P9-CEZ-954

compiled by May Hill Arbuthnot

TIME FOR TRUE TALES

A representative collection of realistic stories

for children; to be used in the classroom, home, or camp;

especially planned for college classes in children's

literature; with a general introduction, section

introductions, and headnotes for the individual stories

TIME FOR TRUE TALES *and almost true*

Illustrated by Rainey Bennett, designed by Hal Kearney

Scott, Foresman and Company

Chicago Atlanta Dallas New York

To children everywhere
and especially to the children of Demington Drive,
who find life wonderful
and make it so for grownups,
this book is gratefully dedicated.

CONTENTS

TODAY IN OTHER LANDS 200

HISTORICAL FICTION AND BIOGRAPHY 258

BOOKS AND CHILDREN

Time and the child

Only grownups know the swiftness of time's passing. To children and young people it moves as slowly as a snail, with long intervals when nothing seems to happen. In those intervals, between play and routines, the child needs something to feed upon. Food for the body is essential but there must also be food for the mind and spirit of the child. And what do children find to feed upon in this modern age! They may turn to soap operas, television cowboys, the comics, or little gilded books with abbreviated content —pacifiers, not food, designed to kill time, not to fill it richly and fully. If they turn to these pacifiers, it is often because many adults have no respect for the child's time. They say, "Don't bother me just now. Go turn on the television." Or they ask, "Where is that pretty book I bought for you at the grocery store?" They don't even remember the title. It doesn't matter. It is just something to keep the child occupied and out of the way. Yet who should know better than adults the touching swiftness with which childhood passes? And who should be more aware than they of its exuberant eagerness, its hungry curiosities? What happens to a child's dreams and his hungers if he is fed only intellectual chaff? And what may happen if his curiosities are met with strong books which feed his young spirit and give him something to grow on?

Clifton Fadiman, exploring recent books for children, makes this statement,

> Consider, though, how little the child actually *does* read. Librarians estimate that about 500 books represent the *maximum* the average child can get through between seven and fourteen. That's about 70 per year. Hence the child simply cannot afford the commonplace.[1]

Perhaps Mr. Fadiman is a bit too exacting. Perhaps if grownups can lull themselves happily with pulp fiction or "whodunits" from time to time, their offspring might be allowed a few commonplaces. But, in the main, Mr. Fadiman's concern is sound. Childhood *is* brief. Its reading is even briefer. The least adults can do is to see that children encounter a variety of fine books and some of the great books which can minister most effectively to their maturing minds, growing responsibilities, and changing needs.

Books and children's needs

But how can grownups learn to know and select the best books for children from the enormous mass of juveniles available? First, they should understand that children should find in reading vicarious satisfaction for their basic needs. In the opening chapter of *Children and Books*[2] there is a full discussion of those needs and the kinds of books which help to meet them. For example, *security*—physical or material, emotional, spiritual, and intellectual—continues to be a basic need even in an age of social unrest, wars, and atom bombs. Children and men alike dream of being safe, comfortable, wealthy, and wise. It is the superman dream that persists no matter how far short of the goal individuals

[1] Clifton Fadiman, "Party of One," *Holiday*, August 1952, p. 6

[2] May Hill Arbuthnot, *Children and Books*, Scott, Foresman, 1947, Chapter 1

and the world may fall. Fairy tale fantasies on the one hand and the biographies of real heroes on the other minister to this dream and keep young spirits soaring.

The *need to achieve,* to do or be something worthy of admiration, is even more pressing than the need for security. This is fortunate or the human race would grow too cautious to survive. Stories built around adventure from *Peter Rabbit* to *Treasure Island* satisfy this need grandly. Stories for the oldest children along with adventurous action begin to emphasize moral achievement. Kate with the help of the Good Master becomes a self-controlled and useful child. Johnny Tremain abandons his plans for revenge in a self-forgetting absorption in the prerevolutionary plots. Achievement has progressed from riding up a glass hill to moral victory over self.

The *need to belong,* to be an accepted and liked member of a group, motivates the child's desire to achieve and is a part of the maturing process. Stories about family life, neighborhood and gang activities are built around this need to be a part of a social group as well as around the child's *need to love and to be loved.* These latter needs give rise presently to the romance literature of adolescence.

But neither life nor the child is always in earnest and there seems to be a healthy rhythm of work and play rising out of a basic *need for change.* Humorous verses and stories meet this desire for fun and change, either realistically as in "The Story of Johnny Head-in-Air"[1] and *The Adventures of Tom Sawyer,* or fantastically as in "Alas, Alack!" and in such tall tales as *Pecos Bill.*

And finally there is the *need for aesthetic satisfaction.* We know that children are lusty little animals, but we know that they are far more than this. They reach out for beauty as well as food. They respond to the beauty of the world around them and to the beauty of decent human beings doing the best they can, and to the varied expressions of this beauty and goodness as we find them in the arts. So children need to discover in books this nebulous experience that we call aesthetic satisfaction—a sense of the significance of life in terms so arresting and so beautiful that life takes on richer meaning.

This brief review of children's basic needs omits one important consideration—namely, that no two children bring precisely the same needs and interests to a book. One child may be developing happily and normally in his social relationships but with a tight literalness of mind that knows nothing about imaginative play and brooks no nonsense. Such a child needs imaginative beauty in his reading, a little fantasy and sheer hilarity to keep him flexible. Another child is pampered and therefore socially immature. He needs stories that will help him to see himself in relation to other people and to develop increasing social responsibility. The withdrawing child, the overly aggressive one, the indecisive or the insensitive youngsters are all victims of maladjustment to the tasks with which they are confronted. Probably books alone cannot cure their maladjustments, but two things are certain. Trashy, trivial, or second-rate reading may afford these children temporary entertainment and escape from their problems, but it will give them no insight into dealing with those problems. On the other hand, strong books, worth-while books, even while they entertain young readers, will also supply them with clues to a better understanding of themselves and other people.

Qualities that make a child's book worth while

Probably no two people would agree upon all the qualities that must go into a book for children to make it worth while. But there may be a few qualities without which, most people would agree, no book can hope to win both the approval of children and critics of literature.

Of course, poetry is a special kind of writing that must be considered by itself. It is generally difficult to define the qualities that set authentic poetry apart from the commonplace, but many of the criteria have been discussed in the introduction to *Time for Poetry.* Melody and movement or, as Walter de la Mare calls them, "tune and runningness" are the qualities that set poetry apart from prose most conspicuously. In light verse or nonsense jingles the melodies are gay and the movements light, dancing, and

[1] May Hill Arbuthnot, *Time for Poetry,* "The Story of Johnny Head-in-Air," p. 118; "Alas, Alack!" p. 110

strongly marked. The child soon discovers that the Mother Goose verses hop, skip, walk, run, gallop, or swing as tunefully as music. As he progresses to poetry with more content, the melodies are more subtle and the movement less marked and more varied. But in good poetry there is always a compatibility between the tune and runningness and the action, mood, or meaning of the poem. The words poetry employs are used with precision and chosen for their rich sensory and associative values. These in turn stimulate a sensory response in the person who speaks or hears poetry. Melody and movement, sensory imagery, and the associative values of words all work together with magical results to make experiences suddenly stirring and to give them a significance that was lacking when they were merely experiences.

But prose is another matter. If children were literary analysts, they would probably insist that the first requisite of a good story is lively *action* or *plot*. It is true that children accept and even like gentle, charming stories without plot, especially if they are illustrated, but the prime favorites, the stories that survive for generations, the stories children wear out with rereading or wear out the grownups with rereading or retelling are plot stories. Such favorites as "The Three Little Pigs," *The Five Hundred Hats of Bartholomew Cubbins, The Adventures of Tom Sawyer, Caddie Woodlawn,* all have lively plots, with a great deal happening and with the heroes progressing merrily from deed to deed or escapade to escapade. Even the long descriptions in the idyllic *Wind in the Willows* are endured by children because of the unexpected scrapes Toad gets into and the exciting action involved in getting him out.

The stream of consciousness style of writing, the stories which begin in the middle and end up in the air, may pass with adults, but they won't with children. They like stories in which there is a brisk introduction that launches the plot, a development full of action and growing suspense, and conclusions that settle everything including the villain. To be sure, the plots for the nursery age are pretty mild, but even *Angus and the Ducks* has a definite plot, amusing action and suspense, and a satisfying conclusion with Angus safe and sound under the sofa.

An interesting *idea* or *theme* is essential to the development of a good plot. The theme is not always easy to define, but one explanation is that it is the motivating idea for the whole story. *Treasure Island,* for example, has a theme clearly indicated in the title and one sufficiently robust to support a thriller whose popularity has never waned in the more than thirty years of its existence. *The Good Master* is, of course, a gentle, juvenile version of the old *Taming of the Shrew* theme, and *Angus and the Ducks* turns upon the dog's curiosity. But whether or not a theme can be readily defined, it is the backbone of a story. The absence of a dominant idea results in a lot of the "so what?" type of stories that may be beautifully illustrated and momentarily entertaining but which will soon be forgotten.

Another characteristic of a superior book for children is *unique and memorable characters.* Stereotypes are soon forgotten, but unique, salty, vivid characters capture the imagination and affection of young readers. Rumpelstiltskin, Padre Porko, Br'er Rabbit, Ping, Smoky, Pinocchio, Huck Finn, Heidi and her grandfather, Long John Silver, Young Fu, Hetty and Hank, the Defender, Mr. Jerome Kildee—such characters as these are not easily forgotten. They add spice to reading and to life. Young readers are apt to say, "Oh, I wish I could have known"—Kate or Caddie or Tom or Jancsi or whoever the character happens to be. Or when they are grown up, they still chuckle over the wickedness of Long John Silver or the pranks and cockiness of Br'er Rabbit. Book characters like these broaden children's understandings and deepen their responses to people, animals, and life in general.

The fourth requisite of a first-rate story is that nebulous quality called *style.* Unfortunately, the lack of good prose style is not always noticed, particularly in the field of children's books, but good style makes itself felt in many ways. The text moves and flows smoothly. Reading is effortless and agreeable, not because of a denuded vocabulary and short sentences but because words and meaning are compatible and the phrasing is staccato or sonorous, serene or brisk, according to mood and meaning. If the text reads aloud delightfully, it has good prose style. Folk tales are obvious examples of this. Notice their dramatic dialogues, which characterize without descriptions. Sometimes the narrative has a cadenced swing, sometimes it is literally in a minor key. The beginnings often set the mood and tempo of the whole story and the conclusions are likewise gay or grave or romantic in the mood of the adventure. There are similar virtues in the modern fairy tales. The books of Dr. Seuss or A. A. Milne or Wanda Gág cry out for reading aloud, so delightful is their style. In the field of realism the style is different but may be equally well done. The laconic vernacular of *Smoky* suits the story. Not a word of *Tom Sawyer* can be changed to advantage.

There are, of course, other requisites to good fiction[3] such as close unity of interest centered in the theme, a decent economy of incidents, and balanced proportions in the parts of the story. These contribute, too, but for a child's story, the essentials are *plot* growing out of a worth-while *theme, memorable characters,* and *distinguished style.*

Values from books

Taking for granted that grownups know something about the basic needs of children in general and the particular needs of individual children and have also adequate criteria for judging the worth of poetry, stories, and biography for children, what may they hope from a program of exposing children from their early years to good literature? What should fine books do for children?

Insight into living

One virtue of good reading is that it widens the child's limited experience and teaches him more about himself and others. Intensely personal in his interests, the small child identifies himself with story characters. *He* is the wise, clever pig. No wolf can get him. He would never think of being as foolish as Henny Penny or Budulinek. He would outwit them all, like Br'er Rabbit, or astonish them like William or Yonie. By way of stories, the child discovers that prying curiosity or irresponsibility may get him into hot water. But though these gay, first stories show him the cause and effect of behavior or teach him manners and morals, they do so with a smile.

As the child and his reading mature together, he begins to see himself with ever-widening social relationships and social responsibilities. Ellen Tebbits pays dearly and absurdly for an inadvertent misrepresentation. The All-of-a-Kind family suffer acutely over the loss of a library book. The Wilder boy learns the meaning of money in terms of human labor, and Steppin has to get over his high-and-mighty opinion of himself before he makes much progress as a dancer. Standards of home life, of loyalty to a friend or a member of the family, family struggles, and family frolics may become a part of a child's social concepts as a result of his reading.

As the young reader acquires a widening knowledge of people, he also explores the world of nature, of pets and of wild animals—especially of animals that exist in a secret world and order of their own. He soon discovers that some people and animals enjoy security while others must face dangerous insecurity, that some people and animals are accepted and others rejected by the group they value. Children never forget the touching rejection of Wanda by her school group in *The Hundred Dresses.* In biography, the child sees his hero suffering humiliation, failures, even defeat, before he achieves success. Gradually, from the vicarious experiences of reading, the child's insight into his own personal problems grows and his understanding of people and creatures outside his immediate experience is enormously increased.

Reverence for life

That remarkable and dedicated man, Albert Schweitzer, used the phrase "reverence for life" as the summation of his philosophy of living. In this day of wars, atom bombs, and a growing callousness toward violence and death, "reverence for life . . . all life capable of development" is an ideal to cherish for ourselves and for our children. It is an extension of our own self-respect and self-love to a respect and love for others. Good books without sermonizing reinforce this attitude toward life. *The Blind Colt, Smoke Above the Lane,* and *Kildee House,* for example, leave children not only with a bet-

[3] For detailed discussion of these see May Hill Arbuthnot, *Children and Books,* Chapter 11

ter understanding of animal life but also with a deep sympathy and tenderness for animals. *The Defender,* with its unforgettable account of the hunted mountain rams, also gives a picture of social injustice which rouses the reader's pity for the misjudged and rejected man. Books which show animals or men suffering from cruelty or misunderstanding, or sacrificing themselves for another's welfare build in young readers an abiding reverence for the valiant spirit that won't be downed. Poetry develops the child's sensitivity to beauty, to the significance of brief moments or great episodes, in short, to the significance of life and loveliness in all their strange variety. Biography reveals dedicated human beings and cannot help but nourish the child's response to goodness and decency and his "reverence for life . . . all life capable of development."

Zest for life

Finally, most children come into the world with exuberant energy and a zest for life that is glorious to behold. Alas, before they have reached maturity these may be sadly diminished. That is a pity. Life can be tragic or dull, but it can also be triumphant and gay. Sometimes it is downright comic. Also, human beings are endowed with a mechanism denied to animals, namely laughter, and it is good for man to use all of his endowments. So children should discover in their experience with books some reasons for laughter. There are drolls in the fairy tales, humor and nonsense in poetry, and delicious absurdities in realistic stories and even biography. Top off a dull day by reading a selection from this rich store. "Life is real and life is earnest" for most of us most of the time. But the therapy of laughter is a healthy medicine to be administered frequently. Some forgotten philosopher from the teaching profession once said, "Count the day lost in which your children have not laughed." Sometimes a smile or even a sudden twinkle in the eye means as much as a laugh. It means that tensions are broken and the young spirit is relaxed and at ease. A renewed zest for life will follow soon.

These, then, are some of the desirable outcomes of good reading. Supply the child with worth-while, entertaining reading and share it with him and he will gain *insight* into his own behavior, his social relationships, and responsibilities. He will grow in *reverence for life* and sensitivity to beauty and goodness. And he will keep his God-given *zest for life* and the gift of laughter.

May Hill Arbuthnot

Cleveland, 1953

Stories about animals are so popular with modern children that it is sometimes a problem to get them to read anything else. Perhaps the reason is that over half the world's population is now living in cities and the urban child misses the everyday contact with animals which is the rural child's heritage.

To meet children's demands for exciting chronicles of animal adventure, authors and publishers are turning out such stories in quantities. There are books about every kind of beast from rabbits to elephants, from minks to mustangs. Many of these books are excellent, most of them are fairly good, but some of them are stereotypes or juvenile thrillers, as sensational as fights and gore can make them. To appraise this offering,

ANIMAL STORIES

it is well to know something about the different types of animal stories, their values and limitations.

Animals as prototypes of human beings

The animals of folk tales and fables are not, of course, authentic animals at all, but symbols or even caricatures of human beings. "The Three Little Pigs" behave like foolish or wise people and "The Fox and the Crow" are flatterer and flattered. These ancient stories are ancestors of modern allegories like *Nothing at All* and modern fables like *Copy-Kitten*. When illustrators add clothes to these creatures, as in *Peter Rabbit,* their similarity to people is even more apparent. Oddly enough, this scientific generation, young and old, thoroughly enjoys animal tales in which the beasts are used as prototypes of human beings. Small children still love "Henny-Penny," their older brothers and sisters weep over "The Ugly Duckling," and both children and adults chuckle at the absurdities of "Donald Duck," "Bugs Bunny," and "Pogo." Ourselves in fur or feathers seem irresistibly comic or pathetic, both in stories and pictures.[1]

Animals as animals but talking

The second type of animal tale is partly make-believe and partly natural science, a hybrid form. The animals in such stories are portrayed with fidelity to the nature and behavior of the species, but they are given the human attributes of thoughts and speech. To be sure, the beasts don't discuss politics, but they do talk at length about their own affairs. The classic example is not *Black Beauty,* in which the horse is much too human for horse nature, but Felix Salten's *Bambi.*[2] In *Bambi,* the deer talk, are puzzled or afraid, warn each other, grieve or rejoice in words, but always in terms of deer life and deer problems. For example, the deer parents do not admonish their fawns to be courteous to their uncles and aunts, but they do warn them to be on watch for the pale, hairless creature which walks upright and carries a stick that sends out fire and death to animals far away. This type of story is difficult to write with integrity. If the animals are overly humanized, they cease to be authentic animals, and the story tends to become didactic or mawkishly sentimental. Not that children object to sentimentality or moralizing. Like adults, they will take considerable second-rate reading matter, but they deserve better fare.

[1] See May Hill Arbuthnot, *Time for Fairy Tales,* Scott, Foresman, 1952, for the following stories: "The Three Little Pigs," p. 10; "The Fox and the Crow," p. 203; "Nothing at All," p. 259; "Copy-Kitten," p. 259; "Henny-Penny," p. 12; "The Ugly Duckling," p. 291; "Puss in Boots" (The Master Cat), p. 102; "Ask Mr. Bear," p. 257.

[2] Not the altered Disney versions but the original stories.

Animals objectively reported

The third type of animal story is told from the outside, as if the narrator were able to observe everything the animal does. The best of these stories re-create with scientific accuracy the animal and his environment within the framework of an exciting plot. Whether the animals are household pets, farm animals, or denizens of forest, swamp or jungle, they speak no words, but the noises they make are subject to general interpretations, as the cat's purr of contentment, a dog's bark of welcome, a lion's menacing roar or the loud churr of Mr. Kildee's "Old Grouch," which marked a full stomach and a dry, warm shelter. Beyond such guesses at meaning, which all humans seem to indulge in, the reader knows nothing about the inside workings of the animal's thoughts and emotions.

It is this third type of animal story which is enormously popular with children today. Even when they are still accepting the folk tale animal fantasy like "Puss in Boots," and "Ask Mr. Bear," they will also enjoy *Hodie* or one of the *Blaze* books and other stories that are scrupulously objective, realistic, and possible. It is this latter type of animal story, in contrast with the fanciful animal stories of *Time for Fairy Tales,* which has been chosen for this book.

These stories were selected with certain criteria in mind which may serve as standards for evaluating other animal tales. In addition to the usual criteria for evaluating any story for children—interesting plot, strong theme, memorable characters, and good style—there are also specific standards for judging the merit of this third type of animal tale. The first is, of course, integrity to the species of animal described. Hodie, for instance, has the gaiety and clownishness that are characteristic of the French poodle, but he also learns with true poodle quickness and amiability. The Wahoo Bobcat saves a little boy's life, not from any humanitarian motives, but from sheer blind rage and the instinct to defend a cub. The baby skunk in *Smoke Above the Lane* makes friends with the tramp because of desperate fear and hunger. The authors of the stories in this section never allow their animals to function from human motives, nor do they sentimentalize them, but the creatures run true to species.

Second, if there are people in these animal tales, they should be real people, not stereotypes of cruelty or goodness. Both Marguerite Henry in her horse stories and Jim Kjelgaard in his dog stories give children unique human characters, who are as memorable as the animal heroes of the books. So, the old man in that remarkable story *The Defender* is unlike any other character in children's books. Delightful as the wild mountain rams are, it is the old man, the defender, who gives the story greatness.

Avoidance of unnecessary cruelty and violence is a third criteria for evaluating animal stories. Because animals are vulnerable and suffer both from man and from other animals, some of the stories in this field go to sensational lengths to achieve a high degree of reading interest. They play up suffering and brutality to a disproportionate degree. The animal stories presented in this book often show animal tragedies and frequently man's injustice or brutality to beasts, but they are written with compassion, and the gory details are kept within bounds. Too much brutality can rouse latent sadism in young readers or develop in them a callous tolerance of suffering. This field of animal stories is one in which adults who guide children's reading need to distinguish between necessary violence and sensationalism.

Values of animal stories for children

Well-written animal stories have unique values for young readers. Over and over again, they teach him the curious vulnerability of animals, at the mercy of man with his guns and his greedy desire to exploit animals. The animal's lack of language subjects him to injustice and misunderstanding. The dog can't explain that he did not kill the sheep, nor can he help himself if his master wishes to sell him or give him away. It is this helplessness of animals which calls out the child's pity and love. And it is quite as important for the child to wish to love and cherish another creature as it is for him to be loved. In many city homes the animal story is vicarious satisfaction for the pets the child is not permitted to own.

Animal stories also give the child vicarious experiences with a variety of wild animals he cannot know in any other way. He learns the habits and needs of a great many beasts, and his admiration for them grows as he understands their problems, their nature, and their hazardous lives. A book like *Kildee House* or *My Friend Flicka* supplies him with considerable information on the biology of mating, birth, and death, which comes in casually and naturally in the midst of an exciting story. Indeed, poor Jerome Kildee's survival in his unique house came to depend upon his ability to cope with the birth of more and more baby animals. The way nature marches on in the animal world takes on meaning for children who read this story.

Finally, animal stories are good for children because they find in their animal heroes the virtues they most admire in human beings and would like to achieve themselves. Look over any first rate group of animal adventures and see if these virtues are not paramount—courage in the face of danger, fortitude under suffering or injustice, loyalty to cub, mate, or master, and, above all, a shining zest for life that is like the child's own. Colts, cubs, kittens, children take life gaily with splendid prancings and cavortings. And even mature animals seem to find life good and go proudly and gallantly to meet its challenge. These are some of the reasons why children love good stories about animals and should have them, the soundest and the best to be found.

Animals we know best

ANGUS AND THE DUCKS

Marjorie Flack

Marjorie Flack is an artist with words as well as with brush. Her long series of picture-stories for small children—her Angus *books,* Wag-tail Bess, Tim Tadpole, Walter the Lazy Mouse, Ask Mr. Bear (Time for Fairy Tales, *p.* 257)*—have set high standards for the literature of the early years. Each story is unique, each has a well-defined plot, delightful style, and just enough suspense or surprise to keep children interested.*

Once there was a very young little dog whose name was Angus, because his mother and his father came from Scotland.

Although the rest of Angus was quite small, his head was very large and so were his feet.

Angus was curious about many places and many things:

He was curious about what lived under the sofa and in dark corners and who was the little dog in the mirror.

He was curious about things-which-come-apart and those things-which-don't-come-apart; such as slippers and gentlemen's suspenders and things like that.

Angus was also curious about things-outdoors but he could not find out much about them because of a leash.

The leash was fastened at one end to the collar around his neck and at the other end to somebody else.

But Angus was most curious of all about a noise which came from the other side of the large green hedge at the end of the garden.

The noise usually sounded like this: Quack! Quack! Quackety! Quack!!

But sometimes it sounded like this: Quackety! Quackety! Quackety! Quack!!

One day the door between outdoors and indoors was left open by mistake; and out went Angus without the leash or somebody else.

Down the little path he ran until he came to the large green hedge at the end of the garden. He tried to go around it but it was much too long. He tried to go over it but it was much too high. So Angus went under the large green hedge and came out on the other side.

There, directly in front of him, were two white ducks. They were marching forward, one-foot-up and one-foot-down. Quack! Quack! Quackety! Quack!!!

Angus said, WOO-OO-OOF!!!

Away went the ducks all of a flutter. Quackety! Quackety! Quackety! Quackety! Quackety!!!

Angus followed after.

Soon the ducks stopped by a stone watering trough under a mulberry tree.

Angus stopped, too. Each duck dipped a yellow bill in the clear cool water. Angus watched. Each duck took a long drink of the cool clear water. Still Angus watched. Each duck took another long drink of cool clear water.

Then Angus said: WOO-OO-OOF!!!

Away the ducks scuttled and Angus lapped the cool clear water.

Birds sang in the mulberry tree.

The sun made patterns through the leaves over the grass.

The ducks talked together: Quack! Quack! Quack!

Then: HISS-S-S-S-S-S-S!!! HISS-S-S-S-S-S-S!!!

The first duck nipped Angus's tail!

HISS-S-S-S-S-S-S!!! HISS-S-S-S-S-S-S!!!

The second duck flapped her wings!

Angus scrambled under the large green hedge, scurried up the little path, scampered into the house and crawled under the sofa.

For exactly three minutes by the clock, Angus was not curious about anything at all.

HODIE

Katharine and Bernard Garbutt

Mrs. Garbutt writes, Mr. Garbutt draws, and Hodie is their own dog. They live in California where even in some of the polite suburbs of Los

Angeles the coyotes hunt dogs and howl dismally when they miss their prey. Hodie now knows better than to follow these creatures when they smile at him. He is still gay and friendly and well able to take care of himself as well as the turkeys.

Hodie was a city dog.

He lived in an apartment. As he grew bigger and bigger the apartment grew smaller and smaller. He ran into the walls, and the furniture was in the way. Little tables tipped over as he raced by and his ball got lost under the large chairs.

So one spring he went to the country to live on a farm.

The Farmer had a horse and a cow and a goat and a pig and chickens and, of course, a cat. But he had mostly turkeys.

The minute Hodie reached the farm, he ran round and round in circles. He jumped on the Farmer and tipped over the milk pail.

The Farmer did not like it at all. He said, "Why! He can't stay here. I need a sensible dog that can work on the farm. This dog will chase the cat and frighten the chickens and annoy the goat and bother the pig and worry the cow and scare the horse and kill my turkeys. He's just a spoiled city dog. He can't stay here!"

What the Farmer did not know was that Hodie was really just a happy dog. He did not want to scare anything or kill anything. He only wanted to make friends and play. He wanted to please everyone.

The cat found that out at once. Hodie played gently with her and she purred.

Hodie followed the horse and the horse felt comfortable to have him close by.

He lay quietly beside the cow and she liked him too. Hodie jumped up and down in front of the goat. The goat pretended to butt. It was just a game between them. He rubbed noses with the pig in the pigsty.

Once Hodie ran over a hen's nest and broke an egg. The hen pecked him on the nose and after that he watched where he ran. The chickens learned to go about their business as if he were not there.

Hodie could look at the turkeys only through a fence. He sat down to do that and spent hours each day watching them. They grew used to him too.

Hodie was the first one to see the eight baby pigs the morning they were born. That was very exciting.

The cat had her four kittens in the barn. As soon as they were old enough she taught them to play with Hodie too. And the goat let him play with her kid. And the cow let him play with her calf.

When the colt was born Hodie liked him the best. They played tag and hide-and-go-seek and were very gay together.

Hodie was careful not to touch the twelve baby chickens because their mother asked him not to. And all the baby turkeys were out of reach behind the fence.

"Well," said the Farmer. "He's friendly and he does no harm, but what good is he? I can't be feeding him just to play around all day. As soon as the summer is over, he'll have to go back to the city."

Early one morning the Farmer rode the horse over the hill to the river. He let the colt and Hodie go along.

The sun was not yet up and the sky was gray with red streaks in the East. Hodie ran happily on ahead, out of sight. "Ki-yi-yi-yi!" the Farmer heard and he galloped his horse fast around a curve to see what had happened to Hodie.

Nothing had happened to Hodie. He was just looking at a coyote. She was the one who was screaming, "Ki-yi-yi-yi!" at Hodie. Then the coyote saw the Farmer and ran away, but she glanced back over her shoulder and smiled at Hodie.

Hodie started to follow her. And another coyote came out of the bushes behind him.

"Hodie, come here!" yelled the Farmer. He knew the coyotes would kill Hodie if he went with them. So Hodie had to turn and trot back with the Farmer, though he did not want to.

"Hodie is the silliest dog I ever saw," said the Farmer when he reached the farm. "Why, he even likes *coyotes!* He's no use, I need a dog like Jake."

Now Jake was the neighbor's dog and he was different. He was cross but he worked hard. One day he saw Hodie and wanted to fight. He put his hair up along his back. But Hodie did not even notice. He wanted to play.

First Jake was just surprised. Then he decided he liked Hodie after all. He smoothed his hair back again and wagged his tail. The dogs were friends after that.

Jake did not know how to play but he knew how to work. He herded cows at home and so he showed his new friend how to herd. They practiced on the chickens. When the chickens wandered from the barnyard, Jake showed Hodie how to drive them back. Jake walked slowly, now behind them, now this side, now that, never scaring them or hurrying them. He let Hodie help.

Later when the baby pigs got out, Hodie found them. He was able to herd them gently back to their mother all by himself.

When the summer was nearly over, Hodie saw the coyote again. She was near the end of the turkey yard. This time she did not smile at him. He didn't think she should look at the turkeys the way she did. It bothered him, and he waited until she went away.

But the Farmer did not see the coyote. He was too busy to watch Hodie. He did not know Hodie was learning to herd and to guard. He did not think that Hodie was learning anything.

One evening when the sun went down, the Farmer went to feed his turkeys. Hodie was not in sight and the Farmer thought again how useless he was.

"He'll have to go back to the city tomorrow." he said. Just then the Farmer reached the turkey yard.

"HEY!" he shouted. "The gate is open! A lot of my turkeys are gone!" The Farmer was worried. He could hear the coyotes calling over by the river and coyotes eat fat turkeys. But nobody knew where the turkeys had gone.

Nobody knew except Hodie. He had seen them wander away. When the turkeys did not come back he was worried too. He thought they should stay where they belonged. Hodie set off to follow them and found them eating by the river.

It was getting dark and the coyotes were hunting. Their "Ki-yi-yi-yi!" sounded nearer. Hodie knew he must herd the turkeys home. He drove them carefully as Jake had taught him, now behind them, now this side, now that, never scaring them or hurrying them.

Soon the Farmer saw his turkeys coming back over the hill and he saw Hodie driving them. Hodie looked happy because it was such fun. He herded them all the way through the gate and behind the fence. The Farmer closed the gate. Not a turkey was missing. The Farmer was astonished.

"I didn't know he had it in him," he said. Suddenly he knew that the turkeys were not afraid of Hodie because he was so friendly and happy. But what surprised the Farmer the most was that even work was play to Hodie. "Why, he *likes* to work!" said the Farmer.

The Farmer patted Hodie on the head and smiled at him. "The farm is all yours," he told him.

Hodie danced with joy because the Farmer praised him and he loved the Farmer and the farm. Now he could stay and herd the chickens and the turkeys. He could play with the horse and the cow and the goat and the pig and the cat and all their babies.

Hodie was a farm dog now.

MICHAEL WHO MISSED HIS TRAIN

Dorothy and Marguerite Bryan

This delightful story of an unwanted but ingratiating puppy has remained a favorite ever since it first appeared in 1932.

One morning the expressman delivered a large box to the mother of Mary and David. The children wondered what was in it.

It humped! It heaved! It sniffed!

A shiny eye peered out between the slats that were nailed across the side. Then there was a bark!

"It's a dog!" shouted Mary and David.

"Yes, it's Michael from Boston," said their mother. "But we already have Patsy, and we really cannot keep more than one dog on this small place, so Michael will have to go back to Boston as soon as he has had a little rest."

When Michael was taken out of the box, he proved to be a very friendly Sealyham terrier with big feet, big brown eyes, and a fine, strong tail for wagging.

He did not have the big brown spot over his right eye that Patsy had but he had small spots on his ears.

Mary and David and Patsy decided that they did not want Michael to go back to Boston. So they all met out under the dogwood tree to plan what to do about it.

Michael Who Missed His Train, by Marguerite and Dorothy Bryan.

"Mother loves Patsy and wants *her* to stay," David said. "Do you suppose it is because Patsy does tricks?"

They all turned and looked at Patricia.

She sat up and waved her paws.

"Patsy sits up," said Mary. "Why don't you sit up, Michael?"

Michael tried very hard, but when he had lifted his big front paws off the ground he leaned way toward one side, then way toward the other side, then w-a-y, w-a-y back, and over he rolled!

But Michael tried again and again until he could sit up, too—though he did not look very steady.

What to do? Michael was so willing—so loving—so anxious to make himself wanted.

Michael chased balls and sticks.

But he chased the cat next door, and *that* did not help!

They all ran indoors to Mother. "Sit up," Mary ordered.

Patsy sat up very straight, lightly waving her paws.

Michael tried once and fell over; tried twice and fell over; tried the third time, and sat up! His chest stuck way out; his paws dangled way

down; he wobbled and he tottered—but he did *not* tumble over.

"That is very smart," admired Mother. "But one beggar is bad enough around this house. What would we do with two? Michael must go back to Boston."

Michael stretched himself tenderly on Mother's feet whenever she sat down.

But he stretched himself tenderly on the best silk cushion when he was lonesome for Mother's feet and that did not help!

When Patsy was eating her dinner, Michael just sat and watched politely, and no matter how s-l-o-w-l-y Patsy mincey-moused her dinner he would not steal a crumb.

But he brought home a large soup bone that belonged to somebody else and that did not help!

Michael taught himself to sing softly—woo! woo!! woo!!!

But he taught Patsy to sing, too, and whenever those two were left alone on the front seat of the automobile they w-o-o! w-o-o!! w-o-o-ed!!! together, louder and louder until everybody came running to see what the trouble was.

And that certainly did not help!

Whenever Michael did anything wrong, he put himself in the corner behind the door and tried not to do it again.

But somehow he was apt to forget to be a good dog, and that did not help at all!

So Mother said, "Michael means well, but he *must* go back to Boston."

Mary, David, Patsy, and Michael all met out under the weeping-willow tree. Patsy sat close beside Mary and kissed the tip of Michael's nose. "What shall we try now?" asked David.

"We will have to try a brand new surprise trick," answered Mary. "We must all put on our thinking caps."

So Mary made them each a newspaper hat, and they sat thinking—and thinking—and thinking—and thinking.

Then strange sounds began to come out from under the weeping-willow tree—whistlings and tootlings and thumpings and excited yippings. And a whole barrel of ginger snaps was used up as rewarding tid-bits.

After a long, long time Mary, David, Patsy, and Michael went tramping in to Mother.

David kept whistling the first few bars of "Yankee Doodle," over and over.

They all came to a stop in front of Mother's chair.

Patsy and Michael listened carefully. Everything was very quiet. Then—"Ta-Ra-Ra-Ra-Ra-Ra Boom!" said David.

At the word "Boom!" Patsy and Michael fell on their sides and lay just as still as still.

"Di-Yay!" cried Mary.

Patsy and Michael jumped to their feet as though they had been pulled by one string.

"They died for their country," explained David.

"And came alive again for you," added Mary.

"That is very clever," applauded Mother. "But Michael must really go back to Boston!!"

Mournful Michael!

So Michael was put into his box again and the slats were nailed across the side.

Mary and David counted out enough dog biscuits to last during the whole trip to Boston.

Crunch! Scrunch! Munch-munch!! went Michael—and all his meals for his trip to Boston were eaten up before he had even started. Michael was very loving and very sad at leaving—but, somehow, he was *always* hungry.

When the last biscuit crumb was licked up all was still.

The box humped! It heaved! It sniffed!

A sorrowful eye peered out between the slats nailed across the side.

Then there was a moan!

"I will get out the car and take Michael to his train," Mother said hastily.

"Oh, please! Won't you let us carry him down ourselves?" begged Mary. "He isn't heavy."

"And it isn't far," added David.

"Well, all right," said Mother. "Be careful. Good-bye, Michael. I am sorry to see you leave, but we really cannot keep more than one dog on this small place, so you must go back to Boston." She patted Michael's nose through the slats and went quickly into the house.

"Let's give him some soft leaves for a bed on his way to Boston," Mary suggested.

So they put down the box and gathered oak leaves and pushed them between the slats.

Michael scratched round and round and made himself a cosy nest.

Slowly, slowly they moved on.

"He likes to toss pine cones," David said. "Let's find a nice big one for Michael to play with on his way to Boston."

So they put down the box and Patsy found a big pine cone that they squeezed in between the slats.

Michael nosed it and nibbled it but he could not toss it very well. There was not enough room. So he buried it under the oak leaves.

Slowly, slowly they trudged on.

"Do you want to change hands?" Mary asked. "My right arm is getting tired."

"All right," answered David. "So is my left arm."

So they put down the box and changed sides. They both patted Michael between the bars on the way around the box.

Slowly, slowly they tramped on.

Mary and David had just changed hands again when—

Toot! Toot!

"It's the train!" cried Mary.

"And we haven't Michael's ticket or anything," shouted David. They started to run.

The box kept bumping their legs.

Michael rolled from side to side, barking and scratching.

Patsy ran, too.

Just as they rushed around the last curve in the path, Toot! Toot—Toot!! the train gave a warning whistle and Puff—*puff—puff*, it pulled out of the station.

They put down the box.

"Michael has missed his train!" cried David.

"So he has," said Mary.

Mary and David pulled Michael out of the box and put him down beside Patsy. Slowly, slowly they trudged back to Mother, who was waiting at home, feeling rather lonely.

"Michael has missed his train," cried Mary and David.

There was a pause. They waited anxiously.

"What! Michael has missed his train," said Mother. "Well, then, of course—

"Michael *cannot* go back to Boston."

from BLACK BRUCE

Margaret S. and Helen Lossing Johnson

Harry Simpson's collie dog, Black Bruce, was injured during their stay in Newfoundland and had to be left behind to recover. The pup was overjoyed when he was reunited with his master, and the two of them set sail for Prince Edward Island, where new and happier adventures began for Bruce. Margaret Johnson and her mother have done many dog stories together. Each book concerns a particular breed of dog, and the story turns upon the peculiar gifts of that breed. In this book, Bruce does not come into his own until he finds farm animals to herd.

[*A Collie Finds His Work*]

When Bruce jumped out of the wagon in the big barnyard at "Fair Acres Farm," his ears were pricked, his plumy tail was wagging, and there was an interested light in his brown eyes.

A herd of cows, which to him were like large goats, were standing near one of the barn doors, quietly chewing their cuds and regarding the strange dog doubtfully. The collie felt a rush of friendliness for these creatures, and he went forward to make friends. But in the same way that Bess had warned him away from the goats, so the strangest-looking dog he had ever seen now warned him away from the cows. Short-legged, broad-chested, brindle and white in color, with a huge head and undershot jaw, Topsy, the English bulldog, trotted towards him growling low in her throat.

Bruce was only too ready to defend himself, but he meekly retreated before Topsy's fierce rush, for no dog will willingly fight a female dog. Duncan McGregor spoke sternly to Topsy and said: "I hope she will decide to like Bruce; a bulldog's grip is a dangerous thing, and we will have to watch her."

It was evident that the collie liked Topsy, and he walked around with her with wagging tail and a pleased expression. After sniffing him scornfully, Topsy apparently made up her mind that she would not hurt him for the present, but she would keep an eye on him and see that he did just what she told him to do.

Harry and his uncle drew a breath of relief. "Well, I guess she's going to let him stay," said Mr. McGregor. "Topsy is a grand watchdog and sleeps in the stable, where I have some valuable horses; but she's no good at caring for cattle and sheep; that will be Bruce's job." Harry looked at his collie and hoped that Bruce would be as fine a shepherd dog as some of his illustrious ancestors had been.

Mrs. McGregor and the two children, Mary, eight years old, and Bob, six, were very glad to see Harry again and welcomed and admired the beautiful dog whom they had heard so much about.

Bruce had never known any children and drew back when Mary and Bob came near, and Harry told the two that they had better leave the young collie alone for a few days, until he had become accustomed to his new home.

When Harry first took Bruce to the beautiful hillside pasture, bordered by woods of beech and birch and maple, where the fine flock of sheep was kept, he held the collie's collar, for he was not sure what Bruce would do when he saw his first sheep.

"Steady, boy, steady," said Harry, walking quietly towards the sheep. Raising their heads, they stopped cropping the short grass and pointed their ears towards Harry and the collie, ready to run at the slightest quick movement. Bruce, walking softly, was deeply interested in these timid creatures and waved his tail and whined eagerly, but was puzzled by their strange woolly coats. Suddenly he heard a familiar sound, a gentle "baa," which was quickly repeated several times, and he saw a beautiful lamb run to its mother. With a joyous look in his eyes, he turned to his master, begging Harry to release him, for he believed the young creature might be his beloved baby goat whose life he had saved in Newfoundland.

Bruce had to learn many new things during the next few weeks, while the long, warm days and cool nights went slowly by, filled with the work of the big farm and the happy companionship of his master.

By the end of August, Bruce was able to drive the big herd of cows to the pasture, and if one tried to stray down the road, eating the roadside grasses, she would be quickly driven back by the collie and forced to go through the gate with the others. Then Bruce would stand in the gateway until someone came to close it. In the evening the gate would be opened, and Bruce would dash off across the pasture, and soon the cows would all walk into the barnyard, the panting, watchful collie at their heels.

When the sheep broke out of the pasture one Sunday morning while the family were at church, and immediately made their way into a field of ripe oats, it was Bruce who put every sheep and lamb back where it belonged and stood guard at the break in the fence, barking until one of the men found him and repaired the fence.

Gradually Bruce gained the confidence of every living creature on the farm except Topsy. She still expected him to do something for which she would have to punish him, and she never allowed him to set one paw inside the house. Even on Sunday afternoon when Harry took the children and the two dogs for a walk in the woods, Topsy waddled along close to Mary and Bob and rolled a warning eye at Bruce when he came near. The collie was so wildly happy at being with his master, and the woods were so delightful with the mossy paths and sweet-smelling ferns, that he forgot his sober dignity and was like a playful puppy again.

One path in the woods led steeply down to a

broad stream, and here Bruce loved to swim. Topsy was fond of the water, too, and once in it, it was hard to persuade her to come out. She swam around happily, and here Bruce dared to play with her, for his longer legs made him a faster swimmer, and he teased Topsy by always keeping just out of her reach.

After Bruce had shown his intelligence by putting the sheep back in the pasture all by himself, Duncan McGregor decided that Bruce should have the freedom of the farm at night, as well as in the daytime. So a big, warm kennel was built for him and placed under a shed, and when this kennel was filled with sweet-smelling hay, Bruce decided that it was the most comfortable bed he had ever had.

Bruce began to feel that everything on the farm was under his care, especially helpless creatures like young calves and sheep, and it was not long before he included the two children. As it turned out, it was fortunate for the youngsters that he felt that way about them.

Mary and Bob went to the little, country school about a mile from their home, and each morning they started off, Mary carrying the lunch box filled with sandwiches and cake.

One golden afternoon early in September, Bruce had nothing to do, for Harry had gone off for the day, and the men were all in a distant part of the farm cutting a big field of grain. The collie knew it was nearly time for the children's return and trotted down the road to meet them. Soon he saw the two little figures and ran gaily forward, sure of an enthusiastic welcome.

"Oh, Bruce, I'm so glad you came!" said Mary. "Now I know it will be perfectly safe for us to go to the woods to find raspberries. I know where there are a lovely lot of late ones, and we can fill our lunch box with them."

Bruce was delighted at the prospect of a ramble, and the three adventurers climbed a fence and crossed a big pasture, making for the distant woodland. The light was dim, and the air was cool in the shadow of the big trees, and Bob drew back a little, feeling that his sister was being rather daring in going farther into these green depths.

Even Mary hesitated, but Bruce was running cheerfully down the mossy wood-road, coming back to the children from time to time, then dashing off after squirrels, and she felt encouraged to go on. After what seemed a very long time, the three emerged into the bright sunlight again; they had come to a clearing, where the trees had been cut off, and here the raspberry bushes grew in a wild tangle.

Mary picked berries busily for a while, Bob occasionally dropping one into the box; but there were not so many as they thought there would be, and the best ones seemed always to be in the center of the prickly tangle. Bruce had found a rabbit in a pile of brushwood and was trying to dig in to it, panting and barking, and the children encouraged him for a while. At last they gave up, and Bob said, "Mary, I'm tired and *awful* thirsty; I can't walk any more unless I have a drink."

Then Mary remembered a quiet little brook which ran through a deep ravine in the woods, and she decided to go there before returning home. "Father showed me some lovely, big mushrooms there last Sunday," said the little girl. "We can fill our box with them."

So the three turned off into the woods again, following no road this time but making their way through beds of ferns and over fallen trees. Before long they came to the brook, and the children quenched their thirst, while Bruce wallowed in the cool water. Mary saw and picked a fine mushroom, then there was a group of them farther on, and before they knew it, the children were completely lost and had no idea how to get back to the road.

For some time Bruce had been worried and had stayed behind, trying to make Mary and Bob turn back. He knew it was time to go after the cows, and that Harry would soon be home, and he wanted to go back to his master; but the children were in his care, and he couldn't leave them alone, so the faithful collie was very unhappy.

Bob commenced to cry from weariness and fear, and Mary was very near tears. She was a brave little girl, however, and told Bob not to worry. "Bruce will take us home; he knows the way. Go home, Bruce, find Harry," she said, and was delighted when he barked and wagged his tail and started off confidently. The climb up the steep sides of the ravine seemed twice as long as the trip down to the tired children, and they stumbled over logs, and caught their feet under roots, trying to keep up with Bruce. Mary dragged Bob along, and the collie stopped and waited for them several times, wagging his tail, and licking their faces to comfort them. When the three finally found the wood-road again, it was growing dark in the woods, and chilly, and soon the autumn night would close down. The walking was easier on the road, and the children hurried after Bruce, and soon came to the edge of the woods, and the field. At the gate stood Topsy, anxiously peering and sniffing into the dim woodland. When she saw the children, she rushed forward, wagging her stubby tail, and licking their hands with her big wet tongue.

Led by the happy dogs, Mary and Bob crossed the field, and on the other side met their father, starting out to look for them.

"We got lost in the woods," shouted Bob, very brave now that home was in sight, "but Bruce knew the way back, and made us come with him!" Mr. McGregor praised the collie, and Topsy gave him a friendly glance, and much to Bruce's surprise, when the house was reached, the bulldog allowed him to follow her inside, and she lay contentedly beside him while the children told their story. It was the first time the collie had been in the house, and he felt that he now was really a member of the family.

Harry was proud of his splendid Black Bruce, and in November, when Bruce was two years old, the McGregor family gave a birthday party for him. The pleased collie was escorted into the dining room by Mary and Bob, and there he found the whole family and several young friends of the children. The table was covered with plates of cake and sandwiches, and in the center was a special cake with two candles burning.

As the collie appeared, everyone called out, "Happy birthday, Bruce!" and the sensitive dog was so embarrassed that he ran to Harry and hid his head against his master. A crackling wood fire burned in the big fireplace and sent a warm glow over the room.

As Bruce stood beside the fine old mahogany sideboard, over which hung a painting of a beautiful house in the Highlands of Scotland, Mr. McGregor said to his wife, pointing to the picture, "Who knows, perhaps Bruce's ancestors were related to the fine shepherd dogs my grandfather had in that old house in the hills!"

The party was a gay one, and Bruce had his full share of the good things from the table. When all was over, the collie lay before the fire beside Harry, on a soft, bright-colored hooked rug, with perfect contentment shining out of his brown eyes.

All was now ready for winter on the big farm. The barns were full of hay and straw and the bins were full of grain, and in the cellar were apples as well as potatoes and other vegetables. There were warm quarters for all the cows and horses, sheep, pigs, and chickens, and Bruce slept in his cozy kennel, making the rounds of the place at least once during the night, to see that all was well.

The winters are long and cold in that north country, for the ice in the great Gulf of St. Lawrence packs solidly around Prince Edward Island, and the snow lies deep on the ground. Bruce loved the cold and the snow, for his glorious thick coat kept him warm and he was always ready to join in any work or play.

Harry stayed on with his uncle, for he liked a farm better than the sea, and Bruce had plenty to do. One of his great delights was to go to market, following the sleigh drawn by one of the big farm horses, and sometimes riding, tucked in between Harry and Mr. McGregor. Often darkness overtook them and they came home guided by the light of the wonderful Aurora Borealis, or northern lights.

Harry had not forgotten that Bruce was a trained sled dog, and he fashioned a harness and taught the collie to haul wood to the house. Mary and Bob were delighted with this accomplishment of their beloved collie and it was not long before they were riding on the sled; and finally Bruce learned to haul them to school on very cold or stormy days, and the children would unharness him when they reached the schoolhouse. Running home by himself, he would return for them in the afternoon to be re-harnessed, and with his head held high and his tail proudly waving, and the two sleigh bells jingling gaily on his collar, he would bring them home.

There were days when the wind howled and the snow drifted and only the men who had to feed and water the animals ventured outside the house. Bruce was always on hand, full of eager interest, and he thought it great fun to watch the men as they shoveled the snow, making paths from the house to the barn.

But at last the spring came and with it the first melting of the snow.

The large flock of sheep at "Fair Acres Farm" was kept in a barn of their own, with a big fenced-in yard on the south side, where they were allowed to stay on sunny days. One old sheep, the leader of the flock, and several yearlings were in a separate yard, and very early one morning this old leader found a place in the fence which he could manage to crawl under. He promptly made his way to freedom, followed by the five young sheep. Down through the pasture went the six runaways, slipping and sliding in the mud and melting snow, until they came to the stream. A tiny peninsula jutted out into the stream at this spot and here the warm sun had melted the snow very early, and bits of fresh green grass were showing. The sheep immediately smelled and saw this and, overjoyed at the thought of green food after the long winter, they splashed out through the muddy ground near shore and started eagerly nibbling at the grass.

A short distance up this stream, in a ravine, was a sawmill and, above it, a deep millpond. This pond was made by building a dam of stones and logs across the stream. The rapidly melting snow had filled the pond almost to overflowing, and now a heavy rainstorm had increased the pressure on the dam, until it began to give way in the weakest spot. Gradually the break grew bigger, until, with a terrific roar, the whole structure went down and the racing water poured downstream. Suddenly, the six sheep, happily cropping the grass at the tip of the peninsula, found themselves surrounded by foaming water. Fortunately for them, the ground on which they stood was several feet higher than that near shore, or they would have been drowned in the first rush. The water was rising, however, and the runaways huddled close together, helpless and terrified.

Bruce had, as usual, wakened early that morning and he came out of his warm kennel yawning and stretching; turning his cold black nose this way and that, he sniffed the chilly air, then trotted off on a tour of inspection. It was not long before he came to the place where the sheep had crawled through the fence, and his keen nose found their trail, which he followed at a gallop. The collie came in sight of the stream, just as the waters roared down from the broken dam, and he stopped, astonished at the change in the well-known stream. Probably he would not have gone any nearer, but he heard the cry of a sheep in distress and, going to the edge of the wild water, he saw the runaways and recognized them as the ones whose trail he had been following. Half frantic, Bruce barked excitedly and started into the stream; but the current ran so strongly that he drew back, for he was not accustomed to rough water. Hoping that his barking had been heard, the collie looked eagerly about, but there was no one in sight. It was then that the sheep called again, and Bruce saw that the water had risen until it touched the hoofs of the frightened creatures. With a howl he launched himself, but was immediately carried downstream, and struggled back to shore again with difficulty. Twice more he tried, but was defeated, and then his intelligence came to his aid. Going upstream, he struck out and, swimming strongly, he was carried down to the island. Barking, nipping at their heels, Bruce tried to drive the sheep into the water, but the terrified creatures would not move.

Finally, made desperate by their stupidity, Bruce seized one by the wool with his teeth and dragged it into the stream. Guided and partly upheld by the brave dog, the sheep swam shoreward and landed, panting with exhaustion, some distance downstream. Again Bruce swam out, and this time with difficulty he pushed and dragged the old sheep ashore. He was tired now but could not stop until all were safe.

The third sheep was a weak swimmer and once disappeared under the water; and it was only by a great effort that the collie pulled him to the surface again. This time he had to lie down and rest before again braving the flood. The island was all under water now, and the three remaining sheep were in water up to their knees. One more was pulled ashore by the tired dog, and then he looked back to see the other two floating away. Into the water, which was beginning to flow less strongly now, Bruce plunged again and brought one sheep ashore, but the other was carried some distance before it finally crawled out weakly and collapsed on the ground.

For a few minutes Bruce lay panting and exhausted; but the courage of the real shepherd dog was strong within him, and he could not rest until his charges were safe at home. The sheep had recovered and felt safe with the collie, and he soon had them bunched together and started them up the hill. About halfway home, Bruce was met by Mr. McGregor and Harry, running down to meet him. A neighbor had been on the opposite side of the stream while the collie made his splendid rescue, and he had hurried over to "Fair Acres Farm" to tell about it.

"Good dog, Bruce, brave dog!" called Harry, when he saw the wet and bedraggled group toiling up the hill. Mr. McGregor added his words of praise, and Bruce was content. Now that there was someone else to look after the sheep, the collie found that he felt very weary, and he willingly followed Harry into the house and lay down before the kitchen stove, while his master dried his wet coat.

"I won't let you catch pneumonia again, Brucie," said Harry, rubbing him vigorously. Bruce felt a little stiff the next day, but he soon forgot his experience in the flood. Harry and the McGregors did not forget, however, and never tired of telling about the courage of their splendid dog.

from IRISH RED

Jim Kjelgaard

The author says he always has a dog and sometimes "as many as seven at a time." This helps to explain his understanding of and sympathy for dogs. But he knows wild animals too, as his story of a polar bear, Kalak of the Ice, *bears witness. No one who likes dogs should miss* Big Red *and* Irish Red, Son of Big Red. Snow Dog *is equally popular, and all of the Kjelgaard books are well written and intensely exciting. In* Irish Red *Big Red's son, Mike, proved to be a self-willed mutt instead of the great bird dog the Picketts had expected. But Danny still believed in the pup. These two chapters tell of the near-tragedy which changed a silly pup into a disciplined hunting dog.*

White Prison

Danny stirred, and fought sluggishly to a bewildered awakening. For a few minutes he lay still, unable to think where he was or what had happened. Bit by bit, like crooked pieces of a jigsaw puzzle, he fitted the picture together.

He was up on Tower Head, he remembered, where he had come to investigate marten sign. Summer had suddenly become winter, and winter had been ushered in by a terrible wind storm which had ripped through the beech trees. Some had broken. Great boughs had been torn like match sticks from their parent trunks, and one had hit him.

Danny lapsed into a numbed slumber and a second time fought to wakefulness. A thousand drums seemed to pound within his aching head and for a moment he felt very sick. The spasm passed, and when it did he could think more clearly. It had, he remembered, been daylight when he decided to return to Budgegummon. Now inky blackness surrounded him. Danny stretched his hand forth and a warm, wet tongue licked it gently. His exploring fingers found Mike's silky coat. At once he felt a tremendous rush of gratitude. Until now he had not remembered bringing Mike.

He sat up, and when he did his head broke through the fresh, fluffy snow that covered him. It had, then, snowed while he lay unconscious and the fact that it had covered him was the reason why he had not frozen to death. That and Mike, for the red puppy had found him, and was crouching as close as he could get to his injured master. Again Danny gratefully stroked the red puppy's fur.

The snow was still falling fast; even in the darkness Danny felt its soft, deadly caress as he stood erect. He stumbled and almost fell, but by a mighty effort stiffened his legs.

He was aware of Mike pressing closely against his feet, but he could see nothing whatever.

Overwhelmed by another spasm of illness, and weighed down by an unbearable burden on his back, Danny crouched in the snow and gave himself over to sheer misery. When he recovered he felt better and could think more clearly.

The burden he bore was only his pack, Danny realized, and forced himself to be calm. What had happened? First, winter had struck with savage fury. There had been no snow at all during the afternoon, but now it was up to Danny's knees and still falling. He was in the forest, and therefore the snow would not have drifted much. However, there was no possible way he could get to Budgegummon without crossing open spaces where there would be deep drifts, and he had no snowshoes. Even with every possible bit of good luck, it would take him days just to get off the mountain.

Then he did his best to forget it and give his thoughts to immediate problems. Falling snow had prevented his freezing to death, but he was numb with cold and ached in every muscle. Before he did anything else he must get a fire going.

Danny plowed forward, a step at a time, groping hands stretched out before him. A few feet from where he had started, he stopped to rest. He was panting, and beads of sweat clung to his forehead. As soon as he stopped, the cold attacked again; he licked frost particles from his upper lip. Starting forward again, he stumbled over a snow-covered limb, and fell on his hands and knees. For a moment he rested where he was, too tired to get up. A delicious, soothing warmth enveloped him. Then Mike's questing nose touched his face.

Danny fought his way to a standing position. Now he must keep going or die. The snow would not save him again for he had started to sweat. Should he relax for more than a few seconds the sweat would freeze, and if it did he was all through. Danny forced his numb body forward.

He jarred his shoulder against a standing tree and stopped, raising cold hands to feel the tree. It was small, scarcely a foot through, and ragged wisps of paper-thin bark hung like shedding fur from it. A great hope leaped in Danny.

Solely by accident he had bumped into a birch. The parchment-like bark covering the trunk was as thin as paper and burned as readily. Keeping hold of the tree with one hand, Danny trampled a hole in the snow.

Carefully feeling his way, he stripped handfuls of bark from the tree and put it in the hole he had trampled. Then he knelt down, holding both hands firmly against Mike's warm fur. When circulation returned to his hands, Danny felt in his pocket for the metal match box he always carried. He unscrewed the top, extracted one match, and carefully tightened the cover down. Striking the match against the box's rough side, Danny held the tiny flame against his pile of birch bark. The match died, and almost went out. Danny's hand trembled, and a cold shiver rippled up his spine. Then a corner of bark curled, smoldered, and burst into flame. Almost instantly the whole pile was alight.

Danny's happy shout vied with the softly ominous sound of falling snow and the whine of the wind that sighed through the beech forest. Guiding himself by the fire's light, he turned back to the tree and feverishly groped for the outer tips of small dry twigs that broke easily. He filled his hands with them and went back to throw them on his dying fire. Hungry flames crackled their way into this stronger nourishment. Turning back to the tree, Danny wrenched off an inch-thick limb, broke it into sections, and heaped them on the flames. The fire climbed higher.

Danny gratefully appreciated his good luck in having an ample supply of wood practically within reach of his fire. Very few trees on Tower Head were dead, and chance alone had guided him to one of them. Fuel awaited only the taking.

He broke off more and bigger branches and carried them to his fire. He laid them the long way, pushing them farther up as the ends burned, and arranged a layer of dead sticks to sit on. There were blankets in his pack, but Danny was too tired to try making a proper bed. Heat from the fire melted an increasing circle of snow, and Danny changed his seat.

Mike, for once subdued, crouched down beside him. Danny put a hand on the red puppy's ruff and drew him close. Mike had already atoned for all his past sins merely by providing company. Danny spoke softly to him.

"Tomorrow we'll see about getting out of

here, pup. Sure wish I had a pair of snowshoes."

As soon as he had spoken, Danny wished that he had not even thought about what tomorrow would bring. Certainly there was no immediate hope of rescue for he had told Ross that he was going up Stoney Lonesome. Ross would not worry unduly for a couple of days, and if he did start out, it would not be toward Tower Head. If they were going to be helped, Danny and Mike would have to help themselves.

Danny gazed soberly into the fire. It was ordinarily a few hours' walk back to Budgegummon. Now deep snow covered every inch of the way, and progress would be painfully slow. It would take several days to reach Budgegummon, or even to get down into one of the sheltered valleys where, Danny hoped, the snow would not be so deep.

He knew he was in serious trouble, but bewailing the fact, or worrying about what might happen, would not help at all. Tonight, certainly, he could do nothing except sit here by the fire. He pushed a couple of sticks farther up, bent his head forward so that the collar of his jacket came up around his neck, and dozed fitfully. Creeping cold awakened him when the fire burned low, and Danny built it up again.

He was awakened by Mike's warning bark. He jerked erect, one hand stealing to the grip of his .22, but he could see nothing. Mike touched his hand with a cold nose, and Danny lifted his head to find that dawn had come. He stared around in bewilderment.

The once stately forest on Tower Head had become a shambles. Big trees were piled helter-skelter, a Gargantuan jumble of jackstraws. Boughs and branches had blown down among them in a litter of kindling. As Danny plodded over to get more wood for his fire, he thought of the food in his pack.

Expecting to be away for only two days, he had not packed much food. There was a little slab of bacon, flour, syrup, a chunk of meat, salt and pepper, and coffee. There was not nearly enough of anything. Bucking deep snow would require effort and burn up energy fast. The food that Danny had would have to be conserved to the utmost.

Reluctantly he unbuckled the straps that closed his pack and took out the package of flour. He sliced four strips of bacon from his small chunk and put them into the skillet. Melting snow in the coffee pot, he mixed flapjack batter, and pushed the sizzling bacon to one side of the skillet. He poured a flapjack and let it cook. When it was finished he gave it to Mike, along with two strips of bacon.

The red puppy wagged his appreciation, and gulped his food. He looked on with great interest as Danny fixed the same amount for himself. Mike licked his chops eagerly, and begged with limpid eyes. Danny looked at him.

"Nix," he said. "We're on short rations until we find something else. If one of us eats then both of us will, and there'll be no stealing from each other."

Danny washed the coffee pot with more melted snow and brewed coffee. Letting it cool a little, he drank it directly from the pot. Then he brushed snow over the fire, buckled his pack on, and stood for a moment as he tried to pick out a route through the fallen trees.

Danny plunged his foot into deep snow, and almost collapsed as a red-hot iron seemed to flash across his right side. He felt a momentary dizziness, then eased back into his tracks.

Obviously he was hurt more than he knew. He had not felt it last night either because he was partly dazed or because his injury had not had time to stiffen. Possibly he had a couple of broken ribs or internal injuries. Still, there was no one to help him. What was to be done, he must do alone. Days might elapse before anyone thought of looking for him on Tower Head. Danny tried another experimental step, this time with his left foot.

He stepped into deep snow and brought his right foot up. Danny gritted his teeth. The pain was there, but it was not as intense as when he had tried to walk with his right foot forward. He plowed ahead, favoring his right side as much as possible. He had to keep on.

Mike plodded along in the trail Danny broke, the top of his head four inches below the snow line. The red puppy's eyes were anxious, and he whined at intervals. He was worried, but had every faith in the man he was following.

Danny stopped to rest, leaning against a tree to ease the burden on his back. When he cast his eye over the trail he had made he was panicky.

He must have been on the move for half an hour, yet last night's camp was no more than a stone's throw away. He was making very poor time.

It was impossible to go any faster in his condition. He was already panting from exertion. It was turning warmer, too, he noticed. The snow was stopping and the clouds overhead were breaking. A slanting ray of warm sun stole down; the soft snow would soon begin to melt. Danny unbuttoned his jacket, pushed his knitted cap back on his head, and went on.

Two hours later the top of the snow was a soggy mess. Dark wet patches appeared here and there, dips and hollows in what had been a perfectly smooth blanket. Hard to buck before, now the settling snow became doubly difficult to wade through. Danny stopped again to rest.

Hunger that would not be subdued arose within him. Danny licked his lips, and tried not to think of the food in his pack. But he could not help thinking of it, and the very fact that he had food within reach seemed to induce a strange weakness. Danny turned to look at Mike, who was sitting in the snow looking expectantly up at him. Again Danny licked his lips.

The proper course, he had always heard, was to hoard every scrap of food when one had little. But, even though he had come only a short distance, he had burned a terrific amount of energy doing it. It was impossible to continue without eating; he would just have to take a chance of getting some sort of food later on.

Danny stopped and cooked more of his scanty supplies, dividing them equally with Mike. When he had eaten he felt better, but by then it was even more difficult to travel through the wet snow. Every foot he advanced was a foot that had to be fought for, and every step cost pain. He tried counting his steps, then gave it up. The *next* step was the thing. It was all-important, and if he could make that one he could also make the one to follow. Every step he took carried him that much nearer Budgegummon and that much farther away from Tower Head. Distance lost its meaning because of the effort it cost to make that all-important next step.

The sun went down and Danny buttoned his jacket, for with the approach of twilight the cold returned. He stopped to wipe the sweat from his forehead, and considered. He had to rest, for if he tried going on through the darkness he would only exhaust himself and probably fall. Danny glanced at Mike, who sat in the snow, ears erect and tail flat behind him. He whined apprehensively and Danny made up his mind. It was time to camp.

He was very tired, and when he chopped wood for a fire his axe seemed a wooden thing with no edge at all. Danny stopped twice while he was chopping to look at the pile of wood, then wearily turned to cut more. Finally he scooped the snow away, built a fire, laid a mat of twigs, and put one blanket on it. The other he laid on top, and made a pillow with his pack. Mike crowded close to him, and Danny stroked the red puppy's ears.

"Poor pup," he soothed. "You sure got in a fix when you went out with me, didn't you?"

As he comforted Mike, a sudden relief overcame Danny himself. It had been a terrible, endless day. But it had ended, and not until tomorrow must he resume fighting his way through the snow. Tomorrow was a long while away, and they were in camp. At least for the moment their troubles were ended, and within itself that was a relief. The moment was the thing and the future he could work out. Danny prodded the pack with his foot.

"We got this far," he told Mike. "Let's celebrate."

Danny dived recklessly into his store of food and prepared a filling meal for Mike and himself. After eating, he drowsed in front of the fire, then crawled into his blankets. Ordinarily it would have been a hard bed, but not tonight. Danny dropped at once into a deep and untroubled sleep from which he did not awaken until dawn had again come.

He sat up to look at his dead fire. During the night Mike had become cold, and had crawled underneath the blankets to take advantage of the warmth offered by Danny. Now he tumbled unwillingly out of his comfortable sleeping place, stretching and yawning. Danny looked at him and felt comforted just from the puppy's presence.

Yesterday had been a sick day. Still suffering from the effects of the blow when the branch had struck him, Danny had done what he could do. This morning, after a good night's sleep, he could look at their predicament sanely. They were still trapped in a white prison from which there was scant hope of escape, but they must get out if they were to live. It was that simple.

Methodically Danny set about the preparation of a scanty breakfast. He divided the food exactly in half, fed the red puppy and himself. Then he gathered his blankets, shouldered his pack, and started off. After two steps he stopped and looked down at the snow in dismay.

During the night it had turned much colder, and a crust had formed on top of the soggy snow. Mike, climbing up, could run about on it at will. But at every step Danny's foot broke the brittle crust. He shivered, then plodded doggedly ahead.

Mike skipped happily about on the crust, no longer finding it necessary to plod in his master's trail. Danny kept envious eyes on the puppy. If there was some way to make him go there, Mike could reach Budgegummon by nightfall. If Mike came in alone, Ross would set out at once to find Danny. Then he shook his head in despair; it would be hopeless to try to make the obstinate puppy return to the cabin. If only Red were with him!

Mike stopped suddenly, and froze in his tracks. For a moment Danny forgot to breathe; Mike was on partridges! Danny's hand slid to the grip of his .22 revolver.

"Whoa, Mike!" he said tensely. "Whoa!"

Intently he searched the little scattering of evergreens at which Mike was pointing. Partridges were hard to see, but if he could catch one on the ground he had a chance of getting it.

Then Mike went in to flush. There was a thunder of wings and Danny saw five partridges rise. He shot at them, pulling the trigger time after time as he sent the little leaden pellets flying after the grouse. But he knew it was hopeless.

Mike dashed out of sight, and Danny looked after him with sick eyes.

A Rebel's Heart

Trying to keep the partridges in sight, Mike raced happily across the frozen crust. He slipped, went down, and rolled into a small tree. Mike picked himself up and looked about for the birds he had flushed. They were gone, and he could neither see nor smell them. The puppy sat down to puzzle out their probable whereabouts. Then he started toward a copse of evergreens. Halfway there he turned and looked back at Danny. Never before, when partridges were near, had he let anything interfere with their pursuit. But never before had he found himself in a situation such as this one. What should he do?

When the great wind storm had struck, Mike, unlike Danny, had not tried to make his way through it. Instead, the red puppy had curled at the base of a great boulder and waited there, shivering as the mighty beeches trembled and crashed all around him. When the wind died, Mike had started out at once to reach Danny. He had found him before the snow started, lying motionless where he had fallen. The red puppy, sensing something wrong, had tried to awaken Danny by whining, then by pawing, and when he could get no response had curled up beside him. Even though Mike, the rebel, acknowledged no master, the age-old bond between dog and man had instinctively kept him by Danny's side in time of trouble.

So Mike hesitated now, instead of rushing after the partridges, because he knew that Danny was still in trouble. There was an urgency in the way Danny plodded on, and a tense desperation, both of which were entirely foreign to any normal state.

The red puppy turned halfway around to go back. But the will to hunt, as powerful as it had ever been, held him where he was. Mike trembled uncertainly, pulled in two directions at once and wholly undecided as to what he had better do. Then the lure of the hunt prevailed, and he started toward the evergreens.

Because he was certain his game had gone into them, he did not bother to swing downwind where he could get a better scent. He raced full speed toward his objective, then slowed down as he approached it. Wrinkling his nose to clear it, he detected the partridges and stiffened in a point.

He did not rush in at once because there was another faint scent, one he had never smelled before, underlying the odor of partridges. The

smell had something of fear in it, and evil, something Mike did not like. He did not know what it was and because nothing except the porcupine had ever hurt him he eased cautiously forward.

The partridges were in the very center of the thicket, where green branches intertwined so closely that they were almost impenetrable. Mike located the birds exactly and flung himself forward. He heard a partridge's alarmed cluck, and dashed insanely toward the sound. Then his quarry drummed upward and Mike threw himself to one side after it.

A second later and he would have been too late to avoid the beast that had been in the thicket even before the partridges, the thing Mike had smelled and ignored. It was a snowbound puma, a tawny, rippling beast almost invisible in the hemlocks.

The puma had stared with hungry eyes at the partridges when they flew into the thicket, but he had not moved a muscle. They alighted a dozen feet away, too far to let him catch one. But he knew himself unseen; if he did not move one or more of the birds might venture within striking distance.

The hungry puma instantly transferred all his attention to Mike when the red puppy entered the thicket. Here was food in plenty, good food; he had eaten a dog before. He waited until Mike seemed near enough, then launched his lithe spring.

However, the puma did not distinguish between dogs and he had previously caught and eaten only an aging, lost hound. Mike was much younger and infinitely more agile. The puma's outstretched claws missed their target by three inches and Mike dodged out of the thicket.

He ran as fast as he could, with healthy fear lending speed to his legs. Mike had never been hurt by anything except the porcupine, but the law of survival was part of his heritage and he knew that the puma intended to kill him. Furthermore, he knew that it could. Mike raced full speed back toward Danny and found him resting wearily in the snow with his pack braced against a dead stump. Mike slid to a halt beside him and turned around to bristle and bark.

He faced the direction from which he had come, testing the wind with his nose, while the hungry puma lingered behind some brush a few hundred feet away. Having caught man scent, the big cat had no wish to come any nearer. Mike barked again, challenging his enemy, and Danny's hand played around the red puppy's ears.

"What's the matter?" Danny asked. "What's up, Mike? You see your own shadow out there?"

Without understanding the words, Mike sensed the comradeship in the tone of voice.

Danny could not know, nor could Mike himself reason out, that a change had been worked within him. The days when he had been only a senseless puppy, with never a thought except for himself, were definitely in the past. Time, and affection, and now shared trouble, were all combining to work the change. Mike was growing up.

Being a dog, neither the past nor the future mattered to him. The moment was the thing, and now Mike sat on the crusted snow reading the wind that told him of the puma's movements. The big cat had made a circle and gone to one side. Now he lay behind a fallen beech, eyes and ears alert and tail twitching as he studied the situation. The puma had no desire to expose himself to a man, but neither did he have the slightest intention of abandoning the trail until he had caught Mike. Cunning and wise, he would follow the pair until he found an opportunity to catch and kill the dog.

Mike growled low in his throat, and Danny looked questioningly in the direction the red puppy was looking, then turned to go on. Mike stayed behind him, making short little excursions out on the crust to read the wind to better advantage. The puma was coming, slinking along their trail like a tawny shadow. But so woods-wise was he that he never once showed himself. Mike knew he was coming only because his nose told him.

With only a mouthful of cold food at noon, they plodded slowly on. The sun started its downward sweep and with its descent the cold became more intense. Accustomed to being outside, and provided by nature with a suitable coat for all seasons, Mike did not feel it. Danny tried to tighten his jacket and shivered as he stopped in a cluster of big beech trees.

A squirrel chattered in one of the beeches. Mike glanced disinterestedly up, not caring about such game. It was fun to chase squirrels, and to watch them leap with panicky haste into the trees. That was all. But now Mike sensed the change in Danny.

Dead-tired and almost apathetic for the past hour, Danny was now tensely alert. The revolver in his hand, he stood in his tracks and looked eagerly into the towering trees. Nothing happened; the squirrel did not even chatter again. Mike knew what Danny did not, that it had gone into a hole in one of the trunks, but long after the squirrel had found safety Danny continued to stare up into the trees.

Then, with a despairing little gesture, he sheathed his gun and set about gathering firewood. Mike crowded anxiously in, staying as close to Danny as he could get and risking a burned nose when Danny lighted a match with which to start his fire. An eddying breeze brought him the puma's scent. It had come in very close, but when smoke started curling from the fire it retreated. The ravenous cat was not so desperately hungry that he would risk getting near a fire. Mike followed the puma's progress with his nose. He also watched Danny's preparation of their meager meal.

The red puppy had never wondered about the source of his food. He knew only that humans had never let him go hungry. When his belly was empty, they gave him something to fill it and he was sure that it would be filled now. Mike gobbled the tiny piece of meat and the bit of bread Danny gave him, and looked questioningly about for more. He whined when Danny ate an equal amount and sat staring dully into the fire. The red puppy scraped his master's arm with an impatient paw. Danny stirred angrily.

"There's no more!" he half shouted. "See?"

Mike sniffed distantly at the pack when Danny opened it for him. He flattened his ears and rolled appeasing eyes, not understanding the fact that food supplies were practically gone and uncomfortable because he was still hungry. Mike knew only that, for some unaccountable reason, Danny was angry with him and he did not like it.

He retreated to the edge of the light circle cast by the fire, then came back within it, for his nose told him that the hungry puma still lingered in the shadows. It was no place for him. In the semi-darkness, he moved confidently closer to Danny. His paws twitched.

He was hungry, but neither exhausted nor terrified. Mike knew that he had been near death when he met the puma, but now that he was again with Danny, that threat was removed. Today, for the first time, he had learned that he was not self-sufficient, but part of a team. He moved softly over to be nearer Danny, and stared steadily into the unfriendly night.

The puma was creeping nearer. A weak moon had risen, casting moving shadows across the snow, and the puma was taking advantage of them to get nearer the camp. He felt bolder now, for the fire sent up only straggling wisps of smoke. Wrapped in his blankets, Danny had surrendered to exhaustion. Mike snuffled again at the creeping puma, then edged in until his rear paws were braced against the sleeping Danny. There fear left him. Alone he could do little, but together he and Danny could face any threat.

The red puppy growled harshly, and the advancing puma stopped. Then he came on, slowly and furtively. Mike growled again, fiercely this time. The numbed Danny stirred fretfully in his blankets.

The puma was very near now; a little more and he would be within leaping distance. Mike snarled again, and again, as he made ready to repel the attacker. Danny stirred, rolled over, and woke up.

He did not make any noise or cry out when he came awake because he had been born to the woods and wild places. He knew the value of silence, and even sick exhaustion could not make him forget it. When Danny rolled out of his blankets he did so carefully and silently. He inched himself to a sitting position and drew the .22 from its holster.

Mike pricked up his ears and stared intently at a motionless shadow. He knew the puma was there for his nose told him, but he could not be certain he saw it. Danny fixed his eyes on the place, like a hundred other shadows but still unlike any of them. Moving ever so slowly, Danny raised the .22 and squeezed the trigger.

When the little revolver snapped, the shadow melted into the night. The puma, taken by surprise, had silently backed away. He was not hurt and he did not run, for to run would be to expose himself. When he knew he could no longer be seen, the puma turned and loped away after easier game. He had gambled and lost.

Knowing the enemy vanquished, Mike relaxed. For a few minutes Danny remained in a sitting position, the little revolver in his hand. What had he shot at? Had he really seen anything? In any event, Mike was now quiet, so Danny put more wood on the fire and returned to his blankets. When he did, Mike lifted a corner with his nose, crawled in beside him, and snuggled up against Danny's back. They did not awaken until dawn had come.

Mike waited hopefully, expectantly, as Danny built up the fire and brewed a pot of coffee. There was nothing else, and Mike tried to stay his rising hunger by licking his chops. He snuffled at the steaming coffee, then turned his nose away.

When Danny resumed his heartbreakingly slow progress toward the distant valleys, Mike climbed out of the trail he broke to run about on the crust. He liked that better, for in the trail the sharp edges of the broken snow were like glass, and hurt his feet. Mike looked back to see if Danny was coming, then gave all his attention to what lay ahead.

They were crossing a small clearing where blackberry brambles barred their path. Tall weeds had found a rooting in the brambles, and their seeded tops still protruded above the snow. Mike caught the scent of partridges that were eating the seeds, and started toward them. Then he heard Danny's tense voice.

"Whoa! Whoa, Mike!"

The red puppy paused, and looked around. Again he swung his head to drink in the entrancing scent of partridges. He froze into a point.

The old urge was there, the driving impulse to rush furiously upon his game and see if he could overwhelm it. But for the first time something in Danny's voice stopped him. The sound of the familiar command had a new meaning, the end of a long chain of occurrences. Mike was no longer the wild, undisciplined puppy who had escaped from the Haggin estate. A thousand wild chases were behind him, and Red's punishment, and the endless patience and affection offered by Danny and Ross. And fresh in his mind was the realization that he and Danny had faced, and overcome, danger and terror—together. He quivered with eagerness, but held his point.

There was motion in the brambles. One of the partridges thrust a curious head straight up, then sat still. Mike drooled, and tensed his muscles. Before he could move, he heard the snap of Danny's .22.

Utterly bewildered, the red puppy paused. Two partridges thundered away. But another one remained in the brambles, an inert heap of brown feathers. Mike felt an overwhelming flood of excitement; at last his dearest wishes were realized. Everything else was forgotten as he bounded toward the partridge. Mike closed his jaws about the bird, then Danny's voice penetrated his delirious haze.

"Mike. Come here, Mike."

The puppy stood still, not knowing in this joyful moment just what he should do. Again he heard Danny's voice.

"Fetch, Mike."

Then, at long last, Mike gave his whole heart to a master. He started back toward Danny.

Two days later, well down in a sheltered valley, Mike pricked up his ears and looked at the snowbound trees ahead of them. He barked, then started happily forward. Danny's incredulous eyes followed him. A moment later Big Red burst out of the trees. A little way behind him was Ross, on snowshoes and pulling a toboggan.

"Danny!" Ross's voice broke. "Boy, I'm right glad to see you!"

"I'm kind of glad to see you," Danny admitted. "What brought you up here?"

"That Red dog," said Ross. "We looked every other place we could think of, and Red wanted to come up here. I figured I might as well follow him. What happened? You hurt bad?"

"Well," Danny said lamely, "I went up Tower Head to look for marten, only there weren't any, and then a big windstorm came, and a limb hit me, and—"

"Save it," Ross commanded. "Climb aboard."

Danny settled gratefully on the toboggan and let Ross wrap him in warm blankets. He fought the drowsiness that overcame him, for he had a very important message. It had nothing to do with marten, or money, or broken ribs. It was something far more important. He fingered the two partridges at his belt.

"We've got a partridge dog, Pappy." Then he fell asleep.

FACTORY KITTY

Helen Hoke

Helen Hoke writes, teaches writing, and guides young writers in their efforts. She loves cats, and when you have enjoyed this story, you will want to read her Grocery Kitty *too.*

Everybody remembers the day the kitten came to the Ritz Print and Dye Works.

Tony, the head dyer, is the one who started it all. One noontime when the whistle blew, he decided it was such a nice sunny day he would eat his lunch outside. In no time at all, all the other workers brought their lunch boxes outside, too. And the big yard in front of the factory turned into a picnic ground.

And then, suddenly, there was the kitten. Perhaps it had smelled the delicious salami that Mrs. Tony had put in Tony's lunch box. Perhaps it just liked picnics. Certainly, it had no way of knowing it had entered the private property of a big noisy factory filled with machines that clattered and giant cutters that slashed through heavy cloth with a dangerous swish, and great vats of boiling hot dye, all colors of the rainbow.

It was a very small kitten and a very sad-looking kitten, with a torn ear and its ribs sticking out. But it was a very brave kitten, standing there in a strange place, facing all the strange men like a fierce little orange-and-yellow-and-black tiger.

"Well, I'll be," said Tony, "if that isn't a regu-

lar Calico Cat. My grandmother had one . . . a little tiger of a cat, fierce and proud and full of beans."

"Well *this* one's certainly full of beans." Mike laughed because the kitten had quietly begun to nibble at the nice little pot of beans that Mrs. Mike had put in the lunch box.

"Makes himself at home, doesn't he?" said Jake.

"Sure, makes himself at home out here in the yard—but I'll bet he turns scaredy-cat just like the others when we get him *inside* the factory," Mike said.

But Mike was wrong. After lunch, when they all went back to work, Calico followed right along. He gave one small leap in the air when the machinery began to roar. But that was all. Then he began to explore. Delicately, he picked his way between whizzing wheels and rows of cloth that zoomed up and down on a thing that looked like a roller coaster. He stood with his small head cocked beside the dye bath and saw yards and yards of material go in grey and come out red. He watched the workmen load the cloth on little trucks to be carried down to the storeroom. He peered into the quiet office where the Big Boss sat at an ordinary desk, but he didn't stay very long.

"Too peaceful for him around here," the Big Boss said.

There was only one place Calico didn't go. That was down in the basement where the goods were stored. The basement belonged to Big Tom, the black cat who had been with the factory for years. Big Tom would not bother with the rest of the factory. The basement—where there was a danger of rats eating the cloth—was his Hunting Ground. And the big barred iron door to the basement was kept carefully closed.

"Wait till tomorrow—Calico won't be here," the Big Boss said when he left that evening. "No kitten has ever stayed for more than a day. But I hope he does—and that he's a good mouser. Big Tom has all he can handle, downstairs."

"Well, he seems to be settling down for the night," said Tony.

Sure enough, Calico, all by himself, had found an old heap of rags and made himself a bed.

The next morning all the workmen brought something extra in their lunch pails. If that little Calico was still around, he was going to have his reward. And indeed he *was* still around. And what a story the night watchman had to tell!

"That little critter turned up every hour just as if he knew when I had to punch the time clock. He followed me all over the place. And *mice*—he's a born mouser. Little as he is, he's tough! Had 'em laid out in *rows*. Big Tom didn't even need to inspect, upstairs, last night, when I left the door open for him. Only place Calico *won't* go is down in the storeroom. Reckon Big Tom told him that was Private Property."

Within a week, Calico knew just what he liked to do, every hour. He liked to be in the spot with the most action. At seven o'clock he was in the dye room, where he ate the salami that Tony gave him, drank a saucer of coffee, and then sat quietly studying the colors the men were mixing.

"Blue is his favorite color," Tony said.

"Aw—how do you reckon that?" Jake asked.

"Begins to lick himself and purr whenever we make blue," Tony said.

By noon, Calico was hungry again and after lunch he took a nap. He liked to put his head on an old scrap of blue velvet, as soft as his own kitten's fur.

After his nap, he did his exercises, climbing up and down the ropes and sharpening his claws on them. Sometimes the men gave him a ride in a truck with the goods that were being carried off the floor.

"Look at that, turns his claws in so he won't pull the cloth . . . smart cat," Mike said.

"Smart cat" began to be a phrase that was heard often in the factory. Whoever would suppose, the men said, that a little scrawny kitten could turn into such a daring acrobat!

"Better than a tightrope walker," they said when Calico picked his way daintily along a narrow ledge only half-a-kitten wide.

"Better than a whole circus," they said when Calico did his once-a-day Special Trick. Every day, just before the going-home whistle blew, Calico began his long ride down the newly dyed strip of cloth. It was hot. So he kept dancing from one foot to another until *just* before the cloth turned over into the series of steam rollers that dried the wet cloth. At just that moment, easily—no trouble at all—Calico leaped across the space between the two banks of steam rolls, and slid happily down the dry cloth to the heap on the floor below. It made a first-rate toboggan slide, and the men watched, every night just before the whistle, to see Calico do his Special Trick.

He *was* a smart cat all right. He got fooled only once and that was the day that the Ritz Print and Dye Works had the big order to print some leopard cloth. When Calico woke up from his nap, the whole factory was filled with leopards. Up and down the roller coaster came the long lengths of material, yellow with black spots

. . . furry, moving spots. Calico gave a frightened yelp and began tearing up and down the aisles between the busy machines.

"Silly critter—what's got into him?" Tony asked, shaking his head in bewilderment.

When the Big Boss came walking by just then, he began to laugh. "It's the leopards!" he cried. "Stop the machines."

So for the first time since the electricity failed in a thunderstorm, the machines at the Ritz Print and Dye Works were stopped. All because of Calico.

"Now," said the Big Boss, "pick him up, Tony, and show him it's only cloth.

"Reckon you feel pretty silly," Tony said tenderly, as Calico put out a brave paw and touched the leopard cloth.

And Calico must have felt *very* silly because when the machines began to roar again, he stalked with great dignity back to his bed and pretended to be asleep the rest of the day.

It was the next morning that Calico's love of blue got him into real trouble. When he started on his regular inspection of the dye room, there on the floor was a little pan of blue color, as blue as a lake on a summer's day. It was hot in the dye room. And the blue in the pan looked very cool. Suddenly Calico could stand it no longer. He dipped his nose into the cool blue. But it wasn't cool. It was hot. Burning hot. Calico yelped with surprise and misery.

"Jumping Jupiter," Tony cried, "get Miss Alice."

Miss Alice sat in the office with the Big Boss. She was the one who fixed the cuts and burns.

Poor Calico. He had burned his nose. Miss Alice put some salve on it, but Calico kept licking off the salve. And the salve had a horrid taste. Miss Alice finally put a bandage over Calico's nose to cover the salve.

Calico felt very sick. All day long he lay on his heap of rags with his head on the piece of blue velvet. He was very brave, but occasionally the men heard a faint moan and they knew he was suffering.

When it was time to go home, no one wanted to leave him. Finally the Big Boss himself said: "I think I'd better take him home with me. He's a fine brave little kitten, but this noisy factory is no place for him. Jimmy and Jill, my two young ones, will love him and there is a big green lawn where he can play."

Nobody said a word because the Big Boss was usually right about things. But it was a very sad crowd of men who gathered up their empty lunch boxes and started home.

"Reckon we'll miss Calico a lot," Tony said sadly.

"Yes," said Jake, "and what's more—I reckon Calico'll miss us!"

And Jake was right. At first, things happened so quickly that Calico didn't miss anyone. He was whisked into a big automobile and driven to a big white house on a hill. He saw lots of grass, as green as the beautiful green dye Tony mixed. And blue, blue sky, his favorite shade of blue.

Then, as soon as the Big Boss carried him inside the house, things happened even faster. A pretty little girl took him from the Big Boss's arms and hugged him tight. But the Big Boss said: "You'll have to wait till his nose gets better, Jill. Better put him down now. You can play with him all you want when he's well again."

Calico stood in the middle of a big soft rug and stared up at Jill. She was a nice little girl, but he was not at all sure he wanted her to hug him. Then a little boy came running up. He was even smaller than the little girl, and right away he reached for Calico's tail.

"No, Jimmy, no!" said his father. "Poor Calico doesn't feel well. You can play with him when he gets better."

Calico stared at Jimmy and sighed. Jimmy looked like a nice little boy, but Calico was not at all sure that he wanted anybody to pull his tail.

A lady in a stiff, starched dress brought him a dish of warm milk. It was very nice milk, but it did not have the flavor of onions or salami or beans. Calico sighed again.

Then the lady said, "Shouldn't we give him a bath? He must have picked up all kinds of germs in the factory."

"Not yet," the Big Boss told her. "He doesn't feel well enough to have a bath yet."

Calico didn't know what the lady meant by "bath," but he felt it was probably not anything pleasant.

Calico shivered. Everything was so quiet here,

and so strange. He felt sure he wasn't going to like it anywhere nearly as much as he did the factory.

Sure enough, Calico didn't like it. The pretty little girl named Jill dressed him up in her doll clothes and took him for a ride in a buggy. Calico was miserable. It was nothing like the rides in a real truck he had had. The little boy Jimmy pulled his tail every chance he got. And that nurse in the stiff, starched clothes spent all her time giving people—and kittens—baths.

Calico got fatter and healthier, and his nose was all well. But he kept on being unhappy. Sometimes he woke up with a start, thinking it was time for him to catch up with the night watchman. Sometimes in his dreams he heard the whir of the machinery and the swish of the giant cutters. But when he woke, he heard nothing more exciting than the tinkling of chimes of the big clock in the hall.

Then one day Calico saw a big truck outside the door, and the man in the truck was the very same man who had always given him a piece of herring out of his lunch box at the factory. Sure enough, the man was carrying a big bolt of cloth into the house—leopard cloth—the very same yellow cloth with black spots that had scared poor Calico so much.

Calico jumped all the way down to the ground from the second-story window and, before anyone saw him, hopped up into the truck and hid under a big parcel. When the driver came down the walk and got back into the truck, Calico's heart beat fast with excitement. He was with his friends again.

Whizz-grrr went the engine of the truck. *Squeak* went the brakes. And off they went.

After a long ride, the truck stopped and Calico peered out. His heart stopped beating. No factory. No familiar workmen. This was a big building with a roof, but no sides. And there was noise all around, and whistles tooting all the time. Calico saw two silver rails shining in the sun. The next minute a big black engine came roaring along, and the silver rails were hidden by a long row of cars. And now hundreds of people were suddenly on the platform, most of them carrying suitcases and boxes. Calico began to worry about losing the nice man from the factory who had driven him here in the truck.

Calico scrambled out, looking eagerly for the man who always gave him a piece of herring. But the man had disappeared. Calico knew there was just one thing to do. He must find his friend at once. Like a flash, he streaked across to the platform.

"Get out of here," a strange man said, reaching out with his foot toward Calico. Calico streaked off in another direction. And then, another. His friend wasn't anywhere. And the truck! Where had it gone to? Calico couldn't find it, either.

For days, poor Calico wandered. He found that some people pushed him away; some yelled "S-C-A-T!" at him. Life was a weary round of ducking and dodging and keeping one jump ahead of big dogs and ladies with brooms and bad little boys with sling shots. He slept in strange places. And it wasn't long before he had very little to eat. By this time Calico looked very much the way he had looked that first day at the factory—thin and bedraggled and sad. But he was still a fierce tiger cat at heart. And everywhere he went, he looked for just one thing—his beloved factory where he had so many fine friends.

And then one day he saw a big cat eating a piece of fish. The fish looked delicious. And it smelled very much like the herring from the lunch box at the factory. Calico was hungry. He was much smaller than the big cat, but he was willing to fight for just one taste of that fish.

At first, the big cat did not even bother to fight. He just brushed Calico away with his paw. But when Calico nipped the big cat from behind, the big cat snarled. And in a minute the fur began to fly!

"Just one bite of that fish," thought Calico. "I don't care if I do lose an ear trying to get it."

"Oh," screamed a lady in a big automobile parked at the curb, near by. "Oh, oh!"

And the next thing Calico knew, the lady had come to his rescue.

She waved her umbrella at the big cat.

"Brute," she cried angrily at the big cat, "what do you mean, trying to steal from this little kitty?"

Lickety-split, the big cat ran, and Calico gulped down the fish. It was even more delicious than he had thought it would be. But he was not so happy when the lady picked him up and carried him into her automobile. He already knew that he didn't like trucks that took him to strange places. So, when the engine started up and went *whizz-grrr,* just like the truck, even though there wasn't any squeak, Calico was very much upset.

Then, in a little while, there he was in another strange place. It was an apartment house, and he had to ride in an elevator to get up to the tenth floor, where the lady lived. Calico didn't like her apartment at all. It had too many things in it. He wanted to get out. But when he ran over to the window in the living room, he saw it was much too high to jump down from.

Even though he had plenty to eat, Calico was unhappy. The lady, who was called Miss Muff, patted him too much. Every day she took him for a ride. And whenever she took him for a walk, she put a leather thing around his neck so he couldn't run away. That was even worse than being dressed in doll clothes! Every day, Calico felt more and more bored.

Then a wonderful thing happened. It happened one day when Miss Muff took him for his daily ride. When Miss Muff did that, she never bothered to put the leather thing around his neck. Calico always sat beside her on the front seat on a fat satin pillow, looking wistfully out of the window. Miss Muff thought he was having a good time. But he wasn't having a good time.

Now on this particular day, Miss Muff was driving along when all of a sudden there was a big bang and the car stopped.

"Oh, dear," said Miss Muff. "A blow-out. A real blow-out. What shall I do?"

"There's a garage about two blocks back, ma'am," a man on the sidewalk said. "Walk down there and they'll send someone back to fix your tire."

"Oh, thank you," said Miss Muff. She was so excited about the tire she forgot all about the open window beside her. She almost forgot Calico—but not quite. "Be a good boy, kitty," she called back as she got out of the car and hurried away.

No sooner had Miss Muff disappeared around the corner, than with one flying leap Calico was out of the window and streaking away in the opposite direction. All day long he ran and ran and ran. He hid in alleys and behind bushes, and he wandered for miles and miles.

When at last it was night and the dark was all around him, Calico went more and more slowly. It was a very hot night, and he began to wish he could find some cool water. He suddenly remembered that it had been a long time—hours and hours—since he had had a drink of water. He remembered all the nice cool water at the factory. Oh, to be back at the factory!

Slowly, Calico kept on walking. And after a while he smelled a faint fishy smell. Following the smell, he came to a little canal. The moonlight made stripes of gold on the water. The little canal looked familiar. Was it? Yes, it was! Suddenly he saw a big building rising out of the shadows. It looked almost like . . . it *was* . . . the factory itself! Calico started to run, then stopped in his tracks. For along the canal, a black slow-moving shape came stalking. It was Big Tom out for a walk. Calico slid back into the shadows and watched.

Big Tom stepped slowly along the canal. He seemed to be looking for something in the water. And then, quick as a flash, his paw darted into the water and out it came with something shiny.

"A fish! He's caught a fish," thought Calico.

Big Tom ate the fish and then walked on, once more. He was coming nearer and nearer, and Calico felt his heart beat faster. In the factory, Big Tom had never hurt him. Big Tom had just paid no attention to him at all. Big Tom had merely acted as if Calico didn't belong to the factory. But what would he do now if he saw Calico trying to get into the factory?

Then and there Calico made up his mind. He wasn't going to let Big Tom or anything else scare him away. Now that he had found the factory again, he intended to stay there. So he stepped bravely out into the moonlight where Big Tom could see him.

Big Tom stopped walking. For a long time, he stared at Calico, then came closer and closer. Calico stood still and stared back. After a long time, Big Tom did a most surprising thing. He turned and walked back to the canal. In a second, flash went his paw, and out came another fish. Then Big Tom brought the fish back to where Calico was standing and dropped it in front of him. Would Big Tom fight for the fish? Suddenly, Calico knew he was so hungry he didn't care. Thrusting out his paw, he pulled the fish toward him and started gobbling it down. He ate it all. And Big Tom didn't even growl. He simply stood and watched, then turned around and went back to the canal.

Calico waited a minute. "Well!" thought Calico, "well!" and he knew at once that this was his chance. And quick as a wink, there he was, streaking off toward the factory.

Next morning, what a story the night watchman had to tell Tony and Jake and all the others!

"There he was, smiling, if you please, standing by the time clock when I came to ring in. First he showed me the mice he had caught—lots and lots of mice. Then he went to my lunchbox for something to eat. Then he went right over to that old heap of rags and fussed around until he found his special piece of blue velvet, curled up and went off to sleep. Just too tired to follow me around and help me punch the time clock."

"Told you he could take care of himself," said Tony. "Wonder where he went when he ran away from the Big Boss. He looks pretty well fed."

"Anyway he got back—so who cares where he went," said Jake.

"Do you suppose the Big Boss will want to

take him home again?" Mike asked in a worried voice, as the Big Boss came out of his office.

Calico woke up, stretched himself, and began to purr so loudly that the men were sure he understood what the Big Boss said to Mike then, "Take him home? No, I don't think so. He's a Career Kitty at heart, that's exactly what he is. It's on the job for him from now on!"

Bbbrr-BBBBRRRRRR went the machines as the factory day began and the work got under way. *Purr*RRRRR went Calico happily, head cocked and four feet poised for the flying leap into the big room full of noise and action. He was on the job and so was everyone else—and they were all much too busy to see Old Tom peering around the corner of the basement door with what might almost have been a grin on his battered old face.

BLAZE AND THE FOREST FIRE

C. W. Anderson

The fact that Mr. Anderson calls his country house "The House That Blaze Built" is a testimony to the popularity of his Blaze *books. They are excellent horse stories for children 4 to 8, and the drawings that illustrate them are superb. These simple stories will lead the children, when they are older, to Mr. Anderson's* Salute *and* High Courage *and to his magnificent sketches and brief biographies of race horses,* Black, Bay and Chestnut *and* Deep Through the Heart, *which are enjoyed from twelve years old on. Emphasis on character, both in the horses and human beings, makes Mr. Anderson's books of more than ordinary significance. This story is an excellent illustration of the courage of a horse and boy.*

Billy was a boy who loved horses more than anything else in the world. He loved his own pony, Blaze, best of all. After his father and mother gave him Blaze, Billy spent most of his time with the pony. Blaze would come whenever Billy called. He seemed to like the rides through the woods or along the roads as much as Billy did. Billy felt sure that Blaze understood him when he talked; and the pony really did seem to understand what Billy said.

Billy's dog, Rex, usually went with them on their rides. But one day he was sick; so Billy's mother kept him at home. It was a beautiful day, and Billy decided to ride along a little winding road. It passed through some woods, and not many people used it. Both Billy and Blaze liked to ride through the woods, because there were so many things to see. They always met rabbits and squirrels and saw many birds. Flowers grew along the way, and the big trees were green and cool after the hot dusty roads. The summer had been very warm, and there had been little rain.

They had gone quite a long way when Blaze suddenly stopped. Billy looked ahead and saw smoke coming out of a pile of dry brush at the side of the road. He knew that it was against the law to build fires in the woods during the dry season. It was not a safe thing to do because of the danger of starting a forest fire.

Even as Billy looked, the flames burst out. He knew that these flames were the beginning of a forest fire unless they could be put out. If a breeze came up and carried the fire to the big pine trees near by, the whole countryside might burn. Not only the grass and trees would be burned. Fences and barns and houses would also go up in flames.

Billy had once seen a place where a forest fire had been. He remembered how bare and black it had looked, with burnt stumps where beautiful trees had been. He knew he must try to save the woods he loved so much. He must go quickly and get help.

The nearest place to go for help was a large farm. It was a long way to this farm by the road, and there was no time to lose. Billy knew they could save much time if they cut across country through the fields. But to reach the first field they would have to jump a high stone wall, higher than anything Blaze had ever jumped. But Blaze seemed to understand that they needed to hurry. He jumped the high wall perfectly.

Then they went on as fast as they could across the wide field. Billy did not need to urge Blaze. The pony was going like the wind. If he could only keep up this speed, they would soon reach the farmhouse. Billy could see it far off in the distance.

In the middle of the field was a brook. There was no bridge and no time to look for a shallow place to cross. "Come on, Blaze," called Billy, and Blaze went even faster than before. The nearer they came to the brook, the wider it seemed. It was too late to stop now. They were right at the water's edge. Blaze made a tremendous leap. Billy could feel how hard he was trying. It seemed that they would surely get over the brook safely.

As they landed, the bank gave way under the pony's hind feet. For a moment Billy thought they would fall back into the brook. But Blaze scrambled up the bank, and Billy held on somehow, his arms around the pony's neck.

In a flash Billy had his feet in the stirrups again; and they were off as fast as the faithful pony could go. Blaze was breathing hard now, but the farmhouse was near.

Suddenly Billy pulled Blaze to a stop. There, right in front of them, was a high wall with barbed wire at the top. He looked both ways but there was no gate in sight. Billy almost gave up, but the thought of the fire sweeping across the countryside was too much. They must go on.

"Just once more, Blaze," he whispered to the pony. Poor Blaze was very tired, but he galloped bravely toward the fence. He was straining every muscle for the jump.

They were almost over when Billy felt Blaze's hind legs catch on the wire, and they began to fall. Down went Blaze to his knees, and Billy slipped out of the saddle and up on the pony's neck. It seemed certain that Blaze would go down all the way, taking Billy with him. But, with a great effort, Blaze scrambled to his feet; and Billy, holding on to the pony's neck, stayed on. Then Blaze started at a gallop for the farmhouse, which was just across the field.

They galloped into the farmyard. The farmer and his son hurried over to meet Billy. All out of breath, he told them about the fire. At once they got some things to use in putting it out. Then they climbed into a car and drove off very fast. The farmer's wife quickly telephoned to the neighbors to send all the help they could.

Blaze was covered with sweat and dirt. He was a very tired pony, but he rubbed his nose against Billy and seemed to know that the boy was proud of him.

"You're the best pony in the world, Blaze—the very best!" said Billy, and he felt sure that what he said was true.

The barbed wire had cut Blaze's legs. So the farmer's wife brought warm water and medicine and helped Billy wash the cuts clean and bandage them. They were not deep cuts, and the farmer's wife said she was sure they would soon heal.

Billy and Blaze had a good rest at the farmhouse and something to eat. Then Billy started for home, letting Blaze walk slowly. On the way they met the farmers coming back. They said that they had been able to put out the fire before it did any real harm. They all thanked Billy for what he had done. They made him feel quite grown up. They said nice things about Blaze, too; so Billy was very happy as he rode home.

When Billy got home, his father and mother were waiting for him. The farmer's wife had telephoned to tell them what had happened. Billy's father took some salve and put it on Blaze's cuts so that they would heal more quickly. Blaze got much petting, and had some carrots with his supper. He was very fond of carrots. Billy had some chocolate cake with his supper. He liked that just as much as Blaze liked carrots. Billy's father and mother were very proud of both Billy and Blaze.

One evening, two weeks later, there was a rap at the door. Billy's mother asked him to go and see who was there. It was one of the farmers who had helped put out the fire. He held a big box on which was written "For Billy and Blaze."

Much excited, Billy opened the box. He found a beautiful new bridle, with a silver headband on which was printed one word—BLAZE. The box held also a pair of shining new boots and a fine pair of riding breeches. They were just the right size for Billy. The people of the countryside had bought all these things for him. They wanted to show Billy how grateful they were that he had saved them from a forest fire.

It was hard to sleep that night. It seemed to Billy that daylight would never come. He got up several times to look at the new boots and the beautiful bridle. He wanted to be sure he hadn't dreamed them.

No one else was awake when Billy brought the new bridle down to the stable and put it on

Blaze. Even Rex was still asleep. When Billy got into the saddle wearing his new breeches and boots, he felt fine. He was sure he could ride better because he had them on. Blaze arched his neck proudly. Even in the early dawn the silver headband on the new bridle shone brightly. His cuts were all healed; and he felt fine, too. So the two friends started happily off for their early-morning ride.

from THE BLIND COLT

Glen Rounds

Raised on a ranch, Glen Rounds can spin a tall tale or a western horse story and illustrate them to perfection. "The Camp on the Big Onion," in Time for Fairy Tales, *p. 185, is an example of his robust style. The episode given here from* The Blind Colt *is quite different—poignant, tender, and true to horse and boy nature. Glen Rounds says perhaps he wrote this story because he was homesick for horses, and he adds that there really was such a colt as the one he tells about, blind and smart.*

The Bad Lands

It was near sundown of an early spring afternoon when the brown mustang mare left the wild horse band where it grazed on the new spring grass and climbed carefully to the top of a nearby hogback.

All afternoon she had been restless and nervous, spending much of her time on high ground watching the country around her. Now she stood and stamped her feet fretfully while she tipped her sharp-pointed ears forward and back as she looked and listened. And her nostrils flared wide as she tested the wind for any smells that might be about.

The rain-gullied buttes and pinnacles of the Badlands threw long black shadows across the soft gray and brown and green of the alkali flats below her. A few jack rabbits had already left their hiding places and were prospecting timidly around in the open, searching out the tender shoots of new grass. They, too, threw long black shadows that were all out of proportion to their size.

A few bull bats boomed overhead, and a meadow lark sang from the top of a sagebrush nearby. Below her the rest of the mustang band grazed quietly except for an occasional squeal and thump of hoofs as some minor dispute was settled. Otherwise everything was quiet.

But still the little mare didn't leave the ridge. She stood watching while the flats grew darker, and while the darkness crept up the sides of the buttes, until at last the sun touched only the very tip tops of the highest pinnacles. Then after a look back to where the rest of the horses were bedding down for the night, she slipped quietly down the far side of the ridge and was soon hidden in the darkness.

Next morning she was in a grassy hollow at the head of a dry coulee where the rolling prairie and the Badlands meet. And lying at her feet, sound asleep, was her colt, that had been born during the night.

The early sun touched the top of the rim rock behind her, then gradually crept down until it was warming the grass where the little mustang lay. As soon as the ground had begun to steam and the touch of frost was out of the air, she nudged him with her muzzle and waked him. For a little while he lay there, sniffing around in the grass as far as he could reach, and flapping his tail to hear it thump against the ground, while the mare stood relaxed on three legs and watched him.

But after a while she seemed to figure it was time for him to be up and about so she urged him to his feet. And he was as awkward looking a scamp as you'd care to see as he stood with his long, knobby legs braced wide apart and caught his breath after the effort of getting up.

His body was close knit and compact and his back was flat and strong. His muzzle was delicately shaped but his forehead bulged as all colts' do. His neck was so short he couldn't get his nose closer to the ground than his knees, and his legs were so long he seemed to be walking on stilts. His ears were trim and sharply pointed but looked as though they should belong to a horse much larger than he.

The mare saw all this but she knew that all colts were put together so, and that those extra long legs of his were specially made that way so that by the time he was a day or two old he would be able to travel as fast and as far as the grown horses in case of danger. And besides, she thought that his blue-gray coat was especially handsome.

For a few minutes the colt was kept busy trying to balance himself on his legs while he sniffed and snorted at everything in reach. As long as he stood still he was all right but when he tried walking he found he was engaged in a mighty ticklish business, what with his being so high in the air with nothing holding him up but those four knobby legs. They had to be lifted and swung just so or they got all tangled up and started him kiting off in some entirely unexpected direction.

But he was hungry, and the only way he could get anything to eat was to go after it himself, so it wasn't long before he was able to scramble around against the mare's side. After a little nuzzling around he found her teats and settled down to sucking noisily, flapping his tail with excitement.

Before long his sides began to stick out, he was so full of milk, and he was quite ready to enjoy the business of having his coat groomed by the mustang mare. She was fair bursting with pride, as this was her first colt. She whickered softly and caressed him with her muzzle every now and again as she scrubbed him with her rough tongue. When she hit a ticklish spot he'd flap his tail and squirm and snort his tiny snorts. When he did that she'd nip him gently with her big yellow teeth to warn him that wild young ones must learn to obey, and he'd better stand still until she was done or he might get worse.

And not an inch of his hide did she overlook. The white snip on his nose, his speckled blue sides and flanks and his legs that shaded down to black shiny hoofs, all got their share of combing and washing. By the time he had been thoroughly polished the sun was warm in the hollow and he began practising his walking again, and his smelling, and his hearing.

He started taking little exploring trips, a few wobbly steps in one direction, then another, with much snuffing and snorting as the brittle last year's grass crackled under foot. As he got the hang of operating his walking apparatus more smoothly he became bolder and extended the range of his explorations until sometimes he traveled as far as ten or twenty feet from the brown mare's side.

His black-tipped, pointed ears were fixed to turn in all directions, to help him locate the source of sounds he heard. He pointed them forward and back, and the soft wind that springs up on the desert in the morning brushed against them, feeling sweet and clear and smooth. What few sounds he heard at first seemed to float separately through the warm silence as though there was all the time in the world and no need for two noises to be moving at the same time. Meadow larks whistled from nearby sagebrush, and far off he heard the harsh bickering of magpies as they quarreled over a dead rabbit or gopher.

Later on he discovered that down close to the ground there was a thin blanket of bug sounds. Flies buzzed and grasshoppers whirred. And buryer beetles made clicking noises as they busily buried a small dead snake.

Sniffing through his nose, he caught the sharp clean smell of the sagebrush, and the more pungent smell of the greasewood as the sun began to heat it up. Occasionally he got a whiff of wild plum and chokecherry blossoms from the thickets down below the rim of the Badlands.

Of course, these were the big plain smells, easily discovered. Later on he would learn to identify others that had to be searched for with flared nostrils, and carefully and delicately sifted for the story they could tell him of friends, or danger, or the location of water holes in the dry times. But for now the simpler lessons were enough to keep him busy, and the mustang mare was mighty proud of him.

But for all her pride, she was a little troubled, too. For there was something strange about the colt, although she couldn't tell exactly what the matter was. He was as lively as you'd expect any colt only a few hours old to be. He snorted and kicked up his heels when a ground squirrel whistled close by. And he put on a mock battle with a tumble weed when it blew against his legs, rearing up and lashing out with his front feet. When he came back from his trips he'd pinch her with his sharp teeth, and pretend to fight, like any healthy colt should do. But none the less, she felt that something was wrong.

The sun climbed higher, and the colt finally

tired himself out and lay down to doze at the mare's feet. She thought about starting back to join the mustang band, but it seemed so safe and peaceful there in the pocket that she hated to leave. And by tomorrow the colt's legs would be stronger and he would be able to follow her with no difficulty.

But before the morning was half gone she heard the sound of danger; an iron shod hoof striking a stone, and looked up to see two cowboys between her and the mouth of the pocket.

It was Uncle Torwal and Whitey out to see how their range stock was getting along. Torwal was a slow speaking fellow with a droopy red moustache, and a good many of the horses running in the Badlands belonged to him. Whitey, who was probably ten years old or thereabouts, had lived with him on the ranch for several years. Almost since he could remember. He wore a cast-off Stetson hat of Torwal's and high-heeled riding boots from the same source. They lived alone like any two old sourdoughs and were a familiar sight at all the roundups, and in town of a Saturday, Torwal on a crop-eared black and Whitey on a pot-bellied old pinto named Spot. Torwal usually spoke of Whitey as his "sawed off" foreman.

The little mare had whirled to face them, keeping the colt behind her. With her teeth bared and her ears laid back, she looked half wolf for sure.

"Spunky crittur, ain't she?" Whitey remarked as they rode carefully around, trying to get a good look at the colt.

"She's a wolf, all right," Torwal agreed. "An' if you ain't careful she's agoin' t' paste you plumb outta your saddle. Better not crowd her."

They sat on their horses and watched a while and admired the colt. "Purty as a picture, ain't he, Uncle Torwal?" said Whitey. "Reckon we better take him home so the wolves won't get him?"

"Don't reckon we'll take him anywheres," Torwal told him. "Looks like I'm a-goin' to have to shoot him!"

"Shoot him! Why?" squalled Whitey. "Why he's the purtiest colt on the ranch!"

"Better look him over closer, Bub," said Torwal. "See if you notice anything outta the way about him."

"I don't see anything wrong, myself," Whitey told him, after he'd walked Spot in a circle around the mare and colt again. "He looks to me just like the kind of crittur I'd like to have for a 'Sunday' horse."

"Look at his eyes; they're white." Torwal growled. "That colt's blind as a bat!"

"Aw, them's just china eyes, Uncle Torwal," Whitey said. "Lotsa horses has china eyes. Even ol' Spot has one."

"Them ain't no china eyes, not by a long shot," said Torwal. "If you look close you'll see that they're pure white without no center. He's blind, and we gotta shoot him. Otherwise he'll fall in a hole somewheres or get wolf et."

"Well, even if he is blind do we *hafta* shoot him?" Whitey asked. "Couldn't I take him home an' keep him at the ranch?"

"All he'd be is a mess of trouble even if you got him home, and I doubt that he'd go that far without somethin' happening to him anyways," Torwal told him. "An' besides, he wouldn't be good for nothing."

"Well anyway, do we hafta shoot him?" Whitey said. "Couldn't we just let him go loose?"

"Now quit your squallin'," Torwal told him, patiently. "I don't like it any more than you do, but if we leave him he'll either fall in a hole and starve or else he'll get wolf et. Lookit her tracks where she circled during the night. Fighting off an ol' 'gray,' I bet she was."

While Whitey sat with his lip hanging down almost to his collar, Torwal took another chew from his plug and got his rifle out of his saddle scabbard. But whenever he tried to get near the colt the little mare was there, lashing out with her hoofs and showing her teeth to bite either man or horse that got too near. Before long she was covered with lather and her eyes showed white, and the ground was plowed and trampled in a circle. But still the colt was safe.

Then Whitey spoke up again. "Lissen, Uncle Torwal," he said. "Lookit the way she fights. I don't believe any wolf could get to that colt, the way she uses them heels. If you'll let him go I'll watch mighty close to see if he falls in anything. I'll ride out everyday to see that he's all right. An' if he does fall in I—I—I'll shoot him myself!"

Uncle Torwal thought the matter over awhile.

"You want that colt mighty bad, don't yuh?" he said at last.

"Yeah, I sure do! He's the purtiest thing I've ever seen!" said Whitey. "I don't think anything will happen to him, really, Uncle Torwal! He's too smart lookin'!"

"Well, I tell yuh," Torwal said, doubtfully. "Since you feel like that about it we'll let him go awhile. We'll be a-ridin' over here every day for a while, anyways, so we can always shoot him later."

"But don't go gettin' your hopes up," he added. "The chances are he won't last a week. An' if he does he ain't good for nothing except to eat up good grass an' be a gunny sack full of trouble."

"Nothing is going to happen to him," Whitey exclaimed, "You'll see."

"Maybe," said Uncle Torwal, but Whitey could see that he was glad to have an excuse for not shooting the colt. Uncle Torwal put his rifle back in the scabbard, and they sat for a minute watching the colt, and then rode off to attend to their other affairs.

The little mare watched them until they were out of sight, and finally when she could no longer hear them she turned to the colt. She nuzzled him all over to make sure that nothing had happened to him. Then after letting him suck again she started down the trail toward the place she'd left the mustang band, with the blind colt following close against her flank.

Sounds and Smells

Back with the mustang band, the brown mare and the blind colt settled into the routine of range life. Early mornings they moved to their favorite feeding grounds where they grazed until the sun got hot when they dozed and rested. Late afternoons they grazed slowly towards some nearby water hole for their daily drink.

And the blind colt began learning the thousand and one things that a colt must know before he can take care of himself. Because he was blind he not only had to learn the things all colts must learn, but many others besides. For a week or so he stuck pretty close to the mare's side, and she saw to it that they stayed out where the ground was level with nothing for the colt to run into.

So it was only natural that he soon came to the conclusion that all the world was flat, and that he could travel safely anywhere.

What he did not know was that this Badlands country was criss-crossed and honeycombed with gulleys and washouts of every size, shape and description, and that sooner or later he would have to learn about them.

And sure enough, before long he did. It came about one morning when the horses were grazing on a grassy bench between gray shale bluffs on one side and a deep gulley on the other. The blind colt had wandered off a little farther than usual, when the mare looked up and whinneyed sharply for him to come back. He had learned that she usually punished him with her big teeth when he disobeyed, but he was feeling spooky this morning and figured that a little gallop the way he was going before he turned and came back wouldn't really be disobeying. So he flirted his tail over his back, snorted as loud as he could and made a few buck jumps straight ahead. The third jump sent him over the edge of the gulley and he found there was no more solid ground under his feet!

The sensation was one he never did forget. He turned head over heels and rolled to the bottom unhurt but considerably shaken up, and thoroughly frightened. After he had picked himself up he whinneyed shrilly and stood trembling and snorting until the mare came to the edge of the bank. She made comforting noises to him and with her encouragement he soon found a place where he could scramble back up the bank to where she stood.

For several days after that he stayed almost as close as if he had been glued to the brown mare's side, and carefully felt out the ground ahead at every step. He was afraid it would fall away from under him again.

But after a few days his curiosity got the better of his fear, and he started cautiously exploring again. He soon discovered that it wasn't enough to be careful not to fall over these banks, but that sometimes they stuck up and when he ran into them they were apt to jar the daylights out of him.

However, he learned fast and in a surprisingly short time he developed a sense that warned him of these things in his path even though he could not see them.

Whitey and Uncle Torwal, riding across the range, often saw him as he picked his way cautiously over strange ground or traveled with the rest of the horses to water, pressed up close to the brown mare's side.

"Well, he ain't got himself wolf et so far," Uncle Torwal would say.

"Nossir!" Whitey would answer. "An' he ain't a-goin' to, either. He's too smart."

Uncle Torwal would spit and say nothing.

During the late spring and early summer, the band of mustangs didn't travel much. There was plenty of grass on the flats and the water holes were nearly all full. In the cool hours of the mornings the older horses grazed quietly while the colts ran and kicked among themselves. The long middle hours of the day they spent contentedly dozing in the sun.

One or another of the mares usually was to be found a little distance from the rest, where she could keep a watchful eye on the surrounding country. When it was the brown mare who was standing guard the colt stayed close to her side. When she looked he listened, and when she listened, he listened too, and stretched his nostrils wide to smell. This way he learned many things. Things surrounding him were only Sounds and Smells, as far as he could tell. Unable to see them, they of course had no shapes. Bull bats catching bugs overhead in the evening were only Booming Sounds. Coyotes skulking around about their business of catching small rodents and robbing birds' nests were Rank Furry Smells. Jack rabbits were Furry Smells too, but smaller and dustier. The rabbits were also Small Sneezes and Thumping Noises. He learned to recognize the step of every horse in the band, and could spot the step of a strange horse immediately. He learned to tell the difference between the irregular movements of a loose horse and the steady purposeful gait of one ridden by a man.

The blind colt often heard Whitey and Spot go by these days, recognizing them by the lazy clop of Spot's big feet and his habit of blowing imaginary bugs out of his nose every few steps.

By the time summer came on and the band started climbing to the tops of high buttes in the middle of the day to escape the flies, the Colt's nose and his ears were giving him almost as good a picture of the things around him as if he'd had eyes.

Now most of these things were friendly and harmless, but the slightest taint of wolf smell, even before he knew what it was, would send him racing to his mother, stamping and snorting with excitement. For the fear of wolves has been born in the bones of horses for centuries. Before long he was to learn of other unfriendly and dangerous things.

On a drowsy afternoon in the middle of the summer, the blind colt was browsing among the broken banks of a black shale butte some distance from the other horses. In little pockets here and there were scattered bunches of grass high enough for him to reach.

He didn't really need the grass, but finding it was a sort of game. He had to work his way carefully along the rainwashed banks, exploring each projecting shelf with delicate sniffings, and when he discovered a green stalk he'd reach out his long upper lip and wrap it around the grass to get it in reach of his biting teeth.

When he succeeded in pulling up a mouthful, he'd stand and grind it busily with his small milk teeth, and flap his tail and nod his head with enjoyment.

After a time he noticed an odd smell. One that was new to him. It was sharp, but not very strong. He lowered his head and snorted his nostrils clear, to catch the new scent better. It didn't have the warmth and body of an animal smell, and yet there was something about it that frightened him a little, he didn't know why.

He stamped and snorted, but nothing happened, and there was nothing moving that he could hear. So after a little he went on with his search for grass. He had worked around a jutting shoulder of the butte when he noticed the smell was suddenly stronger and then he heard a buzzing—something like a grasshopper. But a grasshopper's buzzing had never given his skin the tingly feeling he had now. He was puzzled. He listened in all directions, pointing his ears this way and that, but the sound had stopped. As soon as he stepped forward, he heard the buzz again, and this time it was sharper and louder. It came from somewhere on the ground nearby, but as soon as he stopped to locate it, the sound stopped. He stood motionless for sev-

eral minutes, waiting for it to come again, and when it didn't he figured that whatever had made it must be gone, and returned to his search for grass.

But when he stepped forward again the buzz returned, and this time it had a nervous, angry sound. The smell was stronger, too. The colt was frightened, but hadn't been able to figure out where the sound came from so he didn't know which way to run. He stamped his foot, and as he did there was a dry rustling and a sudden movement from under an overhanging ledge at his feet as something struck his foreleg a sharp blow. The colt snorted with terror, whirled and ran for his mother, bumping into things as he went.

He'd been bitten by a rattlesnake that had crawled under the ledge for shade.

The mare fussed over him and worried about him, for in a short time he was a very sick colt indeed. His leg began to swell and he grew sick and feverish all over. Before long he was thirsty. And as he waded around in the nearby water hole he found that the mud cooled and soothed him. By evening his leg had swollen so much he could only hobble around with great difficulty. The rest of the band went away after a time, but for several days the mare and the blind colt stayed by the edge of the water hole. The colt spent the greater part of his time standing deep in the churned-up mud while the mare grazed nearby, coming back to nuzzle him and to groom his hide with her tongue every few minutes.

In a few days the swelling began to go down and before long he was able to travel slowly, by favoring the sore leg, and they set out to find the rest of the horses. A couple weeks more and he was about as well as ever. But after that, the slightest smell of rattlesnake was enough to set him to snorting and plunging with fear.

The Water Hole

As the summer advanced the hot dry winds blew up from the south with the heat from a thousand miles of desert, and the country turned dry and brown. The small springs with their trickles of clear water were the first to dry up. Then the smaller water holes began to show wider and wider bands of dried and trampled mud around their edges, and finally they too were completely dry.

By late August the only water to be found was in the few large sinks and behind the scattered earth dams thrown up by the ranchers to hold snow water in the spring.

Old trails that had lain hard and untracked all summer now were inches deep in dust, ground up by the hoofs of the wild horse bands and the herds of cattle on their trips to water.

With so many bands coming into the few big water holes, the grass near them was soon gone, so the horses had to travel farther and farther from water to feeding grounds. When the weather was cool and overcast, they sometimes went to water only once in three days. But when the hot winds blew they had to drink every day.

Before long the blind colt's band was traveling so far that the trip to water and back left little time for rest or grazing.

The blind colt was still fat and sassy, growing like a weed, but the heat and traveling were beginning to show on the brown mustang mare. Her coat had begun to look rough, and her hip bones and ribs to show.

The trips in to water were full of excitement for the colt. Early in the afternoon the band would start slowly grazing in that direction. The nearer they came to the water the shorter the grass was, having been eaten down by the stock that had passed before. After a time they'd fall into one of the well-worn paths and follow it. Before long they'd see the dust of other bunches moving in the same direction. And the last mile or so there would be flocks of sage hens plodding along in single file, also on the way for their evening drink.

When they finally reached the rim overlooking the water hole, the whole band stopped while the leader looked the country over carefully. If there was another band of horses ahead of them they waited until they'd finished and gone away, for two strange bands will not drink at the same time. And, too, there was always a certain amount of danger connected with these isolated water holes. Wild horse hunters sometimes waited there, and the big gray wolves skulked about looking for a chance to pull down any animal that got trapped in the deep mud.

The blind colt enjoyed these trips, however. His ears picked up the disgruntled cluckings of the waddling sage hens, and he smelled the fresh scent of the sagebrush and any number of other pungent desert weeds drying in the hot wind. And while still a long way from the water hole all the horses would smell the water and hurry a little faster.

When they reached the ridge he stood with the others examining the country for danger, throwing his head high and distending his nostrils as far as he could. When the stallion bugled through his nose, the colt tried to do the same.

When they finally started down the trail he'd kick and squeal with excitement, nipping the flanks and hocks of whatever horse was nearest and generally stirring up confusion.

But the water hole itself always frightened him a little, for it was surrounded by a wide band of mud, dried and cracked on top, and thick and gummy under the crust. It wasn't like the nice squishy stuff he'd waded in earlier in the summer. This mud made strange sucking noises around the horses' feet and seemed to be trying to pull them down.

At first he always stayed on firm ground while the brown mare drank, waiting for her. But as the summer got drier and the colt older the mare's supply of milk grew less and less. By this time the colt was able to graze a little so he wasn't troubled by lack of food, but he did begin to get thirsty. So one day he ventured out across the mud himself, being careful to pick a place that had been packed firmer than the rest. Except for the sucking noises around his feet, nothing happened, so after that he always drank with the others.

But one day he accidently shoved up against a short-tempered old mare and she whacked him in the ribs with her heels. The colt was startled and plunged away, landing in a boggy spot the others had been avoiding.

His hoofs, being small and sharp, didn't give him the support that flatter ones of an older horse would have, and he felt himself sinking. The harder he tried to pull his feet loose the deeper he sank. He whinneyed in terror and lunged with all his power, but all he could do was work himself deeper and deeper into the sticky mud.

The brown mare had left her drinking as soon as she heard him squall, but there was nothing she could do but nuzzle him and whicker encouragingly. By the time he was exhausted he had thrown himself partly on his side and was trapped beyond any chance of escape without help. He lay there, covered with mud, his sides heaving and his nostrils showing their red inner side.

The horses milled round, excited by his struggles and his frightened whinneying, but after a time they all went away except for the brown mare standing guard.

She stood over him and nuzzled him with her nose and wiped mud off with her tongue, comforting him as much as possible. By spells he struggled, trying to get to his feet. But after a time he wore himself out completely and just lay and shivered.

That night was the longest he'd ever known. He heard the sound of other horses coming to drink, and the squeals and thump of hoofs on ribs as the brown mare drove them off.

Somewhere in the night there was the smell of a big gray wolf prowling near, and the snorting and stamping of the mare as she circled between the blind colt and the danger.

In the morning he heard the small sounds of sage chickens and little animals drinking, but

nothing else. He and the brown mare were alone. She grazed nearby, returning to the trapped colt whenever he moved or made a sound.

It was late in the morning when the mare threw up her head to listen for a sound the colt had heard some time before. The sound of a shod horse, and from his steady gait it was plain there was a cowboy on his back. In a little while Whitey showed up on old Spot. There was much to be done these days, what with riding out to check the water holes and the like, so Torwal quite often sent him out to ride alone. And when Whitey saw the colt bogged down he was mighty glad that Torwal was not along this particular morning, because he felt sure Torwal would have argued that the colt had best be shot.

He rode up and sat a minute in his saddle while the mare watched him. This time she didn't show fight. Perhaps somehow she knew there was no need. Whitey talked soothingly to her and to the colt while he took down his rope. Shaking out a noose as he'd seen Uncle Torwal do in such cases, he rode carefully out across the mud as close as possible to the colt. The mare followed anxiously, but still not interfering. After a few unsuccessful attempts he got the loop around the colt's neck and took a dally around the saddle horn. Then, working carefully, he edged Spot towards solid ground. As the noose tightened on the colt's neck he began to struggle again. But now with the pull of the rope to help him, he was soon dragged out to firm ground.

He was a messy looking sight, with all that mud caked on him, as he lay there getting his breath. But luckily he wasn't chilled as he would have been later in the year. The brown mare trotted around like an old hen with a bunch of ducks, snorting and whinneying to herself and smelling and nudging the colt. Working very carefully and without getting out of his saddle, Whitey shook the muddy noose from the colt's neck and rode off a few yards to watch.

For a while the colt was content to lay on the grass and rest while the mare nosed him over to see if he was all right, and licked the mud off his coat. But after being in the mud all night he was mighty hungry, so it wasn't long before he struggled to his feet. His legs were pretty wobbly under him, but beyond that he didn't seem to be damaged any. And by the time the mare had nursed him and polished him from head to foot he looked and felt about as good as new, so they started slowly up the trail the way the other horses had gone.

All this time Whitey had quietly watched them from a distance, with his chest thrown out and as near strutting as is possible for a fellow sitting on a sleepy old pinto horse to be. He'd been busting for some time to get a chance to pull a bogged crittur out of the mud by himself. And for it to be his blind colt was almost more excitement than he could hold!

After the mare and colt had disappeared over the ridge he managed to get his attention back on his business and climbed down to clean the mud off his rope before he coiled it back on the saddle.

When that was finished he cocked his hand-me-down Stetson as far on one side as it would go and rode away, admiring his shadow more than a little. He kind of hoped he'd get a chance to rope a wolf or some such thing to sort of finish his day out right.

from JUSTIN MORGAN HAD A HORSE

Marguerite Henry

No one has written more thrilling tales of different breeds of horses than has Mrs. Henry, who, like the illustrator of her books, Wesley Dennis, knows and loves horses. The little wild horse about whom she wrote a book, Misty of Chincoteague, *lives with Mr. and Mrs. Henry, and eats Christmas dinner with them each year.* King of the Wind, *the story of the ancestor of the famous race horse, Man o' War, won the Newbery Award in 1949. The episode given here comes from a book about the ancestor of a special breed of horses, the sturdy and willing Morgan horse. Little Bub, the horse hero, is given to the schoolmaster Justin Morgan in payment of a debt. Young Joel Goss, who has been apprenticed to Miller Chase and who is also a friend of the schoolmaster, loves the colt from the time he first sets eyes on him, and undertakes to gentle him.*

Little Bub Is Rented Out

Never was a colt so willing to be gentled. After but two lessons, he wore a halter as if it were part of him. Like his forelock. Or his tail.

Next Joel tried the harness, and slipped a bit between his nippers and his back teeth. Bub hated the bit. He did not mind rope or leather things, but this iron was cold and frightening.

One night Joel warmed the bit in his hands, and from then on, the colt accepted it without even jerking.

Whenever Bub behaved well, Joel let him bury his nose in a bucket of oats—all the while telling him what a fine, smart horse he was. "You're my reddish-brown stallion," he would say. "Soon you'll be *big* for your size! And then you've got to be so smart and willing that even an ornery man will have no excuse to touch a whip to you. I couldn't abide that!" he added, his fists doubled.

Some nights Joel fastened a horn lantern to an old two-wheeled cart of his father's. Then, filling the cart with stones for weight, he would drive the horse over the rolling hills. Some nights he rode bareback. He practiced pulling the colt up short. He practiced walking him, trotting him, racing him. Often they would travel ten miles in an evening.

Late on one of these evenings Joel burst into the schoolhouse so full of laughter he could scarcely talk.

The children were gone, and the boy's laughter was so hearty that the schoolmaster joined in without knowing why.

Between spasms, Joel managed to gasp, "You should have seed that little hound-dog run!"

"What little hound-dog?"

"Why Abel Hooper's," giggled Joel, bursting into fresh laughter. "He comes a-tearing out the gate and begins yammering at Little Bub and nipping his forelegs. Oh ho, ho, ho!"

"What did Bub do?"

"What did he *do*?" shrieked Joel. "Why he sprung forward like a cat outen a bag. And that idiot hound was too muddled to go home. He turned tail and streaked down the road with Bub after him."

Joel had to wipe away his tears before he could go on. "Finally," he chuckled, "the hound got so beat out I took pity on him and reined in. Why the way Little Bub can climb hills," breathed Joel, "it's like he had wings!"

When Mister Goss discovered Joe training the colt, he was furious at first. Then he boasted and bragged about it at Chase's Inn: "All that boy knows about horses he got from me!"

But the truth of the matter was that in watching his father train a colt, Joel had learned what not to do, as well as what to do. While his father could break a horse in a matter of hours, his horses often seemed broken in spirit, too. The boy was determined that this should not happen to his colt. And it had not. Little Bub's eyes were still dancy. He still tossed his mane and nosed the sky. He still had a frisky look about him. No, he had lost none of his spirit.

The moon waned and became full again. Not once, but many times. For months the schoolmaster said no more about selling the colt. And about the time when Joel began to think that Little Bub might be his forever, a man came to call on the schoolmaster. He was Ezra Fisk, a new settler.

"I've been watching a lad drive a smallish horse in the moonlight," Mister Fisk said, "and by inquiring at the Inn, I understand the horse belongs to you, sir."

The schoolmaster nodded.

"Now I have fifteen acres of wooded land, and Evans, my hired man, will need a horse to clear it. This Evans is a wiry hand, and I figure that he and a horse with a little getup about him could clear the land in a year's time."

"You would like to buy the horse?" asked Master Morgan.

"No indeed, sir. I do not wish to buy such a *little* animal. I merely wish to rent him. I stand ready to pay fifteen dollars a year, *and* his keep of course. I'll send Evans around in the morning to fetch him."

Joel was setting a log in the sawmill when he heard the cloppety-clop of hoofs coming down the river road. This in itself was nothing to make him stop work, but from the uneven beat of the hoofs he could tell that the animals were not traveling in a team. And then without looking up at all he knew. He knew that the lighter hoofbeats were those of Little Bub. Not until he had started the saw, did he face the road.

It *was* Little Bub all right, not ten rods away. He was tied on to the back of a wagon pulled by a fat ox. His reddish coat glinted in the sunlight. And he held his head high, as if he found nothing at all disgraceful in being tied to an oxcart.

The blood hammered in Joel's head. He might have whistled and felt the hot pride of having the little horse nicker in answer. Instead, he kept murmuring the schoolmaster's words: "I've got to pay off my debts before I die. Will you gentle the colt, lad?"

Well, Bub had been gentled all right. *Anyone* could see that. With a heavy heart, he watched the procession as it clattered over the log bridge and climbed up and up the steep hill. Finally it disappeared over the brow, and nothing was left of it. Nothing but a wisp of dust.

The Pulling Bee

By the time spring came on, Joel and Miller Chase were friends. In the late afternoons, while Mistress Chase napped, the miller often gave Joel a whole hour to himself.

One afternoon early in May Joel stood looking out the inn door. Suddenly the yard began filling with big-faced dray horses and oxen, and men were gathering about a huge pine log.

"Is it a pulling bee?" asked Joel, turning to Miller Chase quickly.

"If Nathan Nye is about, looking mighty important and bossy, you can be expecting most anything. He was ever good at fixing contests."

"He's there!" exclaimed Joel. "And he's got tug chains."

"H'm," mused the miller, tapping his cheek, "if I was a boy now with no chores to do, it seems like I'd skedaddle right out there."

Joel grinned over his shoulder, and in no time at all he was helping Mister Nye fasten the tug chains to a big dappled mare.

The mare's owner, Abel Hooper, was too busy boasting to the farmers to be of any help. "A mighty lucky thing I'm first," he was saying. "Lucy and me'll pull this here piece a kindling to the sawmill in one pull. Then you can all hyper on home whilst it's still daylight."

But Abel Hooper had to eat his words, for Lucy barely caused the log to tremble.

One after another, the beasts had their turn, and no matter how whips cracked or masters yelled, the log seemed rooted to the earth.

"Folks, I guess it's up to the oxen now," Nathan Nye was saying, when into the yard came Evans riding Little Bub.

"Hey, Nathan," called Evans, "what's all the hullabaloo?"

" 'Tis a pulling bee," answered Mister Nye, "but can't none of the beasts pull that there pine log to the sawmill in three pulls or less. Just look at Hooper's big mare! She's roaring from the try. And Biggle's gelding—his muscles are still a-hitching and a-twitching. Even Ezra Wiggins' beast failed. None of them can budge the log."

"None except my one-horse team!" crowed Evans.

Joel held his breath. He felt scared right down to his toes.

The crowd snickered. Then it hooted.

"*That* little flea? Why, he's just a sample of a horse. He ain't no bigger than a mouse's whisker! Besides, his tail is so long, he's liable to get all tangled up and break a leg."

Evans looked over the horseflesh. "Little Bub," he said slowly, "ain't exactly what you'd call a dray horse, but whatever he's hitched to generally has to come the first time trying."

"Take him on home," scoffed Nathan Nye. "When we have a contest for ponies, we'll be letting you know."

Above the man-talk Joel heard the sharp voice of Mistress Chase. "Boy! You come here!"

On his way in Joel stopped only long enough to press his face hard against Little Bub's nose.

At the door Mistress Chase handed him a kettle of hasty pudding and a long stick.

"Hang the kettle over the fire," she said, "and stir and stir until I tell you to quit."

"*Hasty* pudding!" muttered Joel to himself. "It beats me how it got its name!"

Evans strutted into the room just then. "Chase!" he called to the miller. "I'll wager a barrel of cider that my horse can move that pine log to the sawmill in two pulls. But first, pour me a mugful. I'm dying of thirst."

At sound of Evans' voice Joel almost upset the pudding.

"Boy!" shrilled Mistress Chase. "Mind your work. Hasty pudding's not meant to feed the fire!"

For once Joel paid no heed. He tore across the room and grabbed Mister Evans by the sleeve.

"Mister Evans!" he cried. "Little Bub's been dragging logs all day. You hain't going to enter him in the pulling bee?"

Evans gulped his drink. "Go away, Joel," he snapped in annoyance. "When I want advice, I'll not ask it of a whippersnapper."

The little horse meanwhile was feasting upon all the fresh green shoots within his range. They tasted juicy and delicious after the business of logging.

One by one the stars dusted the sky. Nathan Nye brought out a lanthorn so Mister Evans could see to fasten his tugchains to the log.

Joel followed Evans about like a puppy. Evans stood it as long as he could. Finally he shoved the boy aside.

"A nettle hain't half as pesky as you," he growled. "Stand back or I'll clout you."

Now Evans was stepping off the ten rods from the log to the mill.

"Want to give up before you start?" scoffed Nathan Nye.

"No such a thing. Why, I'm actually ashamed to ask my horse to pull such a little log. Now if you'll find me three stout men to sit astride the log, why then I'll ask him."

Joel bit his lips to keep from crying out. He hid his face in the horse's tangled mane. "Oh, Bub, my poor little Bub," he choked, "none of the big creatures could budge the log, and now with three men besides. Oh Bub, Bub . . ."

Laughter rang up and down the valley. "Ho-ho-ho—that pint-sized cob to pull such a big log! Ho-ho . . ."

Nathan Nye had no trouble at all in finding three brawny volunteers. As the men straddled the log, they joked and laughed and poked one another in the ribs.

"Look to your feet, men!" warned Evans. "This horse means business. Something's got to give."

Nye held the lanthorn aloft. It lighted the circle of faces. They were tense with excitement. Some of the men were placing last-minute bets with one another. Some were whittling like mad. Others twirled their whips nervously. Joel was white with anger.

Nye repeated the warning. "Look to your feet, men!"

Someone tittered.

Evans felt to see if the little horse was hitched securely. Then, "Git up!" he roared, as he slashed the whip across Bub's back.

The little horse galvanized into action. First, he backed ever so slightly. Then his powerful neck bent low, as if to give every muscle a chance to get going. Now he was straining forward. You could see his muscles grow firm and swell up like rubber balls. You could see the white foam come out on his body.

Joel, too, was drenched in sweat. The silence was heavy, like a gray blanket.

At last there was the groaning of chains. The log trembled. Slowly it moved. It kept on moving. It was more than halfway to the saw!

The little horse stopped. His sides were heaving. Joel breathed in and out with the horse. He felt as if his lungs were on fire. There was no sound at all from the crowd. Overhead a baby robin, trying to get settled for the night, chirped insistently.

Now Evans commanded again. And again the horse went through the same motions. He backed slightly. He bent his head. He strained every muscle. Again the log was moving, moving, moving. This time it did not stop until it reached the sawmill!

And still nobody had made a sound. The three men were as silent as the log they sat upon. Only the horse's breathing pierced the quiet.

Then everyone began shouting at once. "Hooray for Morgan's colt! Hooray! Hooray! Hooray for the big-little horse."

Joel had his arms around Bub's neck. His whole body ached, as if he had moved the log himself. "It's over! It's over! You did it, Bub! You did it!" he kept repeating. Then he sobbed a little from exhaustion and relief.

The horse lipped Joel's cheek and neck. He almost tried to say, "It's all right, Joel; don't be taking it so hard." He was steaming and tired, but it was good to be near the boy again. It was good. He nickered softly.

A RANGE COLT

Will James

Will James was a cowboy, and he wrote in the cowboy vernacular. But don't be deceived by the bad grammar. The story of Smoky the cowhorse is told with consummate skill and feeling. It sets a high standard for telling stories about animals of any sort because it is told with complete fidelity to the species. Smoky lives, enjoys, and suffers as a horse, never as a human being. This book won the Newbery Award in 1927, and its popularity has never waned.

It seemed like Mother Nature was sure agreeable that day when the little black colt came to the range world, and tried to get a footing with his long wobblety legs on the brown prairie sod. Short stems of new green grass was trying to make their way up thru the last year's faded growth, and reaching for the sun's warm rays. Taking in all that could be seen, felt, and inhaled, there was no day, time, nor place that could beat that spring morning on the sunny side of the low prairie butte where Smoky the colt was foaled.

"Smoky" wouldn't have fitted the colt as a name just then on account he was jet black, but that name wasn't attached onto him till he was a four-year-old, which was when he first started being useful as a saddle horse. He didn't see the first light of day thru no box-stall window, and there was no human around to make a fuss over him and try to steady him on his feet for them first few steps. Smoky was just a little range colt, and all the company he had that first morning of his life was his watchful mammy.

Smoky wasn't quite an hour old when he begin to take interest in things. The warm spring sun was doing its work and kept a-pouring warmth all over that slick little black hide, and right on thru his little body, till pretty soon his head come up kinda shaky and he begin nosing around them long front legs that was stretched out in front of him. His mammy was close by him, and at the first move the colt made she run her nose along his short neck and nickered. Smoky's head went up another two inches at the sound, and his first little answering nicker was heard. Of course a person would of had to listen mighty close to hear it, but then if you'd a-watched his nostrils quivering you could tell that's just what he was trying to do.

That was the starting of Smoky. Pretty soon his ears begin to work back and forth towards the sound his mammy would make as she moved. He was trying to locate just where she was. Then something moved right in front of his nose about a foot; it'd been there quite a good spell but he'd never realized it before; besides his vision was a little dim yet and he wasn't interested much till that something moved again and planted itself still closer.

Being it was right close he took a sniff at it. That sniff recorded itself into his brain and as much as told him that all was well. It was one of his mammy's legs. His ears perked up and he tried nickering again with a heap better result than the first time.

One good thing called for another and natural like he made a sudden scramble to get up, but his legs wouldn't work right, and just about when he'd got his belly clear of the ground, and as he was resting there for another try at the rest of the way up, one of his front legs quivered and buckled at the elbow, and the whole works went down.

He layed there flat on his side and breathing hard. His mammy nickered encouragement, and it wasn't long when his head was up again and his legs spraddled out all around him the same as before. He was going to try again, but next time he was going to be more sure of his *ground*. He was studying, it seemed like, and sniffing of his legs and then the earth, like he was trying to figger out how he was going to get one to stand up on the other. His mammy kept a-circling around and a-talking to him in horse language; she'd give him a shove with her nose, then walk away and watch him.

The spring air, which I think is most for the benefit of all that's young, had a lot to do to keep Smoky from laying still for very long. His vision was getting clearer fast, and his strength was coming in just as fast. Not far away, but still too far for Smoky to see, was little calves, little white-faced fellers a-playing and bucking around and letting out wall-eyed bellers at their mammies, running out a ways and then running back, tails up, at a speed that'd make a greyhound blush for shame.

There was other little colts too all a-cavorting around and tearing up good sod, but with all them calves and colts that was with the bunches of cattle or horses scattered out on the range, the same experience of helplessness that Smoky was going thru had been theirs for a spell, and a few hadn't been as lucky as Smoky in their first squint at daylight. Them few had come to the range world when the ground was still covered with snow, or else cold spring rains was a-pouring down to wet 'em to the bone.

Smoky's mother had sneaked out of the bunch a few days before Smoky came, and hid in a lonely spot where she'd be sure that no cattle nor horses or even riders would be around. In a few days, and when Smoky would be strong enough to lope out, she'd go back again; but in the meantime she wanted to be alone with her colt and put all her attention on him, without having to contend with chasing off big inquisitive geldings or jealous fillies.

She was of range blood, which means mostly mustang with strains of Steeldust or Coach throwed in. If hard winters come and the range was covered with heavy snows, she knowed of high ridges where the strong winds kept a few spots bare and where feed could be got. If droughts came to dry up the grass and water holes, she sniffed the air for moisture and drifted out acrost the plain which was her home range, to the high mountains where things was more normal. There was cougars and wolves in that high country, but her mustang instinct made her the "fittest." She circled around and never went under where the lion was perched a-waiting for her, and the wolf never found her where she could be cornered.

Smoky had inherited that same instinct of his mammy's, but on that quiet spring morning he wasn't at all worried about enemies. His mammy was there, and besides he had a hard job ahead that was taking all of his mind to figger out: that was to stand on them long things which was fastened to his body and which kept a-spraddling out in all directions.

The first thing to do was to gather 'em under him and try again. He did that easy enough, and then he waited and gathered up all the strength that was in him. He sniffed at the ground to make sure it was there and then his head went up, his front feet stretched out in front of him, and with his hind legs all under him, he used all that strength he'd been storing up and pushed himself up on his front feet, his hind legs straightened up to steady him; and as luck would have it there was just enough distance between each leg to keep him up there. All he had to do was to keep them legs stiff and from buckling up under him, which wasn't at all easy, cause getting up to where he was had used up a lot of his strength, and them long legs of his was doing a heap of shaking.

All would of been well maybe, only his mammy nickered "that's a good boy," and that's what queered Smoky. His head went up proud as a peacock and he forgot all about keeping his props stiff and under him. Down he went the whole length of his legs, and there he layed the same as before.

But he didn't lay long this time. He either liked the sport of going up and coming down or else he was getting peeved; he was up again, mighty shaky, but he was up sure enough. His mammy came to him. She sniffed at him and he sniffed back. Then nature played another hand and he nursed, the first nourishment was took in, his tummy warmed up and strength came fast. Smoky was an hour and a half old and up to stay.

The rest of that day was full of events for Smoky. He explored the whole country, went up big mountains two feet high, wide valleys six or eight feet acrost, and at one time was as far as twelve feet away from his mammy all by himself. He shied at a rock once; it was a dangerous-looking rock, and he kicked at it as he went past. All that action being put on at once come pretty near being too much for him and he come close to measuring his whole length on Mother Earth once again. But luck was with him, and taking it all he had a mighty good time. When the sun went to sinking over the blue ridges in the west, Smoky, he missed all the beauty of the first sunset in his life—he was stretched out full length, of his own accord this time, and sound asleep.

The night was a mighty good rival of what the day had been. All the stars was out and showing off, and the braves was a-chasing the buffalo plum around the Big Dipper, the water hole of The Happy Hunting Grounds. But all that was lost to Smoky; he was still asleep and recuperating from his first day's adventures, and most likely he'd kept on sleeping for a good long spell, only his mammy who was standing guard over him happened to get a little too close and stepped on his tail.

Smoky must have been in the middle of some bad dream. His natural instinct might of pictured some enemy to his mind, and something that looked like a wolf or a bear must of had him cornered for sure. Anyway, when he felt his tail pinched that way he figgered that when a feller begins to *feel* it's sure time to act, and he did. He shot up right under his mammy's chin, let out a squeal, and stood there ready to fight. He took in the country for *feet* and *feet* around and looking for the enemy that'd nipped him, and finally in his scouting around that way he run acrost the shadow of his mammy. That meant but one thing, safety; and that accounted for and put away as past left room for a craving he'd never noticed in his excitement. He was hungry, and proceeded right then and there to take on a feed of his mammy's warm, rich milk.

The sky was beginning to get light in the east, the stars was fading away and the buffalo hunters had went to rest. A few hours had passed since Smoky had been woke up out of his bad dream and there he was, asleep again. He'd missed his first sunset and now he was sleeping thru his first sunrise, but he was going to be prepared for that new day's run, and the strength he was accumulating through them sleeps and between feeds would sure make him fit to cover a lot of territory.

There wasn't a move out of him till the sun was well up and beginning to throw a good heat. He stacked up on a lot of that heat, and pretty soon one of his ears moved, then the other. He took a long breath and stretched. Smoky was coming to life. His mammy nickered, and that done the trick; Smoky raised his head, looked around, and proceeded to get up. After a little time that was done and bowing his neck he stretched again. Smoky was ready for another day.

The big day started right after Smoky had his feed; then his mother went to grazing and moving away straight to the direction of some trees a mile or so to the south. A clear spring was by them trees, and water is what Smoky's mammy wanted the most right then. She was craving for a drink of that cold water, but you'd never thought it by the way she traveled. She'd nose around at the grass and wait for spells, so as little Smoky could keep up with her and still find time to investigate everything what throwed a shadow.

A baby cottontail had jumped up once right under his nose, stood there a second too scared to move, and pretty soon made a high dive between the colt's long legs and hit for his hole; Smoky never seen the rabbit or even knowed he was there or he might of been running yet, cause that's what he'd been looking for, an excuse to run. But he finally made up an excuse, and a while later as he brushed past a long dry weed and it tickled his belly, he let out a squeal and went from there.

His long legs tangled and untangled themselves as he run, and he was sure making speed. Around and around he went and finally lined out straight away from where his mammy was headed. She nickered for him and waited, all patience. He turned after a spell and headed for his mammy again the same as tho he'd run acrost another enemy at the other end; and as he got close to his mammy he let out a buck, a squeal, a snort, and stopped—he was sure some little wild horse.

It took a couple of hours for them two to make that mile to the spring. The mother drank a lot of that good water, a few long breaths and drank some more till the thirst was all gone. Smoky came over and nosed at the pool, but he didn't take on any of the fluid, it looked just like so much thin air to him, the same with the tender green grass that was beginning to grow in bunches everywhere; it was just growing for him to run on.

The rest of that day was pretty well used up around that one spot; adventures of all kinds was numerous for Smoky, and when he wasn't stretched out and asleep there was plenty of big stumps in the cottonwood grove that could be depended on to give him the scare he'd be looking for.

But there was other things and more threatening than stumps which Smoky hadn't as yet spotted, like for instance,—a big cayote had squatted and been watching him thru dead willow branches. He wasn't at all interested in the action Smoky was putting into his play, and only wished the colt's mammy would move away a little further when he would then take a chance and try to get him down—colt meat was his favorite dish and he sure wasn't going to let no chance slip by even if it took a whole day's waiting for one to show itself.

A couple of chances had come his way but they was queered by Smoky's mammy being too close, and he knowed better than show himself and get run down by them hoofs of hers. Finally, and when he seen his appetite wouldn't win anything by sticking around that spot any longer, he took a last sniff and came out of his hiding place. Keeping the willows between him and the horses, he loped out till he was at a safe running distance and where he could see all around him, and there he squatted again, in plain sight this time. He hadn't quite made up his mind as yet whether to go or stick around a while longer. Just about then Smoky spots him.

To him, the cayote was just another stump, but more interesting than the others he'd kicked at, on account that this stump moved, and that promised a lot of excitement. With a bowed neck and kinked tail Smoky trotted up towards the cayote. The cayote just set there and waited and when the colt got to within a few feet from him, he started away and just fast enough so as the colt's curiosity would make him follow. If he could only get the colt over the ridge and out of his mammy's sight.

It all was only a lot of fun to Smoky, and besides he was bound to find out what was that gray and yellow object that could move and run and didn't at all look like his mammy. His instinct was warning him steady as he went, but curiosity had the best of him, and it wasn't till he was over the hill before his instinct got above his curiosity and he seen that all wasn't well.

The cayote had turned and quicker than a flash made a jump for Smoky's throat. The generations of mustang blood that'd fought the lobo and cougar, and which was the same blood that flowed in Smoky's veins, is all that saved the colt. That inherited instinct made him do the right thing at the right time, he whirled quicker than lightning and let fly with both hind feet with the result that the cayote's teeth just pinched the skin under his jaws. But even at that, he wasn't going to get rid of his enemy (it was a sure enough enemy this time) that easy, and as he kicked he felt the weight of the cayote, and then a sharp pain on his hamstrings.

Smoky was scared, and he let out a squeal that sure made every living thing in that neighborhood set up and wonder; it was a plain and loud distress signal, and it was answered. His mammy shot up the hill, took in the goings on at a glance, and ears back, teeth a-shining, tore up the earth and lit into the battle like a ton of dynamite.

The battle was over in a second, and with hunks of yellow fur a-flying all directions it wound up in a chase. The cayote was in the lead and he stayed in the lead till a second hill took him out of sight.

Smoky was glad to follow his mammy back to the spring and on to the other side a ways. He didn't shy at the stumps he passed on the way, and the twig that tickled his tummy didn't bring no play. He was hungry and tired, and when the first was tended to and his appetite called for no more he lost no time to picking out a place to rest his weary bones. A thin stream of blood was drying on one of his hind legs, but there was no pain, and when the sun set and the shadow of his mammy spread out over him he was sound asleep, and maybe dreaming of stumps, of stumps that moved.

When the sun came up the next morning, Smoky was up too, and eyes half closed was standing still as the big boulder next to him and sunned himself. A stiff hind leg was a reminder of what happened the day before, but the experience was forgotten far as dampening his spirits was concerned, even the stiffness wouldn't hold him back from whatever the new day would hold. He'd always remember the cayote, and from then on never mistake him for a stump, but that sure wasn't going to take any play out of him.

He was two days old now and strength had piled up fast, he felt there was no trail too long for him and when the sun was a couple of hours high that morning and his mother showed indications that she wanted to drift he sure wasn't dragging along behind. The stiffness gradually went out of his hind leg as he traveled, and by the afternoon of that day he was again shying at everything and sometimes even shying at nothing at all.

They kept a-traveling and traveling, and it seemed like to Smoky that the trail was getting pretty long after all. They skirted the flat along the foot of the mountains, crossed one high ridge, and many creeks, and still his mother was drifting on. She wouldn't hardly even stop for him to nurse, and Smoky was getting cranky, and tired.

The pace kept up till the sun was well on its way down, when it slackened some and finally the mother went to grazing. A short while later Smoky was layed out full length and dead to the world.

Smoky didn't know and didn't care much just then, but his mammy was headed back to her home range, where there was lots of horses and other little colts for him to play with; and when late that night she lined out again traveling steady he wasn't in any too good a humor.

Finally it seemed like they'd got there, for his mammy after watering at a creek went to grazing at the edge of some big cottonwoods; she showed no indications of wanting to go any further. Right there Smoky was willing to take advantage of the chance and recuperate for all he was worth. The sun came up, but Smoky was in the shade of the cottonwoods what was beginning to leaf out. He slept on and a twitching ear once in long spells is all that showed he was still alive.

That day never seen much of him; once in a while he'd get up and nurse but right away after he'd disappear again and stretch out flat on the warm earth.

He kept that up till way in the middle of the next night, and it was well towards morning before he felt like he was all horse again.

He come out of it in fine shape though, and he was stronger than ever. His vision was taking more territory too, and he was getting so he could see near half as far as his mammy could. She was the first to see the bunch of range horses trailing in to water early that morning. Smoky heard her nicker as she recognized the bunch and it drawed a heap of interest as to what she nickering about, for he was right there alongside of her and he couldn't see nothing for her to nicker at, but pretty soon he could hear the horses as they trailed towards him. His ears straightened towards the sound and a while later he could make out the shapes of 'em. Smoky just kind of quivered at the sight of so many that looked like his mammy. He was all interested, but at the same time, and even tho his instinct told him that all was well, he had no hankering to leave his mammy's side till he knowed for sure just what was up.

The mother watched the bunch coming closer with ears pointed straight ahead, but soon as some of the leaders discovered little Smoky there was a commotion and they all begin crowding in to get a look at and greet the newcomer, about which time the mother layed her ears back. It was a warning that none of 'em come too close.

Little Smoky's knees was a-shaking under him at the sight of so many of his kind; he leaned against his mammy half afraid, but his head was up far as he could get it and facing 'em and showed by the shine in his eyes that he liked the whole proceeding mighty well at that. He rubbed nostrils with a strange gelding which was braver than the rest and dared come close, and when that gelding was nipped at by his mammy he had a mighty strong hankering to help her along just for fun, and nip him himself.

The preliminary introduction took a good hour, and the mother stood guard; not for fear that any of 'em would harm Smoky, but she wanted it understood from the start that he was her little colt and she had the say over him. It finally *was* understood, but it took all that day and part of the next for the bunch to get used in having the new little feller around and quit making a fuss over him.

They was all jealous of one another and fought amongst themselves to be the only one near him, and his mother, of course she'd declared herself from the start, and it was took for granted from all around that her place in Smoky's heart couldn't be considered, and all knowed better than try and chase her away from him. Fillies and old mares, young geldings and old ponies and all, had it out as to which was the most fit to tag along and play with Smoky and keep a watchful eye over him along with his mammy. All wanted the job, but a big buckskin saddle horse who all the time had been the boss of the herd took it to hand to show them that *he* would be the all around guardeen for Smoky, and second only to his mammy. He delivered a few swift kicks, pounded on some ribs, left teeth marks on shiny hides, and after taking one last look and making sure that all was persuaded, grazed out towards Smoky who by his mammy had watched the whole proceeding with a heap of interest.

There was three other little colts in the bunch besides Smoky, and each time one of them little fellers came the buckskin horse had to whip the bunch so as he'd have the say over the newest one. Now Smoky was the newest one, and the buckskin horse had first rights as an outsider once again. He was an old horse full of scars showing where he'd had many a scrap; there was saddle marks on his back and at one time he had been a mighty fine cowhorse. Now he was pensioned; he'd more than earned a rest and all he had to do for the rest of his life was to pick out good feed grounds for the winter, shady places and tenderest green grass for the summer, and his other interest in life was them little colts that came in springtime.

Smoky's mother was young, at least ten years younger than the buckskin horse, but the buckskin was like a colt compared to her when it come to be playful. She had the responsibility of Smoky and while she let him play with her, kick or bite at her, she never played with him and once in a while if he'd get too rough she'd let him know about it. She loved little Smoky with all her heart and would of died for him any time, and her main interest was to see that she kept in condition so that Smoky would never be stunted by lacking of rich milk. She had no time for play.

And that's where the old buckskin came in. Him and Smoky was soon acquainted, in a short while they was playing, Smoky would kick at him while the big buckskin nipped him easy and careful along the flank, then he'd run away from him, and the little colt had a lot of fun chasing that big hunk of horseflesh all over the country. The rest of the bunch would watch the two play and with no effort to hide how jealous they felt.

Smoky's mother kept her eye on the buckskin, but never interfered, she knowed, and it was only when Smoky came back to her, tired and hungry, that she put her ears back and warned him to keep away.

It took a few days before the buckskin would allow any of the other horses to get near Smoky, and then he had no say about it for he found that Smoky had his own ideas about things, and if he wanted to mingle in with the other horses that was his business, and all the buckskin could do then was to try and keep the other horses away. That was quite a job, specially if Smoky wanted to be with them. So the buckskin finally had to give it up and do the best he could which was to see that none of 'em done him any harm. But none of 'em had any intentions of doing the little colt any harm, and as it was it looked like Smoky had 'em all buffaloed. He'd tear in after some big horse like he was going to eat him up and all that big horse would do was to scatter out like the devil was after him.

Smoky was the boss and pet of the herd for a good two weeks and then one day, here comes another little feller, a little bay colt just two

days old and trailing in alongside his mammy. Smoky was left in the background and witnessed the same fuss and commotion that was done over him that morning by the creek. The buckskin horse once again fought his way in that new little feller's heart, and right away he forgot Smoky.

But Smoky never seen anything wrong to that, he went on to playing with every horse that would have him and it wasn't long till he picked up with a young filly and afterwards went to mingling with other young colts.

From then on Smoky had more freedom, he could go out a ways without having some big overgrowed horse tagging along, but he never went far and if he did he always came back a heap faster than when he started out. But them spring days was great for Smoky; he found out a lot of things amongst which was, that grass was good to eat, and water mighty fine to drink when the day was hot. He seen cayotes again and the bigger he got the less he was afraid of 'em till he finally went to chasing every one of 'em he'd see.

Then one day he run acrost another yellow animal. That animal didn't look dangerous, and what's more it was hard for Smoky to make out just what it was, and he was bound to find out. He followed that animal plum to the edge of some willows, and the queer part of it was that animal didn't seem at all in a hurry to get away, it was mumbling along and just taking its time and Smoky was mighty tempted to plant one front foot right in the middle of it and do some pawing, but as luck would have it he didn't have the chance, it'd got in under some willows and all that was sticking out was part of the animal's tail. Smoky took a sniff at it without learning anything outside that it shook a little. There didn't seem to be no danger, so the next sniff he took was a little closer, and that done the trick. Smoky let out a squeal and a snort as he felt his nostrils punctured in half a dozen places with four-inch porcupine quills.

But Smoky was lucky, for if he'd been a couple of inches closer there'd been quills rammed into his nose plum up to his eyes, which would've caused a swelling in such size that he couldn't of been able to eat and most likely starve to death. As it was there was just a few of them quills in his nostrils, and compared to the real dose he might of got, it was just a mild warning to him. Another lesson.

It was a few days later when he met another strange animal, or strange animals, for there was many of 'em. He didn't get much interest out of them somehow, but while they was handy maybe it was just as well for him to have a close look at one. Besides he had nothing else to do, and mammy wasn't far away.

His instinct had no warning to give as he strutted towards the smallest one of the strangers which he'd picked to investigate. He wasn't afraid of this animal and this animal didn't seem afraid of him so Smoky kept a-getting closer till one was within a couple of feet of the other. Both Smoky and this stranger was young, and mighty inquisitive, and neither as yet knowed that they'd sure be seeing plenty of each other's kind as they get older, that they'll be meeting thru the round-ups at the "cutting grounds," on "day herd" and on "night guard," on the long, hot, dusty trails. A cowboy will be riding Smoky then and keeping a whole herd on the move, a whole herd of the kind that little Smoky was so busy investigating that day. They'll be full grown then, and there'll be other young ones to take the place of them that's trailed in to the shipping point.

But Smoky wasn't as yet worried or even thought on what was to come, neither was the little white-faced calf he was exchanging squints with; and when the critter called her long-eared, split-hoofed baby to her side, Smoky just kicked up his heels, put his head down, and bucked and crowhopped all the way to where his mammy and the rest of the bunch was grazing.

Animals of field, forest, and jungle

from SMOKE ABOVE THE LANE

Meindert DeJong

Here is told an amusing and touching story of a strange friendship.

[A Tramp and a Baby Skunk]

In the wood there was a tramp—making pancakes. And in the wood there was a little skunk, sitting in a hollow stump—watching the tramp. Beside the wood there stood a long, old freight train. The freight train stood beside the wood, and stretched away beyond the wood, for it was easily a mile long. And there it stood. And it was early in the morning.

It was so early in the morning in this little wood in the far North country, that the morning sun was not even up. It was cold in the wood, even though this was a morning in the first week of September. It was so cold that the big tramp stopped making pancakes to rub his big cold hands.

The big tramp did not know the little skunk was watching him. He was too busy making pancakes. He fried them on a piece of tin over a little fire. Above the fire he had hung a big tomato can—the tramp was also making coffee. No, the big tramp did not know the skunk was there, and he was cheerfully humming as he made breakfast for himself over a little fire on the bank of a creek in the little wood. "Carry me back to old Virginny," he was humming.

But the tramp knew that the train was there! Busy as he was, from time to time he would stop his cheerful humming, and peer under the trees at the long, old freight train. He kept his eye on the train.

The little skunk kept his eye on the tramp. He sat in the dark, hollow stump, watching the tramp and listening to his cheerful humming. He sat and sniffed the wood smoke, and the lovely odor of pancakes and coffee that drifted on the wood smoke. He gurgled happily to himself—a tiny little gurgle. He was waiting for the tramp to leave. Then he would go to the little fire and pick up all the pancake crumbs. He did it every morning—ever since the tramp had come to the little wood, oh, many weeks ago.

The little skunk knew the tramp. The little skunk liked the tramp. He liked the tramp for his pancake crumbs and for his cheerful humming. And often he would follow the footsteps of the tramp—oh, just for fun. Just because he liked the tramp. But the tramp had never seen the little skunk.

This morning the tramp was in a hurry. He hurriedly took a last bite of pancake, he gulped a last swallow of coffee out of the tomato can, he stuffed some hot, left-over pancakes in a coat pocket, stamped out the fire, and hurried to the creek with the tomato can. He rinsed out the

coffee and filled the tomato can with water. He stuffed the tomato can with water into his other coat pocket. Then the big tramp hurried through the little wood toward the long, old freight train.

As soon as the big tramp was gone, the little skunk came out of the stump and ambled to the stamped-out fire. He found a crumb of pancake, he nibbled the crumb. He searched for more, but there were no more. He ambled to the creek, and took a little drink. He went back to the fire, but there just were no more pancake crumbs. So then the little skunk just went to the creek for still another little drink.

But the tramp had reached the edge of the wood, the tramp had come to the railroad fence that ran along the little wood. The big tramp looked carefully up and down the long train. He saw no one, he heard no one, and that pleased the tramp. With all his strength he hurriedly tore a board from the fence. And, with the heavy board on his shoulder, the big tramp hurried along the train until he came to a boxcar that he liked. He took the board and rammed the door of the boxcar open.

Once more the tramp looked up and down the train. He heard no one, he saw no one. He peeked inside the boxcar and saw that it was empty. That pleased the tramp. He grinned, and placed one end of the board in the open doorway of the boxcar. He hurried up the slanting board into the boxcar.

The tramp went to the farthest, darkest corner of the boxcar. He tugged the tomato can out of his pocket, and he carefully set it on the floor. And then he stretched himself down on the floor beside the old tomato can. He did not bother to close the door of the boxcar. He did not bother to throw the board down—it still slanted up into the open doorway. He went to sleep!

In the little wood the baby skunk had gone for still another drink to the clear, cool-water creek. The clear, cool-water creek wound in and out between the trees. It gurgled under fallen trees. It curled around the stumps of trees long gone. The little skunk dug at the foot of one of the stumps. He found a nice, fat grub. He nibbled the grub. He gurgled happily—a tiny little gurgle. It was such a delicious grub! But then he went back to the stamped-out fire. But now he was not looking for pancake crumbs, now he was looking for footsteps—the footsteps of the long-legged tramp. And then he found one!

The little skunk hurried from that first invisible footstep to the next invisible footstep. He began following them through the wood. The footsteps of the tramp were far apart. Here a footstep, there an invisible footstep, but the little skunk followed them as surely as if he could see them. He could not see them—he was a near-sighted little skunk but it was as if he saw them with his little crinkling nose, so surely did he follow them.

The little skunk followed the footsteps, and he gurgled his tiny little gurgle. He knew the tramp! He liked the tramp! And he liked to follow the tramp's big footsteps—just for fun. Just because he liked the tramp.

The little skunk came to the railroad fence. He stopped exactly where the tramp had stopped. But he did not watch the train! He was near-sighted, he could not see that far. No, he was following the footsteps. He followed them under the fence, he followed them along the train, and then he came to the slanting board. He stretched up to sharpen his nails on the slanting board. He smelled the footsteps going up the board. He went up the board! It was a big mistake.

The little skunk had hurried and hurried all the time as fast as a little skunk can hurry. But that was slow as slow. And now, when the skunk

went up the board, the Northern sun was shining over the trees into the doorway of the boxcar. The little skunk felt the warm sun. The sun was warm, the sun was good, the sun was warming his fur and his bones. The little skunk felt so good with the sun, he sank down in the sunny, sheltered doorway, curled his bushy tail over his nose and eyes—and went to sleep!

It was a terrible mistake.

It was a terrible mistake because the long, old freight train, standing on the railroad siding beside the little wood, was waiting for the fast express to come roaring by. Once the fast express train had rushed by on the main track, the slow old freight train would start up, and rattle and bang on its own slow way out of the far North country. The little skunk did not know that. The little skunk did not understand trains.

The tramp lay sleeping in the corner. The little skunk lay sleeping in the sunny doorway. And there—with a roar and a swoosh and a shriek—the fast express went thundering by. The shriek and roar so scared the tramp and skunk, they both jumped up, they both leaped high. But just as the tramp jumped to his feet, there with a mighty jolt and jerk the freight train started into motion. The mighty jerk knocked the big tramp right down again.

The mighty jerk had not only knocked the tramp down. The mighty jerk of the freight train knocked the slanting board out of the open doorway. The mighty jerk rammed the door of the boxcar tightly shut. The door flew shut—the empty boxcar became black and dark.

The terrified little skunk lay flat against the floor—lay trembling. But the tramp had gone down hard and lay where he had fallen—he lay still. He had hurt his head. He was stunned. He did not move.

Far up ahead on the mile-long train, the whistle of the old locomotive moaned and hooted. Far up ahead, the bell clanged. The whole train groaned and shook and rattled as the locomotive huffed and strained away from the little wood, back to the main track.

There went the train. It rolled and banged around a bend, and then the little wood was gone. There went the train, there went the baby skunk. Away from the wood that had been his home. Away from the clear, cool-water creek, and the big trees, and the stumps of trees where he had dug for grubs. Away and away. It was a terrible mistake.

But now at last the long-legged tramp in the corner of the dark boxcar was coming to his senses. He sat up, he rubbed his sore head. "Is that a way to start a train?" he grumbled. "Is that an engineer?" He rubbed his head again, but then he thought of something. He hastily felt around in the dark for the tomato can. He poked a long finger down in the can and felt for the water. "Oh, oh, just as I thought," he groaned. "Knocked more than half the water out. And that man calls himself an engineer!"

Now the tramp's eyes were getting used to the dark. Suddenly he leaned forward. He peered hard at the closed door. He peered again, then he sat back with a jerk. "No!" he told himself. "No, don't tell me that's a skunk! Don't tell me I've got myself locked in here with a skunk. Oh, no!"

The tramp became quiet. He sat studying the flattened little skunk. He sat thinking hard. "Now what am I going to do?" he asked in the darkness.

The big tramp did not dare move because of the skunk. The little skunk did not dare move at all. He kept himself squashed flat against the floor. The little skunk was terrified. He did not understand trains. He was used to solid ground. The solid ground had never bounced and banged, and rocked and rattled. The little skunk did not know what to do. He was too terrified to move a muscle.

When the big tramp saw that the little skunk was too terrified to stir, it gave the big tramp courage. "Look, little fellow," he said to the skunk, "you're scared, aren't you? You don't want to be here, do you? Well, I'm the man to help you. Look, I'll get that door open, then I'll wait until we come to a nice, soft pile of leaves, and then with one swoosh of my foot I'll send you flying into the leaves."

The big tramp sat waiting, as if he were waiting for the little skunk to answer him. "One swoosh," he said again. "But to do it, I've got to get at the door. But you're sitting right in front of the door! And I'm afraid that when you see me coming right at you, you'll get so scared you'll throw your scent—swish it all over with your tail. All over me—all over the boxcar! And I'm just a poor old tramp. I haven't any clothes to change. And I can't get off this train to bury my clothes in the ground for a week to rid them of your awful scent. And I can't take a bath in a tomato can half full of water!"

The tramp stopped pleading with the little skunk. He waited still a little longer, but then he came. He edged along the wall of the boxcar, he inched closer and closer to the skunk, but all the while he kept talking in the softest, friendliest voice. And then he reached the little flattened skunk, who clung to the floor with every nail and every muscle!

Now the tramp could see how really terrified and miserable the little skunk was. "Ah, you little tike," he said softly. "Scared to death, aren't you? You're petrified. Well, you just let me get at that door!"

And then the tramp stepped right over the skunk, and turned to the closed door! The little skunk lay flat and miserable between the tramp's big feet. The tramp took hold of the door to shove it open. He struggled and pushed, he pulled and he grunted. The door would not yield. He dug all his fingers into the old door, and tried again. He broke his fingernails, but the door did not stir. At last the tramp looked helplessly down at the little quivering skunk. "I'm afraid you're in for it, little fellow. That door's rammed shut. It's absolutely stuck. You and I are in here till they let us out."

And now at last the terrified little skunk looked up at the big man.

"Ah, little tike," the big tramp said, "I'd better not scare you any more. I'll get back to my corner. But, look, you and I will make out all right. We've some water and some pancakes. We can hold out until they let us out. Who knows, maybe we can even become friends."

The big tramp moved softly away to his dark corner so as not to worry the little skunk. The big tramp was mistaken. He did not see it as he walked away, but the little skunk lifted his head and looked desperately after the tramp. He kept his head turned, trying to see the tramp. He was afraid of the banging train, not of the friendly, soft-spoken tramp.

In the far corner the tramp stretched himself out to go to sleep. He lay there humming himself to sleep. "Carry me back to old Virginny," he was humming. The little skunk listened to the humming. It was some comfort to the little skunk as the slow old train banged on and on.

That is how they rode—the little skunk at the closed door, the tramp in the far corner. The tramp lay sleeping, but the little skunk sat listening anxiously to every rattling sound as the slow old train banged on. He kept turning his head toward the dark corner. He listened wistfully to every snoring sound from the sleeping tramp—it was a little comfort. But he stayed at the closed door. He did not dare to move.

A mile up ahead the old locomotive whistled and hooted its way around a bend. The whole train slowed as it went around the bend, and when it slowed the boxcar did not bang and rattle quite so much. The little skunk looked longingly toward the far corner with the tramp. The boxcar was a little quieter. The little skunk began moving toward the tramp! He still did not dare to get to his feet. He dragged himself along the floor, inch by slow inch. Oh, it took long! The slow old train went many slow miles, before the little flattened skunk at last reached the big feet of the sleeping tramp. He was so relieved when he got there, so tired from the strain, he cuddled himself tightly against the tramp's big shoe. He pressed himself against it.

Just being pressed against the tramp's big shoe seemed to give the little skunk courage. Now the slow old train went around a long bend again, it slowed again. It was less noisy, less rocky. It hardly swayed. And now the little skunk dared to pull himself up by the big shoe and crawl up on the leg of the man! He crawled along the tramp's long leg while the train went slowly around the bend. And then—then he came to the man's stomach!

There the little skunk discovered something. The man was soft! Softer than leaves! The man was warm! Warmer than a whole pile of leaves in the sun! The man was soft and warm—he did not bounce and rattle! The man swayed with the swaying of the train, the man quivered and jiggled with the motions of the train, but the man was soft and warm. And safe! And for the first time on that terrifying ride the little skunk felt safe enough, and cozy enough, to sink himself down on the tramp. He was so tired from the strain and fright! It was so wonderful to feel safe! He went to sleep.

The big tramp slept. The little skunk slept on the tramp. The slow old banging train rolled on.

The tramp and skunk woke up together. They woke up from the quiet. They woke because the train was standing still. Outside the train a bird sang, and then a cow mooed. The slow old train must be standing on a railroad siding somewhere in the country, it must be waiting for a faster train to pass again.

The big tramp slowly opened his eyes. He carefully peered around the dark boxcar. He searched the darkness for the little skunk. Then his eyes fell on the little skunk curled up on his stomach! "Oh, ho!" the big tramp rumbled. "So there you are! I was looking everywhere, but not on my own stomach. Using me for a mattress, eh? Didn't I tell you we'd be friends? If you aren't as cute as a kitten! If you aren't something!"

The big tramp chuckled and chuckled. The little skunk sat jiggling up and down on the big tramp's chuckling stomach. Suddenly he crinkled his nose, and sniffed. He smelled pancakes! He was hungry! And now that the train was still, the little skunk was bold enough, and hungry enough, to follow his nose right across the tramp, right to the pocket where the pancakes were. The floor was still, the floor was not rocking and banging. The little skunk climbed down from the tramp to get at the pocket with the pancakes. But there stood the tomato can with water! The little skunk was terribly thirsty, too —from all the fright. He put his forepaws on the rim of the tomato can, and peered in.

The big tramp hastily sat up. "Careful, don't tip it," he warned anxiously. "It isn't even half full. We can't waste it. There's no telling how long we may be locked up in this boxcar. Here, let me help you." He took the tomato can and carefully poured a few drops into the palm of his hand. He held out his hand with the water. The little skunk shrank away from the hand. The little skunk was timid, but the tramp was worried too—afraid that if he alarmed the skunk, the little skunk might suddenly throw his awful scent. The worried tramp held his hand steady, but because he was worried, he started humming. When the little skunk heard the humming sound he knew so well, he came to the cupped hand, dipped his chin down in, and drank! "There," said the tramp, and he was so relieved, he took a small drink from the tomato can himself.

"Well, that's all the water for now," the tramp announced, after he had put the tomato can down. "Now let's see about pancakes." He pulled the pancakes out of his pocket, and held them close to his face to count them in the dark. "Hey, only five!" he said disappointedly. "I thought I'd taken more."

He sorted out the smallest pancake and broke it in two. "One half for me, and a half of one half for you—because I'm bigger," he told the little skunk. "Wait a minute—I had breakfast, but I suspect you didn't. Okay, one half of one half for you, and none for me. There's no telling how long we may have to stay in this boxcar."

The big tramp gave the skunk his piece of pancake, but he carefully put the other pieces back in his pocket with the other pancakes. On the floor the little skunk had just begun to nibble the piece of pancake when, with a terrific jolt, the old train started into motion. The tramp grabbed the tomato can with water, but the little skunk lay flat and trembling on the floor.

"Look," said the tramp, now that the tomato can was safe, "you'd better get back on me. It rides better." But the little skunk was too terrified to move.

"Now what to do?" the tramp said. "I don't dare pick you up, I don't dare handle you yet. You might not understand, and then you'd swish your tail and throw that miserable scent of yours all over me."

The big tramp puzzled a while. Then he took the piece of pancake and held it on his hand before the little skunk. Even that wouldn't lure the little skunk to crawl up on his hand—he was too frightened. "Careful now," the tramp warned. "You know I mean you no harm." Quickly he slid his flat hand under the little skunk, lifted him up, and set him on his lap. He slid his hand from under him. "There," said the tramp, much relieved. "Now you feel safer, don't you? And I feel better myself." He placed the piece of pancake on his lap before the little skunk. The little skunk almost began to nibble and eat, but first he looked up at the man.

"You're welcome," the big tramp said. And he chuckled and chuckled until the little skunk sat jiggling and eating in his chuckling lap.

That is how they rode from that time on—with the little skunk in the big tramp's lap when they were both awake, or with the little skunk curled up on the stretched-out man when they were both asleep. And all the time the slow old train rolled on and on.

The train kept going through that day, it kept on going through that night. But the big tramp and the little skunk in the tightly shut boxcar did not know where they were. They did not know where they were going. They did not even know what time it was, or what day it was. It hardly made any difference. They ate when they got hungry—but one small mouthful of pancake was hardly enough for hunger. They drank when they got thirsty—but half a mouthful of water was hardly enough for thirst. They slept when they got sleepy. Mostly they slept—for when they slept they could not feel their hunger and their thirst. It was best to sleep as much as possible.

During the day the tramp would just stretch out and go to sleep, but when night came it was different. When night came he would take his shoes off. "Now it is night," the tramp would say, and then he'd take his shoes off, and that would make it bedtime. The little skunk would curl himself up on the stretched-out tramp, and then they both would try to sleep. It was best to sleep as much as possible.

They would wake up to another day. "We must be in another state by now," the tramp would say the first thing in the morning. Slow as this train runs, we must have come through three or four states by now—we've been on here so long." The little skunk would perk up his head and listen to the talking voice.

The big tramp talked quite a lot to the little skunk on the slow, dark, rattling journey through the countryside that they could not see at all. He would sit and stare at the solid wall of the boxcar, and then he'd suddenly say: "You can see for yourself that now we're going along a lake. Isn't it pretty? Look at the gulls!" And then he'd laugh and laugh until the wondering little skunk sat jiggling in his chuckling lap.

But whenever the train would stop the big tramp would become quiet. He would listen long and carefully until he heard the sound of birds, or a cow lowing, or other farm sounds. "Huh," he would whisper then, much relieved, "I was afraid maybe we were stopping at a station in some city, but there's a cow, so we must be in the country. Guess we're stopping so the old locomotive can take on water again. Guess the old locomotive leaks at every seam—it's so old." The little wondering skunk would listen to his whispering voice.

Suddenly the train would jerk to a start again, rattle and roll on again—endlessly. But sometimes the train *would* stop at a railroad station in a town. And that was altogether different. There would be noises all along the train—great bangings as boxcars were loaded and unloaded. Trucks roared, voices shouted, doors of boxcars slid open, slid shut. "Now we've got to be mighty quiet," the tramp would warn. "Hush now, because if they catch me stealing a ride on this train, they'll march me straight to jail!"

The noises would come and the noises would go. Doors of boxcars slid open, slid shut. But no one ever came to the empty boxcar with the tramp and skunk. No one ever slid that door open. The last truck would roar away, the last voices would fade away into the railroad station, and the old train would slowly roll out of the town.

At first when the train would roll through a town, the big tramp was still jolly and chuckly. He would amuse himself by pointing out things in the town that he could not see at all. "See that blue suit in that window?" he would say. "Now a blue suit is just what I need. I'm getting to be quite a raggedy old tramp. . . . Wait a minute, though! Seeing that shoe store reminded me, I need shoes much worse than a blue suit. There's holes in my soles big enough for one of my pancakes to go through. I should have made my pancakes bigger! No, we'll stop at a shoe store, then I can buy a little leash for you, too. Because you and I have just got to travel together from now on." He looked down at the little skunk. "You know, little tike, you've been great company for me on this miserable, hungry, dark journey. Yes, sir, and I've become mighty fond of you. You and I just have to stay together from now on."

That was the day when they shared the last pancake together. They were too hungry for a half, and half of one half. They ate the whole pancake. The old tomato can was dry. It wasn't even damp any more. The tramp could not shake out so much as a drop to give to the little skunk.

That day the tramp did not chuckle any more. He hardly talked. He did not hum. Only once all that day did he say anything, and then it was to warn the little skunk to be mouse quiet, because the train was rolling into a station in another town. "Just this time yet," he pleaded. "Just this time we'll be real quiet. You know, I could bang on the door, and they'd come to let us out, but they'd march me straight to jail." He peered at the little skunk. "We can hold out this day, can't we? I'd much rather be hungry and thirsty and free—than full of food and water in a jail. And you would be, too, because even if they wouldn't put you in jail, they might put you in a zoo. And that's no better than a jail!"

This time when the train finally rolled out of the town, the tramp did not point out the stores. He was too miserable from thirst and hunger. The little skunk, even though the floor was rocking and banging, made many trips to the pocket where the pancakes had been. It still smelled of pancakes, but in it there was not a crumb. The little skunk crawled in the tomato can and licked the bottom.

"It's bedtime," the tramp said shortly when he saw that. "It had better be bedtime! We'd better sleep, if we can." He hastily took his shoes off.

The slow old train rolled on all through that night, and the tramp did manage to sleep a little in spite of hunger and thirst. But when he woke up early in the morning there were strange sounds inside the boxcar. Sharp nibbling, gnawing sounds. He could hear them above the noise of the boxcar. "Hey, mice!" the startled tramp said. "Don't tell me—mice have got more sense than to get on a car where there isn't even a crumb."

It was the little skunk. The little skunk was sitting in his shoe, gnawing and nibbling at the leather! "Aw," said the tramp, "it's come to that! Well, at the next stop they ought to open that door, they can't leave it shut forever. And then we'll take our chance, little tike. I'll put you in

my pocket, and we'll jump out and run. Listen! Doesn't it sound as if we're rolling into a town?"

The little skunk did not listen—he went on gnawing at the tough shoe leather. The tramp took the shoe away from him. "I'll need it if we're coming into a town, and if they open the door, and we have to make a run for it." But the little skunk looked up at the shoe so pitifully, the tramp did not have the heart to put it on his foot. "Here, then," he said gruffly, and he tore the tongue out of the shoe. "Here, chew on that, I can get along without it. I know how you feel, it just feels better to be chewing on something. Remind me next time to buy better-tasting shoes."

The tramp was suddenly quiet. The train had stopped. The tramp got to his feet, he stood listening hopefully. Soon there were sounds—great sounds, hopeful sounds, great noises all along the train. It sounded as if all along the train the doors of the boxcars were being slid open. Somebody had started at the front and was going along the train opening up the boxcars. The noise of sliding doors came closer and closer.

"Now," whispered the tramp, "now at last it sounds like we're going to be set free. But now you've got to help me, little tike. I'm going to set you right before the door, then when they slide it open—there you'll sit. And if I know anything, whoever it is that's opening the doors, when he sees a skunk, he'll run. That'll be my chance. I'll scoop you up and stick you in my pocket, and then I'll run. Then we'll soon find food and water!" He stopped to listen. "Hush, now," he cautioned. "And stay right at that door!"

The tramp pressed himself against the wall next to the door. He waited. The door of the boxcar ahead slid open with a squealing, grinding sound. "Now," said the tramp to himself.

Outside the boxcar a man's voice could be heard. The man was right outside the door, mumbling to himself. The tramp held his breath. But the mumbling went away, and then the door of the boxcar right behind slid open with a squeal.

"No!" said the tramp. "No, they didn't pass us up again!" But already the door of a farther boxcar slid open.

The disappointed tramp stood listening. Then he looked down at the little skunk where he should be sitting, but the little skunk wasn't at the door. Tiny gnawing sounds came from the dark corner—the little skunk had gone back to the leather tongue. "Aw," said the tramp, "that does it. This can't go on—eating shoe leather! We've got to get out. Okay, I'll take my chances, and if I can get away, I'll be back to pick you up. But if I take you with me and I get caught, then we're both caught. So we'll see." He went to the door, he started pounding on it with all his might. "Let me out! Let me out!" he yelled as loud as he could.

Feet came running along the wooden loading platform just outside the boxcar. A man's voice yelled for other men to come. More feet pounded on the hollow-sounding platform. And then the stuck door of the boxcar was wrenched open by many hands. The big tramp tried to make a leap out of the boxcar over the open space between the loading platform and the doorway, but he had been in the dark so long, the sudden light blinded him. Before he could jump three men had jumped into the boxcar. They grabbed the tramp. He struggled, he wrestled, he threw himself and the three men all over that boxcar. But he was too weak from hunger to tear himself away from three big men. He broke away once and ran to the corner where the scared little skunk sat, but the men seized him again.

In the running and rolling and wrestling all over the boxcar, nobody noticed the confused little skunk. He was pushed here, and shoved there, and then he was shoved right over the edge of the doorway. He fell! He fell between the doorway and the loading platform. He landed under the boxcar.

Nobody noticed, for now in the boxcar the three men had overpowered the tramp. Now they were leading him away down the long loading platform. They were taking him to jail.

At the far end of the loading platform, there were steps that led down to the street. The men were going to lead the tramp down those steps. But just before they came to the steps, the tramp took a sudden, sideways, flying leap right over the edge of the high platform—down into the street. The sudden jump tore him out of the grasp of two of the men, the other man went down with him. They rolled over and over in the street. But the tramp was up first, and then the tramp was free. On his long legs he went flying across the street, into an alley, around a corner, and then the tramp was gone.

The three men chased him, but on his long legs the tramp easily outran them all. The three gave up. They came back to the loading platform, they stopped and peered into the empty boxcar. All three were breathing heavily. "Well, well, that was quite a way to start the day," one of them said, panting. "I'm all tuckered out already."

"So am I," said another voice. "And this is supposed to be a holiday. It's Labor Day today, isn't it? Labor—is right! That tramp sure put up a fight. And how that man can run!"

Under the boxcar the little skunk sat listening to the voices. They moved away, and then the sound of feet and voices disappeared into the railroad station. Everything was quiet. Under the boxcar the little skunk sat listening and waiting. He was waiting for the tramp. Nothing happened. There were no footsteps, the voice of the tramp did not come. Still the little skunk waited. The tramp did not come.

At last the little confused skunk began poking and circling and sniffing under the boxcar. He was searching for the footsteps of the tramp, the way he had always done in the little wood up North. But here were no leaves and grass, here were only bricks. Here were only town smells. The little skunk did not understand town smells.

He circled and searched. There were no footsteps. But he *had* to find the footsteps. If he found the footsteps, the footsteps would lead him back to the tramp, and the tramp would lead him back to the little wood that was his home. Back to the clear, cool-water creek, for he was terribly thirsty. Back to the stumps where he could dig for grubs, for he was terribly hungry. Back to the nest of leaves in the hollow stump, for he was terribly lost. Back to his home! He was a little skunk, he did not understand that since he had been on the train for nights and days, that he was hundreds and hundreds of miles from home.

And since he did not understand about trains, and hundreds and hundreds of miles, the little skunk stopped circling and searching uselessly under the boxcar. He had decided to go home! He walked from under the boxcar, he walked into the street. In the middle of the street, the little skunk found rails! He gurgled at the rails, for he knew rails. He had often followed the rails back home when he had wandered from his little wood. But these were not the rails of a railroad siding beside a little wood up North. These were streetcar rails! And these rails merely led down the main street of this town—into the heart of town. The little skunk did not know that. The little skunk was sure that now at last he was going home. In spite of hunger and in spite of thirst, he gurgled happily—a tiny, little gurgle—as he followed the streetcar rail that led him into the town.

. . . .

"There's a tramp loose in town," the steam-shovel man shouted.

"A tramp loose in town? Isn't it bad enough to have a skunk loose in town?" the alarmed mayor shouted back. "Throw the fellow in jail!"

The news went traveling up Main Street. "The mayor says to throw the tramp in jail."

There everything stood while the mayor's words went traveling up Main Street until they reached the streetcar. Then after a while the news came traveling back from the streetcar: "Tell the mayor the tramp got away. He was too fast, his legs were too long—nobody could catch him." The steam-shovel man shouted it to the mayor. "The tramp is gone. They couldn't catch him. He's gone—they think he ran clear out of town."

"Couldn't catch him!" the mayor fumed. "Well, all right. If that tramp is out of town, let's get that skunk out of town, and get on with our Labor Day parade. Let's get on with it."

"The mayor says to get on with it," the steam-shovel man bellowed up the street. "Never mind the tramp."

There the words went from car to car, and mouth to mouth: "On with it. On with it. Never mind the tramp."

At last the distant words reached the streetcar, the streetcar started up, then the long row of cars started up. Everything began to move again. This time everything could move quite a way, for all the time that things had been standing still, the little skunk had hurried right ahead for water.

Now, with the long row of cars out of the way, the big steam shovel could at last make its turn into Main Street. After the steam shovel, the jeep, the bulldozer, the farmer and his wagon, and last of all the crawling fire engine, could all turn into Main Street. But now that everything was moving at last, everybody became excited, everybody cheered and shouted.

It was a racket and a din, and it alarmed the little skunk. Never had he heard such a noise and such a racket—not even on the rattlebang train. He did not like it, he was afraid of it, but since he was a slow little skunk—too slow to run away from it—he did the only thing he could do. He stopped and turned to face it! He raised his warning tail straight up, he quirked and quirked his warning tail!

The motorman saw it. He hastily stopped the streetcar. When the streetcar stopped, everything stopped. When everything stood still, there was nothing to shout and cheer about, so then everything became quiet. When everything was quiet, the little skunk turned and hurried down the track to find himself some water.

The moment the little skunk went ahead, the streetcar started up. Everything started up. But the moment everything moved again, everybody became excited again. Everybody started cheering and shouting, blowing horns, roaring motors, clanging bells, shrieking sirens.

The little skunk stopped. The little skunk turned. Up came his warning tail! Everything stopped again.

Now that the fire engine was on Main Street, the mayor on the high seat could see what was the trouble. He could see something had to be done, but he did not know what to do, he did not know about skunks.

The farmer standing on the wagon could see what was the trouble, too. "Mister Mayor, Mister Mayor, sir, I've got a plan," the farmer said politely. "And it's the only way to keep the little skunk moving. If you will back out of my way, I'll turn around and go up an alley and get on Main Street between the streetcar and the skunk. Then, with my horses I'll keep the little skunk moving. I'm a farmer and I know about skunks. Skunks don't mind horses, and horses don't mind skunks. They often see each other when the horses are in pasture—they know each other. So when Faber and Elizabeth come clopping on behind the little skunk, he won't be alarmed about all the noise any more, and they will keep him moving."

"Fine, fine," the mayor shouted. "Would you do that? If you'll do that for me, then I'll let you ride in our Labor Day parade."

When the farmer heard that now at last, after ten long years, he was going to ride in the Labor Day parade, the farmer became all excited. He hardly waited for the fire engine to back up, he squeezed his horses from between the fire engine and the bulldozer, he turned them down the side street, he turned them into an alley. When they got in the alley the farmer stood up in the wagon, and shouted so excitedly that his two old horses really flew. The sparks flew. But when they turned into Main Street between the streetcar and the little skunk, the whispering farmer slowed his two old horses to a crawl, so as not to alarm the little skunk. They hardly moved, they hardly lifted their heavy feet as they swung ahead of the streetcar and fell in line behind the skunk.

The little skunk heard the two old horses coming. The little skunk smelled the smell of horses, and gurgled happily—a tiny, little gurgle. He liked the smell of horses, he liked horses—horses were his friends.

Faber and Elizabeth walked sedately on behind the skunk. They lowered their big old heads to look at the skunk. They did not mind the little skunk right before their noses. In fact, they liked the little skunk much better than the oily, machinery smell of the big bulldozer. Faber and Elizabeth had often seen skunks at night by moonlight in their pasture. They liked skunks because skunks were slow and poky—not jumpy and scary in the shadowy, moonlit pasture.

The two old horses clopped on behind the skunk. The little skunk hurried ahead as fast as

a little skunk can hurry, for he was very thirsty.

The little skunk hurried along. The horses clopped along. The streetcar crawled on behind the old farm wagon and the quiet farmer. The cars came creeping on behind the crawling streetcar. Everything came on. But now the fire chief did not clang his bell and shriek his siren, horns did not blow, motors did not roar, people did not cheer and shout. The mayor had forbidden it. The farmer had not heard the mayor's order, but he knew enough to be quiet, now that he was right behind the skunk. He knew about skunks!

In the new quiet, the little skunk hurried down the streetcar track. But all of a sudden there wasn't any more streetcar track. And then there wasn't any more street. Instead, there was a country road. And when there was no more track, and no more street—there was no more town. Instead, there was the quiet, lovely country.

When he saw the lovely country the little skunk sat down. He gurgled at the quiet country. He gurgled at the country and at the little country road, and at the lovely country smells. Here were no town smells and town noises. Here was the smell of trees and grass, of cows and sheep in pastures. And the little skunk got up to go into the lovely country.

The road went straight, the little skunk went straight—straight down the road that led into the country.

Behind him in the little town down south in warm Virginia, the streetcar had reached the end of the track, and there the streetcar had to stop. Then everything and everybody had to stop. But nobody turned away, everybody stayed to watch a little skunk, with his happy, bushy tail straight up, march off into the country. Only the quiet farmer and his two old heavy horses still kept on behind the skunk, to help the little skunk get deep into the country.

And then—then there was a bend in the road. The road went around a bend, the little skunk went around the bend in the road. But the farmer quietly turned his horses there and started to go back to the town.

The crowd at the end of Main Street all saw the little skunk marching around the distant bend. Then nobody could keep quiet any longer. The people shouted and cheered, the streetcar clanged its warning bell, the car horns blew and blasted, the steam shovel and the bulldozer roared and rumbled, and the fire chief clanged his bell and twirled his shrieking siren. But the mayor grabbed the shotgun, and shot the single shell into the air. Now they could hold their Labor Day parade!

The little skunk heard the distant noise and racket, but he paid it no attention, for now the noise was far away, and he was in the country. He heard the horses going away, and now he heard the farmer begin shouting to his horses. "Giddap, Faber! Giddyap, Elizabeth! Now we're going to ride in the parade! Giddap, Faber! Giddyap, Elizabeth! You and I are in the parade." How those two old horses ran. They liked parades. It was much better than plowing.

The little skunk went on alone around the bend in the little road.

At the bend in the little road, there was a narrow country lane. And because the lane went straight out from the bend, and because the little skunk was going straight, the little skunk went down the lane. He left the road and took the lane. But that was good! And that was right! For it was a long lane, and a straight lane, and it did not have a single turning. And since the little skunk was going straight, he would go straight down that straight lane. And at the end of that long lane—there was a wood! There was a little wood, and in that wood there was a creek, and there were trees, and fallen trees, and stumps of trees long gone. The clear, cool-water creek in the wood wound in and out between the trees, it gurgled under fallen trees, it curled around the stumps of trees long gone.

The little skunk did not know that. The little near-sighted skunk could not see that far. He could not even smell that far. But because the lane went straight without a single turning, the little skunk would also go straight—straight to the little wood, and to the clear, cool-water creek.

At last the little skunk was half way down the lane. And suddenly he rose up on his hind legs like a squirrel. He crinkled his nose, he sniffed and sniffed the air. He did not smell the little wood and the clear, cool-water creek—he could not smell that far. No, he smelled something else. And at what he smelled that little skunk gurgled and gurgled. Something came drifting on the air over the fields and down the lane. It was smoke! And in the smoke the little skunk smelled something—he smelled coffee. Then he smelled something else—he smelled pancakes frying. He smelled bacon. Pancakes and bacon!

The little skunk dropped to his feet to hurry down the lane toward the lovely odors. But as he hurried farther down the lane, suddenly the little skunk smelled something else. This wasn't on the air, this wasn't far away! This was right before his nose. This was a footstep, and then another big footstep. These were footsteps coming from the field into the lane, and going down the lane. Big footsteps, far-apart footsteps—the footsteps of a long-legged man. Oh, how that little skunk gurgled! Oh, how that little skunk hurried from one invisible footstep to the next invisible footstep going down that country lane. He crinkled and crinkled his little nose. He gurgled.

In the little wood, on the bank of the clear, cool-water creek, a tramp was sitting by a fire. He was frying pancakes on a piece of tin over the little fire. Above the fire hung a tomato can. The tramp was also making coffee. The tramp was also frying bacon—pancakes and bacon. But now he rose to peer under the trees and spy out the fields to see that nobody had followed him from the town to throw him into jail. He looked across the hills and fields and pastures, but nowhere did anything move. He looked down the lane! At what he saw coming down that lane, the big tramp had to lean against a tree and laugh and laugh and chuckle.

"Well, I'll be kicked! Well, I'll be kicked," he softly told himself. "Don't tell me. Don't tell me that that's the little tike following my footsteps down the lane. Well, I'll be kicked—the little smarty-pants. I told him we had to stay together!"

The big tramp leaned against the tree, and watched and waited for the little skunk. He waited with his pancakes and his bacon for the little skunk to come. He leaned against the tree and chuckled. "Well, I'll be kicked," he said again. "Didn't I tell him that from now on we had to stay and travel together?" He slapped his two coat pockets! "That's it! That's it!" he said excitedly. "One pocket for my pancakes—one for my little skunk! From this time on, we live and travel together." And then the tramp leaned back against the tree and laughed and chuckled loud and long.

Down the long lane came the little skunk, hurrying as fast as a little skunk can hurry. Oh, it would take him long, because the lane was long. But the long lane had no turning, and he would get there sure. Oh, he would get there sure!

And when at last he got there, the little skunk would have his tramp, and he would have a home. The little skunk would have a home again in a little wood with a clear, cool-water creek, and trees, and stumps of trees long gone, where he could dig for grubs. He would have a little wood home almost exactly like his little wood home up North. But this winter his little wood home would not be far up North in the cold, blizzard country, where winter came down, and the snow and ice heaped ten feet deep. This time his home would be down south in warm Virginia!

Down the long lane hurried the little gurgling skunk, as fast as a little skunk can hurry. Oh, he was slow as slow, but he would surely get there. Oh, he would surely get there! For he was following the footsteps.

from KILDEE HOUSE

Rutherford Montgomery

This opening chapter of Kildee House *should lead straight into the book. It is a tender and amusing story about Jerome Kildee's problems in preventing the animals from taking over his house entirely and in resolving the enmity between two strong-minded young neighbors.*

[*Mr. Kildee Makes Friends with Old Grouch*]

Jerome Kildee had built himself a house on the mountainside. It was an odd house because Jerome Kildee was an odd man. He built his house under a giant redwood tree on Windy

Point. Since the days of Julius Caesar creatures had been building homes at the foot of the redwood or in its branches. At the time Jerome built his house most folks did not build on knobs high on a mountainside, even the round-topped, wooded mountains of the Pacific Coast Range.

What the neighbors said or what they thought was of no concern to Jerome. The day he walked out on Windy Point, and looked up at the giant redwood towering into the sky, and stood savoring the deep silence, he knew he was going to stay. When he turned from the great tree and looked down over the green ridges, the smoky valley, into the gray-white haze of the Pacific, he smiled. This was a land of silence, the place for a silent man.

The house Jerome built was not as wide as the redwood; to have made it so wide would have been a waste of space, because Jerome did not need that much room. He toted the biggest window he could buy to the cabin, and set it in the wall which faced a panorama of ridges and valleys. The window was as high as the wall; it was one wall as far across as the door. It had been rolled out as a plate-glass window for a store.

The back wall was the redwood trunk. It made an odd house, one wall curved inward, and finished with shaggy redwood bark. Jerome rented a horse and packed Monterey stone up for a fireplace. The fireplace was a thing of beauty. It filled one end of the room. The cream Monterey stone, traced through with threads of red, was carefully fitted and matched for grain; the hearth was wide, and the mantel was inlaid with chips of abalone shell. It was the last piece of stonework Jerome planned to make, and he made it a masterpiece. In a recess back of the last slab of stone he tucked away the tools of his trade and sealed them into the wall. Jerome Kildee, maker of fine monuments was no more. There remained only Jerome Kildee, philosopher, a silent little man, seeking to become a part of a silent mountain.

Jerome Kildee did not work. He owned the hundred acres of woods and hillside around him, but he did not clear any of it. He bought all of his food, and he had stove and fireplace wood hauled up and stacked outside his door. Jerome hired the Eppys to haul the wood to the bottom of the hill, then up the hill with their tractor because there was only a winding footpath up from his mailbox. The Eppys laughed and made quite a bit of it. Jerome had hundreds of cords of oak and madroña close to his cabin. The farmer and his sons would have cut it and sawed it for a tenth of what Jerome paid for the wood and the hauling.

Jerome had no near neighbors, nor would he ever have any, because he had built in the exact center of his hundred acres. He had gone through life silent, unable to talk to people, expecting them to leave him to his own thoughts. He had never visited the Eppy family after they hauled his wood, although they lived at the foot of his hill on the north side. They put him down as a queer one. The nine Eppys, as they were known locally, were robust folks. The six sons were all over six feet tall. Emma Lou would someday be almost as tall as her brothers. The Cabot place, at the foot of the mountain on the other side of the hill, was certainly not a place where Jerome would care to go. It was a fine estate with landscaped gardens and a swimming pool. The Cabots had one son, Donald Roger, who had never given Jerome more than a brief look.

But Jerome Kildee found he was not without friends. He had a host of friends and he didn't have to talk to them to keep their friendship. In fact, his silence helped to keep them friendly. They were all interested in him, a new experience for Jerome, and he was interested in them. Jerome found that they were not unlike the people back where he had operated his monument shop. They were willing to take advantage of him, they were selfish, and some of them were thieves, like the trade rats who packed off anything they could carry, regardless of whether or not they could use it. He soon learned that none of the raccoons could be trusted inside the cabin. They unscrewed the caps off ketchup bottles as easily as he could do it; they unlatched cupboard doors or opened them if there was a knob on them. One old raccoon, who was the neighborhood grouch, lived in a hole in the trunk of his redwood tree. Old Grouch had refused to move when Jerome built his house. He considered the redwood tree his tree. He made it clear to Jerome that he was trespassing.

The pair of spotted skunks who set up housekeeping under his floor were folks of a different sort from the raccoons. They were not dull-witted stinkers of the sort Jerome had known in his boyhood, dumb fellows who for ages had been depending upon poison gas instead of their wits for protection. They carried guns but seldom used them. The little spotted skunks were as smart as the raccoons, and about as curious. They had a real sense of humor and were always playing pranks on the raccoons. With them around, Jerome always had to get down on his hands and knees and explore the chimney of his fireplace before he built a fire. The skunks liked the fireplace and would gladly have traded it for their nest under the floor. They were not big stinkers like the swamp skunks, so Jerome could always fish them out of the chimney with his broom.

Jerome would probably have been crowded out of his house by the assortment of mice that found his house and the fine bark wall of the redwood to their liking if it had not been for the spotted skunks. The skunks had large appetites, so they kept the mouse population on an even keel. Two big wood mice lived in a bark nest back of a knot in the tree trunk. They furnished dinners for the spotted skunks with a regularity which should have become monotonous. How they could go on having big families, nursing them to a size to go out into the world, only to have them gobbled up one at a time as they left the nest, was more than Jerome could understand.

There was another pair of mice who lived under his bed in a box of old letters, which they made good use of without snooping into the contents, or trying to figure out why Jerome had tied them in bundles. They chewed up all of the letters except those written in indelible pencil. This removed from Jerome's life any desire to brood over the past. The spotted skunks could not get into the box. The mice went in through a knothole in the end. But their families suffered the same fate as the wood mice. And they went on having big families.

Jerome's wooded acres harbored many black-tailed deer and many gray foxes and possums. The foxes never made friends, and the possums ignored him because he never kept chickens. They had no bump of curiosity to draw them to his house. He saw them often and had a nodding acquaintance with them, so to speak. The black-tails visited his garbage pit regularly. The does often brought their fawns into his yard. But they did not bother much with him because he did not grow a garden or set out young fruit trees. He was about like any other dweller on the wooded mountain: he just lived there.

It was during the second year that Old Grouch turned the head of a dainty little miss. She was just sixteen months old, and like many another lass before her, she fell in love with a good-for-nothing. Old Grouch brought her to his nest in the redwood. It was high up on the tree where a burl formed a deep pocket. Old Grouch had learned that a redwood tree was a safe haven. When coon dogs chased him, followed by yelling humans, all he had to do was shinny up the giant tree. The hunters could not shake him out or climb the tree. Of course after Jerome came, the coon dogs and the hunters stayed away.

Old Grouch brought his bride home in January during the heavy rains. In April she presented him with a family. Like many another good-for-nothing, Old Grouch failed to provide for his family, though he did share the nest with them, taking the dry side and grabbing any of the food she rustled which suited his taste. Jerome couldn't climb the tree to look into the nest, but he heard the babies and listened to the family chitchat over them.

Old Grouch mildly irritated Jerome. He was smug and fat, always ready to march into the cabin and demand part of Jerome's fried egg or lamb chop, but never thanking his host for anything, and always staying outside unless there was food. Any friendly advance was always met with a snarl or a snapping of white fangs. He was a surly fellow, but Jerome admired the way he had with the ladies.

His wife was of a different sort. She was friendly and thankful to Jerome for bits of food he gave her. She visited the cabin while he was in it, and not just when it was mealtime. She would have taken over his larder if he had allowed it. Her willingness to shift Old Grouch's responsibility for the family to him gave Jerome a problem. He was forced to invent new catches for his cupboard doors, and to fashion latches for his pull drawers.

Outwitting the slim little bride was no easy matter. With feminine wile she made up to Jerome, letting him stroke her head and scratch around her ears, smiling coyly up at him as he sat in his padded chair, but raiding his cupboard as sure as he went for a walk. Jerome fixed inside catches for the doors worked by wires which went up through the inside of the cupboard and were pulled by strings dangling from the ceiling, well out of reach of a raccoon. The pull drawers became pop-out drawers worked by wires with dangling strings attached to them. Jerome's house was well decorated with strings hanging from the ceiling. A large button dangled at the end of each string like a black spider.

When Jerome wanted an egg for breakfast he pulled a string, and open popped a drawer exposing the egg carton. Then Jerome always had to take out two eggs because the minute the door popped open in popped Mrs. Grouch, and Jerome had to split fifty-fifty with her. He could have closed and barred the door, but then he would have had to sit by the big window eating his egg with Mrs. Grouch's furry bangs pressed against the plate glass, her bright eyes watching every bite he took, her little tongue dripping hungrily.

The rains lasted a long time that spring, keeping on until June. Mrs. Grouch stood the home her old man had provided for her as long as she could. The babies were growing and taking up more room, the roof leaked, and Old Grouch always took the dry side. When the wind blew from the north there might as well have been no roof at all. One afternoon while Jerome was tramping in the woods, snug in oilskins and rubber boots, she moved her babies into the house. Helping herself to the stuffing in his mattress, she made a nest in the oven. She had long ago learned how to open the oven door. The smell of the oven pleased her. It had a faint food smell which was elegant. She could feed her babies and lick the oven walls, nibbling bits of burned meat as she came to them.

Jerome discovered the family at once because the oven door was open. He did not scold about the mattress when she showed him her brood of silky raccoons. But he was hungry and this was Saturday afternoon. Jerome always fixed a beef roast for Saturday supper. Once a week the mailman left the meat in his mailbox at the foot of the hill. Jerome got a wooden box and put it in a corner, then he moved the family. Mrs. Grouch was miffed, but she accepted the change with a sly smile. Later she would slip her family back into the oven.

Old Grouch stamped up on the porch and seated himself in the open doorway. He scolded his wife in proper style; he glared at Jerome and tossed a few nasty cracks at him. Between growls he kept sniffing the roast cooking in the oven, and shaking his fur to get the raindrops off it. With a final warning to his wife he turned about, climbed the redwood trunk, and got into his nest. The wind was from the north, and his wife was not there to keep the rain off his back. He stayed in the nest for half an hour, then he climbed back down the tree trunk and walked to the door. Jerome grinned at him. He was cutting the roast. He sliced off a piece and laid it on a saucer. He set the saucer on the floor.

Old Grouch looked at the saucer. This was

dangerous business. Going into a cabin was like stepping into a box trap. But he was wet and cold; his wife had walked out on him. He needed food and warmth. Ruffling his scruff, he walked into the house. He paused at the saucer and sniffed the good smell of the roast. He took a bite. When Mrs. Grouch scurried across the floor to share with him, he caught up the piece of meat in his forepaws. He sat up and glowered at her. Then he began munching the roast. His wife sniffed eagerly. She looked up at Jerome. He handed her a slice of meat. She took it and seated herself beside her husband. They sat there eating very much like humans, using their small hands to tear bits of meat from the large pieces, then stuffing the bits into their mouths.

By the time Jerome had finished his supper Old Grouch had made up his mind. He had marched to the door three times, and each time the cold rain had spattered into his face. He knew his wife and babies were going to sleep warm and dry inside the cabin. She had already returned to the box, where she sat with her small black eyes just above the edge. Old Grouch felt he could do with some more roast, too. He was still a bit hungry. He would stay in the cabin.

After the dishes were washed Jerome lighted his pipe. He was faced with a new problem. He had been trying for weeks to get Old Grouch into the cabin. Now that the old fellow and his family had moved in he dared not close the door. If he closed the door it was hard to say what Old Grouch would do. Jerome was sure it would be pretty wild.

But the night air was growing chilly. The wind was blowing into the room, wet and cold. Even if he did chase Old Grouch out into the rain he couldn't put Mrs. Grouch and the babies out. Jerome got to his feet. Old Grouch took one look at Jerome towering above him, then scuttled out into the night.

Jerome set the gasoline mantel lamp on the table so the white light would flood the door. He got his tool chest from under the bed. Mrs. Grouch kept her eyes just above the edge of the box. Jerome cut a small door in the bottom of his big door. He swung the small door by a pair of butterfly hinges and bored three holes in it.

As he gathered up his saw and auger and screw driver Jerome realized that the little door would offer welcome to any and all who roamed. It would mean keeping open house to all, except, of course, those neighbors too big to squeeze through the little door. He had never been able to make friends; it might be that the little door would change everything. He took the lamp and examined the chimney of his fireplace. The little skunks were not sleeping on the damper, so he lighted the fire he had laid earlier in the day. Pulling his padded chair up to the fireplace, he set his tobacco jar on the chair arm. As an afterthought he got a saucer and stacked a few squares of roast on it. He set the saucer on the floor beside the chair.

Jerome puffed slowly on his pipe. He watched the red tongues of flame lick around the oak and madroña logs in the fireplace. The beating warmth made him feel drowsy. He was on his second pipe when Old Grouch solved the mystery of the little door. He had peeped in through the three holes and discovered that Jerome had turned out the gasoline lamp, that his wife was snug and dry in the box with the babies. He sniffed and caught the rich smell of roast beef. He was wet and cold. He eased through the little door just as his wife hopped from the box, carrying one of the babies. She had her teeth set in the scruff. Shaking the water from his fur, he watched her put the youngster into the oven. He scowled at her, but he didn't make a sound. The warmth of the fireplace and the smell of the roast in the saucer drew him. He moved warily toward the fire. His experience with men had made him wary. But he was cold and he had an idea he could eat some more. Seating himself in the deep shadows near the chair, he stretched his snout toward the dish. He kept his eyes on Jerome. When Jerome did not move Old Grouch eased forward and picked up a piece of meat. He sat up and began munching it.

Mrs. Grouch had finished transferring her babies to the oven. She sat on the door for a while, watching the two males at the fireplace. Shaking her head, she turned her back upon them and curled up with her brood.

Jerome had never been able to talk with people. He had always known he was missing a great deal, but he had never been able to say the weather was nice or that the weather was bad when people came into his shop. He set his pipe on the arm of the chair and tossed another log on the fire. Old Grouch ducked into a patch of deep shadow, but he came out again and got another piece of meat. The warmth of the fire was beating against his fur. He felt contented and happy. Jerome leaned back and spoke out loud. When he spoke the sound of his voice startled even himself. Old Grouch, now gorged with roast and sleepy from the heat, toppled off the hearth and had to make quite an effort to right himself. Mrs. Grouch thrust her head out of the oven and stared at Jerome wildly. If it had not been for her babies she would have fled into the night.

"When I came up here I was licked," Jerome had said. It was as though a stranger had spoken to him; he heard his own voice so seldom. He felt called upon to answer the stranger.

"And were you licked?"

Old Grouch batted his eyes fearfully. He looked all around the room but saw no human being except Jerome, whom he had ceased to consider a man, because Jerome never shouted or whistled or talked at all.

"I've spent a lifetime carving cherubs and angels on tombstones. I've cut many a nice sentiment on a gravestone, but never was able to recite a single line before company." Jerome pointed his pipestem toward the fire. "It's a sad business, dealing with sad people, and not being able to say a word to comfort them."

Old Grouch braced himself and let his stomach ease down until he was resting comfortably. He had room for a bite or two more, and the fire was very nice. Jerome smiled down at him. Old Grouch looked like a small bandit with the black patches which circled his eyes and extended along his cheeks like black bands, making a perfect mask against the lighter coloring of his fur. He cocked his head. He was in a mellow mood. His stomach was full to bursting; his furry hide was warm. He felt like singing.

He started out with a soft "Shur-r-r-r," then went into a deeper note, a long-drawn, tremulous "Whoo-oo-oo," not unlike the call of a screech owl, only softer and sweeter, much more mellow. Jerome's smile widened. He had never dared venture a note himself. In all of the hundreds of times he had sat alone in his pew in church he had never dared open his mouth and sing.

"I have missed much," he said.

"Whoo-oo-oo," Old Grouch sang, his head swaying sleepily.

From the oven door came an answering trill. Never had Mrs. Grouch heard her husband put so much tenderness, so much romance into his song. It touched her deeply, so deeply she closed her eyes and sang back to him. Jerome laid down his pipe.

Turning to catch the high soprano from the oven, Jerome noticed that the little door was bobbing back and forth. He fixed his attention upon it. A small head with black shoe-button eyes appeared. The head moved into the room, followed by a slim body. A moment later another slim body moved through the door. Two tall white plumes lifted. The little spotted skunks had come visiting. Papa waved his plume and stamped his feet; Mama waved her plume and stamped her feet. Like a good host, Jerome arose from his chair. Instantly the two little skunks vanished through the door. Jerome filled a saucer with canned milk and set it near the door, then he went back to his chair before the fire.

Almost at once the little door opened and the skunks marched in. They sat down and began lapping eagerly. When Mrs. Grouch hopped off the oven door and started toward the saucer, Papa elevated his plume and stamped his forefeet. He rushed at her, did a handstand, flipped his hind feet down again, then stamped some more. Mrs. Grouch knew what that meant, as did every other living thing in the woods. She hastily retreated to the oven door. Papa went back to his milk.

Jerome leaned back in his chair. Old Grouch was in full voice now; his whoo-oo-oo was deep and bell-like. Jerome tried an experimental note himself. He was amazed at its quality. It was a baritone note with feeling and depth in it. But it sent Mrs. Grouch scrambling back into the oven; Papa and Mama left without waiting to stamp their feet. Only Old Grouch was not startled at all. He just sat and swayed back and forth and sang. He seemed to have caught the fine flavor of Jerome's baritone. Jerome tried a few more notes. Mrs. Grouch stayed in the oven;

the spotted skunks stayed under the floor. Old Grouch picked up the last square of roast and ate it slowly. When he swallowed it his stomach bulged bigger. He cocked an eye at Jerome. Jerome tried a few hymns he remembered. Old Grouch joined in. He had only one song, but it blended well with any hymn.

After a bit Jerome began to feel sleepy. He was sleepy and he was happy. He leaned back and closed his eyes. Old Grouch yawned. He ambled toward the oven door. After two tries he managed to hop up on the door. Easing into the oven, he curled up with his family. Jerome sighed deeply. Here among friends he could talk about things he had always wanted to talk about, and he could sing when he felt like it. He got to his feet and took his flannel nightgown from its hook. He smiled as he got ready for bed.

from MASKED PROWLER

John L. and Jean George

John L. George in this talented husband and wife team is a zoologist, and his wife is an artist. Both write, and their books reveal a special sympathy for the creatures man hunts so relentlessly. But the authors are realists too, and the uneven battle of wits between hunter and hunted is not softened. In this chapter, Procyon, a young raccoon, has his first encounter with his lifelong enemies, the hunting dogs. The price of life is eternal vigilance, but Procyon triumphs grandly in the end. Don't miss Vulpes, the Red Fox *and* Meph, the Pet Skunk *by the Georges.*

[*First Adventures of a Young Raccoon*]

When the hay was baled and stored in the mow, the harvesting of the oat crop began. All day the whisk of the binder sounded across the field. At ten minutes to five Joe looked at his big gold pocket watch.

"What time do you have, Gib?" he called.

"Five to five," the farmer answered. Joe's watch was always clogged with chaff and grit from the fields, and at least once a day it stopped. He shook it, set the hands and mumbled, "About chore time."

He turned away from the fields and walked toward the barn. The cows were in the barnyard waiting to be fed and milked. Joe opened the east door and they filed into the barn and each walked to her own stall. He took down the electric milking machines and was well along with the chores when Gib came into the barnyard with the team. He unhitched the horses from the binder and gave them a spank on their broad haunches to let them know they were free. They galloped ponderously to the water tank and from there to their stalls. Gib joined Joe in the barn.

"The white cow didn't come up from the woods," Joe said as he poured a bucket of foamy milk through the strainer.

"She's about due to calf," the farmer said. "If she's got a calf we'd better go back and get her now, or she'll hide it in the underbrush, and it will take us a couple of hours to find it."

They finished the milking and started to the woods. As they opened the gate in the lane, Fanny, the Blue Tick hound, trotted around the grainery to join them. She dashed ahead, searching for meadow mice, but waited for them at the end of the lane.

The men separated in the forest. Joe walked to the woodland meadow, scouted the edges and started back to meet Gib at the sugar house.

"Ka Bos, Ka Bos," he would call from time to time to the cow.

Gib was standing motionless at the corner of the shack. He was peering intently across the hill. Several howls from Fanny signaled the presence of some woodland creature.

"Coon family," Gib mumbled. "Four little ones and a big one." Clinging to the dipping limbs of a sugar maple were Procyon, his brother, sisters and mother. They were staring silently at Fanny barking below them.

"Here, Fanny, come on, come here!" Gib called. "Leave them alone, dog."

Fanny did not respond and he went to get her. She was jumping and clawing at the tree in an effort to climb to the limbs where the raccoons clung. Gib clutched her collar between bounds and looked steadily at the picture above him. Frightened by the man, the mother and two of the youngsters galloped higher into the tree. They disappeared in the dense foliage. The other two did not move, but with eyes and ears fixed curiously upon Fanny and then Gib, they stared down quietly.

Suddenly the raccoons had an unexpected ally. The missing cow rushed from a nearby thicket, lowered her head and charged Fanny. Gib released the hound and she dashed for shelter behind the sugar house. Joe heard the noise and came running. As he passed a raspberry and prickly ash thicket, he found the calf. He prodded it to its feet. The cow, still alarmed, bellowed and rushed him but she stopped short beside her calf. Each of the men picked up a stout club and expertly herded the cow toward the lane. She moved reluctantly stopping frequently to call her calf.

"Whey, Boss, Whey Boss. The calf will follow you, he'll follow," Joe told her. And the calf did follow although occasionally he found his untried legs too far apart to move. Joe would straighten him out with a lift from the rear and he would stumble after his mother.

At the edge of the woods Fanny trotted up to the heels of the men. The cow turned and charged the dog. Gib pushed her off with a well-timed shove on her nose.

"Go on home. Git!" He shouted at Fanny. The hound was only too happy to obey. She slipped under the fence and took the field route home.

Once in the lane, the cow started homeward with more willingness. The calf trotted behind her. Joe and Gib discussed the coon family as they herded the cow and the little bull up the lane.

"Weren't they nice little coons?"

"Sure were," Joe laughed. "Wonder where they came from."

"Whey Boss!" shouted Joe as the cow hesitated.

"Fanny brought them out of that old stream bed."

"Maybe there'll be good hunting this fall. Must be a lot more around."

And so they whooped and chatted as they drove the cow and the newest addition to the herd back to the barn. In the barn the cow headed for her stanchion with her calf at her heels. Gib let the calf nurse, then slipped a collar around its neck and tied it to the wall just behind the cow. The cow turned her head and bawled to her calf, who had now dropped on a pile of sweet yellow straw that Gib had thrown down for him.

Gib took the remaining milk from the cow by hand. It was a thick yellow fluid which she would give for several days. It was designed by nature to make the digestive tract of the new born calf begin its work. In a day or so the white milk would come. Gib did not put this fresh milk in with the milk from the other cows, for he could not send it to the dairy. What the calf did not need he fed to the hogs. After the ninth milking he would put the milk in with that of the herd.

Back in the woods the raccoon family relaxed as the men disappeared down the lane. Procyon had been one of the youngsters who had hidden in the leaves with his mother. His sister pushed close beside him, still hugging him and watching the dark tree so recently alive with a barking clawing hound. She shivered. As the forest quieted down, the mother raccoon whistled to her youngsters and descended to the forest floor. Procyon dug his foreclaws into the tree bark and pushed out from the limb. He swung like a pendulum a few times as he hung by his hands, then grabbed the tree with his hind feet, turned around head first and climbed to the earth. The family reassembled and trekked off to the great marsh that spread to the north of the forest.

Procyon left the group at the edge of the cattail border. He crossed a garden of wild iris, pushed through a relentless mat of sedges and came to a fallen cottonwood, four feet through, that had tumbled from the shore into the marsh. He scrambled up this and walked along it. Beneath him he could hear open water, and ripples lapping around the old tree.

Farther along the trunk he came to a massive limb that sloped downward into the grasses. In the fork of this limb, Procyon stopped. He had come upon the scat pile of a raccoon. He sniffed it, circled the pile with careful steps and followed the limb down to a basin of water. The smell of silt and mud filled his nose. Here he had the feel of pollywogs and frogs.

Procyon lifted his head. To his right the

grasses parted and a giant raccoon moved before him. Procyon could see his black mask and the bulging muscles of his forearms. The spread of that broad tapered face made Procyon back against the log.

The old raccoon surveyed the young hunter solemnly. He moved a few steps closer, sniffed him and stepped into the water. The marsh basin muddied as his feet moved nimbly among the roots and down into the muck. The little coon watched in fascination. He had known no other raccoon of comparable stature other than his mother. Even she had not such tremendous jaws. Her haunches were not as high, nor her wrists as large and powerful. Should this giant decide that Procyon was intruding, there would

be little scuffle, little battle. The power and force of those great legs gave him the right to anything in the marsh and woods.

Procyon did not retreat, rather he pushed up on his toes and walked gingerly into the water. Surprised by the audacity of the youngster's movements, the old coon stopped his fishing and looked up. He snarled gruffly and his white teeth made Procyon uneasy. The young coon knew it was useless to run. The old giant still paused as if wondering whether to permit this young one to remain. He seemed to be waiting for the scurry of the cub's retreat. Procyon dug his toes into the mud. He shifted his feet automatically, his eyes on the big raccoon.

There was a deep snarl—the great male had made a decision. He turned away and went back to his work. As he fished he waded off, paying no more attention to the young one. Procyon lost his fear, and once more admired the greatness of the hunter's size. Still eyeing him, he moved deeper into the water and searched the stem of a bull rush. From it he picked off a water snail and brought it up to his mouth. The old coon heard the shell crunch and turned around. Ferocity seemed to have left his face. Procyon stopped to listen more keenly for he thought he detected the murmur of a purr deep in that round chest. The old one moved on through the shallows.

Procyon watched him go, then turned to find his mother. He climbed back on the log and raced for the cattails and reeds where he had left her and his sisters and brother. He found them not far from the base of the log. They were whistling and calling as they rounded up for the trip home.

Tonight they did not return to the red oak. The mother led her family into a grove of basswoods and willows. Here she selected a tilted tree and took the four youngsters to a dry hollow about twenty feet above the ground. The cavity was deeper than the familiar one in the red oak. In fact, it seemed to the young coons that they climbed right back to the earth on the inside of the tree.

The bottom of the retreat was roomy and Procyon and his brother explored the cracks and crevices with their hands before settling down to sleep. When he had satisfied his curiosity about the interior of this marshland home, Procyon snuggled up to his mother for milk. There was none to be had. He pushed and shoved her, but he had had the last of his mother's milk that morning. This was as it should be, for the litter which had weighed little more than half a pound at birth, now weighed well over twenty pounds. The young cubs were ready to go without milk. For a month their mother had taught them how to find and eat other foods.

The family spent much of their time during late August at the basswood retreat in the marsh. Here Procyon often found the old male coon. He followed him, but the two were never intimate, for Procyon kept a respectful distance. The old coon taught the youngster many secrets of the marshes. Procyon tracked him to the elderberry bushes and the gooseberry bushes. Through the old one he became aware of a vast assortment of foods to be found in August.

On an afternoon late in August, Procyon and his bigger sister were wrestling in the bottom of the basswood den. The rest of the family were out on the limbs where they had sunned themselves during the day. His sister grew tired of the tumbling and rolling and meant to end the play. She bit Procyon sharply on the ear. He jumped on her, growled and returned her bite with a sound nip on the chest. She galloped up the tree. Procyon chased her out of the hole and down the outside. She stopped at the first limb. Procyon nipped her while hanging above her, then passed on down the tree and walked off to the gooseberry bushes.

He ate until he was contentedly full and stretched out to play on the back of an old log. He found a walnut and took it in his paws. Rolling around on his back he tossed it between his feet. He was twisting and biting it when the old coon came by. Procyon dropped his walnut and rolled off the log. He crouched against it looking at the hunter. Suddenly the marshland birds became silent.

The old coon was looking up, the young cub followed his gaze. Above them came the winged hunter, Circus, the marsh hawk. He hovered for a minute over the raccoons. His feet swung half extended as his sharp eyes surveyed the scene. Then gracefully he veered and flew toward an abandoned meadow. Undisturbed, the old coon looked away from the soaring hunter. He did not look at Procyon again, but turned away and bounded off along the edge of the reeds hoping to surprise a vole he scented in the meadow. As he left, Procyon reached out and rolled the walnut, his eyes still focused on the path the old giant had taken.

When the corn had tasseled and eared, the coon family moved back to the red oak den for it was closer to this source of food than the basswood. It was with some reluctance that Procyon left the long grasses, protected pools and tangled avenues of the marshland.

About four-thirty in the afternoon of a September day, Procyon was curled on the limb of the red oak. The air was cool as it came rushing through the woods, and Procyon shifted in his sleep, tucking his nose deeper into his fur. He was awakened by a beetle climbing up his nose toward his ear. He snapped at it, but it winged off and he dropped his head back to the limb to sleep. His eyes would not close. He found himself watching the limbs dip deeper and deeper as a storm circled the woods and emptied itself some miles to the north.

He finally arose and climbed down the tree to the ground. His hind legs and haunches were well developed. They were longer than his forelegs and tilted his body forward, giving him the shape of a plump pear. They no longer wobbled when he walked but propelled him through the woods with agility and sent him galloping along the limbs of the trees as deftly as a squirrel. Procyon now weighed eight pounds. He was big, but not full grown or mature. Despite his power and versatility on land and in the trees,

he was still a comedian. Masked and fuzzy, this harlequin of the woods was a limber acrobat. He hung by his hind legs from limbs, frisked along the narrow avenues of the trees, rolled and tumbled on the ground, and climbed hand over hand along low branches.

Procyon was off to the stream this September afternoon. He ran and trotted toward the water, turning off the trail frequently to investigate a rattling leaf, a smell, a hollow log. At the edge of the stream he heard a noise behind him. He jumped to the foot of a tree, looked around, heard it again and galloped up a few paces.

"Who-oo?" a voice called.

"Who-oo," Procyon answered. He turned around sideways and looked down at his sister who had followed him. Bracing himself with his chin he started down. He came down as always, head first. He hung by his big hind feet that curved snugly around the tree. With this support a forearm shot out, and back to his side. It took the weight while he brought the hind foot on that side forward. In this manner he climbed down to the base of the tree and ran to his sister. He nipped her on the ear and raced to the water. The sister buckled up, danced a few side steps in the leaves and chased after him.

Side by side they took a long drink. Their chins seemed to float on the very surface of the water as they drank, for their lower jaws were so far behind their noses that if they had tried to lap like a dog their noses would have been submerged. Then they resumed their sparring again. Finally Procyon crossed the shallows to the roots of a sugar maple. The tree was being undermined by the creek and tilted across the stream at a forty-five degree angle. Its massive roots still retained the soil above, but were washed out below.

The meandering creek had dug into the ground behind the roots leaving a cave barred by the grill work of interlacing roots. Procyon wove his way through this screen and splashed in the shallow water. This was one of his favorite hunting grounds for it was protected from the woodland; and into the net of roots came many creatures of the stream. After a brief survey of his cave, Procyon stuck his head out through a small opening in the lattice work. He looked brightly around the stream bed and watched his sister hunt water-food then run toward him. She slipped and soaked her tail and hind legs. Ears back, he wedged out through the grill and galloped along the shore. She pulled herself from the water and galloped after him.

As he raced along, his antics frightened a minnow. It swam up the creek ahead of him, trying to escape, and stranded itself in a shallow rapid. Procyon pounced upon it as it flopped helplessly. He rolled it over and over in his paws, flipped it to the bank, jumped on it, picked it up in his teeth and tossed it into the sand. Again he grabbed it, then carried it ten feet up the bank. Here he lost it momentarily, found it again, bit it several times and carried it back to the creek. At the spot where he had caught it, he rolled it over and over in the water as if he were washing it. He was merely feeling it in water just as he had felt it on land. Finally the fish became a pulpy mass that fell apart. The head and gills were carried away by the current. He ate the rest.

Meanwhile his sister had felt her way up the stream beyond him and was crunching loudly on what seemed to be a stone, but what proved to be a fresh water mussel. She could not open it and dropped it. It rocked back to the bottom of the stream, scratched white where her little milk teeth had raked across it. But one tooth would never scratch again. Her vigorous bite had knocked it loose from its shallow socket. Where it had been was the gleaming white tip of her permanent canine tooth.

About this time Gib's herd of cattle came crashing through the woods to the creek for water. Procyon ran up a ten inch basswood that leaned over the stream. His sister went up a large silver maple. While the cattle drank below them the coons descended slowly. A cow at the foot of Procyon's basswood caught his scent, looked up and snorted. Procyon, only a few feet above her wide twitching nostrils, turned around and went back up a short distance.

A black heifer seeing the sister, crossed the creek and went to look at her. The raccoon spiraled to the other side of the tree and came around almost face to face with the heifer. Taken by surprise the heifer leaped backward and stumbled down the bank into the stream. Procyon galloped down the sloping basswood and ran for the base of the washed out maple. Before he could gain the protection of the tangled roots, the cow lowered her head and chased him some thirty feet into the woods trying to bunt him with her nose. The young cow stopped and stared at him. Procyon, unafraid, came toward her taking time to investigate every interesting sight along the woodland floor. The cow charged him again, but this time Procyon curved around her to the creek. He found his sister had also come back to the stream. Little disturbed by the herd, they climbed down the lattice work of roots and resumed their fishing. Several cows stood close together on the opposite bank and for a long time watched them curiously.

When the cattle had wandered back toward the fields, the coons left the security of the maple root grill and worked up stream. After they tired of fishing they climbed a flaky barked sugar maple. They walked out onto the far ends of the branches and fingered the terminal shoots and buds. They dipped and swayed with the limbs as the wind rocked the young tree. Procyon and his sister pulled the twigs to their mouths and picked off the buds with their teeth. The leaves spiraled to the ground as they ate. Occasionally they pried loose a sliver of bark and it plopped to the forest floor.

Balancing on the pencil thin limbs they sparred and fought as easily as they did on the ground. Frolicking, swinging and hanging, the fat cubs entertained themselves on the zig-zag playground of the tree. Presently Procyon climbed high in the maple and settled his haunches in the sharp angle of a crotch. Draping his forepaws and head over the branch above, he fell asleep. His sister dozed in a fork below him.

To the east along the horizon a gaudy moon was rising. The scent of goldenrod and milkweed was on the wind, and the air had a taste of nuts, grapes and plump berries. A great horned owl boomed from the forest to the north, and the eerie howl of a red fox was followed by silence.

After an hour's nap Procyon and his sister rejoined the family. The family feasted on the many woodland delicacies that comprised their varied taste. They enjoyed a wide assortment of foods; that of mice, of fish and water animals, nuts, corn, insects and all berries and succulent fruits. This night they dined from the stream to the highlands. They were ready to go home about midnight, but it was dawn before they reached the base of the big red oak and climbed to the den, for they wandered home slowly, checking each scent and sound. They stole quietly down into the hollow.

One bright September night when the stars glittered through the tops of the trees like fireflies, and the air was so clear that each tree looked crisp and fresh, the coon family awoke and prepared themselves for hunting. Stretching and yawning, they gradually came to life. Procyon rolled his sister's tail between his hands and scratched her stomach with his hind foot. He nipped her until she sputtered and then shoved his brother. His mother moved and Procyon reached out and tapped her cheek. She looked at him casually, then turned and climbed out of the den.

Procyon rolled over on his back with his feet in the air and watched the others leave for their night trip through the September woods.

Somewhat later he poked his head out of the den and smelt the night air. Slowly he climbed to the ground and joined the family in the cornfield. Procyon broke off an ear of corn with his nimble hands and peeled back the husk. Biting and chewing he devoured half of this and began on another when the scent of pheasant rode to him on the wind. He turned away quietly and traced the wind to its source. An old cock pheasant sleeping in a dense pocket of goldenrods and asters that grew along the edge of the field, awoke with a start as Procyon raked a corn stalk. The pheasant clattered into the darkness and flew blindly for the woods. Procyon looked after him. The wind carried off his scent and the coon turned to find his family.

He picked up his mother's trail and wove through the corn in search of her. She was sitting over an ear of corn that she held between her forepaws. As she wrinkled up her lips to sink her front teeth in the kernels, she saw her son galloping up the green corridor toward her. She did not stop eating but purred and pressed back her ears as Procyon rose to his back feet, touched her on the forearm then swung gently away. His brother was behaving strangely, and Procyon found his actions more interesting than his mother's. He crossed into the next alley of corn passing through a cobweb that stuck to his black mask. His brother had a young meadow vole under his paw, and was nipping it as it scurried to get loose. When he saw Procyon he stopped playing with it, killed it quickly and ran down the furrow holding it in his teeth. Procyon chased him, overtook him and knocked his feet out from under him. He snatched the mouse and galloped to the next row of corn as his brother scrambled into action and came charging after him.

While the raccoon family was raiding Gib's cornfield, Ruff, the vagrant wild hound slipped under the gate at the end of the lane and stole toward the woods. He was lean and thin for he did not eat regularly. Occasionally he was fed by a family that lived on Ford Road, but for the most part he lived on mice in the fields, muskrats, woodchucks and anything he could hunt or steal. Ruff had no certain ancestry, he was a mixture of terrier, hound and others. During the day he stuck to the woods almost as wild as a fox or coyote. When he came near the farmhouses he did so with his tail between his legs and his head crouched. He hid from the farmers and was chased by their dogs.

Ruff slunk down the lane to the woods, his nose pressed to the earth, trying to pick out the scent of some animal on the dry ground. He circled the sugar house and trotted up the ravine that ran west through the woods past the red oak den. Ruff turned around suddenly and jogged back a few steps. His tail stiffened as he came upon the trail of the coon family leading south to the cornfield.

Ruff understood that the scent he was following was that of a raccoon. The hound knew from experience that the raccoon was a formidable animal and he stole along the trail silently without snapping a stick. Slinking close to the ground he followed the trail to the fence.

Ruff became tense, he could hear the scrapping growls of Procyon and his brother as they fought over the mouse. They were just beyond the fence, four rows into the cornfield. Ruff glided under the fence, still silent.

The brothers heard the fence rattle and as the dog crashed through the first row, they sped up the furrow toward their mother. Ruff strained into action, the exertion forcing a yipe from his throat. He gained rapidly on Procyon and his brother. With a snarl, Ruff sank his teeth into the fleshy hind leg of the brother. The brother rolled into the dusty earth and turned from the attacking hound. Ruff checked his speed and swung. He lunged again. With a howl the hound went down writhing and yelping in pain. With a vicious snarl the mother coon had caught the dog in complete surprise from the rear. By the time the hound had gathered his wits, the family followed by their mother was through the fence. Ruff bounced to his feet but followed them with less interest.

The wire fence checked him long enough for the coons to put ten yards between them. The brother, slowed by his wounded leg, jumped to the first tree beyond the fence and scurried out of reach of the dog. The sisters who had had more time, had run into the woods about fifty yards before climbing a young maple. They were safely out of reach when their mother and Procyon passed them and took to the security of the next maple. Ruff followed them cautiously. He slid up to the tree and stopped. With tongue hanging from his mouth, he looked into the branches. The raccoons were safe in the trees. Ruff limped off.

from THE WAHOO BOBCAT

Joseph Wharton Lippincott

An animal story by Mr. Lippincott, publisher as well as author, is invariably exciting. In this first episode the bobcat has been discovered by a hound, and begins the adventures that are going to lead to his strange friendship with a boy.

Fight with a Hog

The Tiger, completely taken by surprise, waited to see what the big dog would do, and the dog, a hound, just stood there looking at him in the dim light. The hound was trying hard to understand the weird combination of a wildcat's body and a skunk's smell which made his eyes mistrust his nose. At length, the hair began to rise on his back, and with a bellow of combined glee and fury he sprang at the fence, forcing the cat to leap back to the protection of the bushes. Over the fence then came the hound with a clatter of rails, and after the cat he dashed with bellow after bellow fairly bursting from his chest.

Shrill yaps of delight now sounded behind him as the three other dogs heard the row and could not resist running from the house to join in the chase. Down the hog path went the Tiger in long, easy bounds, toward the Prairie and the swamps that he knew so well, the briar thickets in which he could hide and the deep mud holes over which he could leap. He drew away from the bellows and the thumping feet and sprang out of the path into the thick bushes to confuse his followers and give himself more time to elude them, for instinct told him that a hound like this one would trail him as long as his scented tracks could be followed.

The four dogs were all together now, thrashing about in the bushes to find where he had dodged. Occasionally they yelped with excitement, occasionally too there were distant shouts indicating that a man had joined the hunt. Fiercely the Tiger fought his way through the swamp growth, reached the Prairie and dashed along its edge among the tussocks of heavy grass and the tricky holes that had no bottom, places where snakes lurked and the barbed briars would rip any creature that did not understand their tangles.

Bellows from the black hound began again; he was once more on the trail and coming fast. The cat stopped for a moment to listen and make sure he was not too close, then deliberately turned back and followed his own tracks until he came to a tree whose limbs hung low. With a mighty leap the Tiger reached one of these stout limbs, climbed along it to the tree's trunk and crouched there, twenty feet from the ground, so high that his scent would be caught by the rising currents of night air and kept away from pursuers below. If they discovered him he would jump into the bushes and run again.

He was not afraid now. His pounding heart slowed down and he rested. As presently the dogs came bounding single file along the Prairie's edge on the trail he had left, he stood up to watch them flounder in the mud and fight the tangles. They passed him and reached the place where he had doubled back, but then their glad tonguing ceased and they searched in all directions for more tracks. It did not occur to them to turn back on the trail and look up the tree. Once, a circle made by the black hound in his hunting brought him directly under the cat, but there was no scent on the ground and he did not guess that he was so close to the Tiger.

Gradually the dogs worked their way farther into the swamp and far from the cat, the crashing and splashing sounds they made dying out and the shouts of the man growing dim as he tired of the fruitless hunt in the musk-laden air and returned to his house. The moon was rising and filling the swamp with remarkable shadows; the Prairie shimmered wherever there were grassless pools and the frogs were yelling as if their lives depended on the noise, but no creature appeared to notice the Tiger as he climbed down the tree, backwards like a bear, sniffed at his fur, rolled a few times in a sandy spot and once more hungrily began his search for food.

Everywhere was the smell of musk. It had bothered almost all the little furry creatures and made them hide or travel beyond the reach of the fumes; this meant that some had to go into the pine woods or far down the Prairie's edge, others into holes in the ground or in hollow trees; even the hum produced by the countless insects of the swamp seemed to have changed.

Like a ghost in the deserted swamp the cat wandered, ever on the alert but more and more discouraged. He did not want to go near the home of the dogs, so at length he trotted to the second-best field, arriving at its edge just as dawn grayed the sky and the birds of day began to awake and give their first morning cries. Soon they would sing and play and feed on all sides and the creatures of the night would vanish into hiding. Hunger, however, kept the Tiger on the move. Even more stealthy now, he crept along the fence, looking well ahead for gray squirrels and unwary birds of any kind, ears cocked at every sound and muscles ready for instant leaps.

He belonged to the creatures of the night and therefore was too easily spotted now by his intended prey; the birds scattered before him in alarm and the squirrels barked derisively from safe perches over his head, advertising his presence wherever he went. The Tiger, however, was resourceful; he knew that if he found a good hiding place he could crouch there unseen and spring upon unwary creatures that came near him in their own feeding. Such a place was inside the fenced area, in an unplowed corner where tall briars gave perfect cover. So, after leaping the worm fence to this corner he sneaked, and under the green cover of the thorny tangle he hid himself.

A hundred yards across the field stood the house where humans lived and already were clattering about. Their breakfast was finished and the two children, a boy of nine and a girl somewhat smaller, were out on the back porch playing. But the Tiger was not afraid of children.

The grunt of a hog sounded some distance to the right and presently a lean, brown-black sow grubbed her way under the fence and led six very young black piglets into the forbidden area. She was nearer to him than to the house and at the edge of a strawberry patch where her rooting could do much harm. Under some of the plants went her powerful snout and contentedly she munched the roots and grunted while the piglets clustered around her legs.

The half wild sow was having a very happy time until the little boy happened to see her. He knew that hogs had to be chased out of the field whenever they came under the fence, so he shouted to his parents and, seizing a stick, bravely jumped from the porch and ran at the hogs, waving the stick and still yelling.

The old sow looked up, realized at once that this was an attack on her for trespassing, and, with a grunt of alarm led the piglets towards the hole through which they had come. The little ones toddled after her with might and main but were held back by a stretch of soft, ploughed ground and were continually falling into the furrows and having to climb out. The smallest, a mere runt with tiny legs and a very wrinkled snout, was having the worst time of all and suddenly got into a furrow from which he could not climb.

The runt kept very quiet for a few moments, but when the others left him and the boy came running, he gave a shrill squeal of fear and struggled anew with the crumbling furrow. The boy's first instinct was to help him out, so he stooped and put his hands under the runt, whereupon the tiny pig thought his doom was sealed and let out piercing squeals which went to his mother's heart and brought her back on the run to his rescue.

She charged across the soft ground in wild mother rage, reached the boy, knocked him head over heels with her snout and began to rip at him with her toothed mouth, furiously grunting amid the squeals of the piglet and the sudden howls of the boy who was pummeling her as best he could with his fists. The noise reached every corner of the field and brought the father out of the house in his bare feet, running so fast that he tripped on a bush and fell full length in the sand. Behind him came the yelling mother, brandishing a saucepan, her face white with fear as she ran toward her son. The squeals, grunts, shrieks and yells continued unabated as the sow furiously rolled the boy over and over, biting and rooting at him and trampling him into the sand.

Strangest of all was the action of the wildcat. A sudden fury took possession of his brain and blotted out all else. He rushed along the fence, then cut across the ploughed ground and coming close to the battling mass of screaming bodies, threw himself on top of the sow and hurled her to the ground. Buffeting her head with his two forepaws, he raked at her snout and clawed her sides, bit with all his strength into her thick neck and in spite of her kicks held on and rolled about with her in the heavy sand, now on top now underneath, his screams and growls joining the high pitched voices of the others as he ripped and tore and tried to batter the black, fighting body locked in his embrace.

Suddenly the big sow, with a great heave of her snout, threw him away from her, rose to her feet and stood facing him with mouth open, little eyes sparkling and wicked. The cat got his paws under him and crouched, when suddenly he seemed to awaken. He looked this way and that in a daze. He saw the man and the woman standing over him holding the boy between them in their arms, saw the bare, sandy field around him all white in the sun that was rising over the trees. Gone was the old sow in a whirl of dust and gone all of a sudden was his fury and his courage.

He got shakily to his feet, looked for an instant at the man and woman standing there so oddly quiet, then started for the fence, slowly at first until his legs unlimbered and he could take the furrows in his great, graceful bounds. He scarcely touched the top of the fence as he went over it and he did not stop until he was far in the cool, shadowed swamp, among the silent places, away from all signs and sounds of the strange, wild fight. Throwing himself flat on the ground under the green tangles he lay with heaving sides pulling himself together and getting back his normal balance. Forever in his memory, however, would be the very strange adventure of this day.

Small birds sang as if nothing at all had happened. The gray moss swayed and the leaves rustled in the growing breeze; ants ran up and down the tree trunks; buzzards circled like kites, with flattened wings and tails spread. Gradually the Tiger relaxed, dozed a little, licked his rumpled fur, tested his bitten legs a few times and arranged himself into a ball that could lie snugly among the dead leaves. Night would come again and with it the hunting time, the magic hour, when the rabbits and mice would appear from their hiding places and again the chance would come for him to still his hunger pains. Yes, night would come and night was really cat time; then he would hunt again and eat frogs if nothing better came his way.

Sammy and the Wildcat

The day dawned like any other day. The swamp, never entirely asleep, teemed with life and pleasant sounds as birds and beasts went about their usual pursuits. Cattle lowed and hogs grunted as if to show that man was nearby, and far away a railroad engine tooted mournfully as though tired of sticking to the same old track.

Stretched on a low limb of a moss-festooned live oak, with his four feet under him, the Tiger dozed and dreamed. Occasionally his claws moved and often his ears wiggled to ward off flies, but otherwise he was as motionless as the limb itself. The hours passed until the August sun overhead marked high noon and soon began to sink toward the western horizon, its heat growing slowly less as the rays slanted more and more.

The cat was becoming restless. He stretched his legs and yawned, and he began to look around and listen attentively to the sounds in the swamp. An unusual noise came faintly from the direction of the clearings and at once caught his attention. It was whistling, for Sammy liked to whistle whenever he was alone, and now he was making his way to the Prairie, taking what he thought was a short cut to the boat that his father kept moored at the water's edge. He should have stayed on the little path that led there from the house, but Sammy had ideas of his own and wanted to explore. In his bare feet he found it easier to walk under the oaks where the briars were not so tangled, and he was heading in almost a straight line for the tree in which the Tiger rested.

It was not difficult for the cat to tell by the sounds that only one person was approaching, and this a youngster with no evil intentions. A hunter would keep as quiet as possible and sneak along the paths, instead of whistling loudly and padding carelessly over the dry leaves.

Presently he sighted Sammy's head above the palmettos, then his thin body; there seemed nothing dangerous about this little human and, besides, the cat felt that if he kept still he would not be seen on his limb. As he watched, his memory brought him back to the time when he had seen this boy before, running across the field, and he felt curiosity about this small edition of dangerous man.

Sammy came whistling past the tree and then stopped. The vague feeling that he was being watched had come to him as it comes to many creatures more sensitive than the average. He stood quite still and looked around him. The swamp seemed deserted to his eyes, but he continued to turn them this way and that until suddenly they met the stare of the big cat crouching on the limb not twenty feet away. Sammy wasn't scared, but he was mightily surprised. He could not remember ever having seen a cat one quarter as large as this one, which must be the daddy of them all, the kind he had heard his parents speaking about. They liked cats and so did he.

"Kitty, Kitty! Here Kitty!" said Sammy; but as the cat did not stir and continued to gaze at him he grew disconcerted and took several steps backward. He decided something must be wrong with it because it did not move, and he was troubled by the fixed stare of its round, yellow eyes. He walked farther, still looking back and calling "Kitty," and when it was out of sight he thought about it and wondered whether it was hungry, out here in the swamp all by itself.

He found the boat, pulled a bait can from under the seat and put a white worm on the hook which dangled from a fishing pole he had hidden in the bushes at his last visit. The worm was one of a number he had found under the bark of a fallen and partly decayed pine. The nose of the boat was stuck in the mud and the stern projected into the Prairie to the edge of a little pool surrounded by grass. In this pool he dropped his hook and waited expectantly until the line began to move and he felt a nibble. He gave the fish time enough to swallow the worm, then jerked and brought out a flopping bream the size of a pancake.

The bream flopped about on the bottom of the boat but was soon unhooked. Another worm, then another bream. In all, he landed four before they stopped biting. To carry them he strung them on a little forked stick, one end of which he passed through their gills. Now he was ready to go home, so he hid his pole and started up the path, whistling as before and holding the stick on his shoulder so that the fish dangled behind him. He was feeling happy and carefree until all at once he remembered the cat and again wondered whether it was hungry.

He decided then to leave the path and have another look at the big animal, if it was still in the same place; and this time, when he came near the tree, he saw the yellow eyes immediately.

"Here Kitty," he called. "Here Kitty." The cat did not move, and Sammy went quite close, until he was almost directly under it. This was too close for the Tiger, who immediately leaped noiselessly to the ground and vanished in the bushes, leaving the boy surprised and disappointed by its lack of friendliness. He thought of the fish and, acting on a generous impulse, pulled one off the stick and laid it on the ground. Again he called, but getting no response, decided he would leave the fish for the cat to find, because he was sure all cats were hungry like his cat at home. Now he began to whistle again and continued his walk through the swamp to the field and then to the house, where he gave the three remaining bream to his mother to clean and cook for supper.

"Did you have a nice time?" asked Eliza.

"Oh, yes, and I caught another bream, but I gave that one to a great big cat."

"What?" gasped his mother. "What kind of a cat?"

"An awful big one. It looked hungry."

His mother dropped her dish cloth and sat down in a chair beside him.

"Tell me all about it," she demanded. And Sammy, excited by her interest, gave a very good description of the cat in the tree and how it had jumped down and run away, although he had left the bream for it to find because he knew it was hungry.

For once Eliza was speechless, but when Bill returned from a trip into the woods to feed his wandering hogs a little corn and keep them gentle and tame, she gave him Sammy's story word for word.

"I wonder if it was the Tiger?" mused Bill.

"Aren't you worried about the boy walking in the swamp and running into catamounts like that?"

"Not one bit," he answered. "I was like him when I was a little feller and the swamp was swarming with varmints. Nothing ever happened to me."

"Well, I don't feel it's safe. Suppose that critter had jumped on him?"

"It wouldn't. He's safer with the cats around than if they were all dead; that fuss with the old sow proved it."

Eliza calmed down after that.

"At least, it's better, I guess, for him not to be made timid," she said. And so Sammy was not prevented from continuing his walks to the Prairie.

The Tiger found the bream and ate it. He had gone only a few yards into the bushes and had waited there until Sammy was out of sight; then he returned to the tree to look around and at once saw the fish as well as scented it. Fearing a trap, he walked around it very carefully before daring to pick it up and swallow it with a few guarded chews before the gulp that took down head, bones and all. The good-tasting tidbit was definitely associated in his mind with the tree and Sammy, which led to his resting on the same limb during the next day and listening for the whistling which heralded the boy's approach.

And since Sammy had been greatly interested in his experience with the cat, the two met again in the same place. This time Sammy lingered longer and talked to him.

"Why you stay up there?" he wanted to know. "You come down here or maybe I won't bring you a bream. You're bad; when I call you, you got to mind!" He did bring a bream, however, and this time had the luck to look back just as the Tiger jumped from the tree and picked up the fish.

At the house he told his mother that the poor cat had only half a tail as if it had been run over by a wagon. He wanted to know who owned it.

"You own it as much as anyone," his mother told him. "That cat's wild. It stays in the swamp and never goes near anyone's house."

"It's my cat?" he asked just to make sure.

"Yes, it's yours just as I said, as much as it's anyone's."

"It's my cat!" he repeated several times. After that he never caught bream without leaving one and sometimes two of them under the tree. If the Tiger was not on his favorite limb, the fish were left anyway with much calling of "Kitty." And never was a fish wasted because sooner or later the Tiger always came to look for it and to follow Sammy's trail as far as the field as if hoping he would drop others. There came the day when he jumped from his limb to take the fish as soon as the boy left it, and later the day when he circled the boy on the ground, waiting for him to drop the fish.

Sammy now accepted his timidity as he accepted everything when he got used to it, and so gradual was the cat's growth of confidence that the boy was not at all surprised when the big, beautiful animal at last followed him to the boat and sat on its haunches watching him fish. Sammy talked to the Tiger as he would to a companion, and if the cat did not understand the words, at least he knew that they indicated good feeling between them. The Tiger, indeed, while in awe of the boy as a superior being, had no longer any real fear; he knew that Sammy was a very friendly benefactor, and he liked Sammy. He was restless and nervous whenever the boy did not come on time or was kept in the house on account of rainy weather.

Bill and Eliza knew what was going on and never ceased to marvel. They would see the boy and the bobcat come out of the swamp together, the cat trotting ahead of the lad or directly behind him until the field was reached, whereupon the cat would stop and the boy would turn around to talk to him and say goodby.

"I can't understand it," Eliza would exclaim again and again. "It isn't human; maybe we ought to stop it."

"What for?" Bill would ask. "The boy is healthy and happy and keeps up his work. He's got a way with animals that seems to make them trust him. It's a sign of character. Let him develop it."

"But we're not raising a son of ours to be a wild animal trainer in a circus!"

"That's true, but he's nearly ten and there are no boy companions his age around here. That's hard on him, and certainly he won't play with doll babies like Mary does."

"Well, keep your eye on them and don't let anything happen to Sammy," was Eliza's final word. "A catamount is always a catamount even if he gets tame."

Those were warm days, when the black hound did not feel like going into the swamp to hunt cats or anything else. They were beautiful days that made the acorns fatten and the berries and seeds develop over all the land as if in preparation for the autumn chills that were sure to come. The young birds and animals grew large and strong and learned to shift for themselves in the big world, and the snakes began to grow lazy with all the food they could hold, and the fish swarmed in the tepid water of Wahoo Prairie.

JUNGLE BROTHERS

Kenneth Gilbert

Cappy, Dirk Fallon's little Capuchin monkey, sat in the strange forest gazing mournfully at his motionless master.

Exhausted by tropical fever, Dirk, a broad shouldered young gold hunter, lay beside an animal trail that twisted here and there under the thick canopy of the Guatemalan rain forest.

"Jungle Brothers." Used by permission of the author, Kenneth Gilbert

When the first hot dizziness warned him that he had been stricken with the dread jungle malady, he knew a weakening moment of terror at the thought of dying alone in the wilderness. Then he grew delirious, and finally he fell into the coma of the crisis. Eventually, he would awaken clearheaded and free from fever, or he would slip into eternal slumber, reaching adventure's end there in the jungle—alone.

And yet he was not alone, for Cappy sat on guard. He crouched beside Dirk, bewildered by the strange unresponsiveness of the big, kind man-god and fearful of the unseen menace that seemed to lurk everywhere in the dense bush. This was the land of Cappy's ancestors, but the little gray monkey was seeing it for the first time. Before this, Dirk Fallon had done his exploring in more temperate regions, but stories of the gold to be found along the Guatemalan rivers had lured him to the tropics, and he had brought Cappy for company.

"You can look up all your relatives, Cappy," he had grinned, and Cappy had no way of telling him that Dirk meant more to him than a treeful of relatives.

Now Cappy crouched miserably beside Dirk, well-aware that something terrible had happened to his master. He knew too that darkness was creeping over the rain forest, and that the jungle life was awakening. Instinctively he feared the night prowlers, most of them dangerous to little monkeys who foolishly stayed on the ground instead of taking to the trees. He whimpered and with soft little paws rubbed Dirk's fevered cheeks, trying to say that it was time to leave this dreadful place. But Dirk lay there motionless, and Cappy's features wrinkled as though he were close to tears. Yet he would not leave the man he adored, even though remaining might mean swift death.

His bright eyes observed ghostly butterflies and giant moths drifting among the trees, but he was not in the mood to pursue them. There were vague stirrings and rustlings near-by that would ordinarily have demanded curious investigation, but now they only alarmed him. He heard the raucous cries of parrots, and their harsh calls seemed to awaken old memories buried deeply in his brain. Suddenly he heard monkey voices speaking his own language!

He had seen no other monkeys in this land, and for a moment he forgot his uneasiness, and sat up to peer about. Again he heard the monkey talk, and this time it came from a point much nearer.

His excitement mounted. Here were friends. His lips shaped themselves, and in his squeaky little voice he called a greeting, to let them know he was lonely and wanted companionship.

He listened intently for a reply, but none came. Soon, however, he saw a slender, thick-leafed limb sway unaccountably, and then he glimpsed gray forms running among the branches and leaping dexterously from one to another, drawing closer. Again he called out, this time questioningly.

Now there came an answer. It was a hoarse, barking reply, and all at once the trees seemed filled with monkeys who were counterparts of himself. Their leader, a surly-looking old fellow with an age-whitened face, chattered excitedly.

Much of it was unintelligible to Cappy, for these were wild brothers and their language was somewhat different from that of the tame monkeys he had once lived with in a zoo, although their coloring was identical. Yet he understood the drift of their talk. The old king was asking where he came from, to which tribe he belonged, and why he traveled with a man-ape.

Cappy answered them, but his actions roused their suspicion. He slapped at the mosquitoes buzzing about Dirk's face, and disgustedly brushed off a red-striped beetle crawling on his master's sleeve. His wild brothers could not understand this and came closer, hurling abuse at him and demanding that he come into the trees and fight. But Cappy had resources new to these jungle dwellers.

Just inside Dirk's pack, which lay on the trail, was a little silver bell of which Cappy was inordinately fond. He used this bell to express anger, joy, or excitement. Now he leaped nimbly to the pack, and his slender fingers hauled forth the precious trinket. He jingled it violently, and looked up at the strangers to see if they were properly astonished.

Apparently they were stricken speechless. Some of them were plainly frightened. Baby monkeys ran to their mothers, and big males drew together in an attitude of defense. These wild Capuchin brothers had never heard such a sound, and it puzzled them greatly. They knew what to expect when they heard the coughing roar of a jaguar, the plaintive yowl of an ocelot, the bellow of a bull alligator, or the hiss of a huge water boa. But this musical tinkle was beyond their comprehension.

The old king's curiosity got the better of his natural caution. With a questioning bark, he dropped to a lower limb, and hung there while he eyed Cappy and the mysterious and shiny thing in the tame monkey's fist. Cappy gave the bell another jingle.

This completely captivated the king. He came closer, making soothing, persuasive sounds deep in his throat. Other members of the tribe, fully a hundred of them, also drew near.

But Cappy did not mistake this advance for friendliness. He saw the avaricious look in the king's eyes, and jingled the bell violently, at the same time wrinkling his lips suggestively in an insulting snarl.

Ordinarily, this would have been sufficient cause for combat, but now the king was wholly bent on getting possession of the marvelously gleaming thing that made such a pleasing noise. He ignored Cappy's defiance and drew even closer. Growing alarmed at the king's determined manner, Cappy backed closer to his unconscious master and tugged frantically at his sleeve to awaken him.

Suddenly the king lost patience. With an angry bark he dropped to a lower limb, raced along it, and gathered himself to leap upon the stubborn Cappy.

But at that instant one of the watchful males in the higher branches gave a frantic cry of alarm. Forgetting Cappy, the king sprang to safety. The ruff of bristly hair around his neck and along his spine lifted, while he bared his fangs and chattered ominously. The mother monkeys shrieked as they tried to gather their young. In the face of imminent danger, the fighting males formed a group that swung low and hurled defiance at a sinuous, mottled length weaving noiselessly in and out of the undergrowth along the game trail.

Never before had Cappy seen a boa constrictor, that dreaded foe of jungle folk, and particularly monkeys, but instinct told him it was an enemy. He hesitated, torn between his longing to flee into the trees with the wild monkeys, and his reluctance to desert his master. Then, in a frenzy of excitement, he jingled the bell, caught up a short length of rotted limb, and hurled the stick straight at the huge snake's head.

The boa, surprised and angered, looped its coils and hissed a warning. Then its flat, expressionless eyes fell on the man lying there as though dead. Instantly it was aroused and alarmed.

Under other circumstances, it is probable that the boa would have avoided the man and been content to go in peace, but the attack Cappy had launched could be interpreted in only one way by the great snake. Therefore, it offered battle.

With another terrifying hiss it prepared to strike, its strong jaws parted for a death grip before it wound powerful coils around the unconscious victim. The boa was not venomous, but its loops had strength enough to crush life even from a big wild boar.

Before the snake could strike, however, Cappy had stirred into valiant action. He caught up another stick and bravely smashed at the fearsome, scaled head with the lidless eyes.

It was a blow that ordinarily would have meant nothing to the boa, whose muscular length had a toughness almost capable of withstanding the fangs of a jaguar. But the move diverted the snake's attention, and instead of striking at the man, it struck at Cappy.

The little Capuchin, however, was too nimble to be caught in this fashion, and he leaped aside with a shriek of derision, at the same time jingling the bell he still clutched. And, as though at a signal, the tribe of wild kinsmen rallied to his support.

With deafening cries they began raining missiles on the hated destroyer. Sticks, small branches, even green coconuts, were hurled unerringly at the boa, who once more coiled in an attitude of defense. A flock of green-and-gold macaws added to the tumult, while in the distance a band of howler monkeys boomed in reply. Tragedy again stalked the jungle, so the wild things believed.

The assault and noise became too much for the boa to endure. Battered on head and body, he was unable to retaliate, and could only lie there and hiss horribly at his swarming foes. After a minute or so of it he gave up, and slid into the cool sanctuary of the undergrowth, where his assailants dared not follow.

This was Cappy's moment of triumph! As if he alone had routed the monster, he sent a shrill paean of victory through the green forest aisles, and rang his silver bell madly.

His jungle brothers did not dispute his claims. Possibly they felt that the bell possessed some power of driving off all foes. Never before had they dared attack a boa. This strange Capuchin from another world had led them successfully against one of their most fearsome enemies. Surely there was hidden magic in the silver bell.

The monkey king looked at the marvelous treasure, and curiosity and greed once more overcame his natural caution. Again he approached Cappy and made clucking, reassuring noises; he made a show of vast friendliness. If he could get near enough, he could snatch the tinkling thing from the little stranger's hand, and perhaps with a bite or a blow teach the upstart what it meant to be defiant of one who ruled a hundred monkeys.

Cappy was fearful. Again he shook the arm of his fever-stricken master, to apprise him of danger from the gray brethren who were swarming closer from every side. But Dirk Fallon, still in that coma which precedes death or recovery, did not respond.

Nearer and nearer came the monkey king, his gray old face masking determination to get the bell at any cost. Yet he was uncertain about the man lying there so still. Was this a trap? It might be, but he would not be satisfied until he had the gleaming thing in his own sinewy fingers.

His boldness gave courage to the others. Of a sudden Cappy found himself ringed by many little-old-man faces that were not at all reassuring. Most truculent of all was the king. He sidled toward Cappy with a soothing mutter, but his eyes glistened purposefully. Cappy clung to his master, chattering uneasily and baring his fangs. The king was not impressed, however, and continued to approach, stretching out his paws as though demanding the precious bell that Cappy clutched more tightly than ever. Suddenly Dirk Fallon stirred and groaned, and the wild monkeys, with exclamations of alarm, fled to the heights, the king with them. Cappy shrieked triumph.

Yet one wild monkey lingered. This was a sleek young female with limpid eyes, and she fascinated Cappy with a show of shy friendliness. Though she withdrew a little when the king voiced alarm, she returned presently and became greatly interested in a white lichen on the bole of a bacaba palm near-by. Deftly she tore it loose, sniffed it, and picked it apart, all the while with feigned indifference watching the strange Capuchin with the silver bell.

Cappy was enchanted—here was a chance for sympathy and understanding. Eagerly he drew nearer. Too late, then, he saw through her guile, for he heard a sound behind him and whirling abruptly, found himself confronting the baleful eyes of the monkey king. Cappy couldn't retreat to the safety of his master's presence for, with a savage snarl, the king leaped.

The next moment Cappy was battling frantically with a skilled and ruthless fighter—a jungle veteran who was king by right of might. Wounded in a dozen places, Cappy was putting up a game but losing battle when the element of chance, which so often determines situations in the wilderness, came to his aid.

For the sounds of fighting were obliterated suddenly by a hoarse, blood-chilling roar. It wiped out the fierce outcries of the tribesmen as they crowded near and shrieked for the monkey king to "kill." Their triumph turned to terror. Cappy, released by the king, caught sight of a huge, thick-muscled cat with a curiously spotted coat, the most fearsome killer in the jungle—a jaguar!

It was a female, savage with hunger, for her cubs were hidden in a near-by den and she had to hunt constantly to keep herself and them alive. Lean and ravenous, she would not have hesitated to attack a man if she discovered him in the vicinity of her den.

Her keen ears had heard the insane chattering of the monkeys when they had driven off the boa, and her cunning told her that here was an opportunity to stalk her excited victims when they would be less on guard. Now she was among them, her evil, painted face snarling as

she struck right and left at the screaming monkeys fleeing for the treetops. Miraculously they escaped, but Cappy and the fighting king were slower. The jaguar charged.

They saw her coming, and separated instantly as though blown apart by a mighty gust of wind, the king leaping for the nearest limb. But Cappy instinctively turned to the one being who had always offered protection in the past, big Dirk Fallon, lying unconscious of peril. As the jaguar missed, she pivoted to follow Cappy—and saw the man but a short leap distant!

At once she crouched, tail twitching, ears flattened to skull, fangs bared in a terrifying snarl that split her mottled face. Her lambent eyes seemed molten with green flame, while muscles rippled under her sleek skin. She feared the man, but there were reasons why she did not run.

She was mad with hunger, and ferocious because this man's presence might be a threat to her cubs. His seeming helplessness there on the ground gave her confidence, and yet she had the feeling of being cornered. She would fight, kill! Her muscles grew taut, rigid, as she gathered herself for a quick spring.

Frozen by terror, Cappy crouched on Dirk Fallon's breast. The little Capuchin did not understand that his own act was bringing death to his beloved master. He was chained to the spot by the hypnotic power of those blazing jade-green eyes. Moreover, this was his man-god, and he would not leave him. Crouching close to Dirk, Cappy bared his puny teeth in defiance—saw the tip of the jaguar's tail lift suddenly as she tensed for the leap.

That very act broke the spell which gripped him. What he did then was an involuntary thing, governed by no reason, but it had magic results. His thin fingers still clutched the bell that he had not given up in fighting the monkey king, and now with all his strength he hurled the thing straight at the jaguar's head!

It struck her with a tinkling clink, and she recoiled at the sound as though bitten by a snake. In a single movement almost too quick for the eye to follow, she leaped aside with explosive snarl. Never before had she heard such a sound as the tinkle of a bell. She was puzzled, fearful again of the man. Doubt and uncertainty replaced her killing urge, and she hesitated.

But as swiftly there came reassurance. The shining thing had not hurt her. The man was still helpless, an easy victim. Her baleful eyes swung on him once more—but at that instant she stiffened as her ears caught a sound too faint for even Cappy to hear.

Now fear did get the upper hand. Only an instant longer she waited, then melted disappointedly into the brush. She would not fight where the odds were against her. A minute later and there was the soft pat of bare feet on the trail as a dozen rubber-workers hurried up.

They were wispy-haired natives, very swarthy and their black eyes widened at sight of Dirk, who was now stirring, strengthened by his long sleep. They understood what was wrong, and they acted quickly. One went for water, while another disappeared in the brush, to return in a few minutes with pungent leaves that he crushed between his palms. A few drops of the juice were mixed with the water in a gourd dipper, and held to Dirk's lips.

He choked at the bitter draught, but after a time his eyes opened, and he stared at the men with his senses rapidly clearing of the fever fog.

"Gracias," he thanked them in Spanish. "Lucky you came along."

"Si," grinned their leader. "You've been ver' sick, but now you be well. Our camp is near. Mos' fortunate, señor, that we hear the tinkle of a bell, and come to fin' you."

Dirk frowned, puzzled. "Bell?" he asked. Then he understood, so he thought, and grinned and stroked Cappy, who was snuggled contentedly against his shoulder. "Oh—my monkey's. He's probably been having a fine time playing around with it while I've been asleep. Even got himself scratched up. But nothing ever happens to Cappy. Does it, fellow?"

Cappy chattered back in great content, not in the least disturbed because he could not tell his master how he, Cappy, one small monkey with a toy bell, had saved them both from the two most dangerous killers of the jungle. What did it matter? The man-god was himself again—and here were treasures. Cappy glanced down happily. In one tiny fist he gripped a handful of bristly hair wrenched from the royal neck of the vanished monkey king, and in the other he held the precious bell that had wrought magic when magic was needed.

from THE DEFENDER

Nicholas Kalashnikoff

The mountain rams, ruthlessly hunted by greedy men, are a noble and pathetic herd, struggling for survival in the remote fastness of the mountains. The man Turgen has been cruelly misjudged by his fellows, and he too has taken refuge in the mountain tops. How he becomes the defender of the mountain rams and of an unfortunate family and finds himself, in the process, is a moving story. "Everywhere there is life and everywhere there are warm human hearts" is the theme of the book.

[*The Wild Rams Find a Friend*]

By stepping on to a ledge outside his door, Turgen on a clear day had a wonderful view of the valley below and the mountains above him. When he tired of watching the tiny figures of men and women scurrying about at the foot of his hill, he had only to turn his eyes upward to see a different and fascinating sight. For there, dodging among the crags, were specks which he knew to be wild rams.

"How do they live?" he asked himself one evening. The hills were barren except for sparse tufts of moss, an occasional thin clump of grass, and now and then a tough, hardy shrub that could not contain much nourishment.

His curiosity and pity aroused, Turgen watched the rams intently all that season and the next. He could make out nine individuals of what he assumed to be a family—or, as he called it, a tribe. In summer one lamb—or it might be two—were added to the number, but they disappeared with cold weather.

Then Turgen began to worry. For with the cold weather came snow to cover the moss and grass and dry up the meagre shrubs. Even at a distance he could sense the animals' despair as they searched avidly beneath the snow for any poor morsel to chew upon. Their grey-brown wool hung loosely on them now, and they moved indifferently, without spirit. Unless there was a hint of danger. Then they would lift their heads proudly and take themselves into the distance with incredible lightness and speed.

"Poor things." Turgen spoke his thoughts aloud. "To think that I used to hunt you to kill you! What harm are you to anyone? You who ask only for freedom."

But pity could not help them. He must find a way to give them practical aid. He considered one thing, then another. At last he fixed upon a plan.

First he built a light sleigh which he loaded with hay. Then, putting on skis, he pulled the sleigh to the ridge of the next mountain, dumped the hay, and returned home. Not a ram was in sight, but he could feel their inquisitive and fearful eyes upon him from behind the boulders farther up the hill.

From his own door he watched them approach the hay warily, circle it and trample it, and stoop to nibble at it. They seemed to fear a trap. But when he went back to the spot the hay was gone. After that he took frequent offerings of food to them, and gradually the rams came to accept his gifts without hesitation. Although they never approached him when he visited the feeding ground, he caught glimpses of them in hiding, awaiting his coming. In order to gain their greater confidence, he made it a point never to carry a gun. He even gave up his habit of carrying an iron-tipped stick which helped him in climbing. For he knew that all animals fear the rod which gives forth noise and fire.

It was not easy to conquer the fear of these wild creatures. It needed patience as well as understanding. But Turgen had both. Season after season he gave them care and attention, and was rewarded by knowing that they accepted him and depended upon him even though they did not fully trust him. A time came when they no longer hid from him but stood watching from a safe distance as if to determine what sort of being this was from whom they received nothing but good. And he had another satisfaction. The food he gave them worked a miracle in their appearance. They were no longer the sad, dishevelled animals of former days.

His heart leaped for joy one day when he went to the feeding ground and discovered the entire ram family gathered in a group on a little mound near by.

"Eh!" Turgen declared with pleasure. "You are truly a good-looking band—strong and healthy. And you eat now as if you enjoyed it."

The rams eyed him gravely, with an expression that might have been gratitude on their long homely faces.

"Yes," they seemed to be saying. "Perhaps your pampered cattle down below would not thrive on this fare, but for savages like us it is nourishing. You see, we are not looking to put on fat, merely to survive."

With these friends, who had become like his own children, Turgen knew that he would never again be lonely as before.

[*New Life on the Mountains*]

"A good man greets each new day as if it were a holiday." Turgen thought of this proverb upon waking every morning now, because it described exactly the way he felt. By becoming the protector of these defenseless animals, he had found a mission which used all the warmth of his lonely heart. He only regretted that the idea of feeding the rams had occurred to him so late. "But why waste time in regret?" he reflected. "Better rejoice that the idea came to me at last."

In order not to give the rams occasion for fright, it was necessary to change certain of his habits. For one thing, he did no hunting at all in the neighborhood of his yurta and the rams' feeding ground, but travelled some distance before permitting himself to fire a shot. He was gratified to discover before long that with the coming of spring birds and small animals, especially squirrels, flocked to his mountain side in great numbers. It was as if a rumor had spread that his place was their assurance of safety. The next spring and the next it was the same. Gay and charming visitors he had never known before came to delight him with their presence, and he felt himself being drawn into another world. How wonderful to be looked upon as a friend rather than as an enemy of these creatures!

In three years the rams, too, showed growing confidence in him. He fed them regularly, even when the snow melted and the crevices of the rocky hills revealed young grass and tender new shoots on the shrubs.

One sunny day he had gone as usual to the Rams' Mountain and was standing on a ledge near the feeding ground waiting for them to appear. Soon he saw three coming cautiously toward him. Quickly he stepped out of sight. By their watchful movements he judged that they had been sent to reconnoitre, and he was more sure of this a moment later when they bleated a piercing "Ma-a! Ma-a!"

He could not doubt that this was a signal to inform hidden companions that all was well, for the entire ram family now appeared, led by a huge powerful fellow who held his head with its sharp spiralling horns proudly. "What strength!

What assurance!" Turgen thought, enchanted. The long beard and tail indicated that the leader ram was not young, but his legs were slender and built to endure. He had a reddish-brown coat flecked here and there with white. By his extraordinary size and confident attitude he impressed his authority on the herd.

When the leader after a brief survey had satisfied himself that there was no danger he spoke calmly to his charges. "Ma-a!" he said. Whereupon all the rams fell to eating.

Turgen counted them: six females and three males—with two lambs not more than three weeks old, which he had not seen before. Unlike the lambs he had noticed briefly in previous seasons, these were gay and frisky and seemed prepared to enjoy a long life. Two lambs to six females was not a large increase. Still they were promise of new generations. Turgen was overjoyed. Surely the smaller one must be a girl, the larger one a boy. He watched them drink greedily of their mothers' milk, then pick at some grass only to reject it disdainfully and return to their mothers. Clearly they preferred milk to the food of grown-ups.

Turgen could not take his eyes from the rams, his wild mountaineers. In his imagination he saw this little family grow into a great herd.

. . . .

[*Tragedy*]

September came, bringing its customary changeable weather. One damp and windy day when all the furies seemed loose, Turgen went as usual to take food to his charges and stand watch.

"Though why anyone should come out in this weather I don't know," he thought. "Even the rams will surely keep under shelter."

But no. He had time only to drop the hay and retreat to his watching post when there they were in full strength—the whole family. The rain annoyed them and they shook themselves from time to time. Otherwise they showed no discomfiture. While the leader and two other males circled the clearing on the alert for danger, the rest stood quietly in the lee of the cliff waiting for the rain to abate. Looking for the lambs, Turgen saw them lying snugly under their mothers' bellies.

At the first sign of the weather's clearing Turgen's favorite jumped up and ran to urge the second lamb to romp with him. She refused, preferring her comfort.

He then advanced on the older rams, trying by all the wiles he could command to get their attention. Turgen almost laughed aloud watching his antics.

"What a show-off!" Then he worried. "It is cold and wet for one so young. He will get sick. —But that's an absurd idea. He is not made of clay that he will melt."

Soon after this the rain stopped and Turgen started for home. He had gone only a few steps when a shot rang out. There were hunters somewhere in the hills nearby—too far away to menace the herd of rams but the sound of gunfire alone was enough to cause panic. While the echo was still curling around the mountains the rams crowded around the leader as he stood irresolute, his head raised, his nostrils distended to test the air. It was he who must say what they should do.

In a minute the old ram turned and came at a light trot across a narrow stone abutment that formed a natural bridge between the clearing and the adjoining hill where Turgen stood. Without hesitation the other rams followed him in single file, males and females alternating. Turgen's lamb was behind his mother and just in front of the male ram who brought up the rear. The bridge led to a labyrinth of caves where escape was easy. That it led past Turgen seemed a matter of no concern to the rams in the face of great danger.

The bridge was no doubt slippery but the rams were sure-footed and they did not give way to panic. They were moving in a direction away from the gunfire. But Turgen had another plan. He would go toward the place from which the shot came. Should he meet the hunter, the hunter would understand that he was trespassing and leave the neighborhood—for such was the custom. Only one hunter was allowed to a region.

But before Turgen could act on his resolve, there was another shot. The ram at the rear of the line, hearing it, jumped, made an incautious step, and knocked against the lamb, who fell from the bridge.

Turgen's heart turned in him as he watched the small body hurtle down the crevasse. Then, peering over, he saw the lamb lying motionless on the mountain slope. Quickly, he made his way to the spot, fearing that wild animals would get there first.

The lamb's eyes, raised to his, were black with terror. It tried convulsively to rise but could not.

"Thank God, he's alive," was Turgen's first thought. "There's a chance I can save him."

With that he stooped and lifted the lamb gently.

"Ma-a," said the lamb in a weak, childish whimper. And from a distance came a mournful answering bleat. "Ma-a! Ma-a!" that might have been the old leader. Then fog enveloped the mountain.

The lamb was surprisingly heavy, but Turgen hardly noticed the burden in his anxiety and excitement. Carefully he made his way to the yurta through the darkness, and as he went he murmured reassurance to his patient, who made no further effort to escape.

"It is not far to go. Be quiet. Rest. Do not fear —I'll do you no harm." Over and over Turgen said it, like a chant.

At the yurta Turgen laid the lamb on some soft pelts to examine him. Noticing fresh blood stains, he looked for a wound and found a flesh cut under the right front leg. It took but a minute to wash it clean and cover it with a poultice of plantain leaves to stop the bleeding.

The lamb's fright returned now and he struggled to gain his feet. But his hind legs would not obey him.

"There, there, lad," Turgen soothed him with tender strokes and pats. "What are you afraid of? I will soon make you well and take you back to your family. Who am I but an old man? There is no harm in me. Besides, who would dare to lift a hand against such a splendid fellow? Lie still. Trust me."

Pain, weariness, and the strange but unterrifying sound made by a human voice finally had their effect. The lamb rested while Turgen explored more thoroughly for possible injuries. There were scratches and bruises, none of them serious. And one hind leg was plainly swollen.

"God forbid that it should be broken," Turgen thought in dismay. For he was expert with animals and he knew the difficulty of keeping a wild young thing quiet while bone mended.

Fortunately, he found that the injury was no more than a dislocation, but extremely painful to the touch. With practiced skill, while the patient bleated piteously, he swathed the whole body to keep it immobile except for the head. Then, quickly and deftly, he set the bone, bandaged the leg and hoof between splits and satisfied himself that the lamb could do no harm to the injury should he get on his feet. As he worked the lamb regarded him with fixed and startled eyes. It was breathing heavily and clearly would have liked to offer resistance.

The bandaging operation finished, the lamb grew calm, fright gave way to weariness.

"Why," Turgen thought. "There is the same look in his eyes that I saw in Tim's when I set his arm. Children are alike. They suffer more from fright than pain." To the lamb he said: "That other little fellow drank some milk and fell asleep when I had doctored him. And so should you."

Fortunately, Turgen had only the day before brought milk from Marfa's cow. It stood untouched in the cellar. He poured some into a large wooden bowl and offered it to the lamb. At first the lamb turned his head away in distaste, but when by accident a few drops found their way into his mouth he smacked his lips with enjoyment. After that he drank willingly, with relish, looking at Turgen as if to say: "Really, this isn't bad at all."

Turgen was beside himself with joy as his charge finished his meal and promptly went to sleep.

"Food and attention—that's all anyone wants," Turgen reflected. "Just food and attention."

It was late when he himself was ready for bed, and after the agitating events of the day he slept fitfully. Whenever he wakened, as he did frequently, his first thought was for the lamb—and this stranger in his yurta seemed not a wild ram but a person close and dear to him. By going to his rescue, Turgen had found someone to share his yurta.

It is true, he marvelled, what our people say: "Misfortune can sometimes bring happiness."

The world the child lives in is to him an endless source of wonder and curiosity. People and places, birds, beasts, and stars, cities and farms, all the modern means of communication and travel engage his attention. Good factual books in the fields of science and social studies answer many of his questions, but so far as human relationships are concerned, sound, lively stories tell the child more about himself and his ever widening social world than encyclopedias or other factual books possibly can. Realistic stories help the child to understand himself, and they orient him in the wide and varied world of people in which he lives. Such stories can be as

TODAY IN THE UNITED STATES

exciting as fairy tales and as full of humor or adventure or romance. The difference lies in their plausibility. A realistic story is one in which everything that happens is possible and seems probable. The plot may turn simply upon a child's need to stoop down and tie his shoelaces (*Wait for William,* p. 105), or it may involve a tremendous adventure like the Little Paiute's difficulties in leading his grandmother across the mountains and desert to her home. But whatever the action of the realistic story, it must carry the conviction of complete plausibility so that the reader can identify himself with the hero and believe in his mistakes or triumphs as if they were his own and had really happened.

Didacticism past and present

Such is the pattern of the modern realistic story, which, oddly enough, has its roots in the didacticism of the past. In the eighteenth and nineteenth centuries, little juvenile tracts in story form with children as the characters were designed to teach the young to be pious or industrious or honest.[1] Many years went by before *Hans Brinker, Heidi, Tom Sawyer,* and *Little Women* broke this pattern of unrelieved didacticism. These remarkable books were thoroughly entertaining, moral but not moralistic, and so popular that their success would seem to be sufficient to wipe out forever the juvenile tract type of story. But not so. Didacticism in books addressed to children seems to rise in one form or another in every generation. The theological didacticism of the Puritans hung grimly over the heads of their children. And the intellectual didacticism of the eighteenth century and the moralistic didacticism of Maria Edgeworth in the early nineteenth century were almost equally oppressive. Now we are developing a kind of sociological didacticism for children that closely parallels the "How to Win Friends and Influence People" sort of books for adults. Today there are little stories about a child who goes to kindergarten, knocks over the other children's blocks, and grabs their possessions until he is shunned by all. Then, one day he learns to share and lo, he becomes a beloved member of the group, immediately. This sort of thing might seem harmless enough, except that it induces the same kind of priggish self-righteousness that the *Elsie Dinsmore* books used to breed. Upon hearing such a story, normally grabby five-year-olds remark piously, "Wasn't he *bad? I* never do that." And momentarily the little hypocrites believe it. A story about a child's rejection of his small brother as a pest brought horrified condemnation from a family of four children who were normally fond of each other but were always protesting the hampering presence of the baby sister. These stories are numerous today. Their realism is not real, but is a priggish picture of sinning and reforming to the point of perfection. Besides being dull reading, such stories promote unwholesome feelings of self-righteous superiority.

There have even been some picture-stories for young children on interracial relationships, stories about white sheep with one black brother or white rabbits with one spotted brother. In both cases the black or spotted animal has been shunned by his family although the children can never see why. The solution of these problems is as synthetic as the situations. Good race relationships are not taught this way. They develop from agreeable first-hand contact with people of another race or from vicarious experience through books in which peoples of other races are shown to be more like than different from ourselves. Adults who read *Heidi* when they were children can remember how much they wished to know Swiss children and to see Heidi's mountain home. They were predisposed to like the Swiss people because of Heidi. So white children who enjoy *Steppin and Family* discover, in the midst of a thoroughly entertaining story, that this Negro family is much like other families they know and that Steppin, once he gets over his cockiness, is the kind of boy they would like. *Steppin and Family* is not a tract on race relationships but a picture of normal, likable people, making mistakes and enjoying occasional triumphs—in short, it is a good story.

Didacticism is not dead, and something called bibliotherapy may nurture its continuance. But, on the whole, the fine realistic literature written for the modern child is free of this taint. The adult, who guides children's reading, needs to know the books he selects for children so that he can avoid the dull little tracts and select the fine vigorous stories which give children insight into their own personal problems and social relationships without smugness.

Values of realistic stories

Realism for the youngest begins with himself, his personal problems and needs, and those of other children like himself. The children's mistakes are often shown, but their stories are full of reassurance. Paddy has to learn that church is no place for pets. Andrewshek, in *Poppy Seed Cakes,* is saved from the sad results

[1] See May Hill Arbuthnot, *Children and Books,* Scott, Foresman, 1947, p. 21

of his irresponsibility by the all-enveloping love of Auntie Katushka. William, although deserted by his impatient brothers and sisters, who won't wait for him, triumphs grandly. And Dr. Trotter's visit turns out to be a delightful event with a surprise ending, thanks to the doctor's gold watch and ingenuity. Family life in stories for the youngest is full of affectionate reinforcement and understanding. Such stories build the small child's confidence and keep alive his sense of being loved and of finding life full of delightful possibilities.

Gradually, stories for young children spur them on to further achievement and responsibility and, at the same time, orient them into the everyday institutions of their community and their country. Hank and Hetty want "squeaky, creaky shoes," but know they have to earn them by their own efforts. The insatiable curiosity of Yonie Wondernose proves invaluable to his family, and Roger's patient persistence wins him a glimpse of the fox and more. Even in this small selection of stories from the great body of realistic tales for children, the stories for the sixes, sevens, and eights show the characters living in cities and suburbs, on farms, deserts, and mountain tops. The children go to school, dancing school, church, stores, the county fair, the library, the circus, and even live joyously on a riverboat bound for the south.

Children who read these stories or hear them read share vicariously these experiences. Moreover, they discover in the process that their country is made up of different kinds of people living in different parts of the country, with different problems, different religious customs but with the same family affection and loyalties—mountaineers, riverboat people, cotton pickers, Pennsylvania Dutch, Indians, Negroes, Japanese, Jews, Poles, and Quakers, all citizens of the same country. Here, indeed, in the realistic stories for children is a little cross section of "life in these United States." Through such stories, sometimes hilarious, sometimes serious, but invariably representative of the people and the section of the country in which they live, children will begin to take this variety for granted. They may even sense the underlying unity of these people. Certainly young readers of these stories will grow in social sympathy and understanding.

The writers of realistic stories

The stories in this section have been chosen for their content, age appeal, and variety, but the table of contents reveals the fact that this group also includes a cross section of major writers in the field of realistic fiction for children. Not all the outstanding writers are here, but it is a representative selection. Marguerite de Angeli, Newbery Award winner, 1950, has written a series of delightful books about minority groups in this country—the Pennsylvania Dutch, Quakers, Negroes, and a Polish community in a big city. Florence Crannell Means has also made notable contributions, chiefly for adolescents, to the literature of minority groups. Lois Lenski's regional stories are some of the most important contributions of the last decade to children's social understandings and entertainment. They are distinguished by a unique gallery of characters brought vividly to life. They may be migrant workers, berry pickers, or astonished beneficiaries of a gusher oil well. They may be ignorant, inefficient, or downright ornery, but they are lifted out of their sordidness by warm family affection and pride. No child who has identified himself with Shoestring Slater or Joanda could make fun of "Crackers" or "Oakies." These stories build respect for people, all kinds of people.

Marjorie Flack has made a notable contribution to literature for the youngest, and Carolyn Haywood for the next age group, the sixes, sevens, and eights. Lavinia Davis writes for children of various ages, and her books have a warm, earthy quality that is well illustrated by the selection in this group, *Roger and the Fox*. Robert McCloskey, Eleanor Estes, and Beverly Cleary have written some of the gayest stories children have enjoyed since Tom Sawyer was set to whitewashing a fence. So each author could be singled out for a unique addition to the realism of the modern child in his modern world. It is hoped that the samples in this section will send children to the books of each author and to the stories of other excellent writers listed in the bibliography. Meanwhile, here are stories as real as the children next door, stories which will give children a clearer understanding of themselves, greater social insight, a happy sense of life's gaieties and a warm liking for the people who make this country.

PADDY'S THREE PETS

Mary G. Phillips

This lends itself to storytelling and is a favorite with the four- and five-year-olds.

Once upon a time there was a big fat father who had a fat little boy named Paddy. One evening, when fat Father came home from the office, he wiped his feet on the mat, opened the door with his jingly key, and whistled. Down the stairs ran fat Paddy as fast as his short legs would carry him—paddity-pat, paddity-pat, paddity-pat. First he hugged Father then he put his hand into one of the big overcoat pockets. And what do you think he pulled out? A white guinea pig with pink eyes.

"Squeak! Squeak! Squeak!" cried the guinea pig.

"What will you do with him?" asked fat Father.

Fat Paddy stroked the soft fur of the little guinea pig. "I'll give him some lettuce and play with him," he replied. And so he did, until the guinea pig grew fat and fatter.

One evening, when fat Father came home from the office again, he wiped his feet on the mat, opened the door with his jingly key, and whistled. Down the stairs came fat Paddy as fast as his short legs would carry him—paddity-pat, paddity-pat, paddity-pat! First he hugged Father then he put his hand into one of the big overcoat pockets. And what do you think he pulled out? A little gray kitten with white paws.

"Paddy's Three Pets." Used by permission of the author, Mary G. Phillips

"Miaow! Miaow! Miaow!" cried the kitten.

"What will you do with him?" asked fat Father.

Fat Paddy stroked the soft fur of the little gray kitten. "I'll give him some milk and play with him," he replied. And so he did, until the kitten grew fat and fatter. Paddy and the guinea pig and the kitten all played together.

One more evening, when fat Father came home from the office, he wiped his feet on the mat, opened the door with his jingly key, and whistled. Down the stairs came fat Paddy as fast as his short legs would carry him—paddity-pat, paddity-pat, paddity-pat. First he hugged Father then he put his hand into one of the big overcoat pockets. And what do you think he pulled out? A little brown puppy with one black ear.

"Bow-wow! Bow-wow! Bow-wow!" cried the puppy.

"What will you do with him?" asked fat Father.

Fat Paddy stroked the soft brown puppy. "I'll give him some milk and play with him," he replied. And so he did, until the brown puppy with one black ear grew fat and fatter.

One Sunday morning fat Paddy, the fat guinea pig, the fat kitten, and the fat puppy were all playing together on the sunny porch. It was a quiet day. No grocer's wagon rumbled over the street. No children's feet skipped and

scuffled on the way to school. Far away fat Paddy heard the church bell.

"Ding-dong! Ding-dong! Ding-dong!" it called and that meant "Come to church! Come to church! Come to church!"

Fat Paddy scrambled to his feet and gathered his pets gently in his arms. He said to them, "It is time for me to wash my face and hands and put on my best suit and new shoes, for I am going to church with Father. I will put you, fat guinea pig, and you, fat kitty, and you, fat puppy, in a warm, cozy place for a nap."

Hanging in the hall was fat Father's overcoat. Into one deep, warm pocket he put the kitten; into another the guinea pig; and into the inside pocket, dark, deep, and warm, he squeezed the puppy. Then fat Paddy went upstairs—up one step, up two steps, up three steps, up, up, up, up went his feet to the very top.

When he was quite ready for church, he came down the stairs—paddity-pat, paddity-pat, paddity-pat—and there was fat Father waiting for him in the hall. Fat Father had on his overcoat. The pockets bulged and were quite heavy, but then Father's pockets always did bulge, and they always were heavy, for he kept lots of nice things in those pockets. Fat Paddy was thinking of his own best suit and his own new shoes. He did not remember what was in those deep, warm pockets.

Around the corner fat Father and little fat Paddy walked together and their feet kept time with the bell which was calling again: "Ding-dong! Ding-dong! Ding-dong! Come to church! Come to church! Come to church!"

Fat Father and little fat Paddy walked together into the church and up the wide aisle. They walked very quietly with hushed feet, for the church was still. At one pew they stopped and fat Paddy sat down. Fat Father took off his coat and put it over the back of the seat. Bump! went the fat guinea pig's sides against the pew.

"Squeak! Squeak!" cried the guinea pig, waking from his nap.

Quickly fat Father picked up his coat, but he did not see the guinea pig. The people sitting near by smiled. Fat Father turned the coat around and again put it over the back of the seat. This time the kitten's fat sides went Bump! against the pew. The gray kitten woke up.

"Miaow! Miaow!" cried the kitten.

People near by smiled again and so did Paddy. Father did not smile. He was puzzled. Where did the sound come from? Once more he picked up his coat. This time he squeezed the fat sides of the brown puppy. The puppy awoke from his nap.

"Bow-wow! Bow-wow!" cried the puppy.

More people smiled and Paddy leaned over to Father and whispered, "They are taking their naps in your pockets."

Fat Father smiled at Paddy and whispered back, "Home is the place for naps. I'll take them home and come back." Then fat Father picked up his coat very carefully and walked softly down the aisle.

And after that the guinea pig with pink eyes, the gray kitten with white paws, and the brown puppy with one black ear each had a little box in the garage for naps.

THE PICNIC BASKET

Margery Clark

Stories for small children repeatedly sound a reassuring note. Andrewshek is irresponsible, but Auntie Katushka's all-enveloping love saves him over and over again. The "author" of this favorite book, Poppy Seed Cakes, *is really plural. Two librarians, Margery Quigley and Mary Clark, combined their names and their talents in composing these stories which they say grew up around two children they knew.*

One cool summer morning Andrewshek's Auntie Katushka said, "Andrewshek, I think I will put some sandwiches and some cottage cheese and some poppy seed cakes and two eggs in our picnic basket. Then we will go to the park and eat our lunch there, near the water."

"May I go with you, Auntie Katushka?" said Andrewshek.

"Of course you may go to the park with me," said Auntie Katushka. "But first we have a great many things to do, before we can start to the park. I must go into the garden and catch the white goat. I will tie her up so she will not run away. Please find the kitten, Andrewshek, and put her in the cellar, so she will not worry the chickens while we are gone."

"Yes, indeed, I will find the kitten and put her in the cellar," said Andrewshek, "so she will not worry the chickens while we are gone."

But all Andrewshek really did was to lift up the red and white napkin which Auntie Katushka had laid over the picnic basket and look at the eggs and the poppy seed cakes and touch the sandwiches and taste the cottage cheese.

The goat was not easy to catch. The goat wanted to go to the park, too. She galloped round and round the garden.

At last Auntie Katushka caught her and tied her firmly to a post.

Then Auntie Katushka went into the house to get Andrewshek and the lunch basket. She saw Andrewshek peeping under the red and white napkin and tasting the cottage cheese. He had forgotten all about the kitten.

The kitten was nowhere to be found. "I think she must be paying a visit to the Mouse family," said Auntie Katushka.

Then Auntie Katushka put on her bright shawl and took her umbrella with the long crooked handle under one arm. Then she picked up the lunch basket with the red and white napkin on top and she and Andrewshek started for the park.

They went down the hill and across the tracks and past the market and down a long street until they came to the park by the water.

Andrewshek sat down on the grass beside a little stream. Andrewshek's Auntie Katushka laid her umbrella with the long crooked handle and the basket of lunch on the grass beside Andrewshek.

"Andrewshek," said Auntie Katushka, "I must go to the spring and get some water for us to drink. Please watch the basket with the eggs and the sandwiches and poppy seed cakes and cottage cheese while I am gone."

"Yes, indeed, I will watch the basket of lunch," said Andrewshek.

But what Andrewshek really did was to say to himself, "I would like to take off my shoes and my stockings and wade in the little stream. I believe I will!"

Andrewshek took off his shoes and his stockings and went wading in the little stream.

A big white swan came floating calmly down the stream. He saw the picnic basket lying on the grass. He stopped and stretched and stretched his long neck, till he could touch the basket. "Honk! honk! honk!" said he. "I wonder what is under the red and white napkin."

The big white swan lifted the napkin with his red bill and looked in the basket. "Oh, oh, oh! Won't Mother Swan be pleased with this nice lunch!" said he. "Sandwich bread makes fine food for baby swans."

He picked up the basket in his strong red bill and floated it ahead of him down the stream.

Andrewshek could not wade after the big white swan. The water was too deep.

"Stop! Stop! White Swan!" cried Andrewshek. "That is my Auntie Katushka's picnic basket and it has our lunch in it. Please put it back on the grass."

"No, indeed! I will not put the basket back," honked the big white swan. "Sandwich bread makes fine food for baby swans and I have ten baby swans to feed."

The big white swan gave the picnic basket a little push with his red bill. The basket floated on down the little stream. The big white swan floated calmly behind it.

Just then Andrewshek's Auntie Katushka came hurrying up with the spring water. She saw the big white swan floating down the stream, with the lunch basket floating ahead of him.

Andrewshek stood in the middle of the stream, crying.

Auntie Katushka picked up her umbrella with the long crooked handle. Auntie Katushka ran along the shore until she overtook the big white swan, with the lunch basket floating ahead of him.

She caught the handle of the picnic basket in the crook of her long handled umbrella. She drew the basket safely to shore.

"Well! well!" said Auntie Katushka, as she spread the red and white napkin on the grass, and laid the sandwiches and the poppy seed cakes and the cottage cheese and the eggs upon it. "It always pays to carry an umbrella to a picnic."

DR. TROTTER AND HIS BIG GOLD WATCH

Helen Earle Gilbert

The amusing device of a wise old doctor for allaying the fears and worries of his small patients should work vicariously for those who read or hear this story.

One fine afternoon, in the little village of Green Hill, Dr. Trotter was getting ready to go out and make his calls.

Ting-a-ling-a-ling went the telephone.

"Is that you, Doctor?" asked a worried voice. "Will you please come over? Baby Agatha's cheeks are all puffed up."

"Be right over," the doctor answered in his deep, comforting voice. "Sounds like the mumps to me. Who did you say it was?"

"This is Mrs. Cousins. Please hurry. And thank you."

Dr. Trotter picked up his hat and his doctor bag. Then he felt in the left-hand pocket of his Scotch-plaid vest, as he always did when he was going to call on a child, to be sure that he had his big watch with him.

Not that there was much chance of his losing it. For this old-fashioned round gold watch was fastened to one end of a heavy gold chain. On the other end, in his right-hand vest pocket, was the small new silver watch by which he took pulses and told the time.

"Dr. Trotter and His Big Gold Watch" by Helen Earle Gilbert. Used by permission of Silver Burdett Company.

Then he went out to his car. He hurried, for of all the people Dr. Trotter took care of, his favorites were the children. He was a friend to all of them. What is more, every one of them would do whatever he wanted, the moment he asked.

Baby Agatha's cheeks were plump and pink, but she was all right. Mrs. Cousins drew a long breath of relief. She bustled about to make the doctor a cup of tea, piping hot and strong. For although she had not lived on Green Hill very long, she knew, as everyone did for miles around, that the doctor liked his tea.

Dr. Trotter took the cup with a sigh of pleasure and sat down in the big corner chair. Nubbin, the little gray kitten, climbed out of her basket and up into his lap. "Ouch!" the doctor said as her claws went in. But he let her stay.

In the yard outside, Katherine and Tom Cousins, with the Butterworth boys, Hank and George Jr., were climbing in the cherry tree. They began to see how high they could climb and then jump.

Mrs. Cousins glanced out with a worried look. "I'm so afraid one of them will fall," she said.

"Tell me, Doctor, what it is that you do or say

to make the children do whatever you want, the moment you ask?"

"Well, well!" The old doctor set down his cup. "Children can always keep a secret, can't they?" He leaned back and felt in the left-hand pocket of his Scotch-plaid vest. "It's really not my secret but my grandfather's. He was a doctor, too, and this was his watch."

He pulled out the heavy old-fashioned round gold watch.

Mrs. Cousins leaned forward.

Dr. Trotter opened the back of the watch, and there was a little round keyhole.

From his right-hand vest pocket he drew out the other watch (the small new silver one with which he took pulses and told the time) and there —beside it on the heavy gold chain—hung a little shining gold key. Dr. Trotter took it off the chain and thrust it into the keyhole.

Just then the telephone rang. Mrs. Cousins ran to answer it.

"It's for you," she said. "It's Mrs. Oldfield. The minister's cut his thumb. They want you right away."

Dr. Trotter put back his watches and picked up his bag.

Nubbin yawned, curled up in her basket, and dropped off to sleep.

Out in the cherry tree the children climbed higher and higher.

The little old car carried Dr. Trotter to the minister's house where Mrs. Oldfield met him at the door. The doctor dressed the minister's thumb (which wasn't very badly cut after all). Then he went on to the Dwinney's where Jane Dwinney, who was nine, had broken out with a rash.

Just as Jane was putting out her tongue for the doctor, the telephone rang. It was Mrs. Oldfield again.

"Is the doctor there?" she asked. "Will you send him right back to the Cousins'? Tommy's fallen out of that cherry tree and hurt his ankle."

"Be right over," the doctor promised.

"Now Jane, I'll stop in on my way home. You know what for. . . . I think it's measles," he said to her mother. "Keep her warm." And he was gone.

People along the roadside and at their windows saw the doctor's car flying past and wondered. "What's happened now?" they asked. He turned the corner into the Cousins' driveway in a great cloud of dust.

Dr. Trotter saw that the yard was empty. There was no one in the cherry tree.

With one hand in the left-hand pocket of his Scotch-plaid vest, he hurried up the steps.

He found Tommy lying on the couch, with his swollen ankle on a pillow. He was trying not to cry. The other children stood around him. Mrs. Cousins was hurrying with ice in one hand and a hot-water bottle in the other. (In the excitement she had forgotten which one was right for swellings.)

The instant he saw, with his professional eye, that it was only a sprain, Dr. Trotter reached for his watch. Tommy wiped his face and smiled. The children looked at one another.

Out came the big old round gold watch. The doctor reached into his right-hand pocket, and out came the small new silver watch. He looked on the chain for the little gold key.

But the little gold key was gone!

Dr. Trotter felt in all his pockets. He hunted through his bag and poked down into the sides of the corner chair.

Katherine and Hank looked under the sofa. George Jr. looked under the rug.

Mrs. Cousins lifted the kitten basket carefully, not to wake little sleeping Nubbin, and looked under that.

But no one could find the little gold key.

"Wait!" cried Mrs. Cousins. "I may have a key that will fit!" She ran and got her key ring, her key case, and an old desk drawer full of keys. But not one of them fitted the little round keyhole.

"Maybe the Oldfields have one!" shouted Tommy.

Mrs. Cousins rushed to the telephone. She was so excited that Mrs. Oldfield got excited, too.

"A key for Dr. Trotter, you say?" she asked. "Well, I'll see. And I'll call up the neighbors and ask them."

In no time at all Mrs. Oldfield was at the door.

"Here's my key ring," she puffed. "Here's the key to our front door, to the garage, to Fred's case of stuffed birds, and to the minister's typewriter. . . . The neighbors will be right along with their keys," she added.

Tommy laughed.

In bounced Mrs. Dwinney. She had got a ride with the bread man. "Here's the key to our barn," she said, "and to our front-hall closet. Here are some drawer keys and keys to two chests and to the station wagon."

"My goodness!" exclaimed Mrs. Cousins. "All we want is a little bit of a watch key."

In trotted Miss Fuller, the milliner. She had a bunch of Yale keys on a ring and an old satchel. "This," she said with pride, "has in it all the keys that have been in our family for sixty-seven years."

Behind her came Mr. Pound, the grocer, with the keys to his store.

Then came Mrs. Pound with two very ancient clock keys, and Mrs. Trotter with all the doctor's other keys.

"The sexton's even bringing the key to the church," cried Mrs. Cousins from the doorway, "and it's thirteen inches long!"

The door flew open again. There stood Grandma Stepney, the oldest person for miles around.

"It was *tea* you wanted, wasn't it?" she asked, panting a little. "I couldn't quite hear over the telephone, but you said it was for the doctor."

On a tray she held her pink luster teapot, steaming hot, and a large plate of warm cinnamon buns.

Katherine ran to bring her a chair.

Mrs. Cousins took the tray and said, "Thank you."

The doctor looked a little worried.

But Tommy's eyes were bright with excitement.

Just at that minute Nubbin stood up in her basket. She rounded her back, rolled out her red tongue, and yawned. Down in the basket something glittered.

"What's that?" shrieked Tommy.

Katherine rushed over and picked it up.

"Nubbin, you bad kitty!" cried Tommy. "You went to sleep on the little gold key!"

Dr. Trotter took the key and hurried over to Tommy. He opened the back of his big round watch, thrust in the key and turned it a few times.

Then he lowered the watch into Tommy's outstretched hands.

Tick-a-tick-a-tick-a-tick! Everybody listened. Tommy held the watch tight against his ear.

"Before we begin," said the doctor as he took the iodine and dressings from his bag, "where would you like to have me set my watch Tom? At what time?"

His fingers moved deftly over Tommy's anklebone. "Some people," he went on, "like to have it tell them how old they are. What will you have?"

"I'll have twelve," Tommy answered firmly. "That's the highest one. And anyway, I'll be twelve in two years more."

Dr. Trotter nodded. He set the hands at two minutes before twelve o'clock.

"Ssh-sh-h-h!" cried all the children.

The room grew very quiet. Mrs. Cousins stared, her finger on her lip. Grandma Stepney stopped rocking. Mrs. Pound looked at Mrs. Dwinney and smiled.

Tommy's eyes shone. He hardly felt the old doctor's gentle hands on his ankle. He hardly felt the dressing that Dr. Trotter was putting on.

Tick-a-tick-a-tick-a-tick went the big round watch against Tommy's ear.

And then!

RING-RING-RING-RING-RING-RING-RING-RING-RING-RING-RING-RING!

Tommy's face broke into a smile.

"A watch that strikes," said Mrs. Cousins. "Well, I never!"

DOWN DOWN THE MOUNTAIN

Ellis Credle

It is especially good for city children to encounter stories about mountaineer children whose environment is less complex and more challenging than their own. The ingenuity and self-reliance of Hetty and Hank in solving their problems and achieving their heart's desire are admirable.

Once upon a time, in a little log cabin away up in the Blue Ridge Mountains, there lived a little girl named Hetty and her brother Hank.

Although their home was a small one, it was a cozy place to live. There was a big stone fireplace at one end. That was where Mammy cooked beans and cornmeal mush and fried pork in a big, black, frying pan.

There was a big bed in one corner and a little bed in the other corner, and in the middle of the room there was a long table made of planks. That was where Mammy and Pappy and Hetty and Hank ate their dinner every day.

All kinds of things hung from the rafters, strings of shucky beans, bunches of bright red peppers, ears of popcorn all tied together, hams, and sausages, and baskets full of this and that.

Never in all their lives had Hetty or Hank had a pair of shoes. In the summer it was fun to run around barefoot, but when winter came, and the snow lay on the mountains like a chilly white blanket, their little feet were blue with cold and they longed for a pair of shoes.

They each wanted a beautiful shining pair that sang, "Creaky—squeaky—creaky—squeaky," every time they walked.

They begged their mammy to buy them some shoes, but she said, "You can't find shoes like that in these hills! Such shining shoes come from the town, away down down at the foot of the mountain."

So they asked their Pappy, but he said, "There's not a cent of money in this household. We've everything we need right here in these hills."

Hetty and Hank felt very sad, but they did not give up.

"Let's ask our Granny," said Hetty. And they did.

"Some shining shoes?" chirped Granny. "I'll tell you how you can get them yourselves."

"How? How?" cried Hetty and Hank.

"Plant some turnip seeds," said Granny, "and when they have grown into fine big turnips, you can take them all the way down to town and trade them off for some shining, creaky, squeaky shoes."

"Thanky' Ma'am, that's what we'll do," cried Hetty and Hank.

They raced away and planted some turnip seeds in a tilted field right next to Pappy's corn patch.

Home they went singing,

"Our fields are high up in the air,
We wouldn't dare plant pumpkins there,
For pumpkins grow so big and round,
They'd break right off and tumble down.
But turnips grow on hills or vales,
Because they twist their little tails
Around the rocks and hold on tight
And don't let go for day or night!"

When Hetty and Hank got home it was dark. The whippoorwills were calling sadly from the

Down Down the Mountain, by Ellis Credle. New York: Thomas Nelson & Sons deep woods, "Whip-poor-will! Whip-poor-will!" and a little owl was asking "Who? Who-o-o?"

Mammy was waiting for them. She gave them a nice supper of corn bread and butter and yellow honey. Then she tucked them snugly into bed. They dreamed all night about shining shoes that played a creaky, squeaky tune, just like Pappy's fiddle.

The next day they climbed up the steep, steep mountain-side to see if the turnip seeds had come up. But they had not, and Hetty and Hank had to wait and wait and wait, before they spied the baby turnip leaves peeping out of the ground.

Then there was plenty of work for Hetty and Hank! They had to chop away the weeds each day, and chase away the worms and the bugs and the grasshoppers that come for a taste of nice green turnip leaves.

When there was no rain and the little turnips felt dry and thirsty, Hetty and Hank had to bring big buckets of water to make them fresh and green again.

The little turnips were very grateful. They grew and grew until they were the finest and the biggest turnips to be found any where in the hill country.

Then Hetty and Hank brought Granny and Mammy and Pappy up to see them.

"Sakes alive!" cried Mammy, "I never saw such big turnips!"

"Yes siree!" smiled Granny, "These are mighty juicy turnips."

"And they'll fetch a fine price in the town," said Pappy. "Hetty and Hank shall have the old gray horse to take them down the mountain."

So Hank quickly brought the gray horse. Then they pulled up all the beautiful turnips and packed them into a big bag.

Pappy laid the bag proudly across the gray horse's back, then he gave Hetty and Hank a boost and settled them safely right behind the turnips. Now they were ready to go.

"It's no trouble to find the town," said Granny. "Just you keep to the road and it will lead you down. Sometimes it's steep—just like the stair. Sometimes it's narrow—like a hair. It turns and twists and winds around, but at the end you'll find the town!"

"We'll keep to the road," promised Hetty and Hank. Hank pulled on the reins. Hetty gave the gray horse a slap on the side, and they were off.

"Goodby!" cried Granny and Mammy and Pappy.

"Goodby!" waved Hetty and Hank. And away they went, clippity, cloppity, down the road to town.

They had not gone very far before they came to an old man cutting sugar cane in a field beside the road.

"Howdy young ones!" he called. "What have you in that big bag?"

"Some turnips we're taking to sell in the town," said Hank proudly.

"Oh, my! Turnips!" cried the old man. "How I'd love some nice juicy turnips for my dinner. Couldn't you spare me just a few?"

"I suppose we wouldn't miss just a few," said Hetty, and she gave him some.

On they jogged between great bushes of pink mountain laurel, and after awhile they came to an old woman who was making soap in a big black kettle.

"Howdy, children!" she called. "What have you in that big bag?"

"Some turnips we're taking down to town," said Hank.

"Turnips!" cried the old woman. "Mercy me! How I'd love just a taste of turnip for my dinner. Couldn't you spare me just two, one for my old man and one for me?"

"I suppose we wouldn't miss just two," said Hetty and she gave her two big ones.

Down, down, down they went between the rows of tall blue mountains, down, down, down until they came to a little stream flowing over the rocks. There the little road ended. They looked here, they looked there they looked everywhere but it was nowhere to be seen.

But just then along came a woman on horseback, splishing and splashing right down the middle of the stream.

"What's the matter young ones?" she called.

"We've lost the little road to town," said Hank.

"Follow the creek," said the woman. "That's all the road there is in these parts."

So Hetty and Hank went splashing along and along and pretty soon they spied the little road leading up from the water.

They said goodby to the kind woman and gave her a bunch of turnips for her dinner.

On they went along the little road beneath the tall pine trees. After awhile they overtook a man who was driving a flock of turkeys down to town. "Howdy," greeted the man. "What have you in that big bag?"

"Some turnips we're taking to sell in the town," said Hank.

"Oh my stars!" said the man. "Turnips! and I've had nary a bit to eat since break of dawn. A nice, juicy turnip would taste mighty good now, for I've been running after these turkeys 'til I'm nigh worn out."

"We'll have to give him a handful of turnips," said Hetty. And she did.

"Thanky, thanky," said the man, "you're kind and generous young ones!"

Now they were very near to town. They could look down and see the roof tops in the valley.

The little road became so smooth and straight that the gray horse broke into a gallop.

"Here's the town!" cried Hank.

Along they went, clippity clop, clippity clop, past the schoolhouse, past the church, past the courthouse, and suddenly there was the little red store.

"Whoa!" cried Hank, pulling on the reins. "Here's the place to trade our turnips off for some shining shoes!"

They climbed down and lifted off the sack. Somehow it felt very light and very, very empty. Had they given all their turnips away?

Hetty put her hand into the bag and brought out one large, fat, lonesome turnip. It was the only one left.

And there—shining through the store window were those beautiful, creaky, squeaky, shining shoes!

Hetty and Hank gazed at them longingly. But one turnip would not buy a pair of shoes.

Two big tears began to roll down Hetty's cheeks.

"There! There!" said Hank. "No use crying. We'll just walk around and see the sights. Come on."

So they walked along the little road looking this way and that way. They saw the big covered wagons, all loaded with apples, come rumbling down from the hills. They saw the men trading horses in the courthouse square. Then a train went thundering past and they watched it with round eyes.

Along and along they went and after awhile they came to a field where there were many, many people. A big sign over the gate said "COUNTY FAIR."

Hetty and Hank went hustling and bustling about in the crowd. Pretty soon they came to a long row of tables, each one groaning with a different kind of vegetable. There were tomatoes on this one, and beans on that one, and pumpkins on the other one.

"Oh, here are some turnips!" cried Hetty.

"Are they as big as ours?" asked Hank.

Hetty held up her turnip. It seemed larger and juicier than the rest.

"Howdy, young ones," said the old man who was looking at the turnips. "Do you want to enter that turnip in the contest?"

"What contest?" asked Hank.

"Why there's a prize offered for the finest turnip at the fair," replied the old man.

"Mercy me!" said Hetty. "Let's try it."

"You bet your life!" said Hank.

So the old man wrote their names on a tag and tied it to the fat turnip. Then he laid it carefully among all the other turnips.

"You are just in the nick of time," he said, "for I was just a-getting ready to do the judging."

He began to examine the turnips. He weighed each one to see how heavy it was. He felt each one to see how firm it was. And when he had tried them all he held one large turnip high above his head.

"Folks!" he cried. "Here's the finest turnip at the fair. It belongs to a little girl and a little boy!"

Hetty and Hank listened with all their ears.

"Come forward, young ones and receive the prize!"

Hetty held out her hand and there shining up at her was a bright five-dollar gold piece.

"Oh thank you sir!" cried Hetty and Hank. "Now we can buy our shining shoes!"

They dashed along past the beans and tomatoes. They ran past the squash and skipped past the potatoes. They dodged through the hustle and the bustle on the fair grounds. They raced

along the street until they came to the little, red store.

The storekeeper was standing behind the counter.

"We want to buy some beautiful, creaky, squeaky shoes!" said Hank all out of breath.

The storekeeper got down his brightest shoes, and Hetty and Hank each chose a pair that played a creaky, squeaky tune.

Then they bought some gifts to take home with them. A yellow hat for Pappy, a bright sash for Mammy and a big, red handkerchief and a package of needles for Granny.

And off they started on the long trip home. Up, up, up they wound, round and round the mountain, past the pink laurel flowers, along the little stream and underneath the tall pine trees.

After a long, long climb they reached their own little cabin. There sat Mammy and Pappy and Granny waiting on the porch. How pleased they were to see Hetty and Hank and all the new things they had brought!

The next day was Sunday, so they put on their beautiful things and went to preaching.

Hetty and Hank walked proudly into the meeting-house. Their shoes were playing such a creaky, squeaky tune that all the people craned their necks to see who could be wearing such beautiful shoes.

YONIE WONDERNOSE

Marguerite de Angeli

There could hardly be a more appealing introduction to the Pennsylvania Dutch than Yonie. *Young children will also enjoy Marguerite de Angeli's* Henner's Lydia, Thee, Hannah! *and many others, and when they are a little older, her medieval story* The Door in the Wall, *which won the Newbery Award. Mrs. De Angeli's beautiful illustrations for her books add to their charm.*

Yonie was a little Pennsylvania Dutch boy. He was seven. He lived with Mom and Pop, Malinda, Lydia, and little Nancy on a farm in Lancaster County. His brother Ammon was grown up and had been away for a long time. Granny lived on the farm, too. She lived in her own part of the house. But most of the time she was in the kitchen helping Mom and Malinda.

Yonie's real name was Jonathan, but everyone called him Yonie. Pop called him "Yonie Wondernose" because he was so curious. He wanted to know about everything. If Pop brought a package into the house, he must see what was in it. If the Bishop came to talk to Pop, he must listen. If Mom had a pot boiling on the stove, he must lift the lid to see what was cooking. Sometimes the steam burned his nose, but it didn't keep him from looking the next time. If Malinda was baking a cake, Yonie was sure to open the oven door to see what kind it was.

"A Wondernose you are for sure!" she would scold. "Look now how it falls so fast!"

When Yonie and Lydia were on their way to school, he stopped so many times that they were often late. He hung over the fence to watch the men filling the wagons with stones from the stone crusher. He stood watching while a man changed a tire on a car, or while Nathan Straub seeded the bean field.

"We'll be late!" wailed Lydia. "Come now!" But she stood to watch, too!

Yonie's jacket was fastened with hooks and eyes instead of buttons. Pop didn't have buttons on his suit either. That is because he was an Amishman. And the Amish people never use buttons unless they are necessary. Yonie wore a broad hat just like Pop's hat, too—a straw one in summer and a black felt one in winter. And Mom cut Yonie's hair around a bowl, just like she cut Pop's. But Pop wore a beard such as all Amishmen wear.

This afternoon Pop and Mom were going visiting. They were taking Malinda and Lydia with them in the Germantown wagon, and they would stay overnight. Granny, Yonie, and Nancy stood in the doorway to see them off.

"Good-by," said Pop. "Don't be a Wondernose, now, and forget what you are doing!"

"No, Pop, I won't," Yonie answered.

"Remember, you are the man of the house now," said Mom.

"Ya, I will." Yonie nodded and stood straighter.

"Take good care of the barn creatures," called Pop again. "Feed and water them well. Don't forget, if anything happens, be sure to look after the horses first. They get scared so fast. Next, look after Dunder the red bull. He cost a lot of money, so take good care of him, don't forget! We see, now, if you are a man!"

Then he winked, and Yonie knew what he meant. Pop had promised him something when he was old enough to be trusted like a man but no one, not even Mom, knew about that promise. It was a secret between Pop and Yonie.

"I won't forget!" he called back.

As the wagon drove off, he thought, "Now Pop thinks I'll be a Wondernose, but I'll show him! I'll show him how big and smart I can be! When he comes home tomorrow, he'll see that I can take care of the animals by myself. Then, maybe, he'll let me do what he promised!"

"*Ya,* vell," said Granny. "Soon it makes time for supper. More rount-wood I need for the fire, and the cistern water iss all! The last I used for sprinkling the plants and for scrubbing."

Cistern water was soft rain water that Granny liked best for washing dishes and such things. Pop teased Granny because she was always scrubbing.

"It's a wonder you don't scrub the hoe handles and the fence posts, you are so clean!" he would say.

But Granny only said, "Better so, as like some I know, with floors all smeary and things all hoodled up!" and went on scrubbing. Yonie knew he must pump a lot of water to keep Granny supplied. He must get the wood for the kitchen stove. But he must take care of the animals, too.

He went first to the pasture for the cows, Blossom, Bluebell, and Buttercup. As they ambled down the lane, a squirrel scolded at Yonie from the fence rail, then scampered up a tree and into a knothole. Yonie *must* see where he went. Up the tree he scrambled and peered into the hole. He thrust his finger in to see what he could find. But he drew it out again in a hurry, for Mr. Squirrel gave it a sharp bite!

"Ach!" Yonie scolded himself, "here I am, being a Wondernose, just like always."

When he climbed down from the tree, the cows had scattered to nibble the grass at the edges of the lane. It took Yonie some time to get them started again in the right direction and to their places in the cowshed. He hurried to throw down fresh straw for their beds, while Granny milked. He carried water for them and called Nancy to come and put milk in the cats' dish for Malta and the four kittens.

He took the horses to the trough for water. He patted Star's broad back and thought of what Pop had promised. Then he went to look after Dunder. Dunder was kept in a pen and shed of his own on the far side of the barn.

Yonie had helped Pop, but he had never taken care of Dunder by himself as Ammon always had. He knew he must speak quietly to the great beast. He knew how to use the staff that Pop kept handy, too, and how to attach it to the ring in the bull's nose. So he felt safe, even though Dunder was so big and fierce.

The summer was really over. The hay was in the barn and the harvest gathered. But it had turned very warm again. Yonie's shirt was damp from the heat, and his yellow hair clung to his forehead. He wished he could stop work and go wading in the creek. The Little Conestoga ran through the meadow, and Yonie knew how cool it would be in the shade of the willow tree on its bank. He dropped the bucket he was carrying and started toward the creek. Then he remembered his promise to Pop—and Pop's promise to him. He picked up the bucket and went to pump more water for the rest of the animals and the chickens.

"Ach, vell," he told himself, "I can douse good, once, when I get the chores done."

He grunted as he lifted the heavy pail out of the trough. The water spilled a little onto his bare feet. It felt good and made clean patterns where it washed off the dust. He carried the bucket as full as he could. The chicken pans had to be filled, the calves needed a drink, the pigs had to be fed, and there was still the water to carry in for Granny.

When Yonie had filled the pans in the chicken yard, he made sure to lock the chicken house door. He knew the eggs had been gathered, so he didn't bother to look inside again.

He picked up the buckets in a hurry to water the calves and then stopped. Was that an airplane he heard? He couldn't see it but now he remembered that Granny wanted the roundwood for the fire.

"Rount-wood gives a hot fire," she had said, "and supper makes soon."

So Yonie went to the woodpile to get it. He could see Nancy under the big tree happily playing with her doll.

He started to gather the wood, and again came the deep purr of an airplane. This time he was sure. It might even be a new kind. He dropped the wood and ran to the corner of the house where he could see better.

As he craned his neck to follow the flight of the plane, he heard Nancy call, "Wonderno-ose Yonie! Wonderno-ose Yonie!" she teased.

He made a face in Nancy's direction, but turned back to the woodpile. When he carried the wood into the kitchen, Granny wasn't there. Something was bubbling on the stove. It smelled so good! He *must* see what was inside! Could it be apple dumplings? He lifted the lid. Ouch! The steam burned his nose, as usual.

He wondered where Granny could have gone, leaving the supper to cook by itself. But there was more work to do, so he went out to pump water for the calves. The water made him think again of the cool Conestoga. How he wished he were in it! It wouldn't take long for a splash, he thought, and it would feel so good! Suddenly he dropped the pump handle and started for the creek. He had his shirt and trousers off almost before he got there, and then—in he went.

The coolness and the quiet murmur of the creek made Yonie stay longer than he meant to. Then in the stillness he heard the bleating of the calves, and suddenly remembered that they were thirsty. He pulled on his clothes as best he could without drying and hurried back to the pump.

When he opened the barnyard gate, the calves came running to get at the water. The little black-and-white one nipped at Yonie's trousers, butted him with his knobbly head, and licked at his hands to see if he had any sugar.

Yonie thought, "That little runt now, if he was mine, I'd call him Wondernose like Pop calls me, the way he's nosing into my hand for sugar! I wish he *was* mine! It would be more fun to water them if one could be mine. If Pop would give me even a little pig the next time there are any, I'd take care of it till it grew big."

But more than he wanted the calf, more than the little pig, Yonie wanted what Pop had promised. He closed the gate and hurried to get the sour milk for the pigs. He could hear them squealing around beyond the corner of the barn.

When they saw Yonie coming with their supper, they squealed more loudly than ever. There were vegetable parings, bits of bread, and celery tops floating in it. But the pigs thought it was delicious. The great big old sow put both feet in the trough so as to be sure and get her share.

When Yonie went to the kitchen with the water for Granny, she still wasn't there. He thought, once, that he heard her call. But when he listened again he heard nothing.

The food in the kettle had boiled over and didn't smell so good as it had before. He called up the stairs, "Granny! Oh, Granny! Somesing smells like burning!" But there was no answer.

He called again, then listened. But there was still no answer. Then he went upstairs and looked in all of the rooms. But still he saw no one and heard nothing. He went downstairs and over into Granny's part of the house.

"Granny!" he shouted, but only the ticking of the clock answered him.

As he stood wondering where Granny might be, his eyes lighted on the painted chest. There Granny kept the old book. It was full of stories that Yonie loved to hear. Granny never allowed the children to open the chest themselves.

She always said, "The things in it are over two hundred years old. That's when your great-great-

great-grandfather came with his family and many others from the old country. They came so they might worship God in their own way."

Yonie thought, "It wonders me, now, what else is in there besides the book. I could just look once, and Granny would never know."

He went to the chest where it stood under the window and lifted the lid. But before he could even begin to see anything, he seemed to hear Pop's voice, saying, "Yonie! Yonie Wondernose!"

He stood for a second, then was sure that he heard a voice.

It sounded like a real voice coming through the open window.

He listened. He could just barely hear it. But it called, "Yonie! Oh, Yonie!"

He dropped the lid with a bang! Out he flew, through to the kitchen, to the porch, down the yard, through the arbor, and to the chicken house.

Now he could hear the voice plainly, and it was coming from inside the chicken house. "Yonie! Ach, Yonie! Let me out of here!"

He turned the lock and opened the door and out fell Granny! She had been shut up in the heat of the chicken house ever since Yonie filled the water pans! Yonie helped her to a seat in the arbor and ran to get her a drink of water.

When she could speak, she said, "Ach, Yonie! Why didn't you be *this* time a *Wondernose?* Always look *first* inside, *then* lock the door." But Yonie looked so sorry that Granny had to laugh.

"Never mind," she said. "You locked the door like your Pop said. You didn't know Granny was in there. Next time—look inside first." She sniffed the air. "Somesing smells like burning," she said. "Supper, I guess. Ach, vell, ve have spreadin's anyways on our bread, and shoofly pie. Call Nancy."

They went in to supper.

Nancy helped Granny put the "spreadin's" on the table. There was apple butter, currant jelly, stewed apples, and piccalilli. Then there was the pie. It was a shoofly pie made with soft molasses cake baked in a piecrust. Yonie was very fond of it. While they were eating, Granny told how it felt to be shut up in the chicken house.

"Hot as seven in a bed it was in there! I count the chickens over and over. They stare at me, and cluck like I don't belong in there. And I stare back. I try to get out by the place where the chickens go in, but for a long time now I'm too big for that!"

Yonie and Nancy laughed to think of Granny down on her hands and knees trying to get through that little opening. Yonie thought how it would be to sleep seven in a bed!

"Whew!" he said.

Yonie wished he could douse again in the creek, it was so warm in the kitchen. Granny looked warm, too, and fanned herself with her apron. Even Nancy pushed little wisps of hair up onto her braids.

Suddenly, as they finished eating, the spot of sunlight faded from the table, and there was a growl of thunder.

"It makes like a storm, ain't, Granny?" said Yonie.

"Ya," agreed Granny. "The heat iss something wonderful. It makes a storm, maybe. Make everything fast by the barn."

Nancy ran out to get her doll. And Yonie went to make sure he had done all that Pop told him to do. Yes, he had fed and watered the barn creatures. They were all quiet for the night. When he came in, it was time for him to go to bed.

There was another grumble of thunder, but Yonie didn't hear it. He was asleep.

Suddenly a bright flash woke him with a start. With the flash came a sizzling "bang" of thunder! Yonie jumped out of bed. He knew the storm had broken right overheard and that something might have caught fire from the lightning.

"Ach!" he thought. "Somesing does happen maybe, like Pop said. Now I have to see if Star and Blackie are all right and Dunder."

He reached for his breeches just as Granny came hurrying to the foot of the stairs. She called, "Yonie! Oh, Yonie! Come quick!"

But she didn't need to tell him the barn was afire. He could see it as he ran past the window and down the steep, twisty stairs. Then the rain began.

Yonie didn't wait for Granny, who was tying her shoes. He ran headlong through the shower toward the barn. Something black flew past him, then four somethings. It was Malta and the four kittens. A cloud of pigeons fluttered about, then flew off toward the woods. They lived in the cupola of the barn.

Now a blaze came out of the barn like a great red flower that grew and grew, even though the rain was coming down faster and faster. Yonie had to hold his breath as he tried to go through the thick smoke that already filled the barn. If he was going to get the horses out he would have to cover their heads. Otherwise, Pop had told him, they would run right back into the fire again.

Yonie knew where to find the old carriage robe that Pop kept hanging near the horses just in case of need. Stumbling toward it, he got it in his hands at last. Then he hurried to hang it over Star's head. Granny came running in with her shawl to put over Blackie and got him out of the barn door just behind Yonie and Star.

Lightning flashed and thunder banged. Rain poured down, but the fire burned fiercer and roared louder, for now it had reached the hay.

"Run!" cried Granny. "Quick now! Over past the house, and we tie the horses to the fence post."

Blackie tossed his head and tried to get away, but Granny held on. Star snorted and neighed and tried to fling off the cover from his head. But Yonie held it tight till they reached the fence. The rain stopped as suddenly as it had begun, and a breeze sprang up.

Back raced Yonie and Granny toward the barn. Granny was breathing hard.

"Run ahead and let loose the chickens!" she cried. "The wind blows that way and sparks soon set fire to the roof."

"Ya!" Yonie shouted, as he turned off to let out the chickens. They ran out scolding and clucking, and scattered over the road and fields.

"It's good I ain't in there still!" panted Granny. "The fire makes worse on this side, so we loose the cows next. Then Dunder."

They got Blossom and Buttercup out safely and left them to run toward the orchard. But before they could get Bluebell out of the way, a burning brand fell across her back. It rolled off, but left a scorched place. She leaped clear of the door in one jump, then ran off after the other cows.

Granny and Yonie got out just in time, and ran to open the calf pen, which was close by.

"How shall we fix poor Bluebell, so the burn won't hurt?" panted Yonie.

"Apple butter," gasped Granny, spreading her skirts to head off the calves so they would go the right way. "Apple butter makes the pain go away. I fix it while you get Dunder out. Get him quick! He's such a fine bull, your Pop gets mad if he's hurt! Quick!"

Granny started off toward the house, and Yonie hurried around to the front of the barn toward Dunder's shed. He could see the bare frame of the roof through the fire. And just as he looked up, a great timber fell.

"It must be right on the ground near the pigpen!" he thought excitedly. "I must see where it went. Besides, what of the pigs and the old sow?"

He turned back the way he had come and went around to where the pigs were shut in beyond the calf pen. The timber had fallen inside the barn, and not on the pigpen. But Yonie opened the door and called to them, making a sucking noise with his mouth as if he were going to feed them. They came rushing up. And Yonie guided them through the gate and down the slope to the field where Pop had been digging potatoes. There they began rooting in the ground, so Yonie knew they were safe.

Back he started across the muddy field toward Dunder's pen, for now he could hear great roars from that direction.

"That Dunder, now," he thought, "he might do me somesing, he's so mad. He bellers wonderful! If only Pop would come home!"

A sudden burst of flame made him stop to look and wonder. A great rafter fell with a shower of sparks as he watched.

"It's like a picture in a book!" he thought.

Dunder bellowed again, more loudly than ever. Yonie set his tired legs in motion. How he wished Pop were here! But Pop wasn't here, and Dunder must be gotten out!

Then, above the whooshing and the crackling of the fire, Yonie heard a new noise. He stopped again. He looked out toward the highway.

The road leading down from it was crowded with people! There were people in wagons, people in carriages, people in automobiles, and people on foot! Yonie stared. Then a siren shrieked, and he heard a bell clanging. That must be the fire engine! He started to run toward the crowd. He must see that beautiful, bright red engine that now turned into the road. It puffed and clanged. It made the horses step lively. It pushed the people off the road and sent the chickens squawking in every direction.

Yonie was so excited that he forgot everything else. He forgot about the tools and farm gear that needed to be moved from the fire. He forgot that Granny might need his help with Bluebell. He forgot Nancy, who was still asleep in the brick house. He even forgot Dunder. All he could think of was that red engine with the shiny trim. Just as he was about to cross the cornfield Dunder bellowed again loud and long. Yonie stopped short.

"Ach!" he thought, "that Dunder!"

He stood for a second, longing to go where the red engine was already at work. He could see the stream of water it was pouring into the fire from the Little Conestoga. He could see the fire dying down.

Then he seemed to hear Pop say, "Wondernose!"

He turned and ran as fast as he could go to Dunder's pen. Beside the gate into the pen Pop kept the long staff with the hook at the end. Yonie made sure to have it securely in hand before he opened the gate. He could tell that Dunder was not very happy.

Yonie crept up toward the big bull's head. Dunder started to roar, and Yonie quickly snapped the staff into place. Dunder tossed his head, but not far! He was stopped suddenly by the pain in his nose, for the staff thrust his head up into the air and he was helpless.

Yonie was very proud to lead him through the gate toward the field that sloped up the hill. He wrapped Dunder's chain around the trunk of a tree and left the staff where it would be handy. But Dunder still bellowed as if he were in pain.

"Now, what makes it that you holler still?" Yonie said out loud. "Maybe you don't like all this fire, but to make so much noise is no good." He turned to go back toward the fire engine. And then he saw the cause of Dunder's bellows. Across Dunder's back where there should have been glossy brown hair there was no skin at all! A burning timber had fallen on the big bull before Yonie had moved him. Yonie ran tearing down the hill to find Granny and the apple butter.

He had to push his way through the crowd of people. Granny was on the back porch comforting Nancy, who stood there crying in her little nightgown.

He could see her in the light from the kitchen where neighbor women were already setting about making coffee.

"Why," thought Yonie, "it's almost like a picnic!"

He started to cross the wagon track. But just then a shiny black car drove in and stopped. Yonie forgot Dunder again. He *must* see that car! Pop said automobiles were worldly, but Yonie loved to look at them. He stood staring.

The door opened and someone got out—someone who looked like Pop! Someone who said, just like Pop, "A Wondernose still!" It *was* Pop! A neighbor had gone to bring him home!

"And are the barn creatures all safe?" asked Pop.

But before Yonie had time to answer, the Bishop and several neighboring farmers came up to tell Pop they would help him to rebuild the barn and get things in order again.

Yonie wished he could see Pop alone for just one minute, then he could explain that Dunder was hurt because he had taken care of the pigs first! What would Pop do when he knew that Yonie almost forgot Dunder because he stopped to look at the red engine?

He stood waiting till the men were through talking. Then he took a long breath and began: "Apple butter makes good for the burns on Dunder's back, Granny says. And I forgot and took the pigs out first." There! It was out!

What would Pop say? Would he say, "Now you are too little still for me to keep that promise?"

But Pop didn't say anything. He just took Yonie up in his arms and held him tight. Then he put him down again, and said, "Now, come, we see where all the animals are. Star and Blackie I saw when we come in the lane. Where's Dunder?"

When they reached the top of the field where Dunder was tied, some of the neighbor women were there, putting a poultice on Dunder's back. Dunder was quiet.

"He's not bad hurt," said Katie Lapp. "We heard him beller as we come over the field. I bring apple butter like always when there is a fire, to put on the animals when they get hurt."

Pop thanked them. Then he and Yonie went on down to the potato field where the pigs were. They were still hunting out roots in the mud, all but the mother sow. She lay over in the fence corner. When Yonie leaned over to see if she was all right, what do you think he saw? Ten little new baby pigs! Pop saw them, too. He laughed.

"Ya, vell," he said, "this time it pays to be a Wondernose! Better Dunder gets a pain in his back as lose the old mother sow!"

Yonie felt happy.

"Now," said Pop, "for being such a big smart boy, one of these little pigs belongs to you. Choose which one."

Yonie didn't speak. He just laid his hand on the little pink one that couldn't find room to get his share of dinner. Now he had a pet that was all his own.

The calves came bleating to the other side of the fence. The little black one put his nose through the rails and sniffed in Yonie's pocket as he leaned over.

"He's a Wondernose just like you," said Pop. "Would you like to have him, too?"

"Ya, Pop," said Yonie. "I'd like fine to have him!"

"It takes a *man* to care for barn creatures and get them safe out of a fire. Soon it makes time for fall planting." He winked again at Yonie. "I need a man for that, too!" he said.

Now Yonie knew that Pop would keep his promise! At last he could do what he had hoped for ever since Ammon left. He was big enough now to guide the two great work horses to harrow the field for winter wheat all by himself. He could see himself astride Star's back, high above the ground, above the fence posts, even above Pop's head! He could hear himself saying, "Gee! Haw!" and whichever way he said, the horses would go! He slipped his hand into Pop's big one.

"Yonie Wondernose!" said Pop.

JIMMY AND JEMIMA

Helen Sewell

This humorous fable could be entitled "Pride goeth before a fall."

When Jemima was born Jimmy thought she was the most beautiful baby sister in the world. And so did his Mother and his Daddy and his Granny.

Sometimes Jimmy took her out in her carriage.

And when she was older he gave her rides in his express wagon.

Or they rode together on his bike.

But when Jimmy was a big boy he joined the Scouts. Then he had no time to play with girls.

Jimmy wanted more than anything else to earn the lifesaving medal. So he took swimming lessons.

One day all the family came to see Jimmy swim five strokes.

Then Jemima jumped in and swam way to

the other end of the pond. And no one knew that she could swim at all!

Jimmy wanted to learn to ride a horse. So he took riding lessons.

The whole family came out to see him ride.

But when the horse stopped suddenly, poor Jimmy slid right on his head.

Jemima climbed up on the horse's back and rode him all the way home!

One morning Jimmy and the Scouts started out very early, for they were going to climb a high mountain. Jimmy said that Jemima could not go because it was much too far for girls.

They climbed and climbed and climbed.

And when they reached the top Jemima was already there!

One day in the winter Jimmy and Jemima went skating.

Jimmy could skate very well but once he slipped and fell down on the ice. Then Jemima was *too* proud and she skated *too* far.

And Jemima fell in.

But Jimmy was a good Boy Scout. He had learned all about lifesaving. He found a board and he fished Jemima out.

When Jemima was safe in bed with a hot-water bottle she thought about Jimmy. It was nice to have a brother to pull her out when she fell into the water.

And when the Mayor presented the lifesaving medal to Jimmy he thought about Jemima.

It was nice to have a sister to fall into the water so that he could pull her out.

WAIT FOR WILLIAM

Marjorie Flack

This amusing little circus story turns upon the most natural conflict in the world—a four-year-old's trouble with his shoelace and the older children's impatience with his slowness. Its conclusion demonstrates delightfully that "The humble shall be exalted."

Once there were three children who lived in a white house in Pollywinkle Lane in the village of Pleasantville.

The oldest of these three children was a big boy whose name was Charles and he was eight years old.

The middle one was a girl whose name was Nancy and she was six years old.

The youngest was a little boy and his name was William and he was just four years old.

One summer morning when William was riding his scooter up and down the walk Charles said,

"Hurry up, William, put away your scooter and we will take you down to Main Street to see the Circus Parade."

And Nancy said,

"Hurry up, William, wash your hands and comb your hair and we will take you down to Main Street to see the Circus Parade."

So William put away his scooter and he washed his hands and combed his hair, and they all started down Pollywinkle Lane on their way to Main Street to see the Circus Parade.

"Hurry up, William," said Charles. "Walk faster, William. We must not be too late when we get to Main Street to see the Circus Parade."

"Hurry up, William, walk faster, William," said Nancy, "or we shall be too late when we get to Main Street to see the beginning of the Circus Parade."

William walked faster but Charles walked faster and Nancy walked faster as they all hurried along down Pollywinkle Lane on their way to Main Street to see the Circus Parade.

"Wait!" called William. "Wait for me, my shoe is untied!"

"We can't wait," said Charles.

"We can't wait," said Nancy, "or we shall all be too late when we get to Main Street to see the Circus Parade."

So William walked faster and faster, but *flap, flap* went the shoestring, so William hopped and William galloped as he hurried along down Pollywinkle Lane on the way to Main Street to see the Circus Parade.

Then *flop,* off came William's shoe, and there he stood with one shoe off and one shoe on. "Wait for me!" called William. "Wait for me, my shoe's come off!"

But Charles and Nancy did not answer. They did not answer because they did not hear Wil-

liam. They did not hear William because they were too far away, as they hurried along down Pollywinkle Lane on their way to Main Street to see the Circus Parade.

So William stopped and he put on his shoe and he tied the shoestring in a tight firm knot, and then he slowly and carefully made the ends into a proper, neat bow.

But when it was all done, Nancy and Charles were gone, they were nowhere in sight! So William ran alone. He ran all alone down Pollywinkle Lane on his way to Main Street to see the Circus Parade.

Then William stopped, he stopped at a corner because he heard Music, William heard Circus Music coming nearer and nearer and then William saw the Circus Parade coming to him, coming to William on its way to Main Street.

First came the horses—then came the band—and then came the Camels—and then came a man leading an Elephant.

The man saw William. He saw William standing all alone, all alone because Charles and Nancy and everybody else, everybody else in the whole village of Pleasantville had gone to Main Street to see the Circus Parade.

"Want a ride?" called the man.

"Yes!" said William.

So the man lifted William up, up high on the Elephant and William and the Elephant paraded along to Main Street.

William was so high the branches of the trees were near him and he looked down, way down on all the people of Pleasantville as they stood on Main Street to see the Circus Parade!

William passed by the Drug Store, he passed by the Grocery Store, and he passed by the church and then, when he came to the Post Office William looked down, way down, and there he saw Charles and Nancy and all their friends!

Charles and Nancy and all their friends looked up, way up, and there on top of the Elephant they saw William riding the Elephant in the Circus Parade!

"Look at William!" shouted Charles.

"Look at William!" shouted Nancy.

"Look at William!" shouted all their friends.

Then they all ran along beside William as he rode the Elephant in the Circus Parade.

They went up Summer Street, and then down High Street, and then they came to the corner of Pollywinkle Lane.

Then the man lifted William down. He lifted William down, down to the ground again.

"Thank you for the Elephant Ride," said William. The man said, "You're welcome." Then the man and the Elephant went away.

"Tell us about it," begged Charles.

"Tell us about it," begged Nancy.

"Tell us about riding the Elephant in the Circus Parade," begged all their friends.

But William said, "Wait. Wait. My other shoe is untied."

So Charles waited, and Nancy waited, and all their friends waited, while William tied the shoestring in a good firm knot and they waited while he slowly and carefully made the ends into a proper, neat bow.

Then slowly they walked, walked slowly with William as he told them about riding the Elephant down Main Street, down Main Street in the Circus Parade.

from KI-KI A CIRCUS TROUPER

Edith Janice Craine

[*A New Act for the Circus*]

Ki-Ki was lost!

Ki-Ki did not know that he was lost.

The little dog did know that things all about him were strange. There was not one familiar pair of feet, not one familiar sniff, not one familiar voice.

Ki-Ki knew that he was tired. He was so tired that he could hardly keep his chin up. So tired there was hardly a wag left in his wee tail. So tired that he straddled his legs wide apart to keep them from doubling under him. The tiredness came from running and running, here and there, from one place to another, in search of something he knew, something familiar. He braced himself against a railing and blinked bravely to keep his eyes open.

Suddenly, an enormous wagon rumbled past and something inside roared furiously as though very angry. It was a fearful sound.

The little dog was so frightened that he forgot his weariness. He did not take an instant to look where he was going. But he jumped as high and as far as he could, and he landed on the cushioned seat of a basket wagon.

With a faint yap, Ki-Ki rolled himself into a tight ball and snuggled down. He tucked his nose under his forepaws, and closed his eyes. Right away he went fast asleep, without knowing where he was, or what had given him such a fright.

While he slept, Ki-Ki dreamed of familiar things and his tiny body quivered happily. He slept and slept and slept. He was awakened by the sound of laughter. It was the sort of laughter that just pops right out of people when there is a pleased, very kindly feeling deep inside them. It comes when something makes them feel so good they have to smile out loud.

That laugh took away every speck of Ki-Ki's tiredness. With a gay little spring he was on his feet. He stood straight and firm now, and he held his head up.

Just ahead, the little dog saw that a great pair of gates was standing wide open, and that he was going forward in a basket wagon. The wagon had shafts at the back, and a spotted pony was harnessed between the shafts, with his head facing the wagon. He was pushing the wagon. A small boy, under a very big hat, was astride the back of the pony, and the jolliest clown was driving.

"It's the clown!"

"He said that he would come!"

"The circus! Oh! Oh! Oh!"

"The clown and his little boy!"

"See the pony. Ha-ha-ha! He's pushing the wagon!"

"Oh, look!"

"Elephants, with royal covers!"

"I hear bears!"

"There are bears. Brown ones. And look, a big white one!"

"Here they come!"

"Real tigers, and real lions!"

"Wild ones!"

"Wild as anything!"

There were so many shouts from all sides that the noise became a great roar that rolled right into the air.

Ki-Ki did not know that those shouts came from boys and girls of a hospital. There were boys and girls, big ones and little ones, who had to be in chairs, or on couches, or had to hold themselves up with crutches until doctors and nurses could make their bodies well and strong.

But, Ki-Ki could tell that they were very, very happy, so he lifted himself right up in plain sight, and barked as hard as he could. To be sure it wasn't very loud barking. Only those who were nearby could hear him at all, but he did not mind that. A big, kindly hand kept him from jumping under the feet of the elephant, or into a cage and down the throat of a lion. The lion was yawning at the moment.

"Hello, Trouper! Want to help with the show?" said the clown, as he lifted the little dog up into his arms.

Ki-Ki did not answer, but his red tongue went out, swift as lightning, in a wide lick on the clown's face. The lick nearly took the clown's paint off.

"There, there. All right, it's settled, but you must not spoil my looks," laughed the clown. He tucked Ki-Ki under his arm where everyone could see the dog and the pair led the great circus parade around the courtyard.

Everywhere boys and girls were watching eagerly. Some were on a platform so low they could reach out and touch the animals, or talk to the performers. Others were on balconies, and they leaned over. There were three rows of those balconies.

Besides the children, there were grown-ups. They all wore smiles that went from ear to ear. Why, there were even twitches and twinkles about the lips and eyes of the most serious-looking doctors.

Around and around went the parade, so that everybody could see every single thing. The elephants poked out their long trunks for peanuts. The lions roared their fiercest, as they balanced on huge balls. Cowboys, on plunging, bucking broncos, whooped and threw their big hats into the air. Their long lariats opened into wide loops with a delightful swish, then poised and dropped. One caught the clown just as he was alighting from his wagon.

"What do you mean, sir?" The clown pretended to be very angry.

"Sorry! So sorry, sir. You see, my rope slipped," said the cowboy very politely.

"I do not see! It is disgraceful," answered the clown. He had the worst time getting rid of that lariat. It tangled first in one place, then another.

The clown's little boy tried to help. Ki-Ki tried to help and was tossed over and over. A little lame girl with a crutch tried to help, and nearly got caught. It was all so funny that the hospital children laughed and laughed until their sides ached.

The doctors and nurses laughed until their sides ached.

"Ladies and gentlemen," someone shouted. "Attention!"

"It is time for ice cream," roared someone else.

"Hurrah!"

"Hurrah for the circus!"

"Hurrah for the clown!"

"We thank you," the clown waved his hat and bowed very low.

"We thank you for giving us such a good time," called the children.

"Ladies and gentlemen," said the clown. "I want to return this lovely little dog." He held Ki-Ki up, but no one seemed to understand. "I guess he belongs to one of you boys or girls. When I first saw him, I thought he was a brown, woolly muff on legs. He is so little, he surely could get lost in my pocket." The clown balanced Ki-Ki on the palm of his hand.

"Hurrah for the little dog," shouted a girl with a crutch.

"Who owns him?"

"He does not belong to us—"

"He doesn't belong to us—"

Ki-Ki did not belong to any boy or girl there.

"Then, he must belong to a doctor or a nurse," said the clown.

"Not to us," said the nurses.

"Nor to us," said the doctors.

"Land of Liberty! Where, in the name of curly lollipops did you come from, Trouper?" said the clown. He was puzzled as he could be.

"Oh, Dad, I saw something jump into the wagon when we hitched up this afternoon," said the clown's little boy.

"Was it this fellow?"

"I was going to get some water for the pony, and did not stop to look. But, maybe it was."

"My word, Trouper. Did you run away?"

"Perhaps he is lost," said a nurse.

"He looks like a thoroughbred toy 'Pom' to me," said one of the doctors.

"We must watch the newspapers and find out who lost you," the clown told Ki-Ki.

The tiny dog snuggled close on the clown's arm, his tail wagging as hard as it could wag, as if to say that he did not feel lost a bit, and that he was quite content to be a trouper forever and ever.

"Cupid! Cupid! Cupid!" The clown's little boy called three times. The little boy was named Peter Webber. He was stretched out on his stomach on the floor, but his heels were in the air, his chin resting on one palm, and his other hand held a newspaper. He was reading about dogs in the Lost and Found column.

A few feet away from Peter, Ki-Ki was lapping water out of a shiny new pan, which was all his own. He knew very well that his name was Ki-Ki, but he couldn't tell that to Peter. Of course, he couldn't tell anyone. After all, what did it matter? He would jump and frisk when they called him Trouper.

"What do you find in the newspaper, Peter?" the clown asked.

"Pom-er-an-ian—"

"Pomeranian?"

"Yes, sir. The newspaper says that the dog answers to the name of Cupid," Peter read slowly.

"This pup does not answer to that name. What else does the newspaper say, son?"

"Two years old—"

"This chap isn't more than a year old. Any more lost dogs?"

"Yes, Dad. Listen to these. Lost, a brindle bull pup—"

"That does not fit."

"Lost, a small brown terrier," Peter read aloud.

"We did not find a terrier."

"A black Scottie. That's all." Peter folded the newspaper, and Ki-Ki was sure it was time for a romp.

"We must keep watching," said the clown. "After a while, we shall find out who owns him."

The clown's name was John Webber and he had deep lines in the corners of his eyes. These lines made his face look as if he were always ready for a good laugh.

"I wonder how the little dog got away from his master," said Mrs. Webber.

"Perhaps he jumped out of an automobile when no one was looking," her husband answered.

"Maybe his owner thought he was asleep among the cushions," suggested Peter.

"He is so little," said Mrs. Webber. "That might have happened."

"And we must be careful he does not do it again," Peter declared. "I am going to keep watch over you, little fellow." Peter caught the dog in his arms and held him close.

A whole week had passed since Ki-Ki had been found on the front seat of the circus wagon, and he had helped the clown give the crippled children at the hospital so much fun.

Now, it was the very last night the circus would be in town. So the clown and his family were in their own dressing room packing boxes and bags for a journey.

. . . .

When Peter awakened, the caravan was not moving. He was in his pajamas, snug in his own cot, where his mother had tucked him gently, hours before. The long caravan had come to a halt, and the cot was in the Webbers' own tent. From outside came familiar sounds. They were sounds that the little boy knew very well were made by men putting things into shape for the opening of the circus.

There were smells too, very pleasant ones. One was the sweet fragrance from a meadow where the hay had just been cut. Another fragrance came from the campfire breakfasts. These were enough to make any boy hurry out of bed and into his clothes.

Peter found that his mother and father were waiting breakfast for him. Ki-Ki was waiting too, but he did not mind because he had eaten a biscuit.

"Good morning, Mother and Dad," said Peter.

"Good morning," they answered.

"Hungry, dear?" asked his mother.

"Hollow as a bass drum," he said.

"Well, pitch in," invited his father.

The boy did not need to be urged. He had nearly finished his breakfast when something popped into his head.

"Dad, this is the country, isn't it?"

"It certainly is."

"You and Mother promised that when we were in the country, I might ride the big elephant, Queen Bess, some afternoon."

"So we did. Are your lessons finished?"

"They are, Dad, every single lesson."

"Very well. I see no reason why you should not ride Queen Bess this afternoon, if Mr. Lawrence does not object. If he says that it is safe, you may."

"Thanks, Dad. I'll find out." Peter had finished his breakfast, so he gave them both a good hug. Then he hurried out to find Mr. Lawrence.

Things were coming along pretty well. The enormous tent was in place. Ropes and braces were being made fast on the outside. Small tents were going up for the side shows. Many-colored flags and streamers, that Peter had seen being packed the night before, were now waving gaily in the breeze. In the sky, not a cloud could be seen. The sun was beaming down on the circus, and crowds of people were gathering to enjoy the fun.

"You will have to stay inside, Trouper," Peter explained as they hurried along, but the little dog only frisked. Soon the small boy found Mr. Lawrence, who said that it would be quite all right for him to ride Queen Bess that afternoon. So Peter raced back to the family tent to tell his mother.

"I'll get you ready, dear," Mrs. Webber said as she set to work adding: "you will be very careful, son."

"Of course, Mother. Will you watch?"

"I can watch the start, at least," she told him.

"Where's my elephant boy?" Mr. Lawrence shouted a bit later.

"Right here. All ready," Peter called. He wore red sandals with a high turban to match, and brown tights.

"Run along," urged his mother.

"Be a good fellow, Trouper," the boy said, as he fastened the leash to the leg of the cot. "I'll come for you soon." He raced off to his place in the parade, leaving Ki-Ki looking dreadfully disappointed. The little dog tugged at the leash and barked woefully.

"Speed up there," roared the elephant-man.

The elephant's trunk coiled gently about Peter's waist.

"Going up!" Mr. Lawrence laughed as he caught Peter's hand to steady him.

"Whew!" said Peter as he took his place between the elephant's great ears.

"Forward—march!"

Queen Bess moved forward majestically and Peter was so happy that he could hardly contain himself. He wished that he could stand on his head, but that would surely spoil the wonderful turban.

Inside the huge tent, the band was playing such lively music that it made everyone quite gay.

The parade formed as it did for the children at the hospital, with the clown in his funny wagon, pushed by the spotted pony. Only this time, there was no small boy astride the pony's back.

Then came Queen Bess with Peter Webber seated cross-legged on her broad head. There were more elephants, followed by cages of wild animals, roaring and snarling furiously.

Through the performers' entrance went the clown, straight to the center ring, under the gay banners and swinging festoons. From all sides of the arena arose a rousing cheer of welcome. Boys and girls, big and little; men and women, large and small, clapped and shouted at the top of their voices. Around the center ring went the grand parade.

Suddenly, it seemed to Peter, that he heard a different sort of sound. As soon as he could, he looked around to see what it was. Peter was so startled that he forgot how high he was sitting. But the man behind him caught hold of his arm.

"Steady, big boy," said Mr. Lawrence.

"Yes, sir." Peter's teeth chattered. "O-o—oh, Trouper!"

The small dog, his leash dragging, was dashing headlong into the center ring. Heedless of swinging tight-rope tackle, tramping hoofs, and busy performers, he leaped on and on. Two men raced to his rescue and tried to toss him to safety, but the small dog slipped from their hands.

Ki-Ki landed on his side and rolled and tumbled before he regained his feet. With an impudent little yap, he started again.

"Hurrah for that dog!"

The audience thought it a part of the show, and cheered lustily.

"Good boy!"

"Go to it, Old Timer!"

One end of the leash caught the end of a pole, but held only an instant, then Ki-Ki pulled himself free.

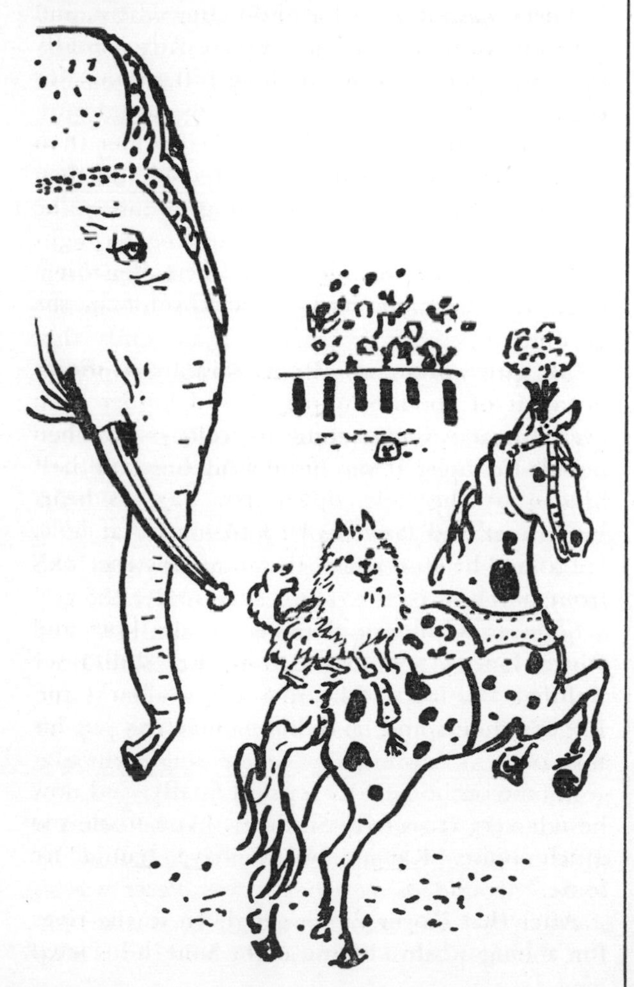

"Woof! Woof!" He headed straight for the parade.

"He'll be trampled. He'll be hurt," Peter choked.

By that time, Peter could not see the dog. Bravely he blinked back tears that welled in his eyes, and gulped down a great lump that rose in his throat. He was sure that Queen Bess would crush the tiny dog. The caravan kept moving steadily, then Peter felt the elephant sway slightly. Her long trunk was swinging from side to side.

Then, just as she had lifted Peter up to his place on her head, so Queen Bess picked up Ki-Ki.

"Oh, Trouper, Trouper!" Peter choked. He could hardly believe his eyes. He leaned forward to catch his pet, but Queen Bess had another idea. She waved the small dog back and forth so that everyone could see him. Then she set him down on the broad back of the spotted pony right in front of her. How everyone laughed!

Of course Ki-Ki had no idea what it was all about, but he understood merry laughs, chuckles, and ha-ha's. He gave his head a funny little shake, then stood on his hind feet, his forefeet waving, as if he were greeting the cheering crowd.

"Good Queen Bess!"

"Cunning pup!"

More cheers and shouts. The shouts were so thunderous that they nearly brought down the tent poles.

"Cheers for the pup! Cheers for the elephant!"

That is how a little lost dog became a really-for-real trouper.

ROGER AND THE FOX

Lavinia R. Davis

This is a sensitively perceptive story about a little boy's interest in a wild creature and his patient, persistent lookout, which is finally rewarded. Such a story has great value in setting a pattern for a boy's approach to wild life, not as a hunter or a molester, but as a thrilled observer of the creature's secret life. Children who like this story will enjoy the second one, The Wild Birthday Cake.

The fall wind swished through the leaves of the trees. The leaves floated to the ground like little umbrellas. And the wind, still chasing and teasing, rolled and tossed them across the road. Roger's feet, in his new school shoes, scuffled through the dried leaves.

Rustle-rustle-crack went the leaves. Roger, who was six, and walking home from school, grinned to himself. He loved the sound of rustling leaves. It was a fine, dry, corn-popping, pie-eating, cider-drinking, *fall* sound.

At the bend in the road the wind died down. Roger heard another noise. It was a little, shy, scurrying noise deep in the leaves. Roger started forward. Then he remembered what Seth had said and he stood still as a fence post and waited. Seth was the hired man on Roger's father's farm and he knew everything.

"If you want to see wild animals," Seth had said, "you can't just rush in on 'em. You have to wait and be patient."

This time Roger didn't have to wait long. There was another stir in the leaves, and then, plain as a pumpkin, out came the chipmunk and darted across the road.

Roger hurried home to tell Seth. He stayed at the house only long enough to help himself to ginger cookies and then he ran up to the barn.

Seth was milking when Roger told him about the chipmunk. "I saw it all by myself," Roger said. "I just stood still and I saw it."

Seth went right on squirting milk into the pail. "Saw a big fox myself this morning," he said finally. "Fine red one down at the river by that ironwood tree that was blown over in the hurricane."

"A fox!" said Roger, and suddenly he felt as flat as a pricked balloon. What was a little old chipmunk compared to a fine red fox?

Roger left the barn and went straight down the long hill toward the Still River. Roger wanted to see that fox himself. Since he and his family had moved to the farm he had seen squirrels, rabbits, field mice, turtles, and of course chipmunks. Once from a safe distance his big brother Dick had shown him a skunk. But until today Roger hadn't even been sure that there were foxes in Connecticut.

Even after Roger reached the river he had a long walk ahead of him. The cold black water twisted and turned between the trees like a pretzel. It was damp and chilly walking along the riverbank, and Roger began to rustle leaves again because the sound made him feel warmer.

It was nearly dark by the time Roger reached the fallen-down tree where Seth had seen the fox. He looked and looked. He couldn't see a thing except the big ironwood tree arching over the river like a shadowy bridge. Roger was colder than ever now and hungry, and there wasn't so much as ginger dust left from his cookies. Pretty soon he started for home. He'd come back tomorrow and bring Scamper with him. Scamper was a fox terrier and almost as smart as Seth's coon hound, Ranger. Roger felt sure if he had Scamper along he'd see the fox.

There was always a lot to do after school, and it was more than two weeks before Roger finally took Scamper down to the long hill to look for the fox.

When he did go, the river looked colder than ever. Even Scamper shivered with cold and then shot through the woods, running as fast as he could to keep warm. By the time Roger caught up with him he was already at the fallen-down tree, yipping and barking and snuffing the ground.

"Be quiet, Scamper!" Roger said, but it didn't do a bit of good. Scamper barked louder than ever. Roger was just going to scold again when he saw the hole! It was quite a big hole and half hidden by the fallen-down tree. Roger's heart beat faster and faster as he looked at that hole. He knew, he just knew, that that was the fox's front porch.

Scamper snuffed and pawed at the hole and Roger looked and looked, but they didn't see a thing. The fox had heard Scamper's barks and Roger's shouts and he didn't so much as put his nose out.

"Come on home," Roger said finally, and now he felt very cross with Scamper. "You made too much noise. Ranger would have had more sense."

After that Roger didn't get down to the river for a long while because every time he started out Scamper came after him. He tried shutting Scamper up, but somebody always let him out and then he was noisier than ever.

Finally one Saturday Dick started to teach Scamper tricks and then Roger knew he was safe. He hurried down to the river, and this time he went very quietly indeed.

He walked through the woods without even rustling a leaf, but he hadn't counted on the crows. He didn't even see the crows sitting in the birches and the oak trees and the thorn apples. But the crows saw Roger. All of a sudden they began to caw, caw, CAW, and flew off, flapping their great black wings. They were so noisy and so unexpected that Roger jumped! The fox must have jumped too! He must have jumped right down into his deep hole because when Roger reached it there was nothing to be seen.

The very next Saturday Roger started off right after breakfast to try to see the fox.

"Seen the fox yet?" Seth asked as he passed the barn. Roger shook his head, but he didn't say a word. He wasn't going to take a chance by boasting to Seth, but in his heart he felt that this would be his lucky day. Scamper was off on a hunting trip of his own, the weather was warmer, he himself had just finished a specially good breakfast, and he just felt like fooling that fox.

Roger walked on tiptoes until he was near the fallen-down tree. Then he hid behind an oak tree and peered cautiously out at the fox hole. He looked at the hole and then he took a deep excited breath! There was something big and reddish-brown. Was it—surely it must be—the fox?

Roger never had a chance to make sure. Just at that moment a big pointer dog jumped through the brush. Right behind him were three duck hunters with their guns under their arms. Roger started forward with his finger on his lips, but it was no use. He had forgotten the cat briers that grew along the riverbank. The next instant Roger tripped over a cat brier and fell flat in front of the hunters!

"Well, sonny," said one of the hunters when they had picked him up and made sure he wasn't hurt, "what are you doing out so early?"

"Fox!" panted Roger, and nodded toward the hole. The three hunters looked and Roger looked, but there wasn't anything there. Even the pointer just sniffed the hole and then went down toward the river looking for duck. "But —but I saw it!" Roger began. "At least I think—"

"Sure, Sonny." The biggest hunter grinned down at Roger. "When I was your size I used to see lions and tigers and giraffes in these woods."

Roger knew when he was being teased, so he started for home. As he walked up the long hill he knew it wasn't his lucky day after all. He didn't mind tripping over the cat brier. He didn't mind the hunter's teasing. What he did mind was that he couldn't honestly be sure if he had seen the fox or just imagined him. And if he told that to Seth he knew he'd be laughed at and he would mind that most of all.

Soon after that the Christmas vacation began and Roger was very busy making his presents. Then the day after Christmas Roger caught a bad cold and had to stay in bed. He spent the time drawing pictures of the fallen-down tree with his new Christmas paints and tracing the outline of a fox in one of his new books. And all the time he wished that the weather would clear up and his cold go away so that he could get back to the river and make sure about the fox.

Roger's cold was soon gone, but the weather wasn't in any hurry to get better. First it rained, then it froze, and then it rained some more. Finally a day came when it was clear and dry, and Roger was well enough to put on his new snow suit and rubber boots and go outside. He felt nice and warm as he started down for the river, but he also felt a bit stiff because the suit and the boots were so very new.

When Roger reached the river the bank was all covered with gleaming sheets of melted-then-frozen snow. It was fine and flat and glistening and just made to be jumped on. Roger took his first jump, and the thin sheet of ice cracked and splintered. He took another jump and listened to the crackle. He jumped again. It was a wonderful noise. It was a sharp, biting, where-are-my-mittens, *midwinter* noise.

Roger jumped almost all the way to the fallen-down tree. It was great fun, but it wasn't the way to see a fox. The fox must have heard all that cracking and splintering a long way off because by the time Roger reached his home no one was there.

There was nothing for Roger to do but turn around and walk up the long, steep hill toward home. He was very tired when he reached the top, and his beautiful new snow suit had rubbed chapped places under his knees.

Seth came out of the barn just as Roger passed it on his way to the house. "Seen the fox?" he asked.

"No!" Roger said, and now he was so discouraged he was sure he never would see the fox. "He's always just gone. Always!"

Seth grinned, but his voice was friendly enough. "You have to be real quiet to see a fox," he said. "Quiet and mighty quick. It wouldn't be easy for a city boy."

Roger hated being called a city boy and he walked away without saying a word. Someday he was going to see that fox all by himself. He just had to see it!

The next day it was Roger's seventh birthday, and that was so exciting he almost forgot about the fox. Mother and Dad gave him skis. Grandma gave him a box of tin soldiers. Dick gave him a duck whistle. And Seth—well, Seth gave him the very best present of all. It was a cap, a regular Dan'l Boone hunting cap, made out of the skin of a coon that Seth and Ranger had caught.

Roger put on his new snow suit, his new coonskin cap, and his new skis. It was easy to wear the cap. It was easy to wear the snow suit now that the new stiffness had worn off. But it was unexpectedly hard to wear the skis. They were longer than Roger was tall, and when he stood up on them they shot out in different directions.

Roger practiced skiing all that week and all the next week. First he learned to glide in a straight line on the flat snow-covered stretch of lawn behind the house. When there was another snowfall Roger and Dick made a huge snow man called Henriques De Pew, and after a while Roger learned to zigzag on skis around Henriques.

In another ten days Roger even learned how to ski down little hills, though he took a lot of snow baths while he was learning. It was very deep snow indeed, and Roger was glad he had his skis to play with because no one, not even Seth, could have walked down to the river through the thick white drifts.

So Roger kept on practicing, and then one day Dad said he could try the long, steep hill that led down to the river. Dad skied down the hill first, and when he reached the valley he turned and waved. Roger waved back. Daddy looked a long way off, but Roger gave himself a push with his ski poles and started after him.

He flew down that hill so fast that he lost his breath. He just swooped down, but he didn't fall once. "Good boy!" Dad said when he reached the valley. "That's skiing."

Well, of course, after that Roger didn't want to stop skiing. Even after Dad left to cut wood he kept right on skiing by himself up and down the long, steep hill. It was hard work zigzagging up to the top, but it was worth it to come zooming down again.

It was quite late, and Roger had just reached the valley after a specially good run when he heard the far-off tinkling of a big cowbell. Roger knew that Mother was ringing that cowbell because it was suppertime.

Roger zigzagged up the hill for the last time. Now that the bell had stopped ringing the world seemed quieter than ever. There were no voices, no crows, no dogs to bark. There was only the cold, lonely wail of the wind in the telephone wires and the faint squeak-squeak of his own ski harnesses.

When Roger reached the hilltop he looked back proudly at the fine, clean tracks his skis had made on all his runs downhill. The snow was pale blue and purple now in the fading light, and the tracks stood out clear and bold.

Roger turned away and skied cross-country toward the house. He was just sliding down the last little slope to the front door when Mother came out to ring the bell again. She had just lifted up the bell when Roger snow-plowed to a stop beside her. She was so surprised she jumped and dropped the bell in the snow.

"Why, Rog!" she said. "You did surprise me. I didn't hear you coming at all!"

When she said that Roger had a wonderful idea. If he had surprised Mother he could surprise the fox! At last he'd found a way to go places that was very fast and very quiet and, what was more, the deep drifts wouldn't bother him a bit. Tomorrow he'd put on his snow suit, his hunting cap, *and* his skis and just fool that fox.

It snowed while Roger and Dick made popcorn that evening. It snowed while they were asleep. It snowed and snowed great, soft, white flakes that covered up the bushes, and covered up the dog kennel, and covered up the fences so that only the tops of the tallest fence posts stuck out like little black rabbit ears.

When Roger woke up the next morning the ceiling in his room glistened with reflected light. Roger lay still for a moment under his patchwork quilts and blinked up at the brightness. Then slowly he understood. There was more new snow. Piles and drifts of it, and he could ski soundlessly over it all and surprise Mr. Fox!

When Roger reached the top of the long hill again there wasn't a single sign of a living creature and there wasn't a sound either. The ski tracks he had made yesterday were gone, and no wind whistled through the telephone wires. There was nothing but new snow and the breathless quiet of the hill listening to itself.

Roger pulled down his coonskin cap and hugged himself because he was so glad he was the first person out in that brand-new world. He felt like a real hunter now, a frontiersman, a breaker of trails.

Roger pushed off and sifted soundlessly down the long, steep hill to the river valley. He never stopped until he reached the wood lot nearest the fallen-down tree. Then he stood so still that even Henriques De Pew, the snow man, seemed like a jitterbug in comparison. There, straight ahead of Roger's nose, was the fox standing beside his hole!

The fox's head was up, his bushy tail was out like a flag. Except for the slight twitching of his whiskers, he was just as still as Roger himself!

All of a sudden the fox put back his head and barked. It didn't sound like Scamper or Ranger. It sounded like nothing on earth but a big, red fox, and it was the wildest, eeriest sound Roger had ever heard.

Only Roger's eyeballs moved as he saw the second fox come out of the hole. She was smaller and lighter-colored and more timid-looking than

the first fox. By this time Roger was so excited he was shaking! He took a step forward to balance himself, and the tip of one ski hit into a tree trunk and knocked the snow from its branches. There wasn't much noise. Just the very soft plopping sound of snow from the trees falling onto snow on the ground. It was hardly a noise at all, but it was enough!

The two foxes disappeared!

One moment they were right there in front of Roger and the next they were not. They had melted away faster than the noise of an exploded firecracker. Roger stared, and then a grin spread from one side of his coonskin cap all the way to the other side. Right before him where the foxes had stood were new, clear tracks in the snow. Roger looked at the tracks and looked again. The tracks were fox paw prints and they were right where he had seen the foxes!

After that Roger did not wait another minute. He made a kick turn and started straight up the hill to tell Seth. This time he hadn't been fooled. He had seen the fox and there were paw prints to prove it. More than that, he had seen two foxes, which was just twice as many as Seth himself had seen!

THE GOLDFISH

Julian Street

This is a wonderful Christmas story, but it is much more fun to tell to children than to read to them.

The first thing Mrs. Harman saw when she opened the nursery door was the cat crouched upon the table, tense and motionless, watching Peter, the goldfish, in his glass bowl.

"Shoo! You're a bad cat! Shoo!" she cried, stamping her foot.

The cat shot her a quick, guilty glance, and was gone like a shadow through the doorway.

"Shoo!" cried Mrs. Harman after her, and turned to her son.

"You shouldn't let the cat in here, Don. She'll get Peter."

Seven-year-old Don was seated on the floor struggling with a shoe lace.

"Now—" he began, "now—I didn't see her, Mother. I've been tying my laces. Mother, will you telephone for Craig to come over and play? You know I was disappointed yesterday and day before, and— Will you, Mother?"

"Have you spotted today?" asked Mrs. Harman.

"A little jelly spot at lunch. It was very little, and—now—I didn't spot at breakfast."

"Very well," said Mrs. Harman, "I'll see if Craig can come."

But Craig could not come and for the third successive day Don was disappointed.

"You see it's near Christmas, dear," the mother explained, "and all the boys are busy."

"I'm not busy," Don told her wistfully.

"I'll tell you what you can do." Mrs. Harman spoke brightly. "You can write a letter to Santa Claus. Won't that be fun? It's only three weeks to Christmas, and he'll be wondering what you want."

"I don't know what I want." His tone was listless.

"Snow shoes?" she suggested.

"Oh, I don't know."

"A sled?"

Don brightened. The sled gave him an idea.

"I know what. I want a brother. Not a little one. A regular brother. Big, you know, with lots and lots of teeth."

"They're hard to get in those large sizes," Mrs. Harman said, "and it's so near Christmas they must be pretty well picked over. The best plan is to write to Santa about it. Here's paper with lines, and a nice sharp pencil."

Don sat down at his little desk and in a round laborious hand began to write. The letter, when completed, ran uphill and down and read as follows:

> Dear Santy
> i am well i hope you are well i would like a boy with teeth the biggest one you can spair for a brother
> yours truly
> D Harman

The paper, originally white, was changed to gray in the process of writing, and smudges had somehow been communicated to Don's face and hands.

"Now," said his mother, "we'll send it."

"Do you think he'll get it tonight?"

"He ought to."

They moved to the fireplace; Mrs. Harman touched a match to the letter and they watched it burn to a black, wavering crisp, and disappear.

That night Mrs. Harman told her husband she was worried about Don.

"He needs boys to play with," she said.

"There seem to be plenty of boys in the neighborhood," Mr. Harman replied.

"Yes, but they're not his age. Craig is Don's age but he lives almost a mile away, and Don doesn't see much of him except at school. I was thinking—" She sighed and broke off.

"What were you thinking, dear?"

"I was thinking of little Fred, your sister Helen's boy. He's just three months older than Don, you know."

"Isn't he getting on all right at Aunt Henrietta's?"

"I suppose so. But your Aunt Henrietta is growing old, and—well, it's not as if he had a father and a mother."

"Look here, Sallie," her husband said, "you've

got something in your mind. What is it? Do you feel that we ought to—" He did not finish the question, for his wife was nodding at him, smiling.

Meanwhile, up in the nursery, Don was eating his supper and his nurse was watching every mouthful.

"Will you never learn to be a little gentleman?" she demanded. "Look at your napkin. One mass of jelly. I'll have to show it to your mother. A big boy like you, and Christmas so near, too!"

"I don't care," said Don, defiantly.

"One mass of jelly," she repeated. "I'll certainly have to show it to your mother." So saying, she took the offending napkin from the boy's neck and left the room.

"I don't care!" he said again, and moved slowly over to the table where, with chin on hands, he sat and gazed at Peter, the goldfish, in his bowl.

He was not thinking of the bowl; he was not staring into it as the cat had stared, but through it at something far beyond—just what, I do not know. Nor do I know how long he sat there gazing beyond the glass and the water and the weeds and the little castle and even Peter himself. It may have been a long time or a short time, but whether it was long or short his attention was at last attracted by a tiny squeaky sound. He listened and the sound grew plainer. Somehow it suggested words—words which at first seemed to come from so far away you couldn't understand them. Then suddenly he realized that the sound was coming from inside the goldfish bowl.

Don looked at Peter. He was not swimming now, but was lying motionless, nose pressed against the glass, staring out into the nursery. His mouth was moving. It opened and shut, opened and shut, and the squeaky little sound continued.

Don leaned forward and turned one ear to the bowl. The sound grew plainer.

"Is that you, Peter?"

"Yes! Yes! Yes! Yes!" the little squeak responded instantly.

"Don't talk so fast," said Don. "What do you want?"

"Help me out!"

"All right," said the boy, but when he dipped his hand into the water, Peter darted to his castle.

"Not like that! You'll drown me!"

"You can't drown a fish."

"Have you ever been a fish?" asked Peter sharply.

"Of course not."

"Then what do you know about it?"

"I'm a boy, and a boy knows more than a fish."

"He thinks he does!" As Peter spoke, four round bubbles issued from his mouth and followed one another to the surface, where they broke with a chuckling sound: "Ha-ha-ha-ha!"

Don did not like to be laughed at by grownups, let alone fish.

"If that's how you're going to talk," he said, "I won't help you."

"Wait a minute! I want to tell you something. Will you promise not to tell?"

"Yes, what?"

"Put your ear close."

Don hesitated. "No tricks, now! If you jump up and nip my ear, or yell in it, or anything like that, I'll grab you out and have you cooked."

Peter looked shocked. "I wouldn't think of playing tricks on you," he said. "May I float belly-up if I would."

"Well, go ahead, then."

"I'm ashamed to tell it." The little fish looked very red. "It happened through my messy way of eating. They all warned me—my mother, my aunt, my nurse—but I—"

"Your nurse? Fish don't have nurses."

"That was before I *was* a fish. It was when I was a boy."

"Were you a boy?" Don was hardly able to believe his ears.

"Yes."

"What happened to you?"

"Spilling did it—spilling food on my napkin and the tablecloth."

"A fish hasn't napkins and tablecloths."

"Of course not; that's just it," said Peter. "That's how I happened to become a fish. They told me I didn't deserve a napkin on a lap. They told me I ought to be kept in water. But I never dreamed I'd come to this." A little groan came from the bowl.

"Don't you like to be a fish?" asked Don. "You don't have to go to school."

"Swimming was fun at first," said Peter, "but I'm awfully tired of it. The bowl's so round—one side just like another. And when my nose tickles I miss my hands terribly. Really there's nothing as nice as being a boy with hands and a clean white napkin and a lap."

"I wish I could get you out," said Don, "but you'd flip around on the table and die, wouldn't you?"

"Yes, there's only one way to turn me back into a boy."

"How?"

"Another boy must do it for me. He has to keep his napkin clean for a week."

"A whole *week?*" Don gasped.

"Only a week. After that I'll be his brother. I can make box kites, and we could dig caves, and keep rabbits, and get some garter snakes, and some—"

"I'll try!" exclaimed Don. "I'll try like everything!"

"Oh, thanks!" said Peter. "I can't tell you what it's going to mean to me!" He looked through the other side of the bowl at the calendar on the wall. "This is the seventeenth. You begin tomorrow morning. You only have to keep your napkin clean until the twenty-fourth, and then—why, my scales! That will be Christmas Eve! How jolly!"

"If I should spot just once," Don asked, "would that spoil everything?"

Peter quivered.

"Don't speak of such a thing!" he begged. "And remember, you are not to breathe a word of what I've told you. If you tell, the whole thing will be—"

"There you are!" cried the nurse, appearing in the doorway. "You're supposed to be in bed. Now, I'll have to tell your mother."

Don turned and blinked at her. Then he arose, shuffled over to his bed, slipped out of his bathrobe and tumbled in.

The week dragged along. The Christmas preparations, the mysterious packages, the crackling of wrapping paper Don heard through the closed door of his mother's room—none of these things occupied his mind as they had the year before. His thoughts were fixed on the tremendous task of freeing Peter. Somehow, somehow he must manage to keep his napkin spotless for a week. He must!

At first he thought the safest plan would be to go without meals altogether; but when he tried it Nurse scolded, and besides he got hungry. His one idea when he sat down to eat was to keep from splattering and spilling. When there was meat with gravy he cut it into little pieces with the utmost care, never allowing his knife or fork to slip. He spread his apple sauce and jelly very thin upon his bread and butter, and saw to it that none was hanging to the edges. He pushed his glass of water or milk far back from the table's edge, and when he drank he took the smallest swallows. As for cereals, eggs and soft, custardy desserts, he ate such little spoonfuls that Nurse could not believe her eyes, and wondered "what ailed the child."

To his surprise he found the task less difficult as meals and days went by. There were little tricks, he learned, to keep from making spots, and the more you practiced them the better you got. But as the work grew easier, responsibility increased. It would be awful to dribble something on his napkin after having kept it clean three days . . . four days . . . five days.

When Nurse was absent from the room he would go to Peter's bowl and whisper reassuring words; but Peter never spoke again, although he looked at Don with sad, appealing eyes, especially during meals.

At breakfast on the seventh day Peter was plainly nervous. At luncheon he was more excited still. And when night came his fins and tail were all a-quiver as he gazed through the glass wall.

This made it hard for Don. He tried not to watch Peter. At lunch he made a slip with some potato but caught it in his hand before it reached his napkin. As this occurred, a great big bubble rose like a sigh from Peter's mouth.

Having safely disposed of the last spoonful of custard, Don gave a joyful cry. He removed his napkin, and raised it like a fair white banner.

"Look!" he cried. "A whole week, and not a single spot!"

"Now, I do declare!" exclaimed the nurse, who thought he was showing it to her. "How good little boys do get when Christmas is coming. It shows what you can do. Look at it, all clean and white! I'll have to show it to your mother." She took the napkin and left the room.

Don placed his elbows on the table, rested his chin in his hands, and gazed intently at the goldfish bowl.

"Peter!" he whispered softly.

But Peter only swam about, as much a goldfish as he ever was.

Don was disappointed. He had hoped the thing would happen after supper, while Nurse was there. He had imagined Peter rising from the water, changing shape, and dropping off his scales—until he stood a full-fledged boy. How Nurse's eyes would bulge! But though this didn't happen, Don never lost his faith; he only sat there wondering how and when the change would come.

"There you are!" cried the nurse, appearing in the doorway. "You're supposed to be in bed. Now, I'll have to go and tell your mother."

Don skipped over to the bed and leaped in. "You such a big boy," Nurse went on, "and this Christmas Eve, and your stocking hanging in the living room! I'll really have to tell your mother." She was muttering and puttering around the nursery as he fell asleep.

"Shoo! Shoo! You bad cat!" It was Mrs. Harman's voice.

Don turned over in his bed and squinted at the early morning light.

"Merry Christmas, dear!"

"Merry Christmas, Mother!" He sat up suddenly and stared with wide eyes at the goldfish bowl.

"Why, Peter's gone!" he cried, jumping out of bed.

"Never mind that now," said his mother. "You must hurry down and see all the lovely things Santa left in the living room. Get into your bathrobe and slippers. Hurry, son!"

As she spoke Don heard a motor in the driveway. Then the slam of the front door and his father's voice in the hall below.

"Dad! Dad!" he shouted, rushing down the stairs.

On the bottom step he stopped abruptly. There, holding tightly to his father's hand, stood another boy, a boy just Don's size. He grinned, and as he did so Don saw that he had lots and lots of teeth.

The two stared at each other for a moment. Then Don moved slowly forward.

"We can make box kites," he said, "and dig caves, and keep rabbits and—"

"And garter snakes," put in the other boy.

EDDIE GOES TO DANCING SCHOOL

Carolyn Haywood

Once the children discover Eddie, they will want to read all three Eddie *books and the* Betsy *books too. No one writes about pleasant family life and the mild adventures of children 4 to 7 more happily than Carolyn Haywood.*

One day when Eddie came home from school his mother said, "Eddie, Mrs. Wallace was here this afternoon."

"You mean Toothless's mother?" Eddie asked.

"Eddie, that's a dreadful way to speak of Anna Patricia," said Mrs. Wilson.

"Well, it's true!" said Eddie. "She hasn't had any front teeth for such a long time that I guess she's never going to get any. And anyway, Anna Patricia is a silly name. Why don't they call her Anna or Patricia? Or just Pat? If I had a name like that I'd make everybody call me Pat."

"I guess Anna Patricia likes to be called by her full name," said Eddie's mother.

"Well, in school we all call her Toothless," said Eddie.

"Mrs. Wallace is forming a dancing class," said his mother. "She came to invite you to join."

Eddie looked at his mother with a face filled with horror. "A dancing class!" he cried. "What would I want to do that for?"

"Now, Eddie," said Mrs. Wilson, "it will be very nice for you to learn to dance. Dancing school is fun."

"Fun for the girls maybe, but not for boys. Are Rudy and the twins going?"

"It's just for the children in your room in school," said his mother.

"That's tough," said Eddie. Then his face brightened. "I know, Mama! You tell her Papa can't afford to send me to dancing school."

"But it's free, Eddie," said his mother. "Only the girls have to pay."

"That's a mean trick," said Eddie. "And I bet I'll have to dance with Toothless. And she lisps!"

"Of course you'll dance with Anna Patricia," said Mrs. Wilson. "The dancing class is going to be held at her home."

Eddie sat down and held his head. "Ugh!" he said. "When?"

"Friday afternoon, at half past four," replied Mrs. Wilson.

"Friday afternoon!" wailed Eddie. "That's when we practice for the Saturday ball game."

"Eddie," said his mother, "you wouldn't want it to be on Saturday, would you?"

"Of course not," Eddie moaned. "But why does it have to be at all? Why do I have to learn to dance? Rudy and the twins don't have to learn to dance. Why do you pick on me?"

"Eddie, you will have a very nice time," said his mother. "Don't raise such a fuss. Go and see."

"If I don't like it can I stop?" Eddie asked.

"Yes, if you don't like it you can stop," his mother replied.

"O.K.!" said Eddie. "But don't tell Rudy and the twins that I have to go to dancing school."

"O.K.!" said Mrs. Wilson.

On Friday, when Eddie came home from school, his mother said, "Eddie, put on your best suit for dancing class."

"You mean my best Sunday suit?" said Eddie.

"Yes, dear," replied Mrs. Wilson.

"Golly! This dancing school business gets worse all the time," said Eddie.

Eddie washed his face and hands and soaked his hair with water. Then he took off his blue jeans and put on his best suit. "What will I do if I meet Rudy and the twins, all dressed up in my Sunday suit on Friday?" Eddie shrieked from his bedroom.

When he came downstairs his mother handed him a package. "These are your pumps, dear," she said.

"My what, Mama?" said Eddie, screwing up his nose.

"Your pumps," replied Mother, "your dancing pumps."

"What do I do with 'em?" Eddie asked.

"You wear them on your feet," said Mrs. Wilson.

"You mean I can't dance in my shoes?" Eddie cried.

"You would step on the little girls' feet, Eddie, in those clumsy shoes," said his mother.

"Serves 'em right!" said Eddie. "I'll walk all over Toothless's feet. Just let me at 'em."

"Eddie, do stop dawdling and get off," said his mother. "Have you money for bus fare? And don't forget to ask for a transfer."

Eddie pulled some change out of his pocket and looked at it. "O.K.," he said.

Just then he heard the twins coming in the front door. Eddie leaped like a deer and was out of the back door in a flash. He did not stop running until he reached his bus stop.

When the bus arrived Eddie stepped in. He knew the bus driver. He often rode with him. His name was Mike.

"Hi!" said Mike. "You look like a movie actor. All you need is a carnation in your buttonhole. Where you going, all dressed up?"

"Don't ask me," Eddie moaned. He flopped into the seat nearest the door.

"Come on, tell me. You'll feel better if you tell me," said Mike.

"You promise you won't tell anybody?" said Eddie.

"On my honor," said Mike.

Eddie got up and whispered in Mike's ear. "I'm going to dancing school. Isn't that horrible?"

"Oh! Cheer up!" said Mike. "I went to dancing school once. And look at me now."

"You did?" said Eddie, with a brighter face. He leaned over and whispered, "And did you have pumps?"

"Sure! Sure!" said Mike. "I was the best pumper in the crowd. You'll learn to pump. It's easy."

"No, Mike," said Eddie. "They're some kind of shoes. They're in this package."

"Oh, I thought that was your supper," said Mike. "Oh, sure! Pumps. Sure, you gotta have pumps."

"I have to change buses at Brewster Road," said Eddie.

"Righto!" said Mike. "Three more stops before we get there."

When the bus reached Brewster Road, Mike drew up to the curb. As Eddie stepped out he said, "So long, Mike."

"So long, pal!" said Mike. "I'll wait for you to cross the street."

Eddie crossed the street in front of the bus. When he reached the opposite corner, he heard Mike calling, "Hey, Eddie!"

Eddie looked back and saw a package flying toward him. It landed at his feet. "Your pumps," Mike called out, as he started the bus.

Eddie picked up the parcel and put it under his arm. He stood on the corner and waited for the other bus. Across the street there was a used car lot. It belonged to Mr. Ward, a friend of Eddie's father. Eddie looked over the cars while he waited. Suddenly, he caught sight of something bright red. Eddie's heart began to beat faster. He ran across the street and over to the lot. Sure enough! It was just what he thought. There was the fire engine he had ridden on at the Fair. A man was lying under it, working with a hammer.

Eddie stooped down and looked under. There was Mr. Ward. "Hello, Mr. Ward!" said Eddie. "I rode on this fire engine once. It was super!"

"You did, Eddie?" said Mr. Ward, pushing himself out from between the wheels. "Well, how would you like to ride on it again?"

"Now?" said Eddie, his eyes shining.

"I want to see how it runs," said Mr. Ward. "I just put in a new part."

"Swell!" said Eddie, climbing right up into the front seat. "This is great!" he added, as the fire engine started.

Then Mr. Ward looked down on the ground. "Does that bundle belong to you?" he asked.

"Oh, golly! Yes," said Eddie. "Stop."

The fire engine stopped and Eddie got down. He ran back and picked up his package. Then he climbed up again. He put the package on the seat beside him and they started off. "I sure like this fire engine," he said.

"You going anywhere special?" Mr. Ward asked.

"Oh, not very special," Eddie replied.

"Got plenty of time?" said Mr. Ward.

"Oh sure!" said Eddie.

"Very well! She's going good. We'll take a spin around," said Mr. Ward.

Eddie held onto the seat and swung his legs. This was wonderful! "Can I pull the bell?" he asked.

"No, we can't ring the bell," said Mr. Ward. "The fire company would object. Might look like a false alarm."

Mr. Ward drove Eddie way out into the country before he said, "I guess I had better get back. Where can I drop you?"

Eddie thought of dancing school for the first time since he had been on the bus. "Oh! I have to go to Beech Tree Road," he said.

"Beech Tree Road?" said Mr. Ward. "What's going on there? By the way, you look all slicked up."

"Yeah," said Eddie. "I forgot all about it. I'm going to dancing school."

"You don't say!" said Mr. Ward. "What have you got in the package?"

Eddie looked sheepish. "Aw, pumps," he said.

"Pumps!" said Mr. Ward. "What the heck are pumps?"

"I don't know," said Eddie. "Something you wear on your feet."

"Well, suppose I take you right over to the place," said Mr. Ward.

"Oh, that would be great!" said Eddie.

Mrs. Wallace was standing at the front door when Eddie drove up in the fire engine. As he jumped down she said, "Why, Eddie! You're very late. I've been wondering why you didn't get here."

"I guess I am a little late," said Eddie. "Mr. Ward gave me a lift."

Eddie could hear the boys and girls laughing. They were all in the dining room.

"It's too bad you missed the dancing class," said Mrs. Wallace. "The children are having their ice cream now."

Eddie's face shone. "Ice cream?" he said. "Gee, that's great!"

"Hello, Eddie!" the children called out when Eddie walked into the dining room.

"Hello!" said Eddie, sitting down at the table.

Mrs. Wallace handed him a large plate of ice cream and Eddie lost no time in eating it. Just as he swallowed the last spoonful, the doorbell rang. Mrs. Wallace went to the front door and opened it. Eddie heard Mr. Ward's voice say, "Is Eddie Wilson still here?"

"Yes, he is," said Mrs. Wallace.

"Well, here are his pumps," said Mr. Ward.

The children had caught a glimpse of the fire engine through the open door. They rushed to the door to look at it. "Oh, here's the fire engine that was at the Fair!" they cried.

"I had a ride on it this afternoon," said Eddie.

"Oh, can we have a ride?" the children shouted. "Can we have a ride?"

"You have on your best clothes," said Mrs. Wallace. "You can't go riding on a fire engine in your best clothes, in your dancing clothes."

"We won't hurt them," the children cried.

"I didn't hurt mine, did I?" said Eddie.

"I'll take them all home," said Mr. Ward.

The children rushed to the fire engine, the little girls in their ruffled dresses and the boys in their Sunday suits.

"Now, everybody sit still," said Mr. Ward. "You have to keep your clothes clean."

Just as everyone was settled Eddie jumped down. "Wait a minute," he said.

He ran into the house and came back with his package. He looked up at Mr. Ward and grinned. "Forgot my pumps," he said.

Mr. Ward dropped the children off, one by one. Eddie was the last. When he drove up to the house, the twins were looking out of the window. When they saw Eddie, they rushed to the front door.

"What's the idea," cried Joe, "riding on the fire engine?"

"Where have you been?" cried Frank.

"I've been to dancing school," said Eddie.

"Dancing school!" cried the twins in chorus.

"Gee, it's swell!" said Eddie, as he waved good-by to Mr. Ward.

When dinner was almost over, the doorbell rang. Mr. Wilson went to the door and opened it and everyone around the dining-room table heard Mr. Ward's voice say, "Here are Eddie's pumps. He left them on the fire engine."

When Mr. Wilson came back to the dining room, he was carrying a package. He put it on the window sill. "Here are your pumps, Eddie," he said.

"Pumps!" cried Rudy and the twins together. "What are pumps?"

"I don't know," said Eddie. "I haven't had time to look at 'em. But dancing school was swell, Mama. Dancing school was swell!"

from BENJIE'S HAT

Mabel Leigh Hunt

[*Hat Trouble*]

Every First Day, which was Sunday, Hamish hitched the horse to the carriage. Grandmother put on her best bonnet and one of her good dresses and her softest, finest kerchief. Benjie cleaned his shoes and scrubbed his cheeks and put on his tow suit and the straw hat bound round with gray flannel. He and Grandmother climbed into the carriage. Grandmother took up the reins, clucked to the horse, and off they went to Meeting.

When they arrived at the meeting-house,

Grandmother patted Benjie's shoulder, and said, "Now thee be a good boy, Grandson," which was rather unnecessary, as Benjie behaved himself very well indeed. He may have squirmed a little when his feet went to sleep, or when the day was warm and his tow breeches scratched, but that was all.

Then he and Grandmother parted, for Grandmother must sit on the women's side of the meeting-house with the women and girls, and Benjie must sit with the men on the men's side. He felt very grown-up sitting there without his father and Milo and Matthew, as at home, and for several First Days this was enough to keep Benjie completely satisfied throughout the long silent meeting. For when Benjie was a little boy, the Friends had no music at their religious services, and only rarely did they have preaching. Children must "wait in stillness upon the Lord," as their elders did, and receive comfort and strength through silent meditation and prayer.

On a certain October morning Benjie and Grandmother went to meeting. There never was a more perfect day. The long needles of the pines glittered in the golden sunlight. The red and golden leaves fluttered lazily down from the trees that were all red and golden. Through the open windows of the meeting-house Benjie could hear the horses moving lazily and stamping at their hitching-rack. From afar came the whistle of quail. For the first time Benjie felt fidgety. The coarse stuff of his clothing made him itch, and although no one paid him any attention, he knew that he must not scratch. The world outside seemed to be saying, "Come out, Benjie. Come out and play in the golden morning." Benjie kept hearing this soft and golden voice, and as there seemed to be no probability of the meeting ever coming to an end, and as the prickles on his legs seemed to be getting worse, he arose at last from his place, very softly. He squeezed past several large knees, whose owners looked at him gravely from under their broad hats. But Benjie knew that they scarcely saw him, for their thoughts were far removed from worldly things. He tiptoed down the aisle of the men's side and out into the meeting-house grounds.

The stillness outside was almost as deep as it had been in the meeting-house, a charmed and golden stillness, and Benjie, now that he had come, scarcely knew what to do with himself. It was very queer, but he didn't itch a bit any more. He looked about, and felt lonely. The world seemed an empty golden shell, with no one in it but the horses and a stranger named Benjamin Bartholomew Barnett. Oh, dear, whatever had made him come? How shocked and sorry Grandmother would be if she knew that he had run away from Meeting! A little lump came into Benjie's throat when he thought of Grandmother, whom he loved so much, and who loved him. Forlornly he wandered to the fence and began to stroke the noses of the horses, since there was no joy for him in the lovely day, after all. He gathered handfuls of grass for them. They nosed him eagerly.

And then a most surprising thing happened.

For all of a sudden Benjie heard a loud crunching noise. His head was jerked violently sidewise. A damp breath blew through his hair, and he looked up to see an old white horse at his shoulder. And he had Benjie's hat in his mouth. He was chewing with all his might and main. He was chewing up Benjie's hat!

"Ow!" cried Benjie. "Gimme my hat!" He reached up as far as he could and began tugging at the object that was no longer a hat, but a crushed and mangled fragment. A long strip of gray flannel hung from the horse's mouth. Bits of straw fell to the ground. The hat was gone, all but one little piece in Benjie's hand—the hat that had been a fine store hat, the hat that had once been Milo's pride, that had been worn less proudly by Matthew, and was, until a moment ago, Benjie's only hat.

Oh, the mean old horse! The meanest old horse in the world! What could Benjie do? He couldn't slip back into Meeting and sit with uncovered head. That was unthinkable, for the Friends wore their hats throughout the Meeting. What would Grandmother say when she found that Benjie had not only "played hooky" from Meeting, but had lost his hat as well. "Wilful waste, woeful want," that's what Grandmother would say. Oh, she would think him a very bad boy! Well, he was, although he hadn't really meant to be. Losing his hat was a punishment for stealing away from Meeting. At last Benjie climbed up into Grandmother's carriage, with the one remnant of his hat in his hand, and made himself as small as possible.

Presently the people began coming slowly out of the meeting-house, looking refreshed and calm and cheerful. They shook hands with each other in the autumn sunshine. There was a pleasant hum of talk.

Benjie screwed himself into a tighter knot on the carriage seat, but kept a weather eye open for Grandmother. Yes, there she was! Beloved Grandmother, folded so neatly into her shawl; her face placid and rosy in its neat frame of bonnet. There! She was looking for him! Oh, dear! Benjie turned his head away sadly. He couldn't bear to see Grandmother looking for the *good* boy that should have come out of the meeting-house with all the good people when Meeting broke.

And then he heard the soft rustle of Grandmother's skirts. He felt her near him.

"Why, Benjie-boy!" she cried. "Is thee ill? Did thee have to leave the Meeting?"

"No, Grandmother," answered Benjie. He turned and looked at her, full of misery. "I didn't have to leave. Just see what happened, Grandmother." He held out the piece of straw. "An old horse chewed up my hat!"

"Thy hat! Benjie! Does thee mean to say that a horse reached into the meeting-house and took the very hat off thy head? Never did I hear the like!" And as Grandmother climbed into the carriage she looked about indignantly as if to say, "Where is that rude creature that ate the hat off the grandson of Judith Cox?"

"Oh, no, Grandmother!" Benjie could not help smiling a little at the impossible picture that Grandmother had imagined. Nothing short of a giraffe could have reached into the meeting-house.

"No, Grandmother," he went on. "I did leave Meeting. It's a nice day, and my pants scratched me, and my feet were going to sleep, and before I thought what I was doing, I was walking out of Meeting."

"Benjamin Bartholomew Barnett!" exclaimed Grandmother. "Thee left Meeting just because thee was fidgety?"

"But I didn't have a bit good time, Grandmother!" cried Benjie hastily. "I wished and wished I hadn't come. And then the old horse grabbed my hat. If he'd just waited a minute I'd have given him some nice grass. I was taking turns feeding them all grass. But he couldn't wait—the old greedy!"

"A just punishment for thee, Benjie," declared Grandmother. "Now thee has no hat. And thee sinned besides." Grandmother shook her head sorrowfully.

"Maybe next year the hat would've been too small for me, Grandmother," suggested Benjie.

"That does not alter the situation, Grandson. Some other boy could have worn it."

The remainder of the ride home was very quiet. Dinner was very quiet. The afternoon bade fair to be very quiet and very long. So that the sound of the music from Hamish's banjo twanging across the October fields was welcome to Benjie, even though it was so surprising. He looked at Grandmother quickly. Her mouth was set in a straight line.

"Someone else sinneth," she said. "Go down, Benjamin, and ask Hamish what he means by playing the banjo on my farm on First Day. And come back the moment thy errand is done."

Benjie went along the edge of the corn-field, going to meet the gay little banjo notes that seemed to be running, in spite of First Day, to meet him. And there was Hamish, seated in his doorway, his head bent over his beloved banjo, his fingers strumming happily. And there was Eliphalet, doing a buck-an'-wing in the red-colored dust in front of the cabin.

"Hamish!" cried Benjie sternly. "Grandmother says thee is not to play the banjo on her farm on First Day."

Hamish's mouth fell open. Eliphalet stopped, frozen in his tracks.

"Ah plum fo'got mahse'f," said Hamish, sheepishly. "Reckon hit am de weathah. Reckon hit am a day foh pickin' de banjo. Reckon dis niggah done los' my min' disrememberin' dat Ol' Miss cain' have no music on Fus' Day."

"Grandmother says thee sinneth," announced Benjie. It was rather pleasant to be able to tell Hamish that he, too, was a sinner.

Hamish's face fell. Tenderly he put down his banjo. He looked so sad that Benjie cried, "But I sinned, too, Hamish." And he told his friend all about the morning's sad incident.

At first Hamish looked very sympathetic. But presently his mouth began to spread. The laughter that seemed to have its home in Hamish's toes was coming up, shaking his body, up, up, until it burst from mouth and nose in snorts and chuckles.

"Yoh mean—yoh mean dat ol' white hoss et up dat hat uv yo-alls? Dat ol' white hoss jus' natchally lean hisse'f ovah an' grab dat hat an' chew an' chew twell hit all chewed up?" Hamish flung up his hands in delight. He rocked back and forth, hugging his mirth.

"An' chew an' chew an' chew," echoed Eliphalet. "De hat, de hoss. De hat, de hoss!"

And soon Hamish and Eliphalet and Benjie, too, for he could not help it, were rocking with laughter. And Dilcey came and stood in the doorway. "Dat ol' white hoss don' need no dinnah dis day," she chuckled. "No, 'deedy. He done had a pow'ful good dinnah eatin' off Benjie's hat."

Benjie wished that he could stay in this jolly place. But Grandmother's word was law, and he trudged dutifully back home. He was relieved to see that Grandmother seemed much more cheerful. She and Benjie carried chairs out to the yard and sat together in the mild autumn sunshine. Presently Jerushy came waddling along, and Grandmother picked her up, and allowed the old hen to rest upon her aproned lap, for Jerushy and Grandmother were great friends, after all these thirteen years together.

And while Benjie leaned against Grandmother's chair, and stroked Jerushy's soft old feathers, Grandmother told him stories. She told him of his great-grandfather, whose home had been on Nantucket Island, but who had spent most of his life at sea, for he had been a whaling master. "A very good man," said Grandmother. "He held silent meeting on his ship every First and Fourth Days, just as if he were in the meeting-house at home." She told Benjie of his great-uncle, who had once lain in prison for many weeks, because he refused to bear arms against his fellow-man. She spoke of Benjie's great-great-grandfather, who had lived in England before sailing to America as a young man, and who had been able to tell his children of the days when George Fox, the great founder of the Society of Friends, used to come to his father's house in that English village where he lived as a boy.

And Grandmother said, "The good people before thee were God-fearing people. *They* had no worldly thoughts at Meeting. None of them would ever have strayed away from Meeting at the slightest excuse, as thee did, Benjamin."

And she looked at Benjie, and Benjie looked at her. It was a long moment, and when it was over, it seemed that Benjie and his Grandmother loved each other even more than ever. And Grandmother reached into her deep pocket, and brought forth a handful of peanuts, and she and Benjie broke them and ate them, which made old Jerushy sit up and jerk her head about, as if to say, "What! Something to eat?" Jerushy made Benjie and Grandmother both smile.

After supper, and six o'clock, when First Day was over, and Benjie was getting ready for bed, he saw Grandmother's eyes begin to twinkle.

Her rosy face grew rosier. She held her apron up to her mouth, and she began to shake all over. Grandmother was laughing! It made Benjie laugh to see Grandmother laughing so hard. And when she had calmed down and wiped her eyes, and tucked Benjie into bed, she looked down at him, and she said, "Don't thee be thinking that I considered it funny of thee to run away from Meeting, Benjamin Bartholomew Barnett. It's just the idea of that old horse chewing up thy hat. All of a sudden it struck my funny bone."

And Benjie said, "Grandmother, next First Day I shall go to Meeting, and I shan't *move,* no matter how much my britches scratch me." He suddenly sat up in bed. "But what shall I do? I can't go to Meeting without a hat!"

"That's true, Grandson," answered Grandmother. "And of course it is almost too late in the season to wear thy tow breeches and thy straw hat, anyway. Why didn't thee bring thy winter hat with thee?"

"It was too little for me," said Benjie. "Mother gave it to Cousin Daniel. Mother said that thee would buy me a winter hat over in Friendship."

"Tut, tut!" exclaimed Grandmother. "Does thy mother think that money grows on my peanut vines, or that I dig it up with my yams? But a hat thee must have. That's plain. We'll see what can be done about it. We'll see."

And as Benjie fell asleep, full of Grandmother's loving forgiveness, he thought to himself, "How nice it will be to have a hat all my own, a hat that is bought just for me!"

But the pine woods through which Benjie ran to school still murmured softly of Indian summer, and he did not really need a hat, except for Meeting. So for two days he almost forgot about the hat which had disappeared down the throat of the old white horse. And while he played *Ant'ny-Over* and *Prison Base* with the boys at recess, the thought of a nice new hat lay half-forgotten, too, but warmly treasured in his mind.

On the evening of Third Day, Grandmother said, "To-morrow thee must march with the other children to regular Fourth Day Meeting. Therefore thee must wear thy new hat to school. Thee didn't know I had a surprise for thee, now did thee?"

She opened the door of the fireside cupboard and drew out a hat.

"There, Benjie!" she exclaimed. "While thee was at school, I was busy plying my needle. There was no need to spend good silver, nor good trade, either, for a store hat, when thy grandfather's nap beaver lay unused in its box. See? I cut a mite off the crown, though it was a pity to waste even that bit. I took some pleats in crown and brim, to make it more thy size. Then I sewed them back together again. And there is thy hat!" She held it up proudly.

Benjie stared and stared. "It's a very peculiarsome hat," he murmured, and burst into tears. "The b-b-boys will laugh."

"Tut, tut, Benjie," scolded Grandmother. "Is thee a girl, to be so vain of thy looks? 'Tis a good hat, and 'twill serve the purpose. Thee should feel honored to wear the hat thy grandfather wore for fifteen years."

Benjie set off for school the next morning, wearing the tall hat. In spite of Grandmother's careful pleatings, it was still much too large for him, and only his ears held it up. In the woods he reached up and felt it carefully. How smooth

and furry it was! No doubt Grandfather had once paid a good round sum for it. Perhaps, after all, the boys would not laugh.

But when Benjie entered the school yard, up went shouts of derision, and soon the whole world, as it seemed to Benjie, was echoing with the chorus:

"Look at Benjie's ha-yat!
Look at Benjie's ha-yat!"

Oh, how red and unhappy Benjie was!

But he laughed as hard as anyone when his tormentors flung the hat into the air, and it caught on the high limb of a tree. He hoped that it would hang there forever. When the hour came to march to the meeting-house, it was very fortunate for Benjie that one of his schoolmates was absent that day, but had left his hat hanging on a nail in the school entry. So Benjie wore it, and was completely satisfied.

He went home that evening to tell Grandmother cheerfully that his new hat was entirely out of reach on the limb of a very tall tree. But the next day, while school was keeping, Grandmother and Hamish came with a long pole and rescued the hat. What a craning of necks as the children watched them through the windows! And presently, to the delight of every boy in the room, Grandmother opened the door, and said, "Benjamin Barnett, thee will find thy hat hanging in the entry." For a few hours after that it seemed to Benjie that he didn't even *like* his grandmother!

Soon Benjie began to feel that nothing on earth could harm that hat. For instance, it blew off one day in a windy gust of rain. He carried it home hopefully, for it was smeared with the gummy red clay of North Carolina. But Grandmother let it dry, scraped off the dirt and washed and brushed it carefully. It looked just as good as ever.

"Is this my hat, Grandmother, or is it Grandfather's hat?" asked Benjie.

"It is thy hat now," answered Grandmother.

So, after thinking it over carefully, Benjie argued to himself that he had a perfect right to give the hat to Eliphalet, for it seemed that the little colored boy was the only one in all the world, except Grandmother, of course, who did not laugh at Benjie's hat.

"Dis heah am a sho-nuff gif'," declared Eliphalet, grinning from ear to ear, and holding the hat reverently in his hands. "Dat ol' Mistuh Beavah, he des' as smove an' slick as evuh he am."

Eliphalet put on the hat, but it would fall down over his eyes, and even over his nose. Benjie could see nothing of his friend's face but a pair of grinning lips, a row of white teeth, and a little black chin. Eliphalet had to perch the hat on the back of his head, to be able to see at all. When Benjie went home, feeling generous, but a little doubtful, he looked back and saw Eliphalet strutting all around the cabin as proudly as a king.

But when Dilcey saw the hat decorating her son's woolly head, she shouted, "Yo-all march straight up to de big house wid dat hat, an' don' be delayin' yo'se'f. Benjie's gran'mammy—she gwine be in a big huff when she fin' dat boy gib ol' dead Massa's hat away. N' ol' Massa's gwine steal back an' ha'nt folkses dat weah his hat when dey ain' got no right."

In a very few moments the hat was lying on Grandmother's doorstep, and Eliphalet running home again with all his might and main, for fear of the *ha'nt*. So the hat was Benjie's once more, and there was nothing to do but wear it.

Whenever he went to Meeting, he could think of nothing but his hat. His ears burned scarlet with shame. He would turn suspiciously, to catch a frosty twinkle in a pair of elderly eyes, or a smothered giggle from some boy.

Therefore one morning, as he and Grandmother rode to Meeting, Benjie said, "I guess *thee* wouldn't wear this hat!"

"Indeed I would, and proud to," answered Grandmother tartly. And to Benjie's horror, she removed her bonnet and put on the hat, sitting as straight as a ramrod, glancing neither to the right nor the left. She looked ridiculous. Oh, dear! Grandmother was certainly very difficult to look after. He couldn't allow *her* to make a laughingstock out of herself. Personal pride was one thing, but family pride was another. He sighed. "Never mind, Grandmother. *I'd* better wear it," he said.

Just then a dog came running out from nowhere, barking furiously. The horse jumped, and thundered down the road, almost shaking Grandmother and Benjie to pieces. Afterward it was discovered that Benjie's hat was missing. He went back to search for it, praying that it had been trampled beyond repair, or that the dog had carried it off. But no! There it was, lying in a fence corner, with only one small dent in the brim.

"A little steaming and pressing will attend to that," said Grandmother.

"Grandfather certainly bought a good hat, didn't he?" remarked Benjie.

"Yes," answered Grandmother. "He had the hat made at Beard's Hatter Shop. A good nap beaver will last a lifetime."

Benjie's heart sank. A lifetime seemed a very long time.

So when next Peter Kersey had an errand to Randolph County, Benjie gave him a letter, secretly, with the request that it be delivered to his mother. It said:

"Dear Mother—

I am middling well, and hope thee is the same. Grandmother is well. Jerushy is still alive and shows no sines of dyeing. But I wish thee would send me a Cap, and oblige

Thy obeedyunt son,
Benjie Barnett."

But when Peter returned, and Benjie unwrapped the eagerly-awaited parcel, there was nothing but a yarn muffler. To tie his head up like a baby! Oh, it was terribly disappointing!

One evening Benjie sat on a stump in the woods. There was a dark scowl on his face. His lower lip stuck away out. At school that afternoon when Susan Bond was supposed to be doing a sum on the blackboard she had drawn a picture. First she had made a very tall hat. Beneath that, two enormous ears. Then she had drawn a teeny-tiny body, and underneath she had printed BENJIE. She had rubbed it out quickly before the teacher had suspected, but most of the scholars had seen it.

So Benjie, very angry, sat alone on the stump. He was angry at everybody in the world.

Presently Peter Kersey came riding through the wood. He jumped off his horse and sat down by the boy. But Benjie did not speak. He only scowled the darker. Peter picked the hat up and turned it thoughtfully in his hands. "Thy grandfather was a fine man, Benjie," he began quietly, "one of the finest North Carolina has ever produced. He and I were boys together. He was my great friend. Did thee ever hear about the time thy grandfather—" And Peter began telling stories about Grandfather Cox—things that Benjie had never heard before. Soon the scowl faded. The sulky lower lip slipped back. Benjie was smiling, and his eyes were shining. He began to think that perhaps he might wear cheerfully a hat that such a fine grandfather had worn.

"And I'll tell thee, Benjie," said Peter, when he had finished, "Thy grandmother is a fine woman, too. There's no one quite like her. But between me and thee, women never understand just how a man feels about his hat. A man's hat is his own. Let it be suitable, and he can face the world with his head up."

Even if Peter Kersey was an Elder, and sat at the head of the Meeting, he understood a fellow!

But the next morning Benjie remembered Susan's drawing, and he said to himself, "I'll not wear this hat to school if I catch the quinsy and die!" So he took to hiding the hat in the woods, and nobody knew.

One afternoon in the early winter Peter Kersey, with his gun over his shoulder, went into the woods after rabbits. He had bagged three and was just turning homeward, when he saw another plump cotton-tail bounding ahead. He took aim, and missed. The rabbit disappeared into one end of a hollow log just as Peter fired his second shot. He walked forward and peered into the log. And there, in the end of it, was Benjie's hat, with the top of the crown almost torn off by the force of the shot, and the dead rabbit trapped inside!

"Now what have I done?" asked Peter of himself. "I'll have to wait for Benjie to come along this way from school."

When Benjie saw the hat—oh, what joy! "Now I'll never have to wear it again!" he cried.

"Don't thee be too sure of that," warned Peter. "Thy grandmother is a very resourceful woman. But now we must go and tell her what has happened."

Very slowly Peter and Benjie walked through the woods toward Grandmother's house. Benjie was wondering just how he would explain the fact that his hat was in the end of the log. And

Peter was wondering just how he could help Benjie. Presently he said, "A thought has suddenly occurred to me. Put on the hat, boy. And can't thee look a trifle pale?"

Indeed Benjie's cheeks were not so rosy as usual, for what would Grandmother say? What would she do?

Arrived at the house, Peter confronted Grandmother bravely. He kept Benjie well behind him. His face was long and serious.

"I have something to tell thee, Judith," he said. "I hope thee will not take it too hard. This afternoon I was hunting in the woods. And I—I shot thy—thy grandson's hat." He reached around quickly and plucked the hat off Benjie's head.

Grandmother stared at the bullet holes. She saw the stains in the crown. She went white as a sheet. "O Benjie-boy!" she cried. "Is thee hurt?"

Benjie could not bear to see his grandmother looking so white and distressed. But neither could he keep his face straight a moment longer. Laughing, he flung his arms around Grandmother's waist. And then Peter began laughing. And as soon as Grandmother heard about the rabbit, her relief was so great that she laughed as heartily as anyone.

"I do declare," she said, "this hat has had so many misfortunes that I'm beginning to believe the Lord never intended that Benjie should wear it."

"Then thee'll throw it away?" cried Benjie.

"Throw this good hat away?" echoed Grandmother. "Just hearken to him, Peter. I'm sure I don't know where he gets such notions. 'Wilful waste, woeful want,' Grandson. Thee knows that other old saying, too—'Keep a thing seven years, and thee will find a use for it.' So of course I won't throw the hat away. It will come in handy for something one of these days. But thee can't wear it any more. As a matter of fact, Peter," she said, gravely, turning to Peter Kersey, "I don't believe Benjie ever liked this hat, fine as it was. I thought it was very suitable for him. But there's no accounting for a boy's taste. So to-morrow, Benjie, we shall drive over to Friendship and buy thee just an ordinary cap."

An ordinary cap! Why, that was just what Benjie wanted! A fellow didn't have to be careful of an ordinary cap. It was all that Benjie could do to keep from turning a handspring or shouting or clapping his hands. But because of Grandmother's feelings about Grandfather's fine hat, it would never do to shout his joy.

But he ran to the stone jar, and he selected the very biggest and brownest cooky for his friend, Peter Kersey. And the next biggest for himself. As Peter accepted the cooky, he and Benjie looked at each other, as man to man, and smiled.

from AUGUSTUS AND THE RIVER

LeGrand

Our hero is a little "grape of wrath" without knowing it. He and his happy-go-lucky family adventure joyously through innumerable books. This episode is the beginning of one of their long and satisfying jaunts.

[*Going South*]

Augustus stood on the low bank of the Mississippi River and shuffled his bare feet in the thick coarse grass. Absent-mindedly picking up a stick with his toes, he looked out over the river.

Below him bobbed the houseboat where he lived with his sister Glorianna, his brother Jupiter, Pop, Ma, Tom Cat and the chickens.

Down the shore a way, he saw Glorianna and Jupiter hunting for doodlebugs. Augustus thought maybe he would get them to play pirate. Then he decided he wouldn't. Jupiter was just five—only half as old as Augustus, and that wasn't old enough to be a good pirate. Glorianna was eight, and old enough, but she was only a girl.

Feeling restless, Augustus picked up another stick with his toes. He kicked it deftly into the air, caught it and tried to balance it on the end of his nose.

On a log near by, a big old bullfrog blinked sleepily, and swelling his throat, rumbled, "Kerchunk."

That was a mistake.

Augustus saw him, and threw the stick. It was a good shot, and he felt a mild glow of pride as the frog squawked and jumped into the water.

The stick drifted out away from shore, and Augustus watched as the current whirled if off down-river.

"Wonder if it will drift clean down to the ocean?" he mused.

There was a quacking overhead and a flock of ducks flew by, headed down-river too.

"Going south for the winter," thought Augustus. "Wish I was going—"

Suddenly he understood the restlessness that had been bothering him. He wanted to go south too.

The ducks were going, the stick was going; why, even the river was going, moving on always past new strange places, way down there beyond where the earth and the sky met.

"We've been living in this ol' bend more than a year now," muttered Augustus.

There was a scrambling on the bank and Glorianna and Jupiter came sliding down beside him.

"What you doing?" asked Glorianna.

"Just wishing I had a boat of my own, so I could go south."

"Bet you'd be scared all alone on the river."

"Huh, would not. I guess I'd show that ol' river something."

Glorianna looked doubtful.

"What you want to go down-river for?" she asked.

"Huh," thought Augustus, "just like a girl—not to understand about things like that."

"Well," he said aloud, "we've been living on this ol' river all our lives, and never been farther south than this bend right here in Iowa."

Glorianna looked puzzled.

"Well, this is pretty far south from Minnesota where we used to live," she said.

Augustus snorted.

"Aw, you don't understand," he grumbled. "I mean really south."

He had a far-off expression as he went on. "Folks say there's some mighty wonderful things to see down there—alligators big as a house—"

Glorianna shuddered.

"—Sugar cane they grind up and boil, and it comes out sugar—"

"Good ol' sugar," said Jupiter, patting his stomach.

Augustus paid no attention to him and went on: "Ol' man Hawkins says there's pirates down there too. An' way down at the end is the blue ocean. I'd mighty like to see the ocean. . . ."

Augustus was thinking so hard about the ocean he didn't notice anything, but Glorianna heard the creaking of oarlocks and looked around.

She jumped up, saying, "Here comes Pop." Turning to Augustus, she added, "Maybe we'll all be going off down-river if the fishing stays bad here. Pop's been talking some about going."

Augustus' face brightened as he said, "Yeh, I heard him tell Ma he was studyin' about it . . . said at least a body could keep warm in the winter if he went far enough south."

The creaking of the oarlocks grew louder and Pop came into sight around the bend, rowing his skiff up to the bank.

"Catch anything, Pop?" yelled Augustus as they all ran down to meet him.

"Nothin' much," grumbled Pop. "Only a few ghoul."

"A ghoul's a right good eatin' fish, Pop," said Jupiter.

Pop looked at him and grinned.

"Trouble is," he said, "only river folks like ghoul. Can't trade 'em down at the store for side meat and beans and coffee and sugar and suchlike."

Augustus helped Pop pull the skiff up on the bank. There was a lot of water in the bottom and it poured out over the stern as the boat tilted.

"Ol' boat leaks worse every day," said Pop. "I aim to fix it sometime. Trouble is, when I'm out on the river I can't fix it, and when I'm on shore I don't need to fix it."

Pop grinned and winked at Augustus, who grinned and winked back. Augustus had yellow hair like Pop's, and they looked a lot alike when they grinned. Ma always said the river had got into their blood, because their hair was so like the color of the muddy yellow water. Glorianna and Jupiter took after Ma and had black hair.

"Are we going south, Pop?" asked Augustus anxiously.

"Maybe," said Pop, going up the narrow gangplank to the houseboat. "I aim to make up my mind right soon."

It was bright and cheerful-looking in the little cabin as they clattered in the door and down the two steps to the floor. The walls were lined with newspapers to keep the wind out. One was a colored funny paper. It looked very pretty, and so did the big calendar Glorianna had fished out of the river one day. The calendar part was gone but the picture part had lots of red roses and white doves and bluebirds and a lady with wings. The lady was spoiled some by the big black mustache Jupiter had marked on her. Next to the calendar hung a map of the United States. It showed the Mississippi River, and Pop had made a mark that showed where the houseboat was.

"Any luck?" asked Ma as Pop came in the door.

"No luck," said Pop. "Nothing but some ghoul. Seems as if all the good fish I can trade have moved on away from here."

Pop looked thoughtful as Ma bustled around getting dinner.

Augustus broke up some driftwood and stuffed it into the potbellied stove. It popped and crackled loudly as Ma fried the fish. Soon there was corn hoecake getting nice and brown in the pan, and the smell of the fish almost brought tears of joy to Jupiter's eyes.

"You Augustus," said Ma, "fetch some water."

Augustus got a bucket of water from the river for washing and another for drinking water. He put the drinking water aside to give the mud a chance to settle to the bottom.

"Now all of you get yourselves cleaned up. The vittles are most done," said Ma.

Augustus filled the tin washbasin and went out on deck. The houseboat rocked in the swells from a passing steamboat. The water in the basin jiggled back and forth, slopping over the edge until most of it was gone. Augustus looked at what was left, thought a while about getting some more, decided he probably wasn't very dirty anyway and managed to get his face and hands damp. Then he rubbed vigorously with the flour-sack towel. A lot of fertile soil went from Augustus to the towel in that process. Then, happily satisfied that he had done all that could reasonably be asked of him, he gave the basin to Glorianna.

By the time everyone had washed, Ma had the food on the table.

She looked hard at Jupiter as they sat down.

"I declare," said Ma, "you haven't done more than wipe the mud off your nose."

"That's the only place there was mud, Ma," said Jupiter in a puzzled tone.

Ma led him out on deck. Mournful sounds drifted into the cabin, followed by splashings and a tinny clattering from the washbasin. When Jupiter burst through the door, his face was pink and shiny.

Pop didn't laugh and carry on as he usually did at dinner; he just sat there dipping his hoecake in the rich side-meat gravy and looking thoughtful. When Pop took a bite, he parted his mustache with one hand as if he were moving a curtain aside. Then he popped the food in and let the curtain fall.

Augustus knew Pop was trying to decide whether to go south or not. He remembered how ol' man Hawkins said if you want someone to do something, you cross all your fingers and look cross-eyed. Then you think about what you want him to do. Ol' man Hawkins said that always worked.

Augustus crossed his fingers and looked cross-eyed at Pop. Scowling fiercely, he muttered under his breath, "Please make Pop go on downriver, because I'm tired of just staying here."

Pop looked up to get another piece of hoecake and saw Augustus scowling at him cross-eyed. Pop's eyes widened slowly and he jerked up in his chair.

"Skin me for a catfish," he said, "what ails you, boy?"

Augustus uncrossed his eyes as quickly as he could, but not before Ma had seen him.

"He needs a tonic," said Ma.

Augustus shivered.

Ma's tonics were a painful subject to the whole family. Whenever anyone stubbed his toe, or looked a little pale, or not pale enough, or ran too hard, or didn't run at all, Ma made a tonic. One thing all Ma's tonics had in common was a bad smell and an even worse taste. Another thing was that she always made everyone take some. She even took a little herself—just to show it didn't taste bad. Ma reasoned that if it was good for one it must be good for all.

So when Ma said "tonic," everyone looked unhappy. Pop pushed his chair back with a clatter and jumped up.

"I've made up my mind," he said. "We'll move on down-river—"

Pop was going to say some more but he didn't get a chance. Augustus jumped up, his eyes shining. He opened his mouth until it formed a perfect circle. Then a wild yell came out.

"Yay, yay!" he shouted. "When do we start?"

Pop blinked and looked startled.

"Well," he said mildly, "I figure we might as well go right soon—maybe in the morning. The fishin's plumb worn out here."

Augustus began to run around the cabin.

"Goin' south!" he shouted. "Yay! Goin' south!"

He butted Glorianna in the stomach. She screeched, and Ma reached for Augustus. He ducked and tackled Jupiter around the knees. They rolled and tumbled on the floor until Ma caught them each by an ear and hauled them to their feet.

"A body'd think you were touched in the head," said Ma, but her eyes twinkled.

Ma liked to travel too, and she was beginning to feel the excitement that is part of going places.

"Goin' south," shouted Augustus and tried to butt Ma.

She boxed his ears and tried to look stern, but her mouth twitched.

"What a young 'un!" said Ma, and began to laugh with Augustus.

Pop had stopped by the door, surprised by all the carrying-on. Pop liked a good time, and when Ma started to laugh, he ran over, grabbed her and started to jig. The floor squeaked under Pop's weight, and the houseboat rolled and lurched.

"I declare," gasped Ma, "I believe you're all jelly-brained."

"Yep," chuckled Pop, "likely we are, but don't we have fun!"

He went to the door and, looking down-river toward the south, shouted, "Look out down there below! We're a-coming!"

Everyone went to bed real early that night because Pop said they had to get up early to get a good start. Augustus was too excited to sleep. Once he heard the whistling sound of wings and the faint honking of wild geese flying past, high over the houseboat.

"We're goin' south too, ol' geese," he muttered happily.

Through the window he could see the moonlight sparkling on the water like a path leading off down-river. Way off down there a steamboat whistled soft and low in the distance. The sound seemed to come up the path of light. And then the two got all mixed up in Augustus' mind. His eyes closed.

"Get up out of there," shouted Pop.

Augustus opened his eyes and groaned. It was still dark and his bed was mighty comfortable.

"Getting folks out of bed in the middle of the night," he grumbled; he blinked as he looked at the lighted lamp, dazzled by the yellow flame.

"Hurry up," said Pop. "I want to start before sunup."

"Start?" thought Augustus. "Start where?"

Then, with a warm glow rushing all through him as he remembered, Augustus jumped up.

Jupiter was bouncing up and down on his bed shouting, "Wheee! Going south!" as loud as he could.

Everybody scrambled around and got in everybody else's way.

Pop stood in the middle of the floor and shouted, "Hurry up, hurry up," at everyone. That was the way Pop was; when he really wanted to do something, he wanted to do it right now.

Augustus rushed through breakfast so fast he scalded his mouth with hot coffee. It burned all the way down. He grabbed a dipper of water and drank it down fast. Finding he had finished his breakfast before anyone else, he went out on the bank to wait for Pop to get through.

It was nice and fresh out on the bank. Everything was pale gray and misty. There was a bright patch in the sky just over the trees on the other side of the river.

A soft breeze came up and made little gurgling ripples that rolled across the river and splashed at Augustus' feet. He stuck his toes out, letting the fresh coolness of the water roll over them. The little waves chuckled against his ankles and clunked against the hull of the houseboat with a thin, musical splashing.

It sounded like a song, Augustus thought, and tried to think of words to go with the music. He had got as far as "Ol' Glorianna looks like a banana" when Pop came out.

Pop stood for a moment, sniffing the damp, cool air. Then seeing Augustus, he said, "All right, let's go."

"Okay, Pop," said Augustus and ran to untie the rope that held the houseboat to the shore. Jupiter and Glorianna picked up the gangplank and pushed and shoved and grunted as they hoisted it up on the roof.

Pop pushed against the bank with the pike pole.

"Here we go," yelled Augustus as he waded out into the river and pushed and pried.

There was a grating noise, the houseboat swung free of the sand and Augustus jumped on deck as the boat drifted off.

"Whee!" yelled Jupiter.

The shore slid past as the current took the little houseboat out toward the middle of the river. Pop got in the skiff, which he had tied to the boat, and rowed to steer the houseboat away from the banks and snags.

Augustus and Glorianna and Jupiter crawled onto the roof. The sun was up now and there was a warm smell from the tar-paper roofing. The chickens in their coop on the roof were cackling sort of drowsily. It was mighty comfortable just being lazy and watching things go past. Augustus sat with his legs dangling over the edge and rolled happily from side to side with the motion of the waves.

The buoys marking the deep-water steamboat channel made splotches of color against the shining water. The red buoys on the left side of the channel and the black ones on the right swayed and bowed at one another with stiff politeness.

Sometimes the narrow channel led almost straight across the wide shallow river, turning back at the bank to make a long slanting crossing to the other side.

On the banks, marking the ends of the crossings, were white wooden towers called "daymarks." Augustus thought that was a silly name for them; they were just as useful at night, he thought, when the lights at the top of the towers were the only marks to guide boats through the darkness. Pop didn't pay much attention to the buoys and daymarks, because the houseboat needed only a few inches of water and could go anywhere.

A steamboat puffed slowly by, pushing a long line of barges ahead of it. The big paddle wheel whirled around, splashing spray high into the air and making swells that rolled across the river, rocking the houseboat.

Zigzagging up the river, the steamboat came close enough for Augustus to see the pilot. High up in the pilothouse, easing the great wheel a spoke at a time, he balanced the long line of barges against the rush of the current.

Augustus jumped up and waved both arms in salute.

The pilot saw him and grinned. Reaching up, he pulled the whistle cord in a series of short, sharp blasts.

Augustus nearly burst with pride. He had been saluted by a steamboat! He started to walk over to Glorianna to make sure she knew what had happened when the houseboat gave a sudden lurch.

Teetering on the edge of the roof, trying to get his balance, Augustus looked over the side and gasped. He was looking straight down into a swirling hole in the water. The houseboat was heeling over into the edge of a whirlpool, swaying from side to side and bucking up and down all at the same time.

"Hold on," shouted Pop from the skiff.

The rope between the skiff and the houseboat quivered and stretched as Pop struggled to pull away from the drag of the whirlpool. Augustus threw himself flat on the roof and held on with both hands.

Ma was out on the back deck holding on to the doorway and shouting, "Look out! Look out!"

The houseboat heeled over farther. The chickens cackled frantically and, flapping their wings, hit the side of their coop as the roof tilted and jerked.

Suddenly Pop stopped trying to row away. He turned the skiff, set its nose against the side of the houseboat and rowed hard, pushing straight into the middle of the whirlpool.

Leaning over the edge, Augustus stared down at the skiff. What was Pop doing? Had he gone crazy?

Digging his oars deep, Pop grunted as he threw all his weight against the blades.

"You're rowing the wrong way!" shouted Augustus.

The houseboat began to spin around crazily. There was a loud "galumph" and a choking sucking noise as the broad flat bottom suddenly slid sideways and covered the hole in the center of the eddying water. Immediately everything was quiet. The water calmed; the whirling stopped; the houseboat straightened and bobbed peacefully off down-river.

"Whew," gasped Pop, wiping the sweat from his forehead; "that was close."

Then he looked up and grinned at Augustus.

"Now you've learned something," he said. "Don't forget it the way I did. Steer right into the middle of an eddy like that, and if your boat is big enough you're all right. Stay off on the side and likely it'll turn you over."

Augustus felt a little shaky. Glorianna was holding on to him. He turned and started to say, "Guess we showed the ol' river," when suddenly he stopped and blinked. Where was Jupiter? He had been on the roof. He wasn't there now. Augustus scrambled down to the deck. Jupiter wasn't there. He wasn't in the cabin either.

"Pop, Pop," shouted Augustus. "Jupiter—he's gone."

Pop's jaw dropped. He sprang from the skiff to the deck as Augustus climbed up to the roof again. Ma clambered up from the other side. Glorianna started to cry.

"He's gone. He's gone," she wailed.

"I am not gone," said a small muffled voice.

Augustus whirled around as the door of the chicken coop opened and a small tousled head popped out. Then the rest of Jupiter followed his head out of the chicken coop. Brushing the feathers off his face, he grinned at everyone and said, "I just got in the chicken coop so's I wouldn't fall off."

Ma came up intending to put her arms around him, but she was so excited she boxed his ears instead. Everyone laughed without knowing exactly why.

"It's a good thing I nailed that chicken coop to the roof," said Pop.

The little houseboat drifted on through the golden autumn day. Augustus sprawled on the roof and wiggled his toes as he soaked up the warm sunlight.

Along about dusk Pop rowed the houseboat to shore in back of a bar. It was a mudbar but the mud wasn't too soft and it looked like a good place to tie up for the night. There were no trees near enough to tie to, so, while Augustus and Ma held the ropes, Pop went up the bank with the ax and cut some stakes. Using the back of the axhead as a hammer, he drove the stakes deep into the mud and tied the ropes to them.

Ma had supper ready before dark really settled down. Augustus laughed and carried on at supper. He poured water on Jupiter's chair and slipped fishbones down Glorianna's back.

"You're so frisky you can just go up on the bank and get some wood for the stove after supper," said Ma.

"Aw," said Augustus.

But he brightened when Pop said, "I'll go along and help you."

"Don't get to walking and forget the wood," said Ma as they went out.

There was a sandy place up above the mud on the bank. The soft sand scuffed out ahead of their feet in little puffs that fell with a dry rattling sound.

"Ouch," said Augustus suddenly as he stubbed his toe on something that clinked.

He poked under the sand and uncovered a big rusty iron ring attached to a cement block.

"Steamboat ring," said Pop, scratching his chin. "Must have been a landing here long ago —maybe even a town."

Augustus looked around at the tangled underbrush and scrub trees that covered the bank.

"I don't see any signs of a town," he said.

"Oh, it was long ago—if there was one," said Pop. "There are a lot of ghost towns along the river. Some of them were busy places too, in the old days. Not a trace of them left now; nothing, except maybe an old rusty steamboat ring like this one."

Augustus chipped at the ring with a stone and broke off a chunk of rust.

"What happened to the towns, Pop?" he asked.

Pop pointed across the river to the lights of a railroad train that wound snakelike around a curve.

"That's what happened," he said. "The railroads came and the steamboats lost out. There wasn't any use for the ol' steamboat towns then."

Augustus watched the train as it crawled out of sight.

"I like steamboats better, anyway," he muttered.

"Most river folks do," said Pop, grinning. "And they're coming back too. They say there's more freight moving on the river right now than ever before."

"What's in those ol' freight barges, Pop?" asked Augustus.

"Well, mostly coffee and sugar and oil, coming up from the south. Going down-river they carry iron and coal, flour and machinery and such."

Pop stopped and shook his head sadly.

"But there are just freight boats pushing barges on the river now," he said. "The ol' packet boats are gone for good. Oh, they were pretty, all glittery white and handsome, fancy carving all over them. Why, some even had pictures of scenery and such painted on the paddle-wheel boxes."

Pop kicked at the old steamboat ring and it clanked sadly.

"Those old boats were back even before my time on the river," said Pop. "I never saw them, only pictures of them."

The stars glittered in the black sky as Pop and Augustus walked slowly back to the houseboat. Far out on the river a steamboat puffed along with a slow even sound like a giant panting. The lights in the windows sparkled brightly and were reflected in bright paths on the water.

The red light that marked the left side of the steamboat was a gleaming spot of bright color that wove through the white reflections. Suddenly the red light blinked out as the steamboat turned, and the green light that marked the right side sparkled where the red had been.

"I think steamboats are still mighty pretty, even if they are just freight boats now," said Augustus.

"Most any kind of boat is pretty," said Pop.

They walked up the gangplank and into the houseboat. Ma looked up.

"Where's the wood?" she asked.

Pop and Augustus looked at each other sheepishly.

"We just plumb forgot it," said Pop. "I'll get some in the morning."

Ma snorted. "Just like a man," she said.

That night Augustus dreamed of a great white steamboat that sailed over the land, throwing rusty iron rings at frightened trains which scuttled off promising never to come back.

"Jumpin' catfish!" Pop was shouting when Augustus woke up.

Pop was standing on deck blinking in the gray morning light. The mist was just rising from the river and the fresh damp smell of early morning, wet wood and mud came through the open door as Augustus scrambled out of bed.

He slipped into his overalls and went out. Pop was looking over the side of the houseboat as Augustus came on deck.

"Look," said Pop, pointing.

Augustus looked.

There wasn't any water under the houseboat —nothing but mud. The river had fallen during the night and left the houseboat high and dry on a mudbank.

"That's a river for you," said Pop. "Up and runs away just when you need it most."

Ma and Jupiter and Glorianna came out on deck. They all stood and looked at the mud.

"Well," said Pop, "only one thing to do . . ."

He rolled up the legs of his overalls and got out in the mud. It was soft and sticky and Pop sank almost to his knees as he leaned against the houseboat and pushed. Augustus jumped down in the mud to help. They pushed and pushed, but the houseboat didn't move.

"No use," said Pop and climbed back on deck.

Augustus started to follow him. He tried to lift his right foot. It wouldn't come. He pulled at his left foot. It wouldn't come, and his right foot sank deeper. The mud oozed up past his knees.

"Hey, help," shouted Augustus. "I'm sinking."

Pop turned and saw him.

"Hold on," shouted Pop.

He threw the gangplank down on the mud beside Augustus and crawled out on it. Pop grabbed Augustus and pulled. The mud made squishy noises. Augustus felt himself lift a little. A little more. With a loud "galumph" his feet came out of the mud and he scrambled up on deck.

"I bet you were scared!" said Jupiter.

"Naw," said Augustus.

Then he saw Pop looking at him. Pop was sort of grinning.

"Well," said Augustus, "anyway—not much."

Pop looked at the river. "She's still a-falling," he said. "Won't be any water anywhere near us by nighttime."

Ma sat down gloomily.

"Likely we'll be stuck here until spring high water," she grumbled.

Glorianna's eyes widened.

"You mean we'll be stuck here all winter?"

"Huh," grunted Augustus, "just you wait. Pop and I will get us off this ol' mudbank."

"How?"

"Oh, that's easy."

"Well, how then?"

Augustus looked all around. He looked down at his muddy feet and wiggled his toes. The mud had dried some and little chunks cracked off and fell in the water. Augustus let on as though he couldn't be bothered explaining things to just a girl and such a small boy as Jupiter.

He looked off up-river as if he expected to see the answer up there somewhere. There was a smudge of smoke over the treetops. Augustus watched it. The smoke swirled closer and a big white steamboat puffed around the bend. It was going down-river and going fast.

"If we had enough money," said Augustus, "I betcha that ol' steamboat would pull us off here pretty quick."

"Hmm," said Pop, "river folks don't have that much money."

The steamboat came roaring past close to shore. The big paddle wheel in the stern slapped around, sending out swells that rolled out across the river and splashed high on the muddy bank.

As the steamboat came closer, one of the swells rolled under the houseboat. Another—and the houseboat lifted and rocked.

Pop jumped up and pushed hard against the bank with the pike pole. The houseboat moved a little. It was afloat! Slowly it slid off the mud, away from shore and out into deep water.

"There," said Augustus. "I guess Pop and I showed you."

from ALL-OF-A-KIND FAMILY

Sydney Taylor

The book from which this episode is taken is a heart-warming story of an affectionate Jewish family that will be enjoyed by all children.

The Library Lady

"That slowpoke Sarah!" Henny cried. "She's making us late!"

Mama's girls were going to the library, and Henny was impatient.

"If it was Charlotte, I could understand," said Ella, who was the eldest and very serious. "I'd know Charlotte was off dreaming in some corner. But what can be keeping Sarah?"

"All the best books will be gone," complained Henny. "Maybe she forgot it's Friday."

"No!" interrupted Charlotte. "Not Sarah!"

No, not Sarah, nor any of the girls could forget that Friday was library day.

Almost no East Side child owned a book when Mama's children were little girls. That was an unheard-of luxury. It was heavenly enough to be able to borrow books from the public library and that was where the children always went on Friday afternoons. Right after school, they rushed off happily to get fresh reading material for the week end. Even Gertie who was not yet old enough to "belong" took the weekly trip to look at the picture magazines.

Where *was* Sarah? Mama was beginning to be concerned too. It wasn't like the child to be late.

At last footsteps could be heard on the creaky back steps. Henny ran to open the kitchen door and poked her head out. "Here she comes," she called.

"Well, it's about time," said Ella. "Come on, let's get our books."

Henny opened the door wider. "What's the matter?" her sisters heard her asking.

A woebegone little figure, face streaked with tears, walked slowly into the kitchen.

"Mama," piped up Gertie, "Sarah's crying."

"Sarah, what's the matter? What's happened?"

Sarah didn't answer. Walking over to the hard brown leather couch, she threw herself face downward, weeping bitterly. Her sisters gathered in a little group around her.

Mama came over and sat down beside Sarah. Gently she stroked her hair and let the child weep. After a while she said softly, "Sarah, tell us what happened."

Between sobs, the muffled words came slowly, "My—library book—is—lost."

Lost! The children looked at each other in dismay. Such a thing had never happened in the family before. "Ooh—how awful!" Ella said, and then was sorry that the words had escaped her for they seemed to bring on a fresh burst of tears.

"Now, now, stop crying, Sarah," Mama said. "You'll only make yourself sick. Come, we'll wash your face and then you'll tell us all about it."

Obediently Sarah followed Mama to the kitchen sink.

"Does it mean we can't go to the library ever again?" Charlotte whispered to Ella.

Ella shook her head. "I don't think so."

"Maybe we could change over to another branch," suggested Henny.

The cold water felt good on Sarah's flushed face. She was quiet now and could talk.

"It wasn't really me that lost the book. It was my friend, Tillie. You know how Tillie never takes a book out herself, but she's always wanting to read mine. When I told her about *Peter and Polly In Winter,* she begged me to lend it to her. She promised she'd give it back to me on Friday.

"When I asked her for it today, she said that she put it in my desk yesterday, but Mama, she didn't! She really didn't!"

"Are you sure?" asked Mama. "Maybe you left it in school."

"I looked a thousand times. That's why I came so late. I kept hunting and hunting all over the schoolroom."

"Maybe you brought it home with you yesterday and left it here in the house."

"Then it should be on the shelf under the whatnot," Ella said.

Hopefully, everybody rushed over to the whatnot where the library books were kept, but alas, there was no *Peter and Polly* book there today.

"I cleaned the house pretty thoroughly this morning," said Mama. "I don't remember seeing the book anywhere. But let's all look again anyway."

How anxiously everyone searched. The children peered into every corner of the two bedrooms and they poked under beds and dressers. No one believed it was in the front room, but still they searched it diligently. They searched and searched until they had to agree that it was useless to continue.

When they were back in the kitchen again, Sarah said tearfully, "How can I go and tell the library that the book is lost?" She was ready to cry again.

"I'm afraid they won't let you take out any more books until we pay for this one," Mama worried. "And a book costs a lot of money."

"But Tillie lost the book," argued Sarah. "She should pay."

"We can't be sure of that," Mama said. "Tillie

claims she returned it. Maybe someone else took it."

"No library could make me pay for any old book." Henny was just trying to cover up how bad she felt too.

"I'm afraid the library will expect you to pay for it. And it's only right," continued Mama. "You borrowed the book and that makes you responsible. The library lets you borrow the book and you're not supposed to lend it to anybody else. I know you wanted to be kind to Tillie, but if Tillie wants to read a library book, then she should take out her own. I wish I could help you pay for this, but you know, Sarah, there's no money for such things."

"But Mama, will you come with me and talk to the library lady?"

Mama shook her head. "No, Sarah, that's something you must do yourself. If you explain just how it happened, I'm sure the library lady will understand that you didn't mean to be careless. Find out what you have to do, and we'll talk about it when you get back. Now you'll all have to hurry. There's not much time left before supper. So, the rest of you, see if you can choose your books quickly today."

Mama had said to hurry but Sarah's feet wouldn't walk. They felt like lead. In her chest was a lump of lead too. Ella put her arm around Sarah's shoulder. Even Gertie forsook her idol Charlotte and came over to Sarah. She slipped her little hand into Sarah's, her brown eyes large in sympathy.

A branch of the New York Public Library was only a few blocks from their home; soon the familiar brown building came into view. Through the high door and up the staircase they went. With each step, Sarah grew more despairing. They'll take my card away, she thought. I just know they will. I'll never be able to take out any more books.

Once inside the room, Sarah hung back, fearing to join the line at the "in" desk. She looked back down the staircase longingly. It would be so easy to run down the stairs and out into the street and just never come back.

"Come on, Sarah," Ella said. "Let's get it over with." Gently she pulled Sarah towards the desk and the five children fell in line.

Henny nudged Sarah. "Look," she said, "isn't that a new library lady? She's pretty!" she added.

Sarah studied the new library lady anxiously. She looked so fresh and clean in a crisp white shirtwaist with long sleeves ending in paper cuffs pinned tightly at the wrists. Her hair is light, just like mine, Sarah said to herself. And she has such little ears. I think she has a kind face. She watched as the librarian's slender fingers pulled the cards in and out of the index file. How does she keep her nails so clean, Sarah wondered, thinking of her own scrubby ones.

It was Ella's turn to have her book stamped. The library lady looked up and Sarah could see the deep blue of her eyes. The library lady smiled.

She has dimples, Sarah thought. Surely a lady with dimples could never be harsh.

The smile on the library lady's face deepened. In front of her desk stood five little girls dressed exactly alike.

"My goodness! Are you all one family?"

"Yes, all one family," Henny spoke up. "I'm Henrietta, Henny for short; I'm ten. Ella's twelve, Sarah is eight, Charlotte is six, and Gertie is four."

"A steps-and-stairs family!" The library lady laughed and the tiny freckles on her pert nose seemed to laugh with her.

"That's a good name for us," Ella said. "Some people call us an all-of-a-kind family."

"All of a very nice kind," smiled the library lady. "And you have such nice names! I'm Miss Allen, your new librarian. I'm very glad to meet you."

Her eyes travelled over the five little girls. Such sad-looking faces. Not a smile among them.

"Better tell the teacher what happened," Charlotte whispered to Sarah.

"She's not a teacher, silly. She's a library lady." Henny's scornful reply was loud enough for Miss Allen to hear. The dimples began to show again.

Sarah stepped forward. "Library lady," she began, twisting and untwisting the fingers of her hands.

Miss Allen looked at Sarah and suddenly noticed the red-rimmed eyes and the nose all swollen from weeping. Something was wrong. No wonder the faces were so unhappy.

"Let me see, now. Which one are you?" she asked.

"Sarah," the little girl replied and the tears began to swim in her eyes.

The library lady put her hand under the little girl's chin and lifted it up. "Now, now, Sarah. Nothing can be that bad."

Sarah said tearfully, "Yes, it can. I—I—" She couldn't go on.

"Here." Ella put a handkerchief to her sister's nose.

Miss Allen went on speaking as if she did not notice anything unusual. "Did you enjoy your book?"

Sarah's voice broke. "I loved it. But nobody else will ever be able to read it again . . ."

"She means she lost it!" Henny blurted out.

"She didn't lose it. It was Tillie." Charlotte rushed to Sarah's defense.

"Oh, I'm so sorry," said the library lady, looking bewilderedly from one to the other. "Who is Tillie?"

Thereupon Ella unfolded the whole story and the library lady listened sympathetically.

"Mama says I must pay for the book and I'm going to—every cent." Sarah was trembling. "But I don't have enough money now."

"How much will she have to pay?" Ella asked.

"I'll have to look it up in the catalogue," Miss Allen answered. She pulled out a big book and began to look through its pages. It really was a shame that this had happened. She knew that the people who lived on the East Side had to count their pennies carefully. Even a small sum would seem like a fortune to these children.

Her heart went out to the little group. How sincere they were and how anxious to do the right thing. She wished that she could pay for the book herself. But she could not risk hurting either the children or their parents by making the offer.

She made her voice as cheerful as she could. "Well, it's not nearly as bad as I thought. Let's see now. Do you have any spending money, Sarah?"

"A penny a day . . . and I can save my pennies. I don't care for candy anyway." She added quickly, "I have seventeen cents saved up in my penny bank."

Seventeen cents! thought the library lady. How can I tell her that the book costs a dollar? "It that all you have?"

Sarah nodded shyly. "Yes."

"She was going to buy a doll." Gertie's voice filled the silence. "A doll with real hair."

The library lady looked at the sad little figure for a moment.

"Sarah," she said, "the book costs a dollar. If you pay the seventeen cents the next time you come, you will owe eighty-three cents. After that, I will make a special arrangement so you can pay one penny each week. I know it will take a very long time to pay the whole amount but you can save for your doll at the same time."

Sarah's eyes opened wide in unbelief. "You mean, I can save for my doll and still pay for the book?"

"That's right," said the library lady, and they both smiled.

Meanwhile the other children were whispering among themselves. Finally Ella spoke up. "Could we help pay? Each of us can bring a penny every week. We've collected three cents right now."

Henny said shamefacedly, "I already spent my penny today but I promise I'll bring it next week like the others."

"That's a wonderful idea! Sarah must be very proud to have such thoughtful sisters."

Sarah was proud. She gave them each a hug. "And when I get my doll, you can all play with her."

"Isn't it nice to have a family to share your troubles?" asked the library lady.

"Have you any sisters?" Sarah asked shyly.

"No, dear. Nor brothers. I'm the only one."

"Isn't that lonesome?" Charlotte asked. The children all felt sorry for the library lady now.

"Yes, dear, it is lonesome. But come now, aren't you going to take out any books today?"

"Can Sarah take out a book too?" questioned Henny.

"Yes, she can, so long as you'll be paying for the lost book."

Sarah clasped her hands together joyfully. "Oh, thank you! I think you're the nicest, kindest library lady in the whole world."

Miss Allen's smile was warm and friendly. "Run along now, dear, and get your book."

As she worked, Miss Allen found herself watching the five little girls. How quaint they were in their stiffly starched white aprons over dark woolen dresses. They looked for all the world like wide-open umbrellas.

Had she been able to peek under those dresses, she would have understood why they billowed out in such a manner. Underneath were *three* petticoats, a woolly, flannel one first, a simple cotton one next, with both of these topped by a fancy muslin garment which was starched to a scratchy crispness. In order to save money, Mama made those petticoats herself. Still further underneath was long woolen underwear, over which were pulled heavy knitted woolen stockings, making thin legs look like well-stuffed frankfurters. How the girls hated those stockings! They itched so! *And they never wore out!* Mama knitted them herself on long needles and she could always reknit the holes the children made.

Miss Allen could see that the stockings were bothering Sarah. She looked very comical as she kept rubbing one leg against the other. Clutching her new book tightly to her, she made her way back to the desk.

"Come on, everybody. It's late," Ella warned.

The children quickly chose their books and gave them to the library lady for stamping.

They raced home on happy feet. They couldn't wait to tell Mama that their beloved Friday afternoons at the library were not going to be spoiled after all.

The Sabbath

The Sabbath begins Friday evening at dusk and for two days Mama was busy with her preparations. On Fridays she cleaned, cooked, and baked. On Thursdays she shopped. Sabbath meals had to be the best of the whole week so it was most important that she shop carefully. Every Thursday afternoon, Mama went to Rivington Street market where prices were lower than in her neighborhood stores.

Usually she left Gertie in Papa's care and set off alone right after lunch. This Thursday Mama was rather late. The children would soon be home from school so Mama decided that it would be nice if for once shopping for the Sabbath could be a family affair.

"Who wants to come to market with me?" she asked the children as soon as they came trooping in.

"I do! I do!" Everybody wanted to go along.

"Gracious, hasn't anybody any other plans for this afternoon?" asked Mama.

"Nothing as exciting as going to market," Ella declared, and her sisters all agreed.

But what about Gertie? It was a long walk for little feet.

Gertie spoke up as if she knew what Mama was thinking. "Oh, Mama," she pleaded, "me too!"

Mama wasn't going to disappoint her. "All right, but I think it would be a good idea to take the baby carriage along."

"Baby carriage!" Gertie was indignant. "I'm too big for a baby carriage!"

"Of course you are," Mama assured her, "but the carriage will come in handy for all the bundles and if you should happen to get too tired to keep on walking, why, we can have the bundles move over and make room for a very nice little girl. Now hurry, everybody. Into your hats and coats."

"Mama," said Sarah, "we'll be passing right by the library. Couldn't we go up for just a minute so you could meet the library lady?"

"Well—I don't know. I have a lot of shopping to do." Mama hesitated. "I would like to see her."

"Please, Mama, for just a minute."

"She's asked us a number of times to bring you over," Ella said.

"All right," replied Mama. "But we can't stay long."

The children were pleased. At last the library lady was going to see Mama. The children were very proud of Mama. Most of the other Jewish women in the neighborhood had such bumpy shapes. Their bodies looked like mattresses tied about in the middle. But not Mama. She was tall and slim and held herself proudly. Her face was proud too.

Once inside the library, the children scrambled eagerly up the stairs while Mama followed at a more sedate pace. They stood in a small group waiting for a moment when the library lady would be free. Then Sarah approached the desk.

Miss Allen looked up and smiled. "Hello, Sarah. It can't be Friday already?"

"No," laughed Sarah. "It's only Thursday, but we brought Mama."

"How nice!" the library lady said, and came from behind her desk to join the family.

"Mama," said Sarah proudly, "this is Miss Allen."

"I'm so glad you came," said the library lady as she extended her hand in greeting. "My, you couldn't possibly be the mother of five—you look young enough to be their eldest sister."

"I don't feel that young," said Mama laughing. "But thank you for the compliment. I've been wanting to meet you for a long time. But you know how it is with a family this size. There's always something to do. The children talk about you so much at home though, I feel that I already know you."

"They've told me all about you, too," replied Miss Allen.

"Sarah has never forgotten your kindness to her," continued Mama. "For that matter, all the children are always telling me such nice things about you. How you're always ready with a suggestion about what they should read, and how interested you are in discussing the books with them. I appreciate that."

"It's a pleasure to help such eager readers," the librarian said, smiling at the upturned faces.

"Well," Mama said, beaming, "I'm afraid we'll have to be running along."

"We're all going to market," Sarah explained.

"Good," said Miss Allen, "and when you come tomorrow, you can tell me all about it."

"Do you like her, Mama?" asked Sarah as they walked downstairs.

"Yes," answered Mama. "She's very sweet—and so pretty too!" Mama was thoughtful for a moment. She turned to Ella and added, "She smiles at you, but somehow the face is wistful, don't you think?"

Back on the street, the children danced along sometimes beside, sometimes just behind Mama. That is, all except Henny. She kept racing ahead and dashing back again, just like a small, impatient puppy.

Already their ears were filled with the shrill cries of street hawkers. Already they could smell the good smells, and in another minute, they were themselves part of the crowd.

"Just look at all the pushcarts!" exclaimed Sarah.

Heaped high with merchandise, they stretched in endless lines up and down the main street and in and out the side streets. They were edged up close to the curb and wedged together so tightly that one could not cross anywhere except at the corners. The pushcart peddlers, usually bearded men in long overcoats or old women in heavy sweaters and shawls, outdid each other in their loud cries to the passers-by. All promised bargains—bargains in everything—in fruits and vegetables, crockery, shoelaces, buttons, and other notions, in aprons and housedresses, in soap and soap powders, and hundreds of other things.

There were stores in which you could buy fish and stores that carried only dairy products. There were bakeries and meat shops, shoe stores and clothing establishments. In delicatessen shops, fat "specials" (frankfurters) hung on hooks driven into the walls and big chunks of "knubble" (garlic) wurst were laid out in neat rows on white trays which bore the sign "A Nickel a Schtickel" (a nickel for a piece). The counters overflowed with heaps of smoked whitefish and carp, and large slabs of smoked red salmon. If one wished, firm plump salt herrings were fished out of barrels for inspection before buying. Men's red flannel drawers and ladies' petticoats flew in the wind from their show-hooks on dry-goods store fronts.

But it was not enough that the merchandise sold behind closed shop doors could be displayed in showcase windows and store fronts. Their owners had to come out in the open too. They built stands which they either used themselves or rented out to others. Almost anything could be bought at these stands. There were pickle stands where the delicious odor of sour pickles mingled with the smell of sauerkraut and pickled tomatoes and watermelon rind. There were stands where only cereal products were sold—oats, peas, beans, rice and barley—all from open sacks. At other stands, sugar and salt were scooped out of large barrels and weighed to order. Here coffee was bought in the bean, for every household had its own wooden coffee grinder.

And wherever there was a bit of space too small for a regular stand, one could be sure to find the old pretzel woman. Her wrinkled face was almost hidden inside of the woolen kerchief bound round her head. Her old hands trembled as they wrapped up the thick, chewy pretzels.

The sidewalks were choked with people. It was not easy for Mama to push the carriage through the narrow aisles left between pushcarts and stands. The children followed behind in twos and whenever Mama stopped either to buy or look, they stopped too.

"Say, Gertie," Charlotte cried out, "how would you like a necklace like that?" She pointed to the garlic peddler who was coming towards them. No need for a store, a stand, or a pushcart for this peddler. With a basket full of garlic on one arm and a spicy necklace of the same looped around his neck, he was all set for business.

The dried mushroom peddlers did business in the same way except that, as Charlotte laughingly said, "They were better dressed." They wore long, heavy mushroom bracelets about their arms as well as necklaces.

How sharply the shoppers hunted for bargains! And what bargains, if one could believe the peddlers. How carefully every article was examined to make sure it was perfect! It always was, according to the shopkeepers. How the buyers haggled over the price of everything. And how the peddlers swore on their very lives that the price of anything was the lowest at which they could afford to part with it! But above and through all the noise and confusion, ran a feeling of great good nature and cheery contentment.

Only one tongue was spoken here—Yiddish. It was like a foreign land right in the midst of America. In this foreign land, it was Mama's children who were the foreigners since they alone conversed in an alien tongue—English.

At the next corner, Henny bought a fat, juicy sour pickle with her after-lunch penny. She ate it greedily, with noise and gusto, while her sisters watched, their mouths watering. "Selfish! How about giving us a taste, huh?"

Henny pretended that she didn't hear them, but before the pickle was half gone, she stopped teasing and gave each a bite.

Inside Mama's favorite fish store the smell was not so pleasing. "Gertie," suggested Charlotte, "let's squeeze our noses tight and talk to each other while we're squeezing."

And that's just what they did, talking about anything at all just so they could hear the funny sounds which came through their squeezed noses. "Look at the big fish with goggly eyes," said Gertie.

"I hope Mama is not getting any live fish this week," Charlotte said. "I like to see them swimming around in the bathtub but I don't like it when Papa cleans them afterward."

But Mama was not getting any live fish this time, only pieces of several different kinds of fish, whitefish, yellow pike and winter carp—that meant gefüllte fish (stuffed fish) for the Sabbath, yum, yum!

"I wish Mama would hurry up," said Gertie. "I can smell the fish right through my squeezed nose. And I do want to buy something for my penny, don't you?"

"Yes, and no fish!"

Out on the street again, the air seemed sharper and colder. Some of the peddlers had been standing in their places since early morning. They stamped their feet and slapped their arms across their chests trying to warm their chilled bones. But the sweet potato man did not mind the cold. Why should he when he had his nice hot street oven to push before him? When Ella caught sight of him, she said at once, "Just the thing for a cold day." The sweet potato man stopped before her and pulled open one of the drawers of his oven. There arose on the air such a delicious smell that Ella smacked her lips expectantly. Inside she saw the plump sweet potatoes in their gray jackets. Some were cut open in halves and their rich golden color gave promise of great sweetness. For her penny, Ella got a large half and as she bit into it, she wondered why sweet potatoes baked at home never tasted half so good. When she rejoined the family, four other mouths helped to make short work of that potato.

The chicken market was the next stopping place. It was smelly and noisy with the squawking of fowl. The children gathered about the crates and watched the roosters sticking their long necks through the slats. Mama donned an apron she had brought with her and began to pluck the fowl she selected.

After Mama finished her plucking, the chicken was wrapped up and added to the other bundles in the shopping bag. The family continued on its way.

Gertie turned to Charlotte. "What'll we buy with our pennies?" The answer to that question was just then coming along the street. Candied slices of tangerine and candied grapes mounted on sticks lay in rows on white trays. The peddler stopped when he heard Gertie's delighted cry. "Penny a stick, little darlings," he said. Charlotte chose grape and Gertie took tangerine. Thus two more pennies were spent.

"I'm almost through," Mama told them, but still Sarah's penny lay warm and snug in her coat pocket. "Aren't you going to spend your penny?" the children asked her. They couldn't be sure because Sarah was saving all her pennies these days—six for the dolly and one penny for the library lady. But today was something special. She had shared in the goodies her sisters had bought. It would only be fair for her to return their generosity. But what could she get?

"Arbis! Shaynicke, guttinke arbislach! Keuf meine heise arbis!" (Chick peas. Fine, nice chick peas. Buy my hot chick peas!)

The hot-chick-pea peddler was singing the words over and over in a funny Yiddish chant as he rolled a small white oven along the streets. Before Mama could stop her, mischievous Henny gave the carriage a big push so that it rolled away from under Mama's hands. She stooped over it as if she were pushing a great weight and began to chant in imitation:

"Arbis! Shaynicke, guttinke arbislach!"

The children roared with laughter. Even Mama could not hide a smile while she ordered Henny to stop. "Leave her alone, lady," the peddler told Mama. "She's helping me in mine business."

Because he was so good-natured, Sarah decided to give up her penny to him. Everyone watched as he fished out the peas. First he took a small square of white paper from a little compartment on one side of the oven. He twirled the paper about his fingers to form the shape of a cone and then skillfully twisted the pointed end so that the container would not fall apart. He lifted the wagon cover on one side revealing a large white enamel pot. The steam from the pot blew its hot breath in the little girls' faces so they stepped back a bit while the peas were ladled out with a big soup spoon. The wagon cover was dropped back into place and the paper cup handed over to Sarah. The peas were spicy with pepper and salt, and how good they were! They warmed up the children's tummies and made them very thirsty.

With the purchase of a pound of pumpernickel bread, the shopping tour came to an end. They left behind the life and activity of the market and started the weary walk home. By now the children were tired. Gertie uttered not a single word of protest when Mama lifted her up and put her into the carriage together with the bundles. The others wished they were young enough to join her.

The next afternoon, when they had chosen their books, they told the library lady all about their marketing trip. Ella was a good actress and could imitate voice and gestures marvelously well. The children and the library lady went into gales of laughter as she mimicked the various peddlers. They made so much noise that the other librarian stared at them reprovingly.

"I guess we'd better be quiet," Miss Allen whispered.

The children started for the staircase walking exaggeratedly on tiptoes and giggling softly.

At home, the kitchen was warm with the smell of fresh-baked white bread. The room sparkled with cleanliness. The table, which wore only an oilcloth covering all through the week, now had on a snowy white tablecloth. On it stood the brass candlesticks, gleaming brightly from the polishing that Ella and Sarah had given them the day before. They were just in time to see Mama saying the prayer over the candles.

The children stood around the table watching her. A lovely feeling of peace and contentment seemed to flow out from Mama to them. First she put a napkin on her head; then placing four white candles in the brass candlesticks, she lit them. She extended her arms to form a circle. Over the lighted candles the encircling gesture was repeated. After that Mama covered her eyes with her hands, softly murmuring a prayer in Hebrew.

Thus was the Sabbath ushered in.

Mama set two braided loaves of white bread on the table at Papa's place. She covered them with a clean white napkin. Then from the whatnot, she took a wine bottle full of the dark sweet red wine which Papa always made himself. She also took a small wine glass and put these on the table next to the loaves.

The children lined up before Papa. He placed his hand on each child's head, asking God's blessing for his little one. When this ceremony was over, Papa left for the synagogue.

It's so lovely and peaceful, thought Ella. Now if only Charlie were here, everything would be just perfect. Had Mama invited him for the Sabbath supper? She hadn't said.

"Is Charlie coming tonight?" she asked.

"No," answered Mama. "Papa tells me Charlie hasn't been in the shop for over a week."

So Charlie was gone again. For how long this time, wondered Ella.

"Where do you suppose he goes?"

"Who knows?" Mama answered with a sigh.

"Doesn't Papa ever ask him?"

Mama shook her head. "You don't ask people about their personal lives."

"It's queer. Charlie isn't at all like the other peddlers, is he, Mama? He seems so educated and so fine. Why does he live like this? What do you suppose happened to him?" Ella's questions caught the attention of the other children.

"I guess he likes it this way," Henny remarked airily.

"Has he a Mama and a Papa?" Sarah asked. She could not imagine life without parents.

"We don't know, Sarah. He never mentions them."

"He comes and goes," began Charlotte.

Henny finished, "And nobody knows."

Papa came in. "Good Sabbath," he said.

"Good Sabbath," each replied.

Papa washed his hands. It was time for supper, but first he must pronounce the prayer in praise of his wife for her fine Sabbath preparations. Then he must say a prayer of thanksgiving for the Sabbath. To do this, Papa filled the glass full of wine, raised it aloft and said a short prayer in Hebrew, then drank some of it. Everyone had a sip from the glass.

Another short prayer was said over the loaves. Papa uncovered them and cut a thick piece for Mama and smaller pieces for the girls. In turn, Mama and the children recited the prayer thanking God for giving them this bread. Now, at last, supper could be eaten.

Such a good supper! *Gefüllte* fish, chicken soup with homemade noodles, chicken, carrots prepared in a sweet way, and applesauce.

Afterward, the children helped with the clearing of the table and the dishwashing. In the lovely hush of the Sabbath eve, they once more gathered around the table, the children with their books, Mama with her magazine, and Papa with his Jewish newspaper. All heads were bent low over their reading while the candles flickered and sputtered. It was quiet except for the whispered sounds of Charlotte's voice as she read aloud from her primer to wide-eyed Gertie.

So they would continue reading until the candles burnt low. Then they would undress and go to bed—for after the candles died out, the room would be in complete darkness. There could be no light struck on the Sabbath. That was the law.

ELLEN RIDES AGAIN

Beverly Cleary

Beverly Cleary is a Californian whose first book, Henry Huggins, *was an instantaneous success. There is now a second book about Henry called* Henry and Beezus, *which is equally funny and popular. Ellen in* Ellen Tebbits *is the feminine counterpart of Henry, and this book is just as hilarious as the other two books and especially popular with girls. As American as supermarkets and completely true to child nature, Mrs. Cleary's stories are hilarious commentaries on modern life.*

The arrival of spring meant different things to different people. To Mrs. Tebbits it meant spring cleaning. To Mrs. Allen it meant planting seeds and setting out new flowers. To Ellen and Austine spring meant something much more important. It meant no more winter underwear.

The two girls were walking home from the library one warm spring afternoon. They felt light and carefree in their summer underwear. It was a wonderful feeling. It made them want to do something exciting.

At the library Austine had been lucky enough to find two horse books. "I wish I could ride a horse sometime," she said.

"Haven't you ever ridden a horse?" asked Ellen.

"No. Have you?" Austine sounded impressed.

"Oh, yes," said Ellen casually. "Several times."

It was true. She had ridden several times. If she had ridden twice she would have said a couple of times. Three was several times, so she had told the truth.

"Where? What was it like? Tell me about it," begged Austine.

"Oh, different places." That was also true. She had ridden at the beach. Her father had rented a horse for an hour and had let Ellen ride behind him with her arms around his waist. The horse's back had been slippery and she had bounced harder than was comfortable, but she had managed to hang on.

And she had ridden at Uncle Fred's farm. Uncle Fred had lifted her up onto the back of his old plow horse, Lady, and led her twice around the barnyard. Lady didn't bounce her at all.

And then there was that other time when her father had paid a dime so she could ride a pony around in a circle inside a fence. It hadn't been very exciting. The pony seemed tired, but Ellen had pretended it was galloping madly. Yes, it all added up to several times.

"Why haven't you told me you could ride?" Austine demanded. "What kind of saddle do you use?" Austine knew all about different kinds of saddles, because she read so many horse books.

"Oh, any kind," said Ellen, who did not know one saddle from another. "Once I rode bareback." That was true, because Lady had no saddle.

"Golly," said Austine. "Bareback!"

Ellen was beginning to feel uncomfortable. She had not meant to mislead Austine. She really did not know how it all started.

"Oh, Ellen, you have all the luck," exclaimed Austine. "Imagine being able to ride horseback. And even bareback, too."

"Oh, it's nothing," said Ellen, wishing Austine would forget the whole thing.

But the next day at school Austine did not forget about Ellen's horseback riding. She told Linda and Amelia about it. They told Barbara and George. Barbara and George told other boys and girls. Each time the story was told, it grew.

Even Otis was impressed and he was a difficult boy to impress. When the girls started home after school, he was waiting on the edge of the school grounds. He had a piece of chalk and was busy changing a sign from "Bicycle riding forbidden at all times" to "Bicycle riding bidden at all times." Otis crossed out "for" every time he had a chance, but the rain always washed away the chalk marks.

"Hello, Ellen," he said, walking along beside her in his cowboy boots. Since Christmas Otis had worn boots instead of Oxfords. He was not wearing spurs today. Miss Joyce had asked him not to wear them to school.

Ellen and Austine ignored him.

Otis kicked at the grass along the edge of the sidewalk. "Say, Ellen, is it true you ride a lot? Even bareback?"

"Of course it's true," said Austine.

"I wish people would stop talking about it," said Ellen crossly. "What's so wonderful about riding a horse, for goodness' sake?"

"Gee whiz," said Otis enviously. "Some people have all the luck."

The girls continued to ignore him. He followed them for a while, kicking at the grass, and then turned down another street.

When the girls came to Austine's house, they found Mrs. Allen on her knees beside a flat box of pansy plants. She was taking them out of the box and setting them into a border along the driveway.

"Hello there," she said. "Since tomorrow is Memorial Day and there isn't any school, how would you like to go on a picnic?"

Ellen did not say anything. She thought Mrs. Allen meant her, too, but she was not sure. She hoped so. That was the trouble with the word *you*. Sometimes it meant one person and sometimes it meant a lot of people. Maybe Mrs. Allen was talking to Austine and not to both of them.

Mrs. Allen said, "Ellen, I have already asked your mother and she says you may go."

"Thank you. I'd love to go." Maybe a picnic would make Austine forget about horses. And if they went on a picnic, Austine couldn't come to Ellen's house to play and perhaps say something about horseback riding in front of Mrs. Tebbits. Ellen was worried about what her mother would say if she found out how Ellen had exaggerated.

"Where are we going?" asked Austine.

"We're going to drive out toward Mount Hood. The rhododendrons are beginning to bloom, and I thought it would be nice to see them blooming in the woods."

The next morning at ten o'clock Ellen ran down Tillamook Street and around the corner to Austine's house. For her share of the picnic she carried eight deviled eggs carefully packed in a cardboard box. Mr. Allen was backing out the car. Mrs. Allen sat in the front seat and Austine in the back.

"Hop in," said Mr. Allen. "Bruce isn't going with us. The boy scouts are marching in a parade."

Ellen was glad she and Austine could each sit by a window. That made it easier to look for white horses and to play the alphabet game. The first one to see a white horse got to make a wish. Ellen was going to wish Austine would forget about her horseback riding.

The girls always played the alphabet game when they rode in a car. Each watched the signs on her own side of the road for the letters of the alphabet. Each letter had to be found in order or it did not count. The *k* in a Sky Chief Gasoline sign could not be used unless a *j* had already been seen. The girl who had a Burma Shave sign on her side of the road at the right time was lucky because it contained in the right order both *u* and *v*, two hard letters to find. The game went quickly at first, because there were lots of signs, but as they neared the mountains the signs became more scarce.

Ellen was looking for a Texaco filling station for an *x* when Austine shouted, "Look, a white horse! I've got dibs on it." She shut her eyes to wish.

Ellen was sorry she had not seen the horse first. She needed a wish. Finally both girls were down to *z*. By then the car was winding along the mountain roads.

"Z!" shouted Ellen. "I win. There was a sign by that bridge that said 'Zigzag River.'"

"That's all right," said Austine generously. "I'm going to get my wish."

It was a few more miles along the highway that Austine saw the horses. "Look, Daddy! Horses for rent, fifty cents an hour! Please stop," she begged.

Mr. Allen drew over to the side of the road near some horses in a makeshift corral. Austine scrambled out of the car and ran to the horses, while the others followed.

"Daddy, please let us go horseback riding. All my life I've wanted to ride a horse. Please, Daddy. You and Mother could go on and look at the rhododendrons and come back for us."

"Would it be safe for the girls to ride alone?" Mrs. Allen asked the man with the horses.

"Please, Mother," begged Austine. "Make my wish come true."

"Sure. Kids do it all the time," answered the man. "They ride up that dirt road as far as the old sawmill and turn around and come back. The horses know the way. Takes about half an hour. Road runs right along the highway."

"They won't be thrown from the horses?" asked Mrs. Allen.

"From these horses?" said the man. "No, lady. These horses worked at a riding academy for years."

"You're sure they're gentle?"

"Yes, ma'am. Gentle as kittens."

"The girls could hang onto the saddle horns," suggested Mr. Allen.

"Oh, Daddy, you aren't supposed to hang onto the saddle horn. Only tenderfoots, I mean tenderfeet, do that. We'll be safe, because Ellen has ridden a lot and I know all about riding from books."

Ellen wished Austine would keep still. She was not at all sure she wanted to ride, especially without a grownup along.

"I suppose it would be safe to let the girls ride for half an hour," said Mrs. Allen. "We could walk along the dirt road and look at the rhododendrons while they rode. That way they would be within shouting distance."

"All right, girls, which horses do you want to ride?" asked Mr. Allen, taking a handful of change out of his pocket.

Ellen thought she had better act brave even if she didn't feel that way. "The spotted horse is nice, but I think I'd rather have the brown one over in the corner of the pen." She thought the brown horse looked gentle.

"I'll take the pinto on this side of the corral," said Austine, glancing at Ellen.

Oh dear, thought Ellen. I've said the wrong thing. I wish I'd read some horse books.

Austine watched eagerly and Ellen watched uneasily while the man saddled and bridled the two horses. "O.K., kids," he said.

Ellen walked over to the brown horse and patted him gingerly. He seemed awfully big when she stood beside him. But he looked down at her with large gentle eyes, and Ellen felt braver.

The man held out his hand, palm up.

Oh, I wonder if he wants me to give him some money, thought Ellen. It must be that, but I'm sure Austine's father paid him. Or maybe he wants to shake hands. A sort of farewell.

"Come on, girlie. Step up," said the man. "Don't be scared. Brownie isn't going to hurt you."

My goodness, thought Ellen. I guess he expects me to step in his hand. I suppose it's all right. His hand is dirty anyway.

She put her foot into his hand and he boosted her onto the horse. The ground seemed a long way below her. And Ellen had forgotten how wide a horse was. The man shortened her stirrups and then helped Austine onto the pinto. Ellen patted Brownie on the neck. She was anxious to have him like her. If only she had a lump of sugar in her pocket.

"Look," cried Austine. "I'm really on a horse."

Ellen knew she was expected to take the lead. "Giddap," she said uncertainly. Brownie did not move.

The man gave each horse a light slap on the rump. They walked out of the corral and ambled down the dirt road as if they were used to going that way. Austine's mother and father followed on foot.

Ellen carefully held one rein in each hand. As she looked at the ground so far below, she hoped Brownie wouldn't decide to run.

"I'm going to call my horse Old Paint like in the song," said Austine, who never missed the Montana Wranglers on the radio and knew all about cowboy songs. "I wish I'd worn my cowboy neckerchief."

"Yes," said Ellen briefly. She didn't feel like making conversation.

When Austine's horse moved in front, Ellen took hold of the saddle horn. It wasn't so much that she was scared, she told herself. She just didn't want to take unnecessary chances.

"I wish we'd worn our pedal pushers," said Austine. "It's sort of hard to feel like a cowgirl in a dress."

"I wish we had, too."

Maybe this wasn't going to be so bad after all. The horses seemed to know the way, and Ellen found the rocking motion and the squeak of the saddle rather pleasant. She was even able to look around at the trees and enjoy the woodsy smell.

Then when they had gone around a bend in the road, Brownie decided it was time to go back to the corral. He turned around and started walking in the direction from which they had come.

"Hey," said Ellen anxiously. She pulled on the right rein, but Brownie kept on going. "Stop!" she ordered, more loudly this time.

"What are you going that way for?" asked Austine, turning in her saddle.

"Because the horse wants to," said Ellen crossly.

"Well, turn him around."

"I can't," said Ellen. "He won't steer."

Austine turned Old Paint and drew up beside Ellen. "Don't you know you're supposed to hold both reins in one hand?" Austine was scornful.

Ellen didn't know. "I just held them this way to try to turn him," she said. She took them in her left hand. They were so long she wound them around her hand.

Austine leaned over and took hold of Brownie's bridle with one hand. "Come on, Old Paint," she said, and turned her horse forward again. Brownie followed.

"Thanks," said Ellen. "My, you're brave."

"Oh, that's nothing," said Austine modestly. "You don't steer a horse," she added gently. "You guide him."

"Oh . . . I forgot." Ellen wondered how she would ever explain her ignorance to Austine. What would her best friend think when she found out how Ellen had misled her?

The horses plodded on down the woodsy road. Through the trees the girls could see the highway and hear cars passing. Austine's mother and father appeared around the bend, and Ellen began to feel brave again.

"Let's gallop," suggested Austine.

Ellen's legs were beginning to ache. "How do you make them gallop?"

"Dig your heels in," said Austine.

"Oh, I wouldn't want to hurt the horse," said Ellen.

"You won't hurt him, silly. Cowboys wear spurs, don't they?"

Ellen timidly prodded Brownie with her heels. Brownie ambled on.

Austine dug in her heels. Old Paint began to trot. At first Austine bounced, but soon she rode smoothly. Then her horse began to gallop.

When Old Paint galloped, Brownie began to trot. Ellen began to bounce. She hung onto the saddle horn as hard as she could. Still she bounced. Slap-slap-slap. Her bare legs began to hurt from rubbing against the leather of the saddle flap. Slap-slap-slap. Goodness, I sound awful, she thought. I hope Austine doesn't hear me slapping this way.

Austine's horse, after galloping a few yards, slowed down to a walk. "Whoa, Old Paint," cried Austine anyway, and pulled on the reins. Old Paint stopped and Austine panted a minute.

"I did it, Ellen!" she called. "It was just a few steps, but I really, truly galloped. I hung on with my knees and galloped just like in the movies."

"Wh-wh-oa-oa!" Ellen's voice was jarred out between bounces. Brownie trotted on. Slap-slap-slap.

Austine began to laugh. "I can see trees between you and the saddle every time you go up. Oh, Ellen, you look so funny!"

Slap-slap-slap. Ellen didn't think she could stand much more bouncing. It was worse than being spanked.

"Ellen Tebbits! I don't think you know a thing about horseback riding."

"Wh-wh-oa-oa!" When Brownie reached Old Paint he stopped. After Ellen got her breath, she gasped, "I do, too. It's just that the other horses I rode were tamer."

The horses walked on until the road curved down to the edge of a stream.

"Oh, look. There's a bridge," exclaimed Ellen, looking up.

"I guess the highway crosses to the other side of the stream," said Austine. "I wonder if the poor horses are thirsty."

There was no doubt about Brownie's wanting a drink. He left the road and picked his way down the rocky bank to the water.

"Poor horsie, you were thirsty," said Ellen, patting his neck.

But Brownie did not stop at the edge of the stream. He waded out into it.

"Whoa," yelled Ellen, above the rush of the water. "Austine, help!"

Brownie waded on.

"Austine! What'll I do? He's going swimming!"

"Here, Brownie! Here, Brownie!" called Austine from the bank. Her voice sounded faint across the surging water.

When Brownie had picked his way around the boulders to the middle of the stream, he stopped and looked around.

"Look, he's in over his knees!" Ellen looked down at the swirling water. "Giddap, Brownie!"

"Kick him in the ribs," yelled Austine from across the stream.

"I don't want to hurt him," called Ellen, but she did kick him gently. Brownie did not appear to notice.

"Slap him on the behind with the ends of the reins," directed Austine from the bank.

Ellen slapped. Brownie turned his head and looked at her reproachfully.

By this time some hikers had stopped on the bridge. Looking down at Ellen, they laughed and pointed. Ellen wished they would go away.

Brownie lowered his head to drink. Because Ellen had the reins wound around her hand, she could not let go. As she was pulled forward, the saddle horn poked her in the stomach.

"Oof," she said. Hanging over the horse's neck, she clung to his mane with one hand while she unwound her other hand.

Brownie looked at her with water dripping from his chin. Ellen thought it was his chin. Maybe on a horse it was called something else.

Austine broke a branch from a huckleberry bush that grew out of an old log at the edge of the stream. She waved it toward Brownie. "Here, horsie. Nice horsie."

Brownie glanced at her with mild interest.

"Oh, go on, Brownie," said Ellen in disgust. She kicked him hard this time. Brownie looked at her sadly and swished his tail.

A couple of cars stopped on the bridge and the occupants looked down at Ellen and laughed. "Yippee!" yelled one of the hikers and everyone laughed. "Ride 'em, cowboy!"

"Do something, Austine," Ellen called across the water. "Our half hour must be nearly up."

"Maybe I could ride back and get the man who owns the horses," Austine yelled back.

"No, Austine. Don't leave me here alone," begged Ellen. "Maybe I could get off and wade. I don't think the water would come up to my shoulders."

"The current's too strong," called Austine. "And anyway, we're supposed to bring the horses back. You can't go off and leave Brownie."

Austine was right. Ellen knew that she couldn't leave Brownie. She might lose him, and the man would probably make her pay for him. At least, she thought he would. She had never heard of anyone losing a horse, so she wasn't sure. "I can't stay here forever," she called.

"Mother and Daddy should catch up with us in a minute," Austine called. "They'll know what to do."

That was just what was worrying Ellen. She didn't want the Allens to see her in such a predicament. What would they think after Austine had told them she had ridden before? Maybe they had wandered off to look at rhododendrons and were lost in the woods by now.

Still Brownie did not move. Ellen wondered what it would be like to try to sleep on a horse. Again she wished she had brought some lumps of sugar. She could have eaten them herself when she became hungry.

One of the hikers climbed down the bank to the edge of the water. "Need some help, little girl?" he called.

"Oh yes, please," answered Ellen gratefully.

Jumping from boulder to boulder, the man drew near her, but he could not get close enough to reach Brownie's bridle. "Throw me the reins, little girl," he directed.

Ellen threw them as hard as she could. They fell into the water, but the man grabbed them as the current carried them toward him.

"Come on, old fellow," he said, pulling at the reins. Meekly Brownie began to pick his way around the boulders toward the bank.

"Oh, thank you," said Ellen, when they reached dry ground. "I guess I would have had to stay out there all day if you hadn't come for me."

"That's all right," said the man. "The trouble is, you let the horse know you were afraid of him. Let the old nag know you're boss and you won't have any trouble."

"Thank you, I'll try," said Ellen, taking a firm grip on the reins. "Good-by."

Just then Austine's mother and father appeared around the bend in the road. "Enjoying your ride, girls?" asked Mr. Allen.

"Oh yes," said Austine. "We just stopped to give the horses a drink."

"It's time to turn back now," said Mrs. Allen.

"All right, Mother," said Austine.

The girls headed their horses toward the corral. Ellen was so embarrassed she didn't know quite what to say to Austine. What would Austine think of her after this? What would she tell the kids at school?

Finally, when Austine's mother and father were a safe distance behind, Ellen said in a low voice, "I guess I didn't know quite as much about horseback riding as I thought I did."

"Your horse was just hard to manage, that's all," said Austine generously.

"Austine?" said Ellen timidly.

"What?"

"You won't tell anybody, will you? You won't tell that Otis Spofford what happened, will you?"

Austine smiled at her. "Of course I won't tell. We're best friends, aren't we? It'll be a secret like the underwear. Giddap, Old Paint."

"Thank you, Austine," said Ellen gratefully. "You're a wonderful friend. And you know what? I'm going to look for some horse books the next time we go to the library."

The horses, knowing they were headed toward hay, showed more spirit. Ellen held the reins firmly. That Brownie was going to know who was boss. She began to enjoy herself. She pretended she was returning to a ranch after a hard day riding the range.

"I didn't know horses had such long hair," she remarked.

"It's their winter coat," explained Austine. "They'll shed it this summer."

Ellen laughed. "Just like winter underwear," she said.

HOME

Lois Lenski

Lois Lenski is giving children a wonderful picture of life in these United States and the diverse people who live here. Strawberry Girl (*Florida*) *won the Newbery Award in 1946. There are also* BoomTown Boy (*Oklahoma*), Bayou Suzette (*Louisiana*), Blue Ridge Billy (*North Carolina*), Judy's Journey (*migrant workers*), Prairie School (*Dakota prairies*), *and* Cotton in My Sack (*Arkansas*), *from which this excerpt is taken. Every one of these is a lively, enjoyable story. What the people in the stories lack in money and education, they make up for in pride and family loyalties. Young readers who share the problems, hardships, and occasional fun of the children in these books will have a deeper understanding of people and of what Albert Schweitzer calls "reverence for life." Joanda in* Cotton in My Sack *is one of the most appealing little girls in the series. This excerpt, together with the song, lends itself to dramatization. Other chapters in this book and many of Lois Lenski's stories will prove admirable for dramatization.*

"Sun up in the mornin'
Hot upon my back,
Got to go start pickin'
Cotton in my sack . . ."

Joanda's voice rang out clearly over the cotton field. She had made up the song herself and its simple tune wavered uncertainly. Then it stopped.

"Oh!" she cried. "Don't you put that worm on me."

"I will so!" answered Ricky.

She ducked to get out of her brother's way.

"There it is *on* you," said Ricky.

"Git it off! Git it off!" screamed Joanda, shaking herself. "If there's one thing I can't stand about cotton pickin', it's worms. Where'd it go? What kind was it—a fuzzy one, or one that's speckeldy-like with lots of feet?"

"I don't know," said Ricky. "You lost it. It's gone now."

"You better git busy and pick," said Joanda.

Five-year-old Ricky sat down in the cotton row. "I *can't* pick and I *won't* pick," he said.

"When you take a notion to pick, you *can* pick," said Joanda.

"What we got to pick for?" asked Ricky.

"This is Daddy's cotton," explained Joanda. "We're pickin' for Big Charley, Daddy's boss-man."

"Is Daddy gonna pay me?" asked Ricky.

"Daddy's *s'posed* to pay *me* for pickin', but sometimes he don't," said Joanda.

"When I git my money, I'm gonna git me a new coat," said Ricky.

"You'll be an old man before you git it," said Joanda.

Ricky slung his tow sack over his shoulder and began to pick. "I'm gonna git my sack full."

Joanda started a game she had made up: "Do you chew tobacco?"

"No," said Ricky, shaking his head.

"Do you dip snuff?"

"NO!" answered Ricky.

"Do you smoke a pipe?"

"NO, NO, NO!" shouted Ricky.

"Do you eat popcorn?"

"No—oh yes! YES!"

"Do you chew gum?"

"YES MA'M, when I can git it!" laughed Ricky.

The small boy held out both hands filled with cotton. "Look how much cotton I got!" He had a sweet smile. His face was plump, but it was very dirty. "For Christmas I want a tractor. I'm gonna be a farmer."

"It's a long time 'fore Christmas comes," said his sister. She stopped in her row and lifted the middle of her seven-foot pick sack to shake the cotton down to the end. Her face was pretty, but had a wistful, sad expression. Dark brown eyes looked out from under her floppy checked sunbonnet. Tangled brown hair hung beside her cheeks. She wore baggy patched blue jeans and a faded red plaid shirt.

"After it's shook down it's not half full," she said. "If I could only git it full once, I'd be happy. Daddy says I won't be even half-a-hand till I git it full."

"Am I a full hand?" asked Ricky.

Joanda laughed. "You? Course not. Mavis is fourteen—she's a full hand, only she can't pick now 'cause she's got a boil on her neck. Steve's twelve, but he's not half-a-hand 'cause he stands and looks around so much. You have to be eleven or twelve to be a full hand."

"Oh!" said Ricky.

"Bless Pat!" cried Joanda suddenly. "That's our baby crying."

"Maybe it's Mr. Burgess's cotton pickers singin'," said Ricky. "I hear our dog barking. *Here, Trouble, here, Trouble!"* He called, but the dog did not come.

The children looked down to the far end of the rows, where three bent figures were picking.

"Listen how the baby's hollerin'," Joanda went on. "Bet she's cryin' to come over here to me. Bet she'd be quiet if she was here with me. Mama won't git her sack full if Lolly keeps on yellin'."

"I'm gonna pull my shoes off," announced Ricky.

"Mama'll whoop you. Daddy'll whoop you," said Joanda.

"No, they won't," answered Ricky.

"Big Charley, the boss-man will whoop you."

"No, he won't!"

"Miz Shands will whoop you."

The song *Cotton in My Sack*. Copyright by Lois Lenski and Clyde Robert Bulla; used by permission of author and composer

"She jest better not try it," laughed Ricky. "She'd have to ketch me first."

"You'll git sandburrs in your feet," warned Joanda.

Ricky walked around in the dirt. "I ain't got no cuckleburrs," he said.

"Pick some more, sugar," said Joanda. "Pick four more pounds, then you can rest."

"I'm tard of pickin'," said Ricky. "I ain't never gonna pick no more cotton as long as I live."

Joanda laughed. The children had picked to the end of their row and now came out on the turn-row between two cotton fields. Here stood the trailer, three-quarters full of cotton. It was an old rickety cotton wagon, with high board sides. Ricky started to climb up the ladder at the back.

"Daddy don't want you to git on the cotton," warned Joanda. "Git down, Ricky." He kept on climbing.

"Cotton feels good on my bare feet, so soft and squnchy," said the boy. He jumped and came down *plop*. He rolled over and over, the fuzzy cotton sticking to his clothes. "I like to go barefooted. It feels good on my toes!"

"We don't have to go barefooted now," said Joanda. "We got shoes to wear. We used to go barefooted when we didn't have money to buy any."

"My shoes hurt my feet," said Ricky. "One time I had some money and I spent it."

"I got $3.45 now, I had $5.00," said Joanda proudly. "I spent it for groceries. I got baloney and bread and two cans of fish and two candy bars. Steve owes me a quarter. He better pick cotton and pay it back. If he don't, I'll make him. He says he's goin' to, but if he don't, I'll take my switch after him."

The Negro pickers in the next field were singing. Joanda stood still to listen:

"Oh, the cotton needs pickin' so bad!
Cotton needs pickin' so bad,
Cotton needs pickin' so bad,
Gonna pick all over dis field" . . .

"Mama and Daddy's pickin' fast," said Ricky. The children looked at the three figures who were coming closer and closer.

"Why is Steve so far behind the others?" asked Ricky.

"He's lookin' at every bird and wishin' it was an airplane," said Joanda. "He's lookin' at the cars along the road." She pointed to the highway off on the right.

"Where's all the cars a-goin'?" asked Ricky.

"To town," said Joanda.

"I don't want to live in town," said Ricky. "You can't make any money in town."

"I do," said Joanda. "You can spend all your money in town. Let's ask Daddy to go to the gin this evenin', when he takes the cotton in."

"Goody, goody!" cried Ricky, jumping up and down.

All the time she had been talking, the girl's nimble fingers had been putting cotton in her sack, as she started on the next row. Her bent back moved from plant to plant, and her thin arms moved in a steady rhythm.

"Why don't you rest a while?" asked Ricky.

"I don't rest, I have to keep on workin'," said Joanda. "I picked twenty-seven pounds one evenin'. Maybe if I try hard, I'll git my pick sack *full*."

"Here, Trouble, here, Trouble!" called Ricky.

A little gray dog came tearing down the cotton middle, barking. Then Daddy came, carrying his bulging sack over his shoulder. He was a thin man with a weathered face, and he wore a slouchy felt hat. Mama came more slowly, dragging her heavy load. Joanda ran to meet her. Mama's load was not all cotton, for there on her pick sack rode the baby, Lolly, as comfortable as a bird in a nest.

"Lolly rolled off back down there," said Mama, "and how she did yell. When I looked around, there was Trouble sittin' in her place as smart as you please, expectin' a ride."

"Betcha he pushed her off," said Joanda. "Can I take her, Mama?"

"Land sakes, yes, git her off," said Mama. "My back's nigh broke. She's as heavy as a ton o' bricks."

"Betcha she was hollerin' for me," said the girl. "Betcha she missed me all right."

Mama had so many clothes on, it was hard to tell whether she was a large or small woman. She wore pants to cover her legs, her cotton dress came to her knees, and over it she wore one of Daddy's old shirts to cover her arms. Brown eyes peered out from under her large slat bonnet. Hot, tired and dirty, she slipped down on her cotton sack to rest.

Joanda took Lolly on her lap, her thin arms squeezed tightly around the heavy two-year-old. The baby was plump and had curly red hair. She was dressed in a khaki coverall suit with red buttons down the front. Joanda looked down at her, adoration in her eyes.

"Lolly pick cotton? Lolly like to pick cotton?" she asked.

Lolly reached over and pulled off a fluffy boll. She began to make a humming sound.

"You singin', Lolly? You singin' *Cotton in my Sack?*" Joanda turned to Mama. "Lolly makes out like she's singin', Mama."

"Only time that young un's quiet is when she's eatin' or sleepin'," said Mama. "She's the noisiest little somebody."

Joanda gave the baby a tight hug.

Daddy began weighing. He tied the two ends of his long pick sack together and hooked them over the scales. "Fifty-two pounds," he said. "Git off that sack, you two."

Mama and Joanda stood up and watched as he weighed the others. Mama had forty-four pounds, Joanda eighteen and Ricky seven. Daddy marked all the weights down in a little green record book. Steve came up, and he had thirty pounds. Daddy shook his head. "We'd a had more if Mavis coulda picked today. Cotton's light. It don't weigh much when it's plumb dry."

Each sack, after being weighed, was thrown up on top of the load. Mama took the baby and Joanda climbed up to help. Ricky and Joanda and Steve and Daddy jumped up and down, emptying the sacks and tramping the cotton. Trouble jumped and bounced and barked.

Mama looked down at Lolly and said, "They're havin' a time, ain't they?" Lolly clapped her hands and laughed.

"Can we go to the gin?" "Oh, Daddy, can we?" "Mama, can we ride to the gin?" begged the children.

Mama looked at Daddy who nodded his head.

"I reckon so," answered Mama. "Come, Trouble. We'll go see if Mavis has got supper cooked." She started across the field, baby in arms and dog at her heels.

Daddy's truck, already full of cotton, had been left parked in the turn-row. He backed it up, hitched the trailer on, and drove out of the cotton field. Joanda threw off her sunbonnet to cool her face in the breeze. The children sat down on the cotton. Their bright faces and figures, seated on the white cotton, made a colorful pattern against the blue of the sky. A radiant sunset threw out flames of red and gold, casting changing shadows across the level Arkansas fields. The truck bumped along the dirt road until it came to the crossroads center, where beside a garage and a country store, stood the White Top cotton gin.

Daddy drove up under the shed until the trailer was on the scales.

A man hurried out. "Hi there, Dave Hutley!"

The children hopped down and the man weighed the cotton. He went in the building to mark down the weight, came out and hooked a tag on the trailer. Then Daddy backed up and he weighed the cotton in the truck.

"O. K., Hutley," the man called out.

Daddy drove the trailer under a large round pipe which came down from the main part of the gin. The man jumped on the load and began to move the pipe about. A loud noise was heard as the motor was turned on and the fan began to operate. The suction pulled the cotton up into the pipe.

"That's the suck!" Joanda explained to Ricky. "See how it sucks up all the cotton?" She turned to Steve. "What do they do with the cotton after they git it in the gin?"

"Don't *you* know?" answered Steve. "They've got big machinery in there. It separates the seeds from the cotton and blows the hulls out in a big pile at the back. The seeds go out in another place. And the cotton goes round and round till it gits clean of leaves and trash, then it's pressed in a bale."

"They put a tow sack around it and tie it with wires," said Joanda. "I know that much."

"Big Charley, our boss-man, took me in and showed me all over one time," said Steve.

"Oh look, what's that up there in our cotton?" cried Joanda. "It's something blue . . . it's . . . whish! There, it's gone. *It was my sunbonnet!*"

"It went so quick!" cried Ricky, laughing. "I saw it go."

"You left it on the cotton," said Steve. "Wasn't it funny to see it go up?"

Joanda didn't know whether to laugh or cry. She started for the door of the gin.

"Where you a-goin'?" called Steve. "Kids are not allowed in there."

"Gonna git my sunbonnet," said Joanda, "before anything happens to it."

Daddy came up and the children explained.

"You're too late, sugar," said Daddy. "It's all chawed up to bits by this time."

"Chawed up?" Joanda blinked. She was used to sudden losses and things she could not help.

After the cotton was unloaded, the man said, "Goin' home now? You live in that shotgun house out on the by-o road, don't you?"

The children climbed into the cab of the truck with Daddy. As they rode along the dusty dirt road, Ricky asked, "Daddy, what's a shotgun house?"

Daddy laughed. "Where'd you hear that, son?"

"The man at the gin said we lived in one," answered Ricky.

"That's right," said Daddy. Now they were close enough to see the house, which was painted red. "It has three rooms in a row. I can take my shotgun and shoot through the front door and the bullet will go out the back door. It will go plumb through all four doors in a straight line."

The children laughed.

"But you won't do it, will you, Daddy?" asked Ricky.

"I got better use for my gun than any sech fool doin's," said Daddy. "Might better go squirrel huntin' over in them woods along the Mississippi River, eh, boys?"

"You bet!" agreed Steve.

The small yard around the house was bare of grass and untidy with trash. Near the back door was a pile of coal and beyond were several rickety sheds. Cotton grew close on all sides. There was just room for Daddy to park the truck and trailer close to the front porch.

The children ran around and went in at the back door. Mama was bent over the stove, putting coal in. Hot bacon fat sizzled angrily and sent up an appetizing odor. A few dishes were set on the oilcloth table.

"I lost my sunbonnet, Mama," said Joanda. "I left it on top of the cotton. It went up in the suck and got chawed to bits."

"Why didn't you keep it on your head where it belongs?" said Mama. "You'll have to find another old one to wear. Mavis didn't even git the fire started. She's still in bed in there. And Lolly's been cryin' so . . . Take her, Nannie."

Joanda picked up the baby and went through to the front part of the house. Mavis lay on one of the two double beds that nearly filled the middle room. Joanda was hot and tired after her all-day picking. A gentle breeze came in at the open front door. Joanda sat on the floor and played with the baby. Then Lolly crawled off to explore. Joanda stretched out full length.

Her tired back felt better when she lay flat on the floor. She rested, not moving, her head placed near the wall. Then she looked up. There on the wall old newspapers were pasted, in place of plaster. They were stained and dirty, but she could still read the words and study the pictures and advertisements. The papers were pasted on upside-down. She could read them better lying on the floor.

Joanda loved to read. There were no books or magazines in the house, only the newspapers on the wall. The words—strange words she did not know the meaning of—had a fascination for her. She used to ask Daddy to explain what they meant. But he couldn't—he only went to the third grade, he said. Joanda could pronounce them, if she took one syllable at a time and tried to say them slowly.

"'Perm—a—nent, permanent—lasts forever.' They do something to the hair, I reckon. $5.00 —that's too much," Joanda said to herself. "But it sure does look purty." She must save up all the hard words she did not know and ask the teacher when she went back to school.

"Supper's ready!" called Mama from the kitchen.

Mama knew how to cook supper, but she did not know the magic of words.

CHI-WEÉ RUNS A RACE

Grace Moon

Mr. and Mrs. Moon have spent years in the Indian country of our Southwest. Mrs. Moon's stories, which her husband illustrates, are not only exciting but also authentic.

Here is a tale of the desert wide,
A tale of the Mesa high,
With sage and sand on every side,
And the blue of a cloudless sky.

Here is a tale of a little maid,
And a boy of a desert band;
Of the things they did and the games they
played,
In far-off Indianland!

Chi-weé wriggled! Chi-weé squirmed! Out there in the sunlight the call of the little hoot-owl had sounded three times. In the broad day when there were no hoot-owls. That meant that Loki was waiting for her, outside in the dancing sunlight where he could hear all the sounds of the desert and see the thousand play places that called louder than voices. And here, in the dark house, she must sit and listen to the words of old Mah-pee-ti while he talked and talked endlessly to her mother.

Her mother had told her she must sit quietly, and the *outside* of her was as quiet as possible,

but no little girl could be quiet *inside* while old Mah-pee-ti talked, and the hoot-owl called, and on the very end of her tongue was a secret so big she had to close her lips *tight* to keep from shouting it out loud to the whole world.

How could big people sit so quietly, and talk and talk when there were such wonderful things to do, and all outdoors called with tongues that would not be still?

Chi-weé belonged to the outdoors. She was a little Pueblo Indian girl and lived in a town built like an eagle's nest high on the top of a mesa. For all the eight years of her life she had lived in this little town overlooking the desert—this queer little town built of stone, that had houses whose flat roofs were the front-door yards of other houses built above them and whose crooked little streets led nowhere in particular except that sometimes they ran to the edge of the mesa so that they too might look out over the desert.

The houses had ladders for stairways and often no doorways at all in the first story. That was because long, long ago when many other tribes were at war with them, each house was really a fort, and to keep the enemies from surprising them at night they would pull up their ladders and then go to sleep in peace knowing that no one could get into the house. But no one came to fight now, as their enemies were not so brave as they used to be and would only steal in secret. There were many children in the little town, and dogs and wild turkeys playing all together in the streets, and women sitting on the roof-tops painting jars and bowls of pottery and stringing long strands of red chili peppers to dry in the sun. They had always many smiles and nods for Chi-weé, who, with her shy little ways, was well loved in the town. Chi-weé was small for her age, with a great mop of black hair and a serious manner, but she was not serious *inside,* and those who knew her well could see in her black eyes a little fairy of mischief ever dancing, and in her heart she said there were wings—wings like those of the little bird for which she was named.

It did not seem that old Mah-pee-ti *ever* would stop—but *now*—he was slowly rising—and at a little nod from her mother Chi-weé was through the door and out to the head of the mesa trail like a tumbleweed blown by a strong wind.

There was Loki waiting as she knew he would be waiting, at the top of the trail that led down the mesa side to the spring below—Loki, who kept sheep in the desert and was Navajo, but who was her very best friend. Better than all else she liked to play with him in the desert, to see the strange places he would find and hear the wonderful tales he would tell. Loki was not very much older than Chi-weé, but he liked to have her *think* that he was very old and wise. Oh, yes—better than with the little chubby baby brother who gurgled, and better than with Ba-ba, her little goat, Chi-weé liked to play with Loki. And now, when she saw him, she called aloud before she came very near.

"Three times must you guess the great surprise secret I have to tell!" she cried, and she jumped up and down in her excitement. "Three times, like *this*—" and she held up three fingers, wiggling them in front of Loki—"and *never* will you guess it!"

"But, how can I guess," he said, with a little pretend-frown. "How can I guess when I do not know what you speak about?"

"W-e-e-ll," said Chi-weé slowly, "I will tell this much—it is about the Trader—a *little* of it is about him. Did you know," she asked excitedly then, "that he had brought a lady wife to the Cañon—a lady with a white face—and she wears shiny clothes?"

"Yes, I know," said Loki. "One time I saw her."

"She knows magic," said Chi-weé with much impressiveness. "*Great* magic she knows—I have seen how she knows it."

"What kind of magic?" asked Loki, and he tried not to appear too interested.

"Listen, and I will tell you," said Chi-weé, and she felt very important, to know more than Loki. Usually *he* was the one who knew everything. "One day—it was yesterday, I think—I found a little flower in the desert. It was one I have not seen before—and, as it was the day when we rode to the trading store, I took the little flower with me and gave it to the white lady. She has a smile that is nice, and she said, 'Oh, but that is a pretty flower, it is one I have wanted to see.' 'Did someone tell you about this flower?' I said, and she said, 'No, I saw it in a book.' Now, that is great magic, to see a flower in a book."

"Pooh!" laughed Loki. "That is nothing—in school places they teach about *everything, all* from books."

"I know about school places," said Chi-weé eagerly. "Once, the mission lady asked me to come in and sit down. It is a very, very bad place."

"Why is it a bad place? I think it is good to know about things," said Loki.

"Oh, but it is bad to sit very still all day in a house, and if you say one *word* the lady says, 'S-S-S-SH!' and waggles her finger at you, and if you move your foot she goes, 'Bang—Bang!' with a little stick on a table, and when the very, very little ones come in with no clothes on she says, 'Shame—shame! Run home to your mamma and get a dress!' No, that school place is a bad place. I do not have to look in a book or ask a teacher lady to know things. If I want to know about a little flower I run out and find it; *then* I know—and how can a book or a teacher lady show to me the sunshine and the little dawn wind and the song of the night hawk? But the magic of the white lady of the trader was different from the books in the school, for she said it had a long, long name, that little flower, and she told me what it was—and she told me——"

"But what is that great surprise?" interrupted Loki. "Listen, I will guess one time—that you go to some place soon?"

"No—no!" cried Chi-weé, all excitement again. "It is a *big* surprise, and maybe a part is for you."

"Then it is seed cakes your mother has made."

"Oh, no!" cried Chi-weé, dancing around him, "and two times you have guessed. Look! Two fingers are gone. Now, one more time——"

Loki grinned. "It is that you can come down in the desert and play with me. Is that the great secret—is it, mesa girl?"

Chi-weé laughed in answer to his grin and made a little face at him. "*That* would be no great secret—many times I come down to the desert to play with you. This is a very different thing. Listen——" and she waited just a little to see if she could make Loki eager to listen, but he made a great show of indifference, and when she waited, he looked across the desert as if he saw something there.

"Well," continued Chi-weé, after a very little, for she was too excited to wait long herself, "listen, Loki—we are to have races and games and prizes"—she was dancing again, up and down—"a whole day—and dances and good things, *many* good things to eat—and——"

Loki too, was excited now, and his eyes sparkled.

"Where will it be—and who will race—and when is this to be?"

Chi-weé laughed joyously.

"I *told* you how it was a great secret. It is that the Trader is very happy to bring the white lady to the Cañon, and in three days from now everyone is to come to the ranch where he lives, and it will be a great day—and *you* will come, Loki—and will play in the games?" she questioned eagerly.

"I will put the sheep in corral that day and I will come," answered Loki joyously, and it was hard to keep his feet from dancing a little jig as the feet of Chi-weé were dancing, but it would not do for him to jump up and down like a little girl.

Those were long days, those three days in between, but at last came the big one. Bright and clear it dawned, and from every direction came people riding to the dance.

"It is like the 'Chicken-pull'!" shouted Loki, when he saw Chi-weé coming down from the mesa; Chi-weé all dressed in her very best, with a green waist and long, brown skirt, and a woven red belt with bobby tassels hanging down. She wore white boots too, and silver bracelets, and a string of silver beads at her throat, and she was very conscious of all this splendor.

"It is like the time at Ganado," called Loki. "*Now* you will see how that was like. I could not tell you much—it is a *see* thing, not a *tell* thing. But now you will know."

"Yes, I will know," shouted Chi-weé in answer, though she was so near she did not need to shout. "And see how I have wings in my feet," and she jumped high with no effort at all. "To-day I could run faster than the wind—to-day the little hares in the desert could not run so fast as I can run. I will be the one that will win in those races—you shall see!"

"If you will talk so much, Chi-weé," called her mother, laughing, "you will have no breath to win races."

But Chi-weé and Loki gave little heed to words. They climbed into the back of the wagon, for Loki was to ride with them this day, and Loki, too, was dressed as Chi-weé had never seen him; with a plum-colored velvet waist with silver buttons and soft buckskin pants, and a woven red belt around his waist and a red band about his black hair, and in his ears bits of turquoise as blue as the deepest blue of the sky. Chi-weé's father drove the wagon and the mother sat beside him holding the fat baby brother, and in the back, on a pile of blankets sat Loki and Chi-weé, and they all felt that they looked very fine in their best bright clothes.

After this they spoke but little, for the eyes of each were big with thoughts of what was to come this day.

Over the glowing desert they drove, down sandy washes and up again—the steep other side—over rocky stretches and past rocks and buttes of the strangest shape and color. Past clumps of pinyon trees, mesquite and cactus, and always, everywhere, were tumbleweed and sagebrush and the little scurrying animals of the wild places. Other wagons, many of them, were driving in the same direction, and people on horses and burros, and many walking. It was the sort of excitement that Chi-weé and Loki loved, and their hearts sang within them.

Finally, they came to the place. It was at the mouth of a broad cañon, and in this sheltered place were the ranch and the store of the Trader.

Now, it was filled with many people and the noise and wagons and confusion made it seem almost like a town, but a town on a holiday, and there was an air of happy excitement over everything.

After a little while, the Trader came out of his store and he told them all that this was a very happy time for him, and that he wanted everybody else to be happy, and so he started the games and said there would be many fine prizes, and especially he said there would be a prize of a big piece of beautiful cloth stuff for the little girl who won in the race. Chi-weé's eyes sparkled at that—and then he said there would be a great feast and everyone was to eat more than they had ever eaten before. The men laughed then, but Chi-weé did not laugh, for it was a serious matter. If she obeyed the Trader she was not just certain what would happen, for there had been times—at other feasts, when good things had tempted very, very strongly—that she had eaten until she had been very sure that she had heard the sewed places of her little dress stretching, and if she ate *more* than that—she wondered if she had better *see* what would happen—and her eyes grew thoughtful for a moment—and then—!

"Look—look!" cried someone. "There go the pony races!" and she ran to where the crowd was thickest, to see. Young men and boys were mounted on ponies and were to race down a place cleared for them. Buried in the sand near one end of the cleared place was a bag with money in it, and just a piece of the neck of the bag stuck out of the sand so the men could reach down and grab for it as they rode past. It was a very exciting race, and many times they grabbed for the bag before one man got it. There were many games that followed the race, some played with balls and some with arrows, and there were other races and tests of strength, and so many things that Chi-weé grew dizzy with trying to see them all. Loki won a game with arrows, and he came running to show how they had given him a beautiful belt with silver buttons on it. And then, at last, came the race for little girls!

When they stood in line for the race, Chi-weé was so excited that at first she could hardly think; and then, very suddenly, she grew quiet and looked around her at the other little girls. Two or three she knew and the others she did not know. They were all as eager and excited as herself and she knew they thought longingly of that beautiful piece of cloth stuff that would make such a lovely warm dress for a little girl. One little girl looked as if the dress she had on could not last much longer than this day. It was very thin and worn and Chi-weé saw that the little girl was thin too. Two red spots were burning in her cheeks and she looked at Chi-weé with eyes that were very bright.

"If I win this race," she almost whispered to Chi-weé, "my mother will be very glad, and I will be glad. I can run fast—I—I think that I will win."

Chi-weé did not answer, for she thought how fast she too could run. And then came the word to be ready, and then—BANG!—they were off!

At first, they ran all together. But very soon first one and then another dropped behind, and then Chi-weé saw that the little thin girl had told true, for just they two together led all the rest and quickly got a great way ahead. They were running very fast now, but Chi-weé could breathe easily, and she heard the breath of the other girl coming quickly in little short sounds.

"I can win," thought Chi-weé, with fast-beating heart. "Something has said that I could win and it told true. That is very beautiful cloth stuff they will give for a prize—and, look—there is the line that makes the race to end, and I am a great way ahead."

It was true—the other little girl had run slower and slower as they came near to the winning place—and then—such a strange thing happened! As she came almost to the line, Chi-weé dug her little toe into the earth and dropped down in a little bunch on the ground.

"Oh!" cried the other girl, panting as she came close, and she would have stopped, but then *another* strange thing happened, for Chi-weé, without speaking, reached up and gave her a push that sent her stumbling across the winning line, and then she got up and walked slowly across the line herself.

"I stumbled my foot on a little stone," said Chi-weé then to the other girl. "I am glad that you won the race. You run very fast."

At first the thin little girl did not know what to do, but the others crowded around her and told her that she had won the race.

"Often people fall when they race," they said, "and that makes them to lose. Look how you have won this beautiful cloth stuff."

"And for *you,*" said the Trader, then turning to Chi-weé with a twinkle in his eye that spoke of understanding, "for you there is *this,*" and he shook out of a little bundle a beautiful shawl, the most beautiful shawl Chi-weé had ever seen, with flowers along the border and a fringe as soft as baby hair. Her eyes flew wide and her little mouth dropped open as she saw it, but longingly her arms reached wide to receive it.

"I—I—do not understand," she said tremblingly. "I did not win a prize."

"You did not *think* you won a prize," said the Trader smilingly, "but for *this* race there are *two* prizes—and this one is for you," and he placed the shawl in her arms.

That night, when they were back in the home place, after a long, long happy day, and Chi-weé was tucked safely in her blankety bed, she held her shawl close to her cheek and remembered the smile of the thin little girl. "How nice to win *two* prizes," she whispered into the soft folds, and settled down to sleep with a great content.

SUGAR HILL

Arna Bontemps

Arna Bontemps is a distinguished Negro writer. His understanding of boys and the problems of the country boy in a big city is evident in Sad-Faced Boy. *Rags, Willie, and Slumber have hitchhiked from Alabama to New York to visit their Uncle Jasper in Harlem. In this chapter the boys encounter a bossy little girl, who starts training them in spite of themselves.*

Slumber stretched out in the warm water of his bath. Rags and Willie had already dried themselves and put on the clean clothes that Uncle Jasper Tappin went out and got for them. Slumber's new things were hanging on a nail, waiting for him. As soon as he could get himself clean, dinner would be ready. Aunt Ludy had already called from the kitchen to remind him of that. And there she was calling again.

"Hurry up, you old slow poke boy. Remember you're in Harlem now. You got to get a move on."

Slumber heard what she said, but he couldn't get a move on. The warm bath felt too good. He had never been in a tub like this one, and he had begun to think that a bath tub was just about the finest thing in the world. He stood up and soaped himself all over again. Then once more he rolled in the water, washing the soap from his body. Yes, a bath tub was a fine thing for sure. Ho-hum, and the warm water was fine, too. It made you feel like closing your eyes and staying there a long, long time. Yes, ho-hum. Slumber closed his eyes. It would just be for a minute. He felt so comfortable in the long tub, the warm water. In one more minute he'd open his eyes and get out of the tub. Ho-hum!

But a minute passed and Slumber had not moved. Two minutes passed, five minutes, fifteen, *twenty-five* minutes! Uncle Jasper Tappin and Rags and Willie took their places at the table. Aunt Ludy started bringing things from the kitchen to the dining room. As she went back and forth, she called to Slumber three times. "Come on, slow poke, we just about ready to eat. Come on, you sad-faced boy, I'm putting the dishes on the table. Hurry up, you Slumber, you."

"Wonder what's keeping that boy," Uncle Jasper Tappin said.

"Maybe he got drowned in that bath tub," Willie said. "Slumber can't swim so good, you know."

The others laughed at little Willie, but they were tired of waiting for Slumber. After a few more minutes Aunt Ludy lost her patience.

"Jasper Tappin," she said, "go in there and see what's holding that boy back. The dinner's going to be all cold."

So Uncle Jasper Tappin went to the bathroom door and opened it. Slumber was not drowned. Nothing was holding him back, either. He was just fast asleep in the bath tub.

"Well, dog my cats," Uncle Jasper Tappin exclaimed. "This beats Jack Robinson, and *he* beat the *band*. Gone to sleep in the bath tub, and all of us sitting at the table waiting for him. You Slumber! You better get up from there, boy. Don't you know the dinner will get cold? Wake up, I say. Rags and Willie and me is about starving. We can't wait for you to take a nap in the bath tub."

Slumber opened his eyes, rolled them sadly. Ho-hum, the warm water felt *so* good.

"I didn't go to do it, Uncle Jasper Tappin. For a fact, I really didn't. But this old bath tub feels so good, this old water is so warm and nice, this old soap smells so good, I just couldn't help it. But I'm coming directly now. I'll be there before you can bat your eye. You just see if I don't."

It did not take Slumber long to get himself dried and dressed, but by the time he reached the table the others were eating.

"Well, that's a new something you bringing up here," Aunt Ludy said, "going to sleep in the bath tub. But never mind, you'll learn to keep your eyes open if you stay up here long."

The dinner was good. The boys finished eating and Uncle Jasper Tappin pushed his chair back from the table.

"Well, has everybody got a plenty?" he asked.

"Yes, sir," the boys murmured.

"No more greens and back bone? No more salad? No more rice and gravy? No more strawberry short cake?"

"No more nothing," Slumber said slowly. "We can't hardly move now. This the best dinner we had in a month or more."

"Well, I'm glad you got enough," Aunt Ludy said. "We'll just have something light for supper when you come in this evening."

"It's most too late to do any real work today," Uncle Jasper Tappin said. "Yet and still we can look the apartment house over and get you ready to do some real helping later on."

The boys followed him out to the elevator and Uncle Jasper Tappin rang the bell.

"Isn't that an elevator over there, too?" Slumber asked as they waited for the door to open.

"Yes," Uncle Jasper Tappin said. "That's what you call the service elevator. We use that for hauling freight and trash. But we're not working just now, so we'll go up on the regular elevator if that boy ever gets here."

The door opened finally, and the three boys stepped in ahead of Uncle Jasper Tappin.

The elevator boy wore a red uniform with large gold buttons.

"Which floor?" he asked.

"Thirteen," Uncle Jasper Tappin told him.

The thirteenth floor was really the roof. The boys, walking behind their uncle, went outside and looked at the blue sky.

Then they walked to the front wall and looked down on the park. They looked at all the roof-tops of Harlem and the streets far below. There was so much to see Slumber scarcely knew what to look at.

"This here is New York?" he whispered.

"Yes," Uncle Jasper Tappin said. "This is New York. See up there . . . That's the downtown part."

"What's that great tall building?" Rags asked.

"The Empire State Building, that is. And up this-a-way is the Bronx. And all down below, all around the park there and up that-a-way towards that other park yonder—well, that's all Harlem."

"There's a plenty to see," Slumber said.

"You mighty right about that. More than you can see in one day, or one week either," the old man said.

Slumber slipped his mouth organ from his pocket and began playing softly. The other two boys leaned their elbows on the wall and continued to look at the sights. After a while Slumber paused to rub his lips and think up a new song to play.

"I always wanted to see New York," he told Uncle Jasper Tappin.

"Well, you boys just look around for a while," the old man said. "I'm going down to see if the halls are all clean. I'll be back soon."

Slumber began a new tune when the three boys were alone.

"What that you playing now?" Willie asked. "I never heard you play that before."

"No, I reckon you never did," Slumber said. "I'm just making it up as I go. It's a song about three country boys in a great big city."

"About you and me and Rags?"

Slumber just nodded his head. He was playing again and he couldn't stop to talk. Soon he began patting his foot. The music trickled out sweetly. Willie sat down and began drumming on a tin can with two sticks. Rags put his fingers in his mouth and whistled like an old train whistling as it leaves Alabama. He shuffled his feet slowly, began dancing.

As he danced lazily to the music of Slumber and Willie, Rags began to think of words to go with the music.

"Aw, blow your whistle, Mister Railroad Train," he said. "Blow your whistle on the Dixie line. Sun in the sky, not a tree in sight. Country boys in a big man's town."

Slumber was playing for all he was worth by now. Willie was trying to beat holes in his tin can. Rags made the sound of that train whistle again and continued to shuffle drowsily. "Aw, blow your whistle on the Dixie line."

Then suddenly Slumber observed that someone else was listening to the music. It was nobody he knew, nobody he had ever seen before. She wore a little checkered skirt with suspender-like straps over the shoulders, and there was a red tam on her head. She had come out of the door quietly, but now that she was near the music, she began to clap her hands. The girl watched the boys for a while, then clicked her heels and made a few little steps of her own.

"Where you learn that music, you sad-faced boy, you?" she said pleasantly. "Who taught you how to blow that harp?"

Slumber shook his head.

"Don't ask me nothing," he told her, pausing. "Don't ask me a thing. We just got to Harlem and we can't sit down."

"Well, listen to me," the girl said, putting her feet down emphatically. "You do right well yourself, old sad-faced boy, but your two brothers here need to learn something if they want to play music in this town. Let me show you how to beat that drum there, little bubber. Move over." She shoved Willie aside. Then, turning to Rags, she added, "When I get through here, I'll show you how to dance, tall boy."

Willie gave up his sticks reluctantly. Slumber rubbed his lips and knocked the harmonica against his knee. Then he began playing again.

"See there," the girl said, catching the rhythm and tapping the can like a real drummer. "It's easy when you know how."

"Hum!" Willie said unpleasantly. "Hum!"

Anybody could see that the happy-faced little girl could do more good drum beating in a minute than Willie could do in an hour. Even Willie could see that, so there was nothing for him to say but *hum*.

Rags had quit dancing and stood beside his small brother observing carefully every move the newcomer made as she beat the traps to Slumber's harmonica playing. When he was thoroughly convinced that she knew her business and that there was no fault to be found with her playing, he said softly, "What's your name, anyhow?"

"Daisy Bee," she said. A little later she asked, "Where did you boys come from?"

"Way down the line," Rags told her. "Alabama. We come up here to see our Uncle Jasper Tappin. We heard a lot of talk about New York and Harlem."

"Oh, he's your uncle! Well, did you ever hear about Sugar Hill?" she asked.

The boys shook their heads.

"Where'bouts is that?" Willie said.

"Right here," Daisy Bee explained. She stopped and pointed with one of the drum sticks. "All the hill up on this side of the park is Sugar Hill. This is about the best row of apartment houses in Harlem, and this one that we're on is the tallest of all. Look down that way and you can see."

Slumber paused to look with the others.

"Oh, yes."

"But we haven't got time for a lot of looking now," Daisy Bee said, getting up from the floor. "Take your drum back, little bubber. Let me see if you can beat it any better since I showed you how. Strike up another tune, sad-faced boy. Come on, tall boy, let me show you how to get those steps right. Maybe I can make something out of you three yet."

The boys didn't exactly like the way Daisy Bee talked. She was high-handed. She simply told you what she wanted you to do and you had to do it. She didn't give you a chance to answer. This irritated Slumber as well as Rags and Willie, but none of them did more than frown a little before they obeyed.

"Take your hands out your pockets and do what she says," Slumber told his brothers. "You can see well as me what we're up against. It's the best thing to let a girl like Daisy Bee have her own way."

The others seemed to agree. They had to let her teach them.

THE HUNDRED DRESSES

Eleanor Estes

Unlike most of Eleanor Estes' other books—the popular Ginger Pye (*Newbery Award*), The Moffats, The Middle Moffat, *and* Rufus M., *which are exceedingly funny—this book is a serious treatment of a grave problem. Children are not likely to forget Wanda, who was rejected by the group, nor the culprits who taunted her.*

Wanda

Today, Monday, Wanda Petronski was not in her seat. But nobody, not even Peggy and Madeline, the girls who started all the fun, noticed her absence.

Usually Wanda sat in the next to the last seat in the last row in Room 13. She sat in the corner of the room where the rough boys who did not make good marks on their report cards sat; the corner of the room where there was most scuffling of feet, most roars of laughter when anything funny was said, and most mud and dirt on the floor.

Wanda did not sit there because she was rough and noisy. On the contrary she was very quiet and rarely said anything at all. And nobody had ever heard her laugh out loud. Sometimes she twisted her mouth into a crooked sort of smile, but that was all.

Nobody knew exactly why Wanda sat in that seat unless it was because she came all the way from Boggins Heights, and her feet were usually caked with dry mud that she picked up coming down the country roads. Maybe the teacher liked to keep all the children who were apt to come in with dirty shoes in one corner of the room. But no one really thought much about Wanda Petronski once she was in the classroom. The time they thought about her was outside of school hours, at noontime when they were coming back to school, or in the morning early before school began, when groups of two or three or even more would be talking and laughing on their way to the school yard.

Then sometimes they waited for Wanda—to have fun with her.

The next day, Tuesday, Wanda was not in school either. And nobody noticed her absence again, except the teacher and probably big Bill Byron, who sat in the seat behind Wanda's and who could now put his long legs around her empty desk, one on each side, and sit there like a frog, to the great entertainment of all in his corner of the room.

But on Wednesday, Peggy and Maddie, who sat in the front row along with other children who got good marks and didn't track in a whole lot of mud, did notice that Wanda wasn't there. Peggy was the most popular girl in school. She was pretty; she had many pretty clothes and her

when they say, 'October's bright blue weather.' "

Maddie remembered that because afterwards it didn't seem like bright blue weather any more, although the weather had not changed in the slightest.

As they turned from shady Oliver Street into Maple, they both blinked. For now the morning sun shone straight in their eyes. Besides that, bright flashes of color came from a group of a half-dozen or more girls across the street. Their sweaters and jackets and dresses, blues and golds and reds, and one crimson one in particular, caught the sun's rays like bright pieces of glass.

A crisp, fresh wind was blowing, swishing their skirts and blowing their hair in their eyes. The girls were all exclaiming and shouting and each one was trying to talk louder than the others. Maddie and Peggy joined the group, and the laughing, and the talking.

"Hi, Peg! Hi, Maddie!" they were greeted warmly. "Look at Cecile!"

What they were all exclaiming about was the dress that Cecile had on—a crimson dress with cap and socks to match. It was a bright new dress and very pretty. Everyone was admiring it and admiring Cecile. For long, slender Cecile was a toe-dancer and wore fancier clothes than most of them. And she had her black satin bag with her precious white satin ballet slippers slung over her shoulders. Today was the day for her dancing lesson.

Maddie sat down on the granite curbstone to tie her shoelaces. She listened happily to what they were saying. They all seemed especially jolly today, probably because it was such a bright day. Everything sparkled. Way down at the end of the street the sun shimmered and turned to silver the blue water of the bay. Maddie picked up a piece of broken mirror and flashed a small circle of light edged with rainbow colors onto the houses, the trees, and the top of the telegraph pole.

And it was then that Wanda had come along with her brother Jake.

They didn't often come to school together. Jake had to get to school very early because he helped old Mr. Heany, the school janitor, with the furnace, or raking up the dry leaves, or other odd jobs before school opened. Today he must be late.

Even Wanda looked pretty in this sunshine, and her pale blue dress looked like a piece of the sky in summer; and that old gray toboggan cap she wore—it must be something Jake had found—looked almost jaunty. Maddie watched them absent-mindedly as she flashed her piece of broken mirror here and there. And only absent-mindedly she noticed Wanda stop short when they reached the crowd of laughing and shouting girls.

"Come on," Maddie heard Jake say. "I gotta hurry. I gotta get the doors open and ring the bell."

"You go the rest of the way," said Wanda. "I want to stay here."

Jake shrugged and went on up Maple Street. Wanda slowly approached the group of girls. With each step forward, before she put her foot down she seemed to hesitate for a long, long time. She approached the group as a timid animal might, ready to run if anything alarmed it.

Even so, Wanda's mouth was twisted into the vaguest suggestion of a smile. She must feel happy too because everybody must feel happy on such a day.

As Wanda joined the outside fringe of girls, Maddie stood up too and went over close to Peggy to get a good look at Cecile's new dress herself. She forgot about Wanda, and more girls kept coming up, enlarging the group and all exclaiming about Cecile's new dress.

"Isn't it lovely!" said one.

"Yeah, I have a new blue dress, but it's not as pretty as that," said another.

"My mother just bought me a plaid, one of the Stuart plaids."

"I got a new dress for dancing school."

"I'm gonna make my mother get me one just like Cecile's."

Everyone was talking to everybody else. Nobody said anything to Wanda, but there she was, a part of the crowd. The girls closed in a tighter circle around Cecile, still talking all at once and admiring her, and Wanda was somehow enveloped in the group. Nobody talked to Wanda, but nobody even thought about her being there.

Maybe, thought Maddie, remembering what had happened next, maybe she figured all she'd have to do was say something and she'd really be one of the girls. And this would be an easy

thing to do because all they were doing was talking about dresses.

Maddie was standing next to Peggy. Wanda was standing next to Peggy on the other side. All of a sudden, Wanda impulsively touched Peggy's arm and said something. Her light blue eyes were shining and she looked excited like the rest of the girls.

"What?" asked Peggy. For Wanda had spoken very softly.

Wanda hesitated a moment and then she repeated her words firmly.

"I got a hundred dresses home."

"That's what I thought you said. A hundred dresses. A hundred!" Peggy's voice raised itself higher and higher.

"Hey, kids!" she yelled. "This girl's got a hundred dresses."

Silence greeted this, and the crowd which had centered around Cecile and her new finery now centered curiously around Wanda and Peggy. The girls eyed Wanda, first incredulously, then suspiciously.

"A hundred dresses?" they said. "Nobody could have a hundred dresses."

"I have though."

"Wanda has a hundred dresses."

"Where are they then?"

"In my closet."

"Oh, you don't wear them to school."

"No. For parties."

"Oh, you mean you don't have any everyday dresses."

"Yes, I have all kinds of dresses."

"Why don't you wear them to school?"

For a moment Wanda was silent to this. Her lips drew together. Then she repeated stolidly as though it were a lesson learned in school, "A hundred of them. All lined up in my closet."

"Oh, I see," said Peggy, talking like a grown-up person. "The child has a hundred dresses, but she wouldn't wear them to school. Perhaps she's worried of getting ink or chalk on them."

With this everybody fell to laughing and talking at once. Wanda looked stolidly at them, pursing her lips together, wrinkling her forehead up so that the gray toboggan slipped way down on her brow. Suddenly from down the street the school gong rang its first warning.

"Oh, come on, hurry," said Maddie, relieved. "We'll be late."

"Good-by, Wanda," said Peggy. "Your hundred dresses sound bee-you-tiful."

More shouts of laughter greeted this, and off the girls ran, laughing and talking and forgetting Wanda and her hundred dresses. Forgetting until tomorrow and the next day and the next, when Peggy, seeing her coming to school, would remember and ask her about the hundred dresses. For now Peggy seemed to think a day

Well, whether Peggy felt badly or not, she, Maddie, had to do something. She had to find Wanda Petronski. Maybe she had not yet moved away. Maybe Peggy would climb the Heights with her and they would tell Wanda she had won the contest. And that they thought she was smart and the hundred dresses were beautiful.

When school was dismissed in the afternoon, Peggy said with pretended casualness, "Hey, let's go and see if that kid has left town or not."

So Peggy had had the same idea as Maddie had had! Maddie glowed. Peggy was really all right, just as she always thought. Peg was really all right. She was o.k.

Up on Boggins Heights

The two girls hurried out of the building, up the street toward Boggins Heights, the part of town that wore such a forbidding air on this kind of a November afternoon, drizzly, damp, and dismal.

"Well, at least," said Peggy gruffly, "I never did call her a foreigner or make fun of her name. I never thought she had the sense to know we were making fun of her anyway. I thought she was too dumb. And gee, look how she can draw! And I thought I could draw."

Maddie could say nothing. All she hoped was that they would find Wanda. Just so she'd be able to tell her they were sorry they had all picked on her. And just to say how wonderful the whole school thought she was, and please not to move away and everybody would be nice. She and Peggy would fight anybody who was not nice.

Maddie fell to imagining a story in which she and Peggy assailed any bully who might be going to pick on Wanda. "Petronski—Onski!" somebody would yell, and she and Peggy would pounce on the guilty one. For a time Maddie consoled herself with these thoughts, but they soon vanished and again she felt unhappy and wished everything could be nice the way it was before any of them had made fun of Wanda.

Br-r-r! How drab and cold and cheerless it was up here on the Heights! In the summer time the woods, the sumac, and the ferns that grew along the brook on the side of the road were lush and made this a beautiful walk on Sunday afternoons. But now it did not seem beautiful. The brook had shrunk to the merest trickle, and today's drizzle sharpened the outlines of the rusty tin cans, old shoes, and forlorn remnants of a big black umbrella in the bed of the brook.

The two girls hurried on. They hoped to get to the top of the hill before dark. Otherwise they were not certain they could find Wanda's house. At last, puffing and panting, they rounded the top of the hill. The first house, that old rickety one, belonged to old man Svenson. Peggy and Maddie hurried past it almost on tiptoe. Somebody said once that old man Svenson had shot a man. Others said "Nonsense! He's an old good-for-nothing. Wouldn't hurt a flea."

But, false or true, the girls breathed more freely as they rounded the corner. It was too cold and drizzly for old man Svenson to be in his customary chair tilted against the house, chewing and spitting tobacco juice. Even his dog was nowhere in sight and had not barked at the girls from wherever he might be.

"I think that's where the Petronskis live," said Maddie, pointing to a little white house with lots of chicken coops at the side of it. Wisps of old grass stuck up here and there along the pathway like thin wet kittens. The house and its sparse little yard looked shabby but clean. It reminded Maddie of Wanda's one dress, her faded blue cotton dress, shabby but clean.

There was not a sign of life about the house except for a yellow cat, half grown, crouching on the one small step close to the front door. It leapt timidly with a small cry half way up a tree when the girls came into the yard. Peggy knocked firmly on the door, but there was no answer. She and Maddie went around to the back yard and knocked there. Still there was no answer.

"Wanda!" called Peggy. They listened sharply, but only a deep silence pressed against their eardrums. There was no doubt about it. The Petronskis were gone.

"Maybe they just went away for a little while and haven't really left with their furniture yet," suggested Maddie hopefully. Maddie was beginning to wonder how she could bear the hard fact that Wanda had actually gone and that she might never be able to make amends.

"Well," said Peggy, "let's see if the door is open."

They cautiously turned the knob of the front door. It opened easily, for it was a light thing and looked as though it furnished but frail protection against the cold winds that blew up here in the winter time. The little square room that the door opened into was empty. There was absolutely nothing left in it, and in the corner a closet with its door wide open was empty too. Maddie wondered what it had held before the Petronskis moved out. And she thought of Wanda saying, "Sure, a hundred dresses . . . all lined up in the closet."

Well, anyway, real and imaginary dresses alike were gone. The Petronskis were gone. And now how could she and Peggy tell Wanda anything? Maybe the teacher knew where she had moved to. Maybe old man Svenson knew. They might knock on his door and ask on the way down. Or the post office might know. If they wrote a letter, Wanda might get it because the post office might forward it. Feeling very downcast and discouraged, the girls closed the door and started for home. Coming down the road, way, way off in the distance, through the drizzle they could see the water of the bay, gray and cold.

"Do you suppose that was their cat and they forgot her?" asked Peggy. But the cat wasn't anywhere around now, and as the girls turned the bend they saw her crouching under the dilapidated wooden chair in front of old man Svenson's house. So perhaps the cat belonged to him. They lost their courage about knocking on his door and asking when the Petronskis had left and anyway, goodness! here was old man Svenson himself coming up the road. Everything about Svenson was yellow; his house, his cat, his trousers, his drooping mustache and tangled hair, his hound loping behind him, and the long streams of tobacco juice he expertly shot from between his scattered yellow teeth. The two girls drew over to the side of the path as they hurried by. When they were a good way past, they stopped.

"Hey, Mr. Svenson!" yelled Peggy. "When did the Petronskis move?"

Old man Svenson turned around, but said nothing. Finally he did answer, but his words were unintelligible, and the two girls turned and ran down the hill as fast as they could. Old man Svenson looked after them for a moment and then went on up the hill, muttering to himself and scratching his head.

When they were back down on Oliver Street again, the girls stopped running. They still felt disconsolate, and Maddie wondered if she were going to be unhappy about Wanda and the hundred dresses forever. Nothing would ever seem good to her again, because just when she was about to enjoy something—like going for a hike with Peggy to look for bayberries or sliding down Barley Hill—she'd bump right smack into the thought that she had made Wanda Petronski move away.

"Well, anyway," said Peggy, "she's gone now, so what can we do? Besides, when I was asking her about all of her dresses she probably was getting good ideas for her drawings. She might not even have won the contest otherwise."

Maddie carefully turned this idea over in her head, for if there were anything in it she would not have to feel so bad. But that night she could not get to sleep. She thought about Wanda and her faded blue dress and the little house she had lived in; and old man Svenson living a few steps away. And she thought of the glowing picture those hundred dresses made—all lined up in the classroom.

At last Maddie sat up in bed and pressed her forehead tight in her hands and really thought. This was the hardest thinking she had ever done. After a long, long time she reached an important conclusion.

She was never going to stand by and say nothing again.

If she ever heard anybody picking on someone because they were funny looking or because they had strange names, she'd speak up. Even if it meant losing Peggy's friendship. She had no way of making things right with Wanda, but from now on she would never make anybody else so unhappy again. Finally, all tired out, Maddie fell asleep.

The Letter to Room 13

On Saturday Maddie spent the afternoon with Peggy. They were writing a letter to Wanda Petronski.

It was just a friendly letter telling about the contest and telling Wanda she had won. They

"Join"—"camp": those words were the keys to one of Hattie's dearest dreams.

Hatsuno had never been in the mountains. All her life she had lived where she could see them, stretching like a purple wall across the end of the dingy downtown street. They were beautiful, with snow-capped peaks shining pink and lavender and gold in the sunrise, and Hatsuno had always longed to explore them; but though they looked so near, they were miles and miles away.

The new school had given her hope. In the new school there was a Camp Fire group; and every summer it spent a few days at a camp far up in the mountains. Hattie had seen pictures of its bark-covered lodges climbing steeply among the tall evergreens beside a sparkling stream. She had heard Patty tell of the campfires and the horse-back rides. For Patty was a Camp Fire girl, and Patty's mother was the guardian of the group. Yet, friendly though Patty was, she never spoke of Hattie's joining. And Hattie was far too shy to bring up the subject.

In her old home she had not been so shy; but the old house had grown too small, and they had had to move to a larger one. Hattie, the first Noda baby, had been followed by five boys, and, as Harry said, each child shrunk the house a little bit more. This spring brought not only a new baby but a new grandmother, and the house was as small as Hattie's year-before-last coat. Even Mother couldn't let out its hems enough to make it do.

Mother could manage almost anything. During the depression, when Father was out of work, Mother had kept the children neat as wax and even stylish. She was always up, working, when Hattie woke in the morning, always up, mending and making over, when Hattie went to sleep at night. Mother was proud that even in the bad years Denver had few Japanese Americans "on relief": almost as few as in jail.

Even Mother could not stretch the house enough for the new baby and Great-Grandmother. So the Nodas had moved, uprooting the children from neighborhood and school. The new school was pleasant; Hattie's teacher, Miss Bender, was lovely; Patty White was the gayest, prettiest girl Hattie had ever met. But Hattie didn't fit in.

So here she was, walking home alone, with Camp Fire and the mountains as far away as ever. Teddy overtook her, making noises like a machine gun—like a railway train—like an airplane. Teddy's face was as round as a button, his eyes as black as coal, his teeth as white as rice.

"Last one home's a lame duck!" he chirped at her.

She did not hurry as once she would have done. Home was a changed place now; changed by Grandmother as well as by the new house.

Though Great-Grandmother had come from Japan ten years ago, Hattie had never seen her till this month. Great-Grandmother had lived with Aunt Kiku in San Francisco, until Aunt Kiku's death had left Grandmother alone.

She was not at all what Hattie had expected; not at all like grandmothers in books, comfortable, plump people who loved to spoil their grandchildren. No, Grandmother was not that kind.

Hattie slowly opened the door, which still quivered from Teddy's banging it. Little gray Grandmother sat stiffly erect, only her head bent toward the sock she was darning, her small feet dangling.

"How do you do, Grandmother?" said Hattie.

"How do you do, Elder Daughter?" Grandmother responded. There is no easy way to say "granddaughter" in Japanese.

Under their folded lids Grandmother's eyes traveled down Hattie. Hattie, feeling prickly, smoothed her hair, straightened her collar, twitched her checked skirt, and finally shifted her weight to one knee as Grandmother reached her feet.

"A cold day for bare legs," Grandmother observed. Hattie thought her look added, *And a great girl twelve years old should wear long stockings.*

Self-consciously Hattie's eyes pulled free from Grandmother's. "Oh," she cried, "Dicky's climbed on the piano again." She ran over and replaced the box of satiny white wood in which her latest—and last—doll always stood on view, fairly safe from the six boys. It was an enchanting doll, with glossy black hair and a silk kimono. "The other boys at least keep off the piano," Hattie scolded, "but not Dicky."

Grandmother's cool eyes seemed to say, *Boys*

have to be excused, since they're so much more important than girls. And why should a great girl of twelve care about dolls?

Hattie hurried on into the good-smelling kitchen. "Mother," she complained, "Grandmother doesn't understand that we're Americans, not Japanese. I bet she'd like me to flop down on my knees and bump my head on the floor the way you used to have to, and say, 'Honorable Grandmother, I have returned.' "

"Wash your hands," said Mother, "and help me get dinner on the table."

Hattie slapped her shoes down hard, as she went to the sink to wash. She wished her heels weren't rubber; they didn't make enough noise to express her feelings.

"Of course you will give proper courtesy to the old," Mother said quietly.

"Why? She doesn't even like me." The question was useless. Hattie had grown up knowing that politeness to the old was as much a law as honesty, industry, self-control—and minding parents.

Mother only said, "Stop and buy grapefruit on your way from school. Be sure to pick out heavy ones."

"Of course," Hattie grumbled. Hadn't she known how to choose good fruit and vegetables since she was nine?

Dinner was Japanese American. Seven Nodas—and Grandmother—crowded around an ordinary American table; but the utensils were chopsticks instead of knives and forks. The fish soup and the pickled radish were Japanese; the *pakkai* were American spareribs and the fluffy white rice was international. Bread and butter were pure American, and the dessert was Japanese gelatin, too firm to quiver. "It's not so nervous as American jelly," Harry said, and made Teddy laugh till his eyes went shut.

Only Grandmother seemed all Japanese; in the way she sipped her soup and tea, with a noise that was polite in Japan but not in America; in the way she refused bread and butter; in the way she greeted an old neighbor of the Nodas', who came in as they were finishing the meal.

Grandmother shuffled across the room, toeing in, because for sixty-five of her seventy-five years she had worn clogs; and she bowed the deep bow of old Japan, her withered hands sliding down to her knees. Why couldn't Grandmother be more American?

The neighbor had come to remind them that tonight was the festival called Buddha's Birthday. Grandmother's eyes brightened at the news. But Mother apologized: she could not go with Grandmother, for Saburo the new baby was feverish, and she could never bear to leave her babies when they were sick. Father? He had to work tonight. Thoughtfully Grandmother looked at Hattie. Hattie excused herself and hurried back to school.

Right up to the time school opened, she kept seeing Grandmother's eyes brighten and grow dull. If Hattie had been with Patty and the others on the schoolground, as she longed to be, she might have forgotten Grandmother. But sitting lonesomely at her desk, pretending to read, she could not forget.

Maybe it was good, after all, to have a rule about being kind to old people whether they like you or not. Hattie thought of Mother, taking care of her and her brothers when they were young and helpless. How dreadful if, when Mother grew old and helpless, they did not take turn about and care for her! Hattie frowned at her book, thinking.

"Mad, Hattie? My, but you're scowling!" teased Patty, pausing as she came in from the schoolground.

Hattie shook her head and smiled. If only Patty would sit down beside her and say the thrilling words, "Oh, Hattie, wouldn't you like to join Camp Fire?" If she would even say, "Can't you come over after school?"

But after school Hattie walked home alone, as usual, stopping for the grapefruit on her way. When she had put them in the home cooler, she hunted up Grandmother, and ducked her head in a shy bow. "Grandmother," she said, "if you want to go to Buddha's Birthday tonight, I'm sure Mother will let Harry and me go with you."

The Nodas were Methodists, so the Buddhist church was strange to Hattie and Harry. Tonight it was crowded, and all through the program small children trotted in and out and climbed over people's feet, with nobody minding. There were songs and dances and pantomimes, graceful kimonos, stately poses, dignified steps; and voices in the high falsetto which was the proper tone for Japanese actors, but which gave Hattie a funny, embarrassed feeling. "Such squeaky doors!" Harry whispered comically.

Coming home by street-car and bus, the three arrived so late that the house was all sleeping. Harry bade Grandmother good-night and stumbled drowsily to his room, but Grandmother lingered, eyes bright and cheeks flushed.

Hattie hunted for something to say. "The dancing was lovely," she said. "And the kimonos."

"I have one old kimono," Grandmother said, turning toward her door. With Hattie at her heels, she opened a dresser drawer and took out a silken bundle which she unfolded and held out, smiling faintly at Hattie's gasp of admiration.

"Chrysanthemums, for your aunt's name, Kiku, Chrysanthemum," said Grandmother. Gorgeous blossoms in many rich colors grew across the heavy blue crepe. "It was the only one saved from the great San Francisco fire. She wrapped it round one of her doll boxes." Grandmother motioned toward the drawer and a white wood box that lay there.

"Could I see?" Hattie stuttered.

"You may," Grandmother answered.

When Hattie slid open the box the breath of the Orient puffed out into her nostrils. She lifted the bag that protected the doll's hair and face, and gazed at the miniature lady, exquisitely moulded, and robed in brocades, padded, corded, embroidered. Clasping the box to her breast with one hand, Hattie pulled out a chair for Grandmother. "I don't know much about the doll festival," she coaxed shyly. "Here in Denver we don't."

She curled up on the floor at Grandmother's feet. "O Kiku San brought her doll set with her," Grandmother said, "when she married and came to America. This one is more than a hundred years old. We were taught to take care of things. The girls' festival—O Hina Matsuri—was a great day. It was play, but it taught us history and manners."

Looking from the doll to Grandmother, Hattie listened with all her might. She missed some words, for the Japanese the Nodas used at home was simple, and, to Hattie's relief, there had

been no Japanese Language School for some years now. Still, she could follow the story, and it made pictures for her in the quiet night: little-girl-Grandmother wearing enchanting kimonos, in charming rooms carpeted with cushiony mats; spending long hours learning to serve tea just so, to arrange flowers just so, to paint the difficult Japanese letters just so; learning to hold her face and voice calm no matter how she felt. Girl-Grandmother, writing poems with her friends and going to view the full moon, valuing beauty above riches. Grandmother, hearing about America, and longing to go where life was free for women. Grandmother, never able to come until she was too old to fit herself into this new land.

When the parlor clock struck one, Grandmother stopped short. "A girl of twelve should be asleep!" she said severely.

Next morning Hattie wondered if she had dreamed that companionable midnight visit, for Grandmother looked coldly at Hattie's bare knees and said, "Since you must run and jump like a boy, I suppose those ugly short clothes are necessary." But even while Hattie was biting her lip uncomfortably, Grandmother added, "Hatsuno, the chrysanthemum kimono and the doll are to be yours. After all, you are our only girl."

Home was beginning to seem homelike again.

That was fortunate for Hattie, since neighborhood and school were still strange. It was a relief to go back to their old district on Sundays, to the Japanese Methodist Church. And once Mother took the older children to an evening carnival at their old school. On the way they stopped at the store where they used to buy Japanese food, dishes, cloth. Clean and bright itself, it was jammed in among grimy second-hand stores and pawn shops. It was queer, Hattie thought, but no matter how clean people were, or what good citizens, if they happened to be born Chinese or Japanese or Mexican, they were expected to live down on these dirty, crowded streets, with the trucks roaring past. Yes, the new neighborhood and school were far pleasanter than the old—if only Hatsuno could fit in.

As Mother's Day approached, Hattie felt lonelier than ever. When she came into school two days before the tea, Patty, Sue and Phyllis were huddled round the teacher's desk. Miss Bender smiled approvingly at Hattie, who was already top student in Seventh Grade. Patty smiled, too, and looked at her expectantly. Hattie's heart thumped with the wish to push herself in amongst them. But how could she? She smoothed her starched skirt under her, sat down, and pretended to clean out her desk.

"It's such a late spring," Miss Bender was saying, "the lilacs aren't out. But I'll bring sprays of cherry-blossoms. And we must find out how many mothers to expect. I hope your mother is coming, Hattie."

"No, ma'am," Hattie said soberly. "The baby has chickenpox, and Mother just won't leave a sick baby."

"Haven't you an aunt or grandmother who could come in her place?"

Oh, dear! Grandmother would be so different from the rest. What would Patty think of her? Then Hattie's head came up. "I'll ask Great-Grandmother," she said.

She thought Grandmother would refuse. She hoped Grandmother would refuse. Instead, Grandmother asked, "Every girl should have mother or grandmother at this tea?"

"Yes, Grandmother."

"And your mother will not leave the baby. Elder daughter, you went with me to Buddha's Birthday. I go with you to school."

Hattie swallowed a lump in her throat. Grandmother was doing this because she thought Hattie wished it. Tea—Grandmother would sip it in Japanese fashion. Would she notice if the girls giggled? She would hide the fact if she did. Hattie thought of Grandmother's long training in the concealment of pain or disappointment. Well, that was a good heritage for anybody. Hattie would use it now. "Thank you, Grandmother," she said. "I will come and get you Friday, after school."

When the two came into the schoolroom that afternoon, the mothers were all there and having their tea, and it seemed to Hattie that everyone stopped talking and turned to gaze. Well, she and Grandmother must look pretty funny, Hattie thought.

Hattie was dressed like the other girls, in white sweater and short white skirt, her white anklets folded neatly above her oxfords, and her black hair out of its braids and done in another favorite style of the season. Grandmother, as short and slim as Hattie, wore a dress nicely made over from a kimono, but looking a little strange; and her gray hair was combed straight back from the withered little face with its slanting eyes.

Politely Hattie introduced Miss Bender to Grandmother, and pulled up one of the visitor's chairs, since Grandmother had never been to a tea where people stood up and balanced the dishes on their hands. Patty brought her a plate, Phyllis the sandwiches, Sue a cup of tea. Then Patty returned, pulling her mother after her. "Mom," she said, "here's Hattie. And here's her great-grandma." Patty dropped her mother's hand and stood beaming.

Hattie looked anxiously at Grandmother. She could not speak a word of English, nor the others a word of Japanese. But, instead of words, Seventh Grade and its mothers were bringing sandwiches and cakes till Grandmother's plate was heaped. And Grandmother sat there, as stately and self-possessed and smiling as if she went to seven teas a week.

Hattie studied her more closely. Others might think Grandmother's little face a mask, but Hattie saw that the eyes were bright again, and that the wrinkled cheeks were pink. Grandmother liked it! Grandmother felt happy and at home!

Maybe even a great-grandmother could be lonesome, especially when she was too old to learn the ways of a new land. Thinking so happily of Grandmother that she forgot all about her own shyness, Hattie squeezed Patty's arm, just as she might have squeezed Teddy's on some rare occasion when he was sweet instead of maddening.

Patty squeezed back—quickly, as if she had been waiting for the chance. "Mother!" she stuttered, in a voice that matched her gay fluff of curls. "Mother, I think maybe I was mistaken. I think Hattie might like to—" She looked eagerly up into her mother's questioning eyes—"You ask her, Mother!" she begged.

"About Camp Fire? Hattie, would you like to join our Camp Fire group?"

Hattie was silent from pure joy and astonishment.

"If I got your name in this week," Mrs. White continued, "you could go to camp with us. A camp in the mountains; do you know about it?"

"Oh, yes, ma'am, *I know,*" Hattie said with shining eyes. "Oh, yes, ma'am!"

STEPPIN'S FIRST PUBLIC APPEARANCE

Hope Newell

This first chapter from Steppin and Family *is a good introduction to an appealing hero and a lively story. Steppin, a Harlem Negro lad, hopes to dance like Bojangles Robinson, and who wouldn't want to, once having seen that remarkable tap dancer? Unfortunately, Steppin starts out with much too good an opinion of himself. His ups and downs are mostly downs for awhile, but he does begin to climb eventually.*

To see Steppin Stebbins racing down the street one warm afternoon in June, no one would have believed that he was on his way to school. Every other school day in the whole year it had needed his mother's warning, "You'll be late," and his little sister Mary Ellis' constant scolding to get Steppin through his lunch and back to his desk before the tardy bell rang. But this day was different.

It was the last day of school. No more lessons, no more homework, no more scrambling out of bed in a hurry, nothing but fun for two blessed months! But it was not so much the thought of freedom to come as the great event of that very afternoon that made Steppin hurry. For he was to do a solo tap dance at the closing exercises of his class. "My first public appearance," he thought proudly as he ran down the street.

A changing traffic light on Eighth Avenue brought him to an abrupt halt. Hopping up and down on the curb, Steppin stared impatiently at the stream of automobiles, trucks and street cars roaring by. The thunder of the elevated trains overhead, the clank and clatter of street cars and honks of taxis went unnoticed. His ears were tuned to city din.

"School is out
Hear me shout,"

he crooned under his breath, while his feet beat out a tap in the same rhythm. Brush, brush, hop with his right foot, and brush brush, hop with the left foot, over and over. While he danced Steppin kept an eye on the green signal light. Was it going to stay that way all day? Wouldn't it ever turn red?

At last it changed and Steppin darted across the street like a flash and scurried down the street. Out of habit he looked up at the street clock which generally told him he was in danger of being late. But today he saw that it had taken him only five minutes to come this far. As school was only two blocks away, Steppin slowed down to a walk and stopped before his favorite window, the pawn shop.

Treasures of all kinds were heaped together in the dusty shop window; guns, tennis rackets, telescopes, banjos, roller skates and jack knives. Steppin always played a game before that window. He picked out the thing he would most like to buy if he had all the money he wanted. He usually spent a long time over that choice, weighing values carefully. But this day he paid no attention to the wonderful display. He had caught sight of his reflection in the gilt mirror that stood at the back of the show case.

He eyed himself proudly. "Boy, I sure do look

like a professional," he murmured, strutting a little and grinning broadly. His coffee-brown face, shining with the scrubbing he had given it, grinned back at him, showing all of his ivory white teeth. His hair under the tight skull cap he wore was slicked so close to his skull that it looked as if it was painted on. His big black eyes took in the navy blue coat of his Sunday suit, the stiffly starched white shirt with a little black bow tie, and the white duck trousers which his friend Charley Kee, the Chinese laundry man, had pressed for him in exchange for errands. Steppin sighed with satisfied approval.

Steppin had pored over the pictures of Negro celebrities who performed in night clubs and theatres, and this costume was the best imitation of his idols that he could manage. Except for one thing Steppin was greatly pleased with the elegant entertainer he saw reflected in the mirror. His shoes were all wrong. He had no soft flexible slippers with metal taps on their tips like a real dancer. He wore a pair of old sneakers and had stuck a cluster of thumb tacks in the tip of each sole to use for taps. They did pretty well, but Steppin was not satisfied with them.

"Oh, well, you can't have everything at once, I suppose," he consoled himself. "Anyway when I get to be a professional I'm going to have six dozen pairs of dancing shoes at a time, with solid silver taps on every single one of them. Even platinum, maybe, if I want to."

Steppin's dreams of the future carried him happily on to school. A few boys were playing ball in the playground. They called to Steppin to join them. "Not a chance," thought Steppin, not when he was about to make his first public appearance as a dancer. He must keep his clothes in order for an occasion like this. So he entered the large brick building and ran up the stairs to his class room.

Steppin hardly recognized the familiar room, it looked so festive with garlands of evergreens on the walls and bowls of flowers on the window sills. Some of the girls, who were helping the teacher, Miss Blair, decorate the room, looked festive too, in their frilly dresses of pink and blue and white, their hair gay with bows of bright ribbons. Miss Blair herself, in a blue silk dress, with her blond hair fluffed out around her face, looked young as a girl, Steppin thought.

Miss Blair's desk had been taken away, and two big jars of lilacs stood one on each side of the platform. A bright poster painted by some of the children served as a back drop. Steppin surveyed it with approval. It looked almost like a stage.

But suddenly he thought of the moment when he would have to step up there before all the boys and girls. Cold shivers went up his spine. A strange sinking feeling gripped him in the stomach. He was scared! Steppin had never thought of that.

"Oh my gosh, I've got to make good, and here I am as jumpy as a cat," he thought as he slid into his seat. His own name, Stephen A. Stebbins, seemed to jump at him from the neatly printed program on his desk. He stared at it and clenched his clammy hands under the desk.

While the other boys and girls, demure and solemn in their best clothes, took their seats, Steppin anxiously went over in his mind the dance routine he had so carefully worked out. He counted out the steps to the tune of *Marching Through Georgia* which his sister, Mary Ellis, was to play for his accompaniment. Brush, brush, hop and brush, brush, hop; and heel and toe and break. "Gee, I wish I could have a tune with some snap to it," he thought. But the few selections which Mary Ellis could play by ear on the wheezy old organ at home did not include pieces with snap.

In a daze Steppin heard Miss Blair make her little opening speech and then announce: "And now we will have the first number on our program, a recitation of Kipling's poem *If* by Martin Burns, Junior." Martin had been speaking that piece on every school program since he was in the fourth grade and never yet had he been able to get through all the "ifs" without help. Steppin had never before felt the slightest interest in his struggles, but now he found himself waiting in an agony of suspense every time Martin hesitated. When for the fourth time he began "Eff you can" and stopped, open mouthed, with imploring eyes fixed on Miss Blair, Steppin knew how he felt. Suppose I forget my dance steps! But Miss Blair, with whispered prompting, urged Martin on to the final line which he knew by heart and which he spoke in ringing triumphant tones. "AND WHAT IS MORE, YOU'LL BE A MAN, MY SON."

spell, 'cause there's somethin' I've got to talk to the sheriff about. There won't be much business here until the double feature is over and I'll be back before then."

Then as Uncle Ulysses went out the door he said, "Uh, Homer, after you get the pieces in place, would you mind mixing up a batch of doughnut batter and put it in the machine? You could turn the switch and make a few doughnuts to have on hand for the crowd after the movie . . . if you don't mind."

"O.K." said Homer, "I'll take care of everything."

A few minutes later a customer came in and said, "Good evening, Bud."

Homer looked up from putting the last piece in the doughnut machine and said, "Good evening, Sir, what can I do for you?"

"Well, young feller, I'd like a cup o' coffee and some doughnuts," said the customer.

"I'm sorry, Mister, but we won't have any doughnuts for about half an hour, until I can mix some dough and start this machine. I could give you some very fine sugar rolls instead."

"Well, Bud, I'm in no real hurry so I'll just have a cup o' coffee and wait around a bit for the doughnuts. Fresh doughnuts are always worth waiting for is what I always say."

"O.K.," said Homer, and he drew a cup of coffee from Uncle Ulysses' super automatic coffee maker.

"Nice place you've got here," said the customer.

"Oh, yes," replied Homer, "this is a very up and coming lunch room with all the latest improvements."

"Yes," said the stranger, "must be a good business. I'm in business too. A traveling man in outdoor advertising. I'm a sandwich man, Mr. Gabby's my name."

"My name is Homer. I'm glad to meet you, Mr Gabby. It must be a fine profession, traveling and advertising sandwiches."

"Oh no," said Mr. Gabby, "I don't advertise sandwiches, I just wear any kind of an ad, one sign on front and one sign on behind, this way. . . . Like a sandwich. Ya know what I mean?"

"Oh, I see. That must be fun, and you travel too?" asked Homer as he got out the flour and the baking powder.

"Yeah, I ride the rods between jobs, on freight trains, ya know what I mean?"

"Yes, but isn't that dangerous?" asked Homer.

"Of course there's a certain amount a risk, but you take any method a travel these days, it's all dangerous. Ya know what I mean? Now take airplanes for instance . . ."

Just then a large shiny black car stopped in front of the lunch room and a chauffeur helped a lady out of the rear door. They both came inside and the lady smiled at Homer and said, "We've stopped for a light snack. Some doughnuts and coffee would be simply marvelous."

Then Homer said, "I'm sorry, Ma'm, but the doughnuts won't be ready until I make this batter and start Uncle Ulysses' doughnut machine."

"Well now aren't you a clever young man to know how to make *doughnuts!*"

"Well," blushed Homer, "I've really never done it before but I've got a receipt to follow."

"Now, young man, you simply must allow me to help. You know, I haven't made doughnuts for years, but I know the best receipt for doughnuts. It's marvelous, and we really must use it."

"But, Ma'm . . ." said Homer.

"Now just *wait* till you taste these doughnuts," said the lady. "Do you have an apron?" she asked, as she took off her fur coat and her rings and her jewelry and rolled up her sleeves. "Charles," she said to the chauffeur, "hand me that baking powder, that's right, and, young man, we'll need some nutmeg."

So Homer and the chauffeur stood by and handed things and cracked the eggs while the lady mixed and stirred. Mr. Gabby sat on his stool, sipped his coffee, and looked on with great interest.

"There!" said the lady when all of the ingredients were mixed. "Just *wait* till you taste these doughnuts!"

"It looks like an awful lot of batter," said Homer as he stood on a chair and poured it into the doughnut machine with the help of the chauffeur. "It's about *ten* times as much as Uncle Ulysses ever makes."

"But wait till you taste them!" said the lady with an eager look and a smile.

Homer got down from the chair and pushed a button on the machine marked, "Start." Rings of batter started dropping into the hot fat. After a ring of batter was cooked on one side an automatic gadget turned it over and the other side would cook. Then another automatic gadget gave the doughnut a little push and it rolled neatly down a little chute, all ready to eat.

"That's a simply *fascinating* machine," said the lady as she waited for the first doughnut to roll out.

"Here, young man, *you* must have the first one. Now isn't that just *too* delicious!? Isn't it simply marvelous?"

"Yes, Ma'm, it's very good," replied Homer as the lady handed doughnuts to Charles and to Mr. Gabby and asked if they didn't think they were simply divine doughnuts.

"It's an old family receipt!" said the lady with pride.

Homer poured some coffee for the lady and her chauffeur and for Mr. Gabby, and a glass of milk for himself. Then they all sat down at the lunch counter to enjoy another few doughnuts apiece.

"I'm so glad you enjoy my doughnuts," said the lady. "But now, Charles, we really must be going. If you will just take this apron, Homer, and put two dozen doughnuts in a bag to take along, we'll be on our way. And, Charles, don't forget to pay the young man." She rolled down her sleeves and put on her jewelry, then Charles managed to get her into her big fur coat.

"Good night, young man, I haven't had so much fun in years. I *really* haven't!" said the lady, as she went out the door and into the big shiny car.

"Those are sure good doughnuts," said Mr. Gabby as the car moved off.

"You bet!" said Homer. Then he and Mr. Gabby stood and watched the automatic doughnut machine make doughnuts.

After a few dozen more doughnuts had rolled down the little chute, Homer said, "I guess that's about enough doughnuts to sell to the after theater customers. I'd better turn the machine off for a while."

Homer pushed the button marked *"Stop"* and there was a little click, but nothing happened. The rings of batter kept right on dropping into the hot fat, and an automatic gadget kept right on turning them over, and another automatic gadget kept right on giving them a little push and the doughnuts kept right on rolling down the little chute, all ready to eat.

"That's funny," said Homer, "I'm sure that's the right button!" He pushed it again but the automatic doughnut maker kept right on making doughnuts.

"Well I guess I must have put one of those pieces in backwards," said Homer.

"Then it might stop if you pushed the button marked *"Start,"* said Mr. Gabby.

Homer did, and the doughnuts still kept rolling down the little chute, just as regular as a clock can tick.

"I guess we could sell a few more doughnuts," said Homer, "but I'd better telephone Uncle Ulysses over at the barber shop." Homer gave the number and while he waited for someone to answer he counted thirty-seven doughnuts roll down the little chute.

Finally someone answered, "Hello! This is the sarber bhop, I mean the barber shop."

"Oh, hello, sheriff. This is Homer. Could I speak to Uncle Ulysses?"

"Well, he's playing pinochle right now," said the sheriff. "Anythin' I can tell 'im?"

"Yes," said Homer. "I pushed the button marked *Stop* on the doughnut machine but the rings of batter keep right on dropping into the hot fat, and an automatic gadget keeps right on turning them over, and another automatic gadget keeps giving them a little push, and the doughnuts keep right on rolling down the little chute! It won't stop!"

"O.K. Wold the hire, I mean, hold the wire and I'll tell 'im." Then Homer looked over his shoulder and counted another twenty-one doughnuts roll down the little chute, all ready to eat. Then the sheriff said, "He'll be right over. . . . Just gotta finish this hand."

"That's good," said Homer. "G'by, sheriff."

The window was full of doughnuts by now so Homer and Mr. Gabby had to hustle around and start stacking them on plates and trays and lining them up on the counter.

"Sure are a lot of doughnuts!" said Homer.

"You bet!" said Mr. Gabby. "I lost count at twelve hundred and two and that was quite a while back."

People had begun to gather outside the lunch room window, and someone was saying, "There

ert, poison springs. The land that had nourished and clothed and sheltered his race since the beginning of time.

It was like looking at part of himself, and it filled him with a happiness that was primitive and simple and satisfying. For the moment the meaning of his own name took on a deep significance—Inyo, the dwelling place of a great spirit.

Moving from dream to dream as clouds form and reform in a summer sky Inyo suddenly realized that the shadows had got long and the mountains were turning cold. He was still far below the trails of the Bighorn sheep. He listened for the soft pad on the pine needles of hoof or paw. But the antelope and the deer had not yet come out of hiding, and the bear must have seen him first.

Then he saw the spirals of smoke drifting up from the woodlands below him, and his hand fell slowly away from his arrows. The smoke was sign that the campfires had been lighted. The boys down there would be running and jumping, the girls on rope swings hung from the branches—ropes made from the strong fibers of the Joshua tree that grows down where the valley borders the desert.

There would be much laughing and singing. The hunters would be showing the game they had brought in, and the squaws would be proud over their full baskets. The porcupines and the rabbits that the hunters had shot would be sizzling over the fires, and the grass nuts roasting in hot ashes. Doomdah's tepee would be already set up and bedded down in soft fir plumes and dried grasses—warm, sweet-smelling grasses. Her basket would be overflowing with big piñon nuts, her fire burning, and the hot stones ready for the pot basket.

The little Paiute shivered. The wind was beginning to whoosh through the treetops. It was time to go, and with a glance back at the heights he had never reached he named the place "Not Shoot Arrows," and broke into a short steady trot down the trail.

Inyo edged into the camp as if he had never been away. His head was downcast, his heart shamed. He had hunted and come back empty handed. But nobody seemed to notice it. Only Doomdah would notice it, Doomdah who had made him the bow and arrows. What would she say to him, what would she ask him: "Where is the game? I have gathered the piñon nuts alone, I have set up the tepee. I have broke off the fir plumes for our beds, and pulled the wild grasses with my own hands. Where is the game?"

Then he would tell her about tomorrow, how tomorrow he would be shooting what he hadn't shot today. Tomorrow the bear would be slower, tomorrow the deer would be less wary, tomorrow the eagle would be flying low. Doomdah would understand. He must find Doomdah and tell her about tomorrow.

But he couldn't see her anywhere. He went from fire to fire looking for his grandmother. If he could have asked: "Where is Doomdah?" someone might have told him. But while one has eyes it is for his eyes to seek out the answers. And his eyes saw everything but his grandmother. They saw the braves making big talk about their hunting, the squaws bending over the fires and cooking, the girls on swings under the trees, and the boys running foot races. And all he wanted to see was Doomdah.

Then he noticed that as he came to each fire the talking there stopped, and those who turned to smile at him—the kindly squaws and the braves who had brought in the meat—smiled without words. Smiles of compassion and comfort. But no words. Some of the squaws made a place for him by the fire. He just looked, and passed on. Where was Doomdah?

When he had gone by all the fires, and when he saw she was at none of them, he looked in all the tepees. And wherever he looked and wherever he stopped there came a hush as if it were something he had brought with him. Finally he went back to one of the first fires and sat down on the outermost edge of those who were sitting there. A squaw brought him food to eat, and he ate it.

When the eating was over the fires were allowed to die down—all except one. More wood was thrown on this one, but not too much, for if a fire is too large the heat and the smoke will drive you back into the cold again.

The Indians had gathered around this special fire. Now was the time for the Chief to speak, and brave after brave settled back on his haunches, and squaw after squaw hushed child and papoose, while all prepared to listen to what would be said—tales of that time when the Paiute heroes walked the earth, stories of those happy days when the desert was all meadows and forests, full of fruits and game.

Inyo had heard all this before, as had the other Indians. Year following year they had heard it, but still they listened. The glow from the pine logs etched each passive copper face against the black night, the occasional cry of a child was quickly stifled, the inattention of the young was corrected with a slight shove.

There was no argument. The talk came from the man who knew. He was never interrupted nor was he asked to prove his statements, but was listened to with a nod here and a smile there, and because what he said set the pattern of life for the Paiute, and because it was full of the wonder and the grandeur and the greatness of the race, the Indian could sit there and listen to it forever.

All except Inyo. He did not want ancestral heroes tonight. He wanted Doomdah. His thoughts went farther and farther away from the speaker, and closer and closer to his grandmother. Where was she? If there was no tepee where would she sleep tonight?

Inyo could not remember ever having had the care of either father or mother. Both had died back in those days when the white man's sickness, cholera, had touched the tribe. Since then it had been Doomdah's love that stood between him and the little griefs of his life. Now it was only Doomdah's stories that held interest for him. For Doomdah was a Chumash, and had come from Far Away, where the Chiefs were called Padres, where there were strange fruits and flowers, where there were sheep who ate from your hand, and cattle—

The little Paiute felt a heavy hand on his shoulder that unbalanced him and sent him sprawling over into the ashes. He looked up into the face of Hard Hoof, the Medicine Man, with the firelight shining back from his deep-set eyes.

"The talk is good," said Hard Hoof.

Inyo wiped the ashes out of his eyes with the back of his hand, and wondered how Hard Hoof had known he wasn't listening. He tried to forget about Doomdah and think only of Hy-nan-u, the ancestor that the speaker was now talking about. Hy-nan-u who was everybody's ancestor, who had taught the Paiute to be happy by going about doing good.

But how could Inyo be happy without Doomdah? From the time he had learned the difference between words and signs he had listened more to Doomdah than to anybody else. And there was more than Paiute words to her talk. She spoke words she had learned from the Padres, and she taught those words to him—Mission words. But this kind of talk was always a secret between them, and only when they were alone did they speak them, these strange, soft words of the Far Away.

Again Hard Hoof's heavy hand brought Inyo's thoughts back to the campfire.

"The talk is good," warned Hard Hoof.

Seeing that it was going to be more comfortable if he listened to what the speaker was saying, Inyo leaned well forward and stared at Chief Jobouri. He was the finest looking of a race of free-living men, straight and of good height, and neither young nor old. The firelight flickered over his headband of yellow quills, and when he waved his arms his skin shone like polished bronze, and his eyes flashed black fire.

"The Paiute never grows old," said Chief Jobouri.

There were nods of assent, and almost without his seeing them there were many quick glances shot at Inyo. The Chief was not looking at him, but most of the other Indians were, and those who weren't seemed to want to be looking.

The Waucobi land stretched from mountain to mountain, from desert to desert, pointed out the Chief. It was a beautiful land, but it was not a big land.

"This home of ours is a good home." The deep, rich voice was like music to those who listened. "The Waucobi gives generously to the Paiute. She gives us food and shelter, the red joy of the hunt and the pale peace of the tepee. But the Waucobi has a law, and only as we keep that law does she give these things to us." He waited for the hushing of a baby's cry before he went on.

"Everything changes—day is ever becoming night, summer keeps birthing into winter, sleep nourishes our activity. But the law itself never changes. As fire is dry and water is wet the law is

verge on the runner, on Keith, no, on Heywood. That big halfback, heavy, powerful, fast, had been slashing holes in their line all afternoon. In the mud and slime he seemed impossible to stop, and Ronny himself had tackled him half a dozen times.

The teams lined up. Heywood took the ball once more for a sizeable gain. But Ronald was noticing something else; he was watching Mike and two others break through and pile up on Keith. It was what they'd been doing ever since the kick-off. To his astonishment some of his teammates hadn't forgotten Goldman's injury of the previous season. They were still trying to pay Keith for his share in it.

There's a guy we don't like, so we'll bang him off at the start. This was their attitude. Ronny knew what they didn't seem to know, that Keith could take it. All the time they were attempting to bang him off, Steve Ketchum and Heywood had plowed through for those touchdowns.

Once again Heywood sliced into the line and out into the secondary. He was nearly clear before he slipped and fell. That's a break, that is. On the next play they made a first down, and then Keith got loose off tackle, his most dangerous run. It was Ronny who, seeing the danger on that sloppy field, managed to knock him outside after a thirty-yard gain. He picked himself up, now as wet and soggy as he had been at the end of the first half.

"C'mon, gang, get in there, get in there and play ball like you can, will ya? Block that end, Mike, watch him every minute; get in low, Jake."

But slowly, surely, steadily, the Academy came toward their goal, toward a fourth touchdown, toward the worst licking the High School had ever taken. Keith charged in low and hard between Vic and Don Westcott who alone seemed to be holding up the center of the line, playing a magnificent defensive game. Don slapped at him and threw him off his stride as Ronny came running up. The whole play was clear before him. Keith with one arm out, stumbling in the mud; Mike and Dave rushing in hard to fall on him so that if he wasn't knocked out he'd at least know he'd been hit. It made Ronald furious. He closed in, determined not to permit them to get away with it, to block off Dave anyway. He did block him off, and as he did so Mike accidentally slipped and hit him on the chin with the full force of his fist.

He saw stars. When he came to they were standing around in the mud. Doc Roberts was leaning over, wiping his face and holding smelling salts under his nose.

"I'm ok, Doc." He rose unsteadily, feeling dizzy, tried to step out a little, managed to trot a few steps. "I'm ok." But he was not ok, and he was mad clean through. This had to end. One thing or the other. They'd have to quit and play ball—or he would.

"C'm here, gang. This way. Look. This has gotta stop. It's gotta stop or I quit. If you guys don't lay off that bird, I'll leave the field, here, right now, and I'll tell Coach why. C'mon, gang, what say, gang, let's go. Let's forget that stuff. Let's get together, let's play against that crowd there, not against each other."

"You're dead right, Ronald!" Jim Stacey, adjusting his headgear, stepped in toward the center. "Listen, you guys, lay off that fella from now on and play ball. I've been watching you, and Ronny's quite right. We've been playing against each other, not together. Let's all shoot together for the team."

"Ok, Jim."

"All right, Jim-boy."

"Sure, let's go, gang."

"Yeah, let's go."

"All right now, get in there, you guys."

The whistle blew. The teams lined up. Ronald looked around. He was standing on the 8-yard line!

It was raining harder than ever. The Academy leaned over the ball. It was snapped to Heywood, who for the first time started a fraction of a second too soon. The ball was over his shoulder, he stabbed at it, deflected it in the air. A wet figure dashed past and snatched at it in the mist. He had it. Never missing a stride he was five yards down the field before anyone turned.

"Go on, Ned, go on Ned-Boy, for Pete's sake, go on. Don't slip, Ned, go on, Ned!"

The two teams picked themselves up out of the mud and streamed along behind him, but the fleet colored boy gained with every stride.

"Yeah, team! Team, team, team. Yeah, team!" The cymbals clashed and clanged from the High

School side of the field. The first chance they had had to cheer since the kick-off.

Now then, we're moving. We're really moving. For the rest of the third quarter the teams slithered up and down the center of the gridiron, both Keith and Ronald punting and handling that juicy sphere as if it were dry and easy to hold. Somehow they managed to cling to the thing.

Then toward the end of the quarter the High School team got moving. A quarterback sneak was good for a long gain. On the Academy 30-yard line, however, they were held for two plays. Third and six. They went into their huddle.

"Ok, gang. 39 on 5 count." He was winded, he puffed hard. This was Meyer's play. They went into formation.

"Hike. 27 . . . 38 . . . 40 . . . hike . . ." He leaned over, his hand on Don's wet rump. The ball came and for once the play was perfectly executed. He faked with his empty left hand to Jake, the halfback, and then in the same motion tucked the ball in Meyer's stomach, continuing back himself as if he were about to throw a pass. Meyer roared off Roger Treadway's end into the secondary, he bounced off Steve, straightarmed Rex Heywood, and carried Keith along on his back almost five yards. The High School stands were jumping, shrieking, yelling.

Then someone shouted. Over to the left in clear territory a figure lay in the wet. Jim had gone down on the play to fake catching a possible forward and draw in one of the defensive backs in their 5–4–2 alignment. Doing so he had turned, slipped, and fallen in the open. When Ronny reached him a group of players was huddled round and he was writhing in agony on the ground.

The Doc rushed up, shoving them aside. He knelt down in a puddle, began feeling of the thigh, the leg, the calf, the ankle.

"Ouch!" Jim perked up. "Ow . . . that hurts . . . ow . . ."

The Doc beckoned to the sidelines. "You lay still, young man. Lay still now, don't move."

Silence came over the field, and Ronny could hear them from the stands. . . . "It's Jake . . . naw . . . it's Perry . . . no, he's up there . . . it's Jim Stacey."

Two managers ran out with a stretcher. They rolled him over, protesting. Ronny saw he was in acute pain. On the bench Jack Train, his substitute, leaned over toward the coach. Then they were carrying Jim from the field.

The team stood disconsolately in the rain. Aw, shoot! Shucks, don't we get the breaks against us! How's that for rotten luck! First this stinking lousy weather. Then we lose our captain, the key of our passing attack, the man who was our best pass catcher.

Jack Train came running on, adjusting his dry headgear. His uniform was unsoiled, his hands were fresh and clean. Ronny looked at him almost with disgust. Heck! What good is he? Couldn't catch a dry ball at ten feet. What use is he on a day like this?

They tried a play. Then another. Something had gone, the mainspring of their nervous energy had snapped, there was no punch left. Baldy was a bear on scouting other teams, and Ronald well knew they'd been told that with Stacey out the High School's passing attack wasn't to be feared. He saw the defensive halfback in one zone slide up. Ideal for a pass if only he had a receiver.

Looking over the situation he called for a fake split buck-end run with Jake carrying the ball. But they were waiting, and although Meyer blocked out the defensive end, the halfbacks smeared the play for a small gain. Third and nine! Shoot! Just as we were rolling, too. That's lousy luck all right. Then he heard a voice at his elbow as they went into the huddle. It was Ned, who never raised his voice, who never spoke unless you spoke to him first—Ned, who was the best defensive end in the State but never carried the ball.

"Ronny. Lemme have a look at that thing. Shoot me that flat pass up the center. I b'lieve I kin hang on to that thing."

Why not? They were stopped now. Why not have a try at it? "Ok, gang. Number 46 on 4. Got it, everyone?" He looked round at their muddy faces, heard their panting, saw their affirmative nods. "C'mon now. Formation T. 46 on 4. Hike. 27–38–40–39 . . . hike . . ." He leaned over, patting Don on his wet back. Here it comes!

Taking the ball, he turned and scuttled to the

It is well for American children to discover early that their country is made up of many kinds of people, of many races, religions, and customs. Then, the transition to thinking about peoples of other countries is an easy and a natural one, founded on familiarity with and liking for many kinds of people in their own land. It is only a step from Hatsuno's charming little grandmother in America to Chinese Little Pear's understanding family. Swiss Kobi's acceptance of responsibility in the terrifying storm is close kin to the Little Paiute's brave decision. Pennsylvania Dutch Yonie Wondernose and French Canadian Pierre Pidgeon are equally full of curiosity and resourcefulness. And Chinese Young Fu and Negro Steppin are both ambitious and well-intentioned boys but subject to mistakes nevertheless. In short, human nature is human nature whether it is the American smart aleck, Jemima, paying dearly for showing off or Hungarian Kate eating too many sausages in an equally absurd bit of exhibitionism.

TODAY IN OTHER LANDS

Like the varied peoples in our United States, the heroes and heroines of these stories of other lands are a lovable group that American children will discover are more like themselves than different. For example, a third-grade class was talking about Kintu's fear of the jungle, and the teacher asked the children what they thought had cured Kintu of his fear. They decided that it wasn't the "charm" because that was "nothing but an old fruit pit." After considerable discussion, they thought perhaps Kintu got over being afraid when he had to stay in the jungle and found out that he could use the skills he had already learned to keep himself safe. Then the teacher asked the children if they had ever been afraid of something that they were not afraid of now. Practically every child had. Fear of the dark, of dogs, of deep water, and of a new school were mentioned most often. In each case, the children decided they had recovered from their fear when they did something about it and found out that they could take care of themselves in the dark or in deep water or in a new classroom or with strange dogs. After this discussion, Kintu seemed more than ever like themselves and fears a common difficulty to be dealt with and banished.

One thing children should find in books about other countries is authenticity in all the details and a true picture of the *everyday* life of the people. For a while, children's books about foreign lands read like travel folders. They presented the bizarre, the unusual, and the exotic. Life was a series of fiestas, gaily costumed and picturesque. The toil and struggle were missing. The stories chosen for this section, unlike such unrealistic tales, present everyday people faced with everyday problems, sometimes worried or frightened, sometimes gay or triumphant, but normally doing the best they can at work and play.

This is what stories about people of other lands should do for children—make them kindred under the skin. From such stories young readers develop a warm interest in people and in ways of living different from their own. What child, after reading *Heidi,* has not wanted a bed of straw in a loft and goat's milk and cheese to eat? The silversmiths of Mexico in "Four Silver Pitchers," the Hungarian ranch of *The Good Master,* Young Fu's work with the coppersmiths, the Iceland farm in *Smoky Bay,* little Pedro's jungle hut so lovingly prepared for his grandmother—these people and their ways of life seem as admirable as the child's own family and community. As a result of knowing vicariously peoples of other countries, children are predisposed to warm and friendly relationships with foreign groups when they encounter them in real life. To this end the stories in this group have been chosen.

SNIPP, SNAPP, SNURR AND THE RED SHOES

Maj Lindman

This story of the Swedish triplets by the author-artist Maj Lindman is one of a series. This little tale has a gaiety about it that matches the colorful illustrations of the original book. It is as popular as that other birthday story Ask Mr. Bear *by Marjorie Flack* (Time for Fairy Tales, *p. 257*).

Snipp, Snapp, and Snurr were three little boys who lived in Sweden.

One day Snipp said, "Mother, dear, tomorrow will be your birthday. Snapp and Snurr and I have talked about it, but we can't decide what to get you for a birthday present."

Snipp said, "I thought you might like a train."

Snapp said, "I thought you might like a pony."

Snurr said, "I know! You would like to have a red wagon!"

Mother thought for a moment. Then she said, "I would like a pair of red slippers, red slippers lined with gold."

Snipp, Snapp, and Snurr decided that mother must have her shoes.

They ran upstairs to their playroom to get their bank which was a white china pig with brown spots. The bank was on the high bookcase.

Snipp brought a chair.

Snapp climbed upon the chair, stood on tiptoe, reached for the bank, and handed it to Snurr. Then he climbed down.

The three little boys ran over to the table. They rattled their bank. They shook it, and

Snipp, Snapp, Snurr and the Red Shoes by Maj Lindman. Albert Whitman & Co., 1932. Used by permission of the publisher

rolled it from side to side to try to get out all their money.

But as long and as hard as they shook it, they could not get out enough money to buy the red shoes.

Snipp, Snapp, and Snurr decided that they must find a way to earn money.

The three little boys asked their mother if they might go out. They ran down the steps and walked toward the corner. All three of them were looking for ways to earn money.

Down the street, near the corner light they saw a neighbor painting a high board fence. It was a very high fence, so high that the man had to stand on a wooden box to reach the top.

Snipp said politely, "Do you need help, sir? I am quite sure that I could finish painting the fence."

The neighbor had many other things to do, so he was glad to have Snipp finish painting.

Snapp and Snurr walked on down the street. They were thinking of ways to earn money to buy the red shoes.

High on the red roof of a house they saw the village chimney sweep. He was cleaning out the chimney with brushes.

Suddenly he called loudly to one of the boys, "Snapp, come and help me!"

Both boys climbed up the tall ladder to the roof, and across the roof, to the very tallest chimney.

The man was nearly as black as the chimney he was sweeping. But he smiled kindly as he

said, "Snapp, you are so little you can get into the chimney and sweep it cleaner than I can. I will pay you if you will help me.

So Snurr left Snapp on the roof and climbed down all alone.

Snipp was painting a bright red fence.

Snapp was cleaning out the very blackest chimney he had ever seen.

Snurr walked on, wondering to himself what he could find to do. He must earn money to help buy the red shoes.

At last Snurr saw a big mill where wheat was ground into flour. Before the mill stood his friend, the miller. He wore a bright red cap and was smoking his longest pipe.

Snurr stepped up to him and said, "Please, sir, will you give me a job?"

The miller laughed, "Well, well, Snurr, what do you say? You want to be a miller? Good! You can begin work now."

All three boys were very happy. Each one had found some way to earn money to help buy the red shoes for his mother.

Snipp drew his brush up and down the fence busily. He felt most important.

The fence grew brighter and brighter until it glistened in the sun.

Snipp worked so fast and used so much red paint that he spilled some of it all over his clothes. He even splashed red paint on his cheeks and his bare legs. So as the fence grew redder and redder, Snipp grew redder and redder, too.

His suit which was once such a pretty blue was all spattered with red.

Snapp's suit was not much better! Snapp pushed the brush up and down the dirty chimney. The black soot flew all over his nose, and his hair and his clothes. Soon his pretty blue suit was gray. Then it grew darker. And the longer he worked the blacker he got.

The cat which sat on the roof watching him was sure that a little black boy was hard at work!

But Snapp was very happy. Soon bright coins would jingle in his pocket which would help to buy the red slippers for mother.

And Snapp worked harder than ever, whistling a little tune as he worked.

Snurr was finishing his work. He had worked hard at the mill. Once he had surprised the miller by carrying a large sack of flour.

Snipp worked painting a fence, and he grew red.

Snapp worked cleaning a chimney, and he grew black.

Snurr worked at the flour mill, and he grew white from head to foot. He looked just like a snowman.

Money jingled cheerily in Snurr's pockets as he left the mill. The miller had been much pleased with his work.

Snurr now had his share of the money to help buy the red shoes for his mother.

Snipp, Snapp, and Snurr all finished their work at the same time.

As they were running happily home they met in the market place.

The little boy in red was Snipp.

The little boy in black was Snapp.

The little boy in white was Snurr.

Each took his money out of his pocket.

When they counted all their money they found that now they had enough to buy the red shoes.

Snipp, Snapp, and Snurr were very happy!

They decided to hurry to the shoemaker right away to see if he had the red shoes.

Down the street they went. It was nearly sunset and they were afraid the shop might close.

They ran into the shoemaker's shop, each carrying his part of the money.

Because Snipp was in the lead, he began, "Mr. Shoemaker, have you—"

Because Snapp was next, he said, "red shoes lined with gold?"

Because Snurr was last he finished, "Shoes that will fit our mother's feet?"

The shoemaker laughed, "Have I red shoes lined with gold that will fit your mother's feet? That I have. They are right here on the shelf, the finest you can buy, near or far."

Snipp, Snapp, and Snurr each gave the shoemaker his part of the money.

The shoemaker wrapped the shoes up in a box, and the three little boys hurried home, each taking his turn to carry the package.

At last they were home. Because Snipp was the first to find work, Snapp and Snurr agreed that he should be the one to give the package to Mother.

"Here is a present for you, Mother!" they cried as they burst into the door.

Mother was surprised to see a red boy, a black boy, and a white boy, instead of her three little boys in blue.

"Snipp, Snapp, Snurr! Where have you been?" she cried.

"We have been earning money to buy you a birthday present, Mother dear, and here it is!" they answered.

Mother untied the string, unwrapped the box, and took out the red shoes lined with gold.

"Why, here are the red shoes that I wanted more than anything else," she cried. "They are the most beautiful slippers in the world!"

She was so happy that she waved her lovely red slippers in the air.

Snipp, Snapp, and Snurr, the three little boys, joined hands and danced around their mother. As they danced, they sang, "Happy birthday!"

PIERRE PIDGEON

Lee Kingman

It is hoped that the children who enjoy this unusual story will, when they are older, discover Lee Kingman's The Best Christmas. *Pierre is French Canadian and the Christmas story is about a Finnish-American family. Both stories have a convincing realism and warmth that are characteristic of this writer's work.*

Pierre Pidgeon was seven years old, waiting to be eight. He lived in a part of Canada called the Gaspé, which is a large piece of land surrounded on three sides by water.

His father was a fisherman who sailed out in his boat every day. Very often, he left early in the morning when Pierre was still asleep.

But every afternoon Pierre went down to the dock to watch his father's boat come in and to help unload the fish.

Since fishing didn't bring in much money to take care of the Pidgeon family, Pierre's mother baked bread in an outdoor oven and sometimes sold it to tourists who came along the road, and Pierre liked to help her.

Pierre liked to do lots of things. He liked to drive a dogcart—and sail on his father's boat.

But most of all he liked to build ship models. It took a great deal of patience to do this, but when he grew tired of it, Pierre would always run down to the beach to play.

He liked, too, visiting the store near the dock where the boats came in. The shelves were full of canned foods and fishing tackle and cloth and clothes for the people who lived in the town, and there were wood carvings for tourists who liked to buy souvenirs. But most of all Pierre liked the shelf halfway up on the right just inside the door. For one day when he walked into the store to buy a spool of thread for his mother, he looked at that shelf and right in the middle of it, he saw a beautiful ship model.

It was the nicest he had ever seen, and he thought it was even better than the ones he made because it was all inside a bottle!

Mr. LeClerc, who ran the store, saw Pierre

Pierre Pidgeon by Lee Kingman. Reprinted by permission of and arrangement with Houghton Mifflin Company, the authorized publishers

looking at the boat-in-the-bottle. "How do you like that ship model, Pierre?" he asked.

"I like it very much!" said Pierre, "but how did the man ever make it inside the bottle?"

"Ah," said Mr. LeClerc, and smiled at Pierre. "There is only one way for ships to get inside bottles. They grow inside!"

Pierre looked at Mr. LeClerc. "But boats aren't alive! How can they grow inside a bottle, if they aren't alive?"

Mr. LeClerc shook his head. "I don't know, Pierre. But ships can move just like dogs and horses and oxen, and how else could a boat get inside a bottle if it weren't very small indeed, as small as a seed bean?"

Every time he went to the store, he stopped to look at the boat-in-the-bottle and wish it belonged to him. Once he asked Mr. LeClerc how much it cost, and Mr. LeClerc put his head on one side and said, "That's a very good bottle. I should say a dollar."

Pierre felt very sad inside, because he knew he would never have a whole dollar all his own to spend.

His mother knew Pierre was seven, waiting to be eight, and one day when they were all sitting out by the windmill, she asked him what he would like for his birthday. Pierre thought of the shelf halfway up on the right just inside the door of the store by the dock and his eyes grew very bright. "I should like the boat in Mr. LeClerc's store!" he cried. "The boat-in-the-bottle!"

Pierre's mother smiled at him. "But you can make boats," she said.

Pierre sighed. "But I can't bottle them!" he said.

One day Pierre walked along the road driving Henri, the ox, to the pasture. Henri was not an ox to be hurried, so Pierre strolled behind, only switching him once in a while when he stopped to munch clover by the roadway.

When they came to the pasture, there was a

fine long view of the sea and Pierre sat down to look at it. As it was a very warm day, he soon put his cap over his face and went to sleep.

But it did not take him long to wake up, when he heard someone calling, "Oh, help!"

He jumped up!

He saw a lady caught in a corner of the pasture fence by a very large ox. His horns were lowered, but Pierre knew from the spots on his back that it was Henri. Pierre ran up and held onto his tail. "He will not hurt you," he told the lady. "Henri is a very gentle ox."

"That may be," said the lady, "but I'd just as soon he stopped staring me in the face."

Pierre tugged at Henri's tail and the ox turned away and went back to the clover. The lady brushed her skirts and picked up the little camp stool and small easel she had dropped.

"I want to paint a picture," she said. "Do you think you can keep that ox from pushing me off the edge of the cliff while I do it?"

Pierre said he thought he could, so the lady set up her camp stool and sat on it and balanced her easel so that it stood up straight. She took out her sketch pad and arranged her paints on the ground. Pierre sat down where he could watch Henri, who was not fierce at all when you knew him. And he also kept an eye on the lady, who squinted out at the ocean as she painted.

"What is that odd-looking rock out there?" she asked Pierre.

"That is the ship of stone," Pierre explained, "because it is shaped like a boat."

The lady worked a long time and Pierre felt that she kept looking at him, too. When she put her paints away and finished washing off her paint brushes, Pierre jumped up. He wanted to see what she had painted.

The lady let him look and right spank in the middle of the picture was Pierre Pidgeon, keeping an eye on Henri.

"That's me!" cried Pierre.

"So it is," said the lady. "And here is something for rescuing me from the ox." She gave Pierre a dollar!

When he had stopped looking hard at the dollar and said thank you, he gave Henri a warm slap and ran off down the road to the village.

There was Mr. LeClerc's store and Pierre stopped short just outside the door. Suppose someone else had bought the boat-in-the-bottle! His heart beat three times as fast as it usually did, when he walked in the door. And then his heart beat even faster than that—the boat-in-the-bottle was still there!

"Good afternoon, Mister Pidgeon," said Mr. LeClerc smiling at him. "Have you come for another look at your boat?" Pierre nodded and looked at it speechlessly. The bottle shone in the afternoon sunlight and the little boat inside looked as if it were sailing along on a good stiff breeze.

Pierre felt the dollar in his hand and then he walked all around the store. There were the big round balls of colored candy that his little sister liked, and there were the silky skeins of embroidery thread his mother liked. But Pierre came back to the shelf halfway up on the right, just inside the door.

"Mr. LeClerc," said Pierre, swallowing hard. "I want the boat-in-the-bottle." He held out the dollar, which was now well crumpled by his fist.

Mr. LeClerc blinked. "Well, well!" he said, and reached up for the bottle. He put it down on the counter in front of Pierre, who picked it up very carefully in both hands.

"Do you want a box for it?" Mr. LeClerc asked.

"No, thank you," said Pierre. "I shall carry it very carefully and take it straight home so it won't break." He looked at it again. "The bottle has much too small a neck for anyone to push

KINTU

Elizabeth Enright

Kintu lives in the African Congo, but his problem is universal—how to get over a particular fear. After the children have enjoyed the story, an interesting discussion can grow out of this problem. What cured Kintu of his fear? Was it the charm, which was only a fruit pit? Let the children argue it out. They will probably conclude that Kintu got over his fear when he discovered that the things he knew how to do kept him safe in the jungle. Ask the children if they have ever been cured of a fear they had when they were younger—fear of the dark, perhaps, or of dogs or of deep water or what not? The conclusion is, of course, that we get over being afraid when we do something about the thing we fear and discover that we can take care of ourselves.

The Jungle Village

Kintu was a little black boy who lived in Africa. He lived with his father and mother and his five brothers and sisters in a big mud hut with a straw roof, shaped like a beehive. The beehive in which Kintu lived was the largest of a great group of beehives in the middle of the jungle, for Kintu's father, Kitomba, was the chief of his tribe, and therefore a very important person. Kintu was his eldest son, which meant that he, too, would one day be a chief.

He had two brothers and three sisters to play with. There was Timbo, who could throw a spear farther than Kintu could, although he was a year younger. And there were Kakopa and Kaku, who were twins and who looked so much alike that Kakopa had to wear a ring in her nose so that people could tell which was which. Then there was Wapi, who was fat, and rather bow-legged, and always eating something. And last of all there was Nomba, who was the baby and who spent most of her time in a little hammock which hung from her mother's shoulders.

They were very busy children; their days were filled with lessons—most exciting ones. Kintu had more of these than anyone else, because he was the eldest son and to be a chief you must know many things.

You must know, for instance, how to throw a spear faultlessly, how to shoot an arrow perfectly; and every day Kintu practiced for hours, hurling his spear and shooting his arrows at a red circle painted on the trunk of a baobab tree.

He learned how to play the drums, and with the palms of his hands make them talk the drum language which in Africa is the way that messages are sent from village to village.

"Look out, look out," say the drums, beating deeply, "an enemy tribe is coming down the river"; or "Look out, look out, an angry storm approaches from the east!" Usually they send warning messages but sometimes they only converse together.

Kintu would sit with his drum (n'goma) before him, his hands thumping on the tightly stretched skin, and for miles around the jungle murmured with the sounds he made.

A chief's son must be able to dance to the drums as well as to play them. Kintu learned devil dances, and fever dances, dances of triumph, dances to bring good hunting, or fine weather, or the rain, and all of them were different. Kintu liked the devil dances best because when he did them, he wore a magnificent headdress made of crimson feathers and telephone wire. (His father considered the telephone wire a great bargain; he had got it from a white trader who had passed that way several years before, and he had only given four leopard skins and a pair of elephant's tusks in exchange for a big coil of it. They used it for all sorts of things: Kintu's mother wove it into their headdresses, and made baskets out of it; it even held their roof together in places.)

The devil dances took longer than any of the others, and were more interesting because there was a great deal of leaping and shouting to them. The drumbeats grew louder and louder till your ears rang with the sound of them, and you kept on dancing till you fell exhausted in the dust, and had to be taken home.

Kintu learned many other things, too. He was taught how to cure the hides of wild animals, and how to make arrowheads and spearheads of metal and stone. He learned how to kindle a fire with two sticks, how to set a trap, how to climb trees almost as fast as a monkey. He learned which berries were poisonous, and which ones were the best cure for snakebite.

Timbo and Wapi had lessons much the same as his own, but Kakopa and Kaku learned other things; they made pottery and cooked and wove mats of grass and palm leaves. They had their dances, too. All of the children were dressed alike in little colored skirts except for Nomba who was attired simply in a bracelet and a head necklace. All of them had brass ornaments on their ankles and around their necks, and would have felt strange without the quiet jingling which accompanied their walking.

Every day the children awoke at the very first light of dawn, and rising from the hard earth which was the only bed they had, shook themselves like little dogs and walked straight out of the hut to work or play as they pleased. Kintu took up his spear and practiced throwing it. Kakopa and Kaku wove their mats; and Timbo and Wapi played leapfrog or pretended to be hunters stalking a panther in the jungle. Nomba was too fat and too young to do anything but lie in the sun, chewing a piece of sugar cane.

In the middle of the morning, their mother made a fire by rubbing two sticks together till a spark caught the leaves and kindling on the flat stone which was her fireplace. Then in a great earthenware pot she cooked their breakfast—corn and manioc root and eggs (and sometimes chicken).

When it was done she called them, and they all sat down around the big pot and dipped into it with their fingers. Wapi usually managed to get the most, and often burned himself because he never could bear to wait for things to cool.

Their only other meal was in the evening and was usually exactly the same as the first; but sometimes as a special treat, their mother made them a delicious pudding of corn flour and palm oil and dried white caterpillars.

After supper the people of the village would gather around a fire and talk or sing. The men spoke of hunting, and the oldest ones had stories to tell of the times when lions were fiercer and elephants bigger than any found nowadays. Kintu, sitting beside his father, would shiver and try not to listen, because though nobody knew it, he was afraid of the jungle!

Magic

Now living in a jungle is very much like living next door to the zoo, except that the animals are not in cages, which makes quite a difference. Sometimes at night Kintu would lie awake and listen to the strange sounds made by wild creatures in the jungle, and be very afraid.

There was an insect which ticked all night long like a little watch, and an insect which made a loud noise like an alarm clock. There were the excited voices of suddenly awakened monkeys, and the croaking of big frogs which sounded like old men talking together in deep hoarse voices. There were panthers and leopards whose snarls were like the sound of thick canvas being torn. And there were the grunts of hippopotami who left the river and walked on land at night. There were noises made by nightjars and cicadas, and all the other hundreds of creatures who preferred to do their talking after dark.

Kintu would lie on his hard earthen bed and shake with fright, because he knew that when he was older his father would expect him to hunt in the jungle and to know it as well as he knew his own village. It would never do for a chief's son to be afraid!

It worried Kintu badly, and finally he decided to go and see the witch doctor and ask him for a spell to make him braver.

So one morning, after breakfast, he stole away from his brothers and sisters and playmates, and all by himself walked to the witch doctor's hut.

It was set apart from the rest of the village, and on either side of the door were little idols carved of black wood. One had a very ugly, cross face, and one grinned from ear to ear showing a double row of square, ivory teeth. Kintu bowed and raised his spear to each of them, then he entered the hut and came face to face with the witch doctor.

The witch doctor was very old and very wise, and he wore a derby hat, which he had got from the same trader who brought the telephone wire. From his great height he looked down at Kintu, without smiling, and Kintu would have shaken in his shoes if he had any to shake in.

"Chief's son," said the witch doctor, "why have you come to see me?"

"Witch doctor," began Kintu bravely, "I am in great trouble. I am afraid of the jungle!" He

paused, and glanced up to see if the witch doctor looked disapproving, but there was no change in the old man's expression, so he continued. "Yes, I'm afraid of it. All of it. Its beasts, its noises and its huge trees. I don't even like the way it smells. How can I ever be a great chief like my father when I am such a coward?"

He hung his head for he was very much ashamed.

"This is bad!" said the witch doctor. "I must think." And he sat down on the floor, pulled his derby hat over his nose and thought. Kintu leaned against the wall and watched him almost without breathing, he was so terribly excited.

After several minutes (long ones, they seemed) the witch doctor stood up, pushing back his hat. Still without smiling he looked down at Kintu.

"Chief's son," he said, "I believe I have a cure for you." He leaned down, took something out of a red earthenware bowl, and put it into Kintu's little black hand.

"Take this," he said, "and tomorrow, when the sun is at its highest, walk three hundred paces into the jungle towards the east. After you have walked for three hundred paces, plant this charm at the foot of the first baobab tree you find; then, when you have buried it, say these words—" (But what the words were I cannot tell you for they were black magic, and a secret.)

"In the jungle? All by myself?" asked Kintu in a timid voice.

"All by yourself, chief's son," said the witch doctor firmly.

Kintu walked slowly home. Once he stopped and opened his hand to see what the charm was like; it was nothing but the dry stone of a fruit and didn't look as though it had much magic in it; but the witch doctor had said it had, and Kintu believed him.

That evening he couldn't eat his supper and his mother was worried about him.

"You have been eating between meals again," she said. "When *will* you learn to leave that monkey-bread tree alone?"

But Kintu only sighed, and said nothing. Very late that night he lay awake and listened to the jungle sounds which seemed louder and more terrifying than ever. He thought the cicadas were chanting a jeering song: "Afraid, afraid, afraid," they cried, over and over again.

"Perhaps after tomorrow you'll be singing another song," whispered Kintu into the darkness; and feeling a little more cheerful, he went to sleep.

In the Jungle

The next day dawned bright and very hot; and Kintu went through his duties in a daze.

When, soon after their morning meal, the sun had ridden to its highest point, and everybody else had gone to sleep in the shade, Kintu picked up his spear (ekonga), and holding the charm in his other hand, tiptoed through the drowsy village and into the jungle.

It was hot and steamy under the great trees; it smelled like the inside of a greenhouse, warm and damp. Everywhere the silk cotton trees raised their great trunks; and high, high overhead a whole, separate airy world existed: parrots called in cross voices, a thousand birds sang different songs, and monkeys leapt nimbly along the boughs, chattering and scolding.

Counting all the time, and forgetting to be afraid, Kintu looked up and stubbed his toe badly on a root. By this time he had walked his first hundred paces and was beginning his second hundred. The farther he walked the wilder the jungle grew, and he had to beat back the undergrowth and tear apart the vines which hung, covered with flowers, from every tree.

Once he surprised a group of little brown monkeys who were sitting sociably on the ground in a circle, eating berries. They simply leapt up the trunk of a palm tree when they saw him, and sat high in the leaves telling him what they thought of him till long after he had passed.

Great moths flew blindly into his face; and once he came upon a hibiscus bush so beautiful, with its flaming red flowers, that he stopped and stared at it.

All this time he had forgotten about being afraid, but now as he came to the middle of his last hundred paces the shadows seemed suddenly darker, and the trees taller than before, and he found himself counting more and more rapidly.

"Two hundred and eighty," said Kintu, leaping over a log, "two hundred and eighty-one—eighty-two—eighty-three . . ." On his right something gave a squeal and plunged into the bushes.

"Eighty-four, eighty-five," shouted Kintu in a loud, bold voice (he was running now), "eighty-six, eighty-seven, eighty-eight, eighty-nine . . ."

At last the three hundred paces were behind him, and he began to look about for a baobab tree.

There were silk cotton trees, and gum trees, and pandanus trees, and borassus trees, and ebony trees, and rubber trees, and mahogany trees, and kakula trees; but there was not a single baobab tree in sight!

Kintu sighed; his heart was beating like a tom-tom and the palms of his hands felt cold and damp; but he had come this far and he simply couldn't turn back till he had buried the magic fruit pit.

So he hunted and he hunted, and went farther and farther into the jungle, and at last he came upon an enormous baobab tree standing all by itself in a clearing.

He felt safer somehow now that he had found it, and with relief he knelt among its great roots and scooped out a hole in the ground with the head of his spear; he buried the charm and covered it with earth. After that, he said the words of black magic which the witch doctor had taught him.

Then he picked up his spear and started back.

It had taken him a long time to find the baobab tree and by now it was the middle of the afternoon; the shadows were growing longer.

A crowd of little gnats circled around his head as he walked, buzzing in high thin voices till his ears rang and he felt dizzy. He kept waving his spear at them to drive them away, but they didn't mind it in the least and came back again as soon as he stopped.

On and on stumbled Kintu, among flowers, and tendrils, and great leaves. He realized that he had lost his way, and that so far the magic had not worked, because he felt more frightened than ever.

He thought about his family all safe together in the village, and wondered when they would miss him and begin to look for him. He thought about the stories told by the old hunters of fierce lions who sometimes come into the jungle at night, of hyenas whose cry is like the laughter of a devil-god, of great elephants with tusks of ivory who can uproot small trees with their trunks. He thought about the buried fruit pit and the magic words, and they seemed small protection against the jungle and its many dangers. He wished that he had never gone to see the witch doctor at all, and that he had allowed himself to be a coward in peace.

Kintu began to cry quietly, because he was sure that he would never see his family again, and he was terribly afraid. He stopped walking and stood very still among great ferns like giant feather dusters: it seemed foolish to go on when whatever direction he took was bound to be the wrong one.

It was growing darker now, and already the

tree toads had begun their evening conversation. "Wack-a-wack-a-wack," they cried in harsh voices from every tree. The gnats, fortunately, had got tired of Kintu's waving spear and had all gone off together to find some other creature to torment; so except for the remarks of the tree toads, and the occasional cry of a bird, it seemed very still.

Then, all at once, quite near, he heard a sound like that of thick canvas being torn in two. The snarl of a leopard!

It no longer seemed useless to go on; in fact, it seemed most necessary to go somewhere very quickly; and Kintu, spear in hand, began to run faster than he had ever run before.

Ahead of him, six little monkeys, who had also heard the dangerous sound, went leaping and skipping along the ground at great speed. Kintu, feeling somehow that they were his friends, followed them; and when they came to a huge tree hung with creepers which the monkeys swarmed neatly up, like little sailors climbing up a rigging, he went right after them as fast as he could go.

Up and up he struggled, with his spear between his strong teeth, and his little black fingers and toes curling around the thick vine almost as cleverly as the monkeys' did. The creeper looped itself over one of the lower branches and returned to earth on the other side, so Kintu began climbing up the boughs; stretch, pull, swing! Stretch, pull, swing!—till he had nearly reached the top of the tree, and then he sat down on a huge limb with his shoulder against the broad trunk, and his spear across his knees. His heart was thumping like anything and he was out of breath, but he felt slightly safer.

The six little monkeys, who didn't seem to mind him at all, sat on a branch just above him, and said things very fast in monkey language about leopards. Kintu wished that he could understand them and join in their conversation; he wanted to ask them if leopards were any good at climbing trees. Still, even if he couldn't speak to them, it was a comfort just to have them there, and he hoped they wouldn't go away.

All about him stretched the strange leaves and branches of jungle trees, and below him he saw the great ferns and flowers through which he had beaten his way. Overhead the sky was a darker blue, with a little purple in it, and already there was a star, pale and cold, shining just over the place where the sun had set.

The air was filled with queer smells. A clump of yellow orchids bloomed in a deserted bird's nest several feet below him and gave off a perfume so strong and heavy that he grew tired of it very soon. There were big red berries on a tree nearby that had an odor rather like cough medicine; and you've been in the monkey house at the zoo, haven't you? So you know how the monkeys smelled.

It was really twilight, now; and Kintu saw the bright busy lights of fireflies everywhere. Huge mosquitoes came whining out of the shadows; cicadas sang at the tops of their voices, and the tree toads almost screamed at each other. An evening wind stirred for a moment in the feathery treetops and moved the branch above Kintu where the monkeys were dozing in a row. It woke them up, and they chattered anxiously at each other for a minute. But they soon went back to sleep; and Kintu, feeling like the loneliest person on earth, continued to stare at the sparkling patterns made by fireflies against the darkness.

Presently the moon rose, huge and lopsided, above the world; each leaf glittered in its light, and the brass bracelets on Kintu's ankle looked as if they were made of purest gold.

The night was full of sounds: rustling sounds and scratchings and scamperings; squeaks and grunts in the darkness below; the singing of the night birds in the leaves above.

Then Kintu heard another sound—a new one. He heard the heavy, soft footsteps of an enormous creature stepping quietly; the snapping of shrubs and the squelching sound of wet earth under huge feet. He leaned forward and peered still more intently into the blackness below him. A tremendous shape, darker than the shadows from which it came, moved gently and ponderously towards the tree where he was hidden. Bigger than a house, it looked; almost as big as a mountain, Kintu thought. Slowly, slowly the Thing approached; then paused directly below him. Suddenly there was a faint sound of scraping, and the tree began to quiver as though in an earthquake; the monkeys jabbered nervously, and Kintu knew that an elephant, the largest of all wild creatures, was scratching his back on a branch.

Then slowly, as before, the great beast went on its way; the noise of snapping twigs and heavy tread grew fainter, and it was seen no more.

Hours passed; the moon was high in the sky; and Kintu, too tired to think of fear any longer, settled himself against the tree trunk and slept with the monkeys.

The Leopard

He must have slept a long time, because when the shrill, excited voices of the monkeys woke him, he saw that the moon had set, and the world was as black as the inside of a pocket.

He looked down wondering what was the matter. At first he saw nothing but the roaming lights of the fireflies. And then a chill of fear ran up the calves of his legs and along his spine to the nape of his neck; for below him he saw two small lights, side by side, which did not move; two small lights which he knew were the eyes of an animal watching him.

Squealing and scolding, the monkeys bounded along the branches, dived into the boughs of another tree and were gone.

Kintu faced real danger, alone.

Once more he heard the low snarl which had so frightened him earlier in the evening. The leopard had found him, after all.

The two lights moved a little; Kintu knew that the animal was crouching, making sure of the distance before he sprang.

Then the eyes leapt forward; there was the swish of a heavy body flying through the air, the impact of it against the tree, and the sound of sharp claws tearing wood.

Determinedly, the leopard climbed the tree towards Kintu.

It was useless to be frightened now. Something would have to be done, and quickly too.

Swiftly and quietly Kintu stood up on the branch. He held on to the trunk with his left hand, and in his right he raised the spear high above his shoulder.

He could hardly see the dark shape of the animal climbing towards him, but he would have to take a chance.

"Now or never," said Kintu in a small voice, and hurled the spear.

Then there was a grunt and the thud of a soft, heavy weight falling upon the earth. After that there were no more sounds at all: and Kintu knew that the leopard would not bother him again. Not this one, anyway.

Trembling all over, but almost shouting with triumph, he climbed, feeling his way, a little higher in the tree. How glad he was, now, that his father had made him practice throwing the spear hour after hour, day after day.

"I certainly won't sleep again," said Kintu; and slept.

Drumbeats

The next time he woke up it was morning. Long pale fingers of early sunlight slanted through the leaves. Every bird was singing as though it were necessary to sing louder than any other bird. The world was golden and fresh and drenched with dew.

Kintu stretched his stiff arms and legs, and yawned with a great noise. He looked for his spear and wondered for a moment if he had dropped it. Then he remembered about the leopard.

Quickly he climbed down the branches and slid along the creepers to the ground.

There, stretched at the foot of the tree, lay the leopard, so beautiful with its tawny dark-spotted fur that Kintu was sorry he had killed it. But when he looked closer and saw the cruel curving white teeth, and the glittering claws half hidden in the soft paws, he was sorry no longer.

"It is better to kill than to be killed," said Kintu wisely; and pulling his spear from the leopard's hide, he started off once more to find his village.

It was a beautiful morning! Wet leaves glittered in the sun like leaves of gold. Great drops of dew fell on his head; and there was a little pool in the cup of every flower.

Feeling thirsty, he tipped a big leaf down to his open mouth, and water poured into it as if from a pitcher.

He was hungry, too, and stopped for a minute to pull some purple berries from a vine. Nothing had ever tasted so delicious.

He felt like a king as he strode through the

jungle, brandishing his spear and singing: "I am not afraid!"

The wild creatures, watching him, knew that this was true.

"He is not afraid," screamed the gray parrots in the treetops. "He is not afraid," sang all the birds together. "He is not afraid, he is not afraid," chattered the noisy monkeys; and great serpents, sunning themselves on branches, watched him through the leaves, and said in slow voices, "He is not afraid."

The leopards saw him, too, and the black panther with golden eyes, hidden behind a screen of flowers. "No, he is not afraid," they said, and turned away into the shadows feeling fear themselves.

Never had Kintu been so happy; he was filled with hope, and was sure that he would find his village, and that everything would be all right after all. He listened with joy to all the shrieking, babbling, singing, chattering noises of the early morning jungle. He liked its noises. He loved the way is smelled.

Then something made him stop, quite still, in his tracks. He held his breath, and listened with ears which had been trained to sharpness by the jungle, to another sound. Far, far to the right of him, there was a faint throbbing in the air. Yes! There could be no doubt about it; it was the beating of drums that he heard and this is what they were saying:

"Chief Kitomba's eldest son has disappeared. Has he been seen? Has he been seen?"

And then, still farther away, to his left, the drums of another village replied, "Chief Kitomba's son has not been seen. Chief Kitomba's son has not been seen."

Kintu's heart skipped a beat. The drums which had spoken first were the drums of his village, he knew. If he turned to the right and followed their sound he would surely find his way home.

He couldn't go fast enough! He ran; and skipped over creepers and leapt high in the air, twirling his spear, and yelling for joy. But he did not forget to stop now and then and make a scratch on the bark of a tree with his spearhead. When he got back to the village he would ask some of the men to get the leopard for him. And he wanted them to be sure and find it.

The jungle was loud with the sound of drumbeats now. All the villages for miles around were answering the message from his village, and relaying it to others still farther away.

It grew very hot; yellow mist rose from the damp ground. The gnats came after him in swarms; but he didn't care: the world was beautiful and exciting and full of adventures, and he was no longer afraid.

Then he saw the hibiscus bush with its scarlet flowers, the very same one that he had noticed the day before; and he knew that he was near his home! He broke one of the bright blossoms from its stem and stuck it behind his ear as a badge of triumph.

There was a shout behind him suddenly, and turning he saw his father running towards him between the trees.

"Father!" cried Kintu, throwing his spear to the ground and leaping into Chief Kitomba's arms.

"I was lost! I spent the night in a tree, I saw an elephant, I killed a wicked n'gwe, and I'm not afraid," said Kintu all in one breath.

"You are safe, my son; you are not hurt?" asked Chief Kitomba anxiously.

"No, but I am very, *very* hungry," answered Kintu.

The Celebration

His mother was so glad to see him that she cooked him the special pudding which is made of corn flour and palm oil and dried white caterpillars. Then she stood over him and watched to see that he ate it all.

His brothers and sisters sat round him in a circle, each of their mouths hanging open an inch, and listened to the story of his night in the jungle. He had to tell it three times.

"Let us play a game about it," said Wapi to Timbo; "you can be the leopard and I will be Kintu in the tree."

"No, indeed," said Timbo; "you forget that I'm the eldest. *I* will be Kintu, and *you* can be the leopard!"

All the people of the village were so glad that Kintu had returned and was unharmed, that Chief Kitomba said, "Light the bonfires; bring out the big n'gomas; we will have a jubilee, as soon as the leopard's brought back to the village."

"A jubilee!" screamed everybody in delight, and clapped their hands and ran to fetch wood for the bonfires. Half a dozen men followed Kintu's markings to the place where the slain leopard lay beneath a tall tree. Cutting a slim strong sapling with their knives they lashed the heavy animal to it and, raising the burden to their strong right shoulders, walked singing and laughing back to the village. When they had reached it they went at once to the hut of Kintu's father, and set the leopard down beside the door. Everybody came to look at it, and said what a big one it was, and what a fine coat it had, and how wicked and dangerous it must have been when it was alive.

Kintu could feel happiness and pride swelling inside of his chest like a big balloon. His ribs felt almost too narrow to hold it. He looked downwards and drew a circle in the dust with his big toe.

"Now we will celebrate," said Chief Kitomba.

Kintu went into the hut and put on his favorite headdress of crimson feathers and telephone wire, for he felt that this was a very special occasion. Then he walked to the central clearing in the village where all the tribe was gathered.

The fires had been lighted, and were burning like five great towers of flame and smoke, soaring and snapping. Half a dozen of the bravest warriors in the village stood behind the big drums, waiting to play them.

"Come here, my son," said Chief Kitomba, and Kintu went to him. Around his neck his father fastened a necklace made of leopards' teeth; and around his waist he tied a leopard's skin so that the tail hung down behind just as it should.

"Now dance," said Chief Kitomba, and Kintu for the first time in his life was allowed to do the Dance of the Victorious Hunter; for had he not killed the leopard, that creature feared and hated by all jungle dwellers, men and beasts alike?

"Boom. Boom. Boom-a-diddy-boom!" sang the drums, and Kintu's feet moved swiftly through the dust, hopping and leaping. Around him all the people of the village clapped their hands and stamped in time to the music.

Kintu finished his dance with a whoop and a yell. And then everybody danced!

Drums boomed, brass anklets jingled, spears clashed together, dry gourds were shaken like rattles, people sang and monkeys screamed in the thickets. Never had there been such a loud and joyful jubilee in the history of the village!

It went on till very late at night. They brought out delicious things to eat: hot things in big earthenware pots, fruits of all kinds on round platters. There were delicious things to drink, too, in tall black jars.

Long after it was dark the fires still burned high, and the village was filled with flickering lights and dark moving shadows.

Everyone was happy, and Kintu was the happiest of all, for his father had said to him, "I am well pleased with you, my son; you will be a good chief to our people when I am gone. Only fear can make a strong man weak, and you have conquered that."

At last, when they had all grown tired of dancing and had eaten too much, they sat down around one of the dying bonfires and asked Kintu to tell them his story.

He told them about climbing the tree after the monkeys and about the elephant who had come unsuspectingly so near to him; he told them all about the leopard. But he did not tell them why he had gone into the jungle in the first place or about the magic charm; that was a secret between the witch doctor and himself and the baobab tree.

Finally, when he was sure that he couldn't stay awake more than two minutes longer, Kintu stood up and said goodnight to all his proud, well-fed relatives and friends. But before he went to his father's hut, he tiptoed through the shadowy village to the hut which was surrounded by little black idols. The witch doctor was leaning in his doorway.

"Well, chief's son," he said, and from his great height he looked down at Kintu without smiling. But this time Kintu was not timid in the least.

"Well, witch doctor," he said, "I am very grateful to you. I did everything you told me to, and then I got lost. I spent the night in the jungle among wild creatures; I even killed a leopard. And this morning when I woke up, I knew I wasn't frightened any more!"

The witch doctor didn't look very much impressed.

Kintu waited for him to speak. At last he

nodded his head slowly up and down and said "Good." That was all, but Kintu felt that it was enough.

Turning, he left the witch doctor's hut and walked slowly through the darkness. It was quieter, now. There were occasional bursts of laughter from groups of people, but the voices were subdued, and the fires had died into heaps of glowing coals.

Kintu entered his hut and removed the headdress of crimson feathers and telephone wire. Then he lay down on the earth against the wall. Above the voices and the laughter he heard the night sounds of the jungle. He heard the tree toads, and the monkeys, and the insects which tick like little watches. Far, far away he heard a sound like that of thick canvas being torn in two. Kintu knew that another leopard roamed the jungle, terrifying all creatures. He reached out and patted the handle of his spear companionably.

But above all these noises he was aware of the song of the cicadas. No longer could he make the words "Afraid, afraid, afraid" fit their chanting. There were no words for it. The thousands of voices pulsed together like the sound of a heart beating and the longer Kintu listened to them the drowsier he became. And at last with his cheek pressed against the earth and with one hand on his spear he went to sleep.

LITTLE PEAR FALLS INTO THE RIVER AND DECIDES TO BE GOOD

Eleanor Frances Lattimore

A little girl exclaimed after reading Little Pear, *"You know he is just like my little brother, always getting into scrapes." The author, Mrs. Lattimore, has spent many years in China and must have known and loved many children there, she writes about them so delightfully.*

It was a hot day in the middle of the summer. The sun blazed down on the village and on Little Pear, who was strolling along the street, eating a cucumber. His bare feet shuffled through the thick yellow dust. "Ay-ah," he sighed, "how hot it is!—and where are all my friends?"

The street was deserted, and the reason was that nearly every one was asleep. It was too hot for most people to want to walk about. It was even too hot for the children to want to play. Little Pear, though, always wanted to be doing something. "I know what I shall do," he thought. "I shall go and watch the boats on the river." Just then he saw a child trotting around the corner. He felt quite excited for a minute, because he had walked nearly through half the village and had seen only a pig and a few chickens. But when the child came nearer he saw that it was only Big Head's baby brother.

The baby was dressed in a little red apron shaped like a diamond. It was all that he had on, because Chinese babies don't wear very much in the summer. His head was shaved except for a fringe of hair across his forehead. He was trotting along in a great hurry until he met Little Pear, who stopped him. "You must not run away," said Little Pear, and he took the baby's hand and led him back to the home of Big Head, who was leaning against the doorway, fast asleep. Little Pear lifted the little brother over the doorstep and gave him the rest of his cucumber. "Stay where you are," he said. "You might get lost if you run away." Then he had a good idea. He took the good-luck chain off his own neck and put it around the baby's. "Now you will be safe," he said, and he patted the baby kindly on the head and strolled on, feeling very good. Again he thought, "I shall go to the river and watch the ships," and he started off in the direction of the river.

It was a long way to the river. Little Pear followed the path that cut across the fields, and soon left the village far behind him. The sun blazed down on Little Pear as he pattered along in his bare feet. The fields were as deserted as the village. There was no sound except for the singing of cicadas in the willow trees as he drew near the river.

Presently he stood on the high bank, looking down at the river. First he looked up the river, and then he looked down the river; and all the time he remembered to hold tight to a willow tree with both hands.

The river was swift and muddy. The sun shining on it made the ripples first brown and then blue. The bank opposite Little Pear, like the bank that he was standing on, was bordered by rough-barked willow trees leaning out over the water. Between the banks the boats went busily up and down. Here everybody seemed to be very wide awake. Little Pear thought of the sleepy village he had left and was glad that he had come to the river.

There were all kinds of boats. Big boats with masts and sails and smaller boats with none, and boats with great fishing-nets spread out like huge spider-webs. There were flat boats, too, laden with things to sell. Some had cabbages, and some had rolls of matting, and some had bags that might be filled with all sorts of interesting things, Little Pear thought.

The big boats had eyes painted on them in front, so that they could see where they were going. The owners of these boats were careful not to let anything hang over the edge in front of the eyes, for then the boats could not have seen their way as they sailed in and out among the smaller boats.

Little Pear wished that he had a boat of his own, but he couldn't decide whether he would rather have a small one that he could row, or a larger one that he could push with a pole, or a *big* one with a sail.

Finally Little Pear decided that what he would like most of all to have when he grew up would be a fishing-boat. For then he could catch fish for his meals and take fish to the city to sell, and what fun that would be!

Little Pear held tight to the willow tree and gazed at the ships going up and down. He was wishing that he would grow up soon, when suddenly he saw, drawing nearer and nearer, the loveliest kind of boat on the river. It was a houseboat!

"That is the kind of boat I should like to have," thought Little Pear, as he watched it drawing nearer and nearer. It was a long flat boat with a real little house on it, with a hole in the ceiling for the smoke to go through, and paper windows. A man was walking up and down the side of the deck, shoving with a long pole.

Little Pear looked admiringly at the clothes hanging out to dry and watched the children playing about the deck, and the boat sailed gayly along until it was quite close to Little Pear.

Suddenly one of the children saw him. He called to his brothers and sisters, and they all flocked to the edge of the boat and waved to Little Pear as he stood alone on the bank. It made him feel very happy, and without thinking he let go of his tree to wave back. *Slip,* went his feet on the steep bank—slip, slide—and *plop,* into the river fell Little Pear! . . .

The brown water whirled round and round him in circles as he rose to the surface, choking and sputtering. "Ay-ah!" cried the children on the boat. "He is drowning, he is drowning!" For Little Pear could not swim, and the swift current was carrying him away from the bank. He splashed around wildly with his arms and was about to sink again when the man on the boat rushed forward and reached out his pole. "Catch hold!" he cried.

Little Pear couldn't hear what the man said,

for there was water in his ears. He could scarcely see the man, for there was water in his eyes! He couldn't say anything himself, for he had swallowed so much water—but he splashed around with his arms—and—he caught hold of the pole! Then he held on tight while the man pulled him to the side of the boat and lifted him safely to the deck.

For some time he lay there, wondering to himself whether he was drowned or not, and thinking that perhaps he would never see his family again. Then he opened his eyes and saw above him a circle of faces. Here he was on the houseboat, and here were the children who had waved to him and the man who had saved him. There was the kindly face of the mother, too, who had hurried out of the little house to see what had happened.

Little Pear smiled at them, and they all exclaimed over him, saying what a wonder it was that he wasn't drowned; and they admired his flowered jacket and the green string around his pigtail.

"Will you stay with us?" asked the children.

But their mother said, "No, this little boy comes from the shore, and his family will wonder where he is. He must go home when we come to the next landing-place."

The boat sailed on down the river. Little Pear sat drying in the sun, while the children sat around him in a circle, telling him about their life on the river, and asking him eager questions about the land. "We have never lived on the land," they told him, "because this boat has always been our home." Then Little Pear told them about his village, and about his family and friends and his canary. As he talked he began to think how glad he would be to see them all again. But the boat sailed on down the busy river, taking Little Pear farther and farther away from home.

When they finally reached the next landing-place, the houseboat stopped and Little Pear was set ashore. He felt very sorry to say good-by to his new friends. He climbed the path up the bank and watched until the boat had sailed on, far down the river. The children were still waving to him, but Little Pear held tight to a tree with both hands, because he didn't want to fall into the water again. The boat disappeared around a bend in the river, and Little Pear started for home.

Away across the fields the sun was setting. Little Pear walked on, and on, and on. The way home was long, as the boat had sailed a mile or two down the river. "Ay-ah," thought Little Pear, "soon it will be dark!" And he hurried his tired feet along more quickly. He wished that he might meet another kind man like his friend who had taken him to the city. But the path along the river bank was deserted, the fields were deserted, and it seemed as though in all the world there was nobody except Little Pear.

Little Pear walked on, and on, and on. The sun had been down for a long time, and the night was very dark, when at last Little Pear saw ahead of him the dim outline of the village. Dogs barked at him as he approached. "Don't bark!" he cried. "Don't you know me? This is Little Pear!" When he reached his own gateway the stone lions on either side of it looked very fierce. "They are roaring now, not laughing," he thought, and he said aloud, "Don't bite me. This is Little Pear!" He ran across the courtyard to the house. "Open the door!" he cried. "It is Little Pear!"

Then the door was flung open, and "It is Little Pear!" cried his mother and Dagu and Ergu all at once, throwing their arms around him.

How glad Little Pear was to be at home again! And how glad his family were to see him! "Where have you been?" they cried. "We have hunted for you all afternoon, and the men are still out with lanterns, looking for you."

Little Pear told them all that had happened, how he had left the village and had gone to the river, and how he had fallen into the river and been rescued. Then his mother prepared some hot food for him while Dagu put the kettle on to boil and Ergu sped away to tell all the village that Little Pear had returned.

Soon there was the sound of many feet in the courtyard, and then the tiny room was filled with people. There were Little Pear's father and the other men who had been searching with him for Little Pear. There was Ergu, out of breath and with shining eyes. There were all the nearest neighbors and best friends. There was Big Head, looking very excited, and Big Head's baby brother, eating a tang-hulur. He still had the good-luck chain around his neck.

"You may keep the chain," Little Pear told him, "for you are very little and something might happen to you. But I am a big boy, and I am never going to run away again."

Then everybody was very happy. They patted Little Pear on the head, and the baby brother gave him the rest of his tang-hulur.

"We all loved you very much when you were naughty," they said, "but we shall love you even more if you are good."

"I will always be a good boy, now," Little Pear promised, nodding his head very hard. Ergu looked at her small brother and suddenly felt rather sad.

"Little Pear is growing up," she said.

A LONELY NIGHT

Mary and Conrad Buff

Conrad Buff, who made the beautiful pictures for Kobi, *is a Swiss and in this story he has recalled his childhood experiences in that beautiful country. His wife Mary Buff wrote them down, and together they made this book. So also they made* The Apple and the Arrow, *a thrilling story of the Swiss people's fight for freedom.* Dash and Dart *is about twin fawns and reflects the Buffs' California life, part of which is spent high in the mountains where deer, squirrel, and other small animals share the forest with them.*

When Kobi had finished milking the cows, he carried the milk into the hut and poured it out into flat wooden bowls, which he put away in the cool milk room. Then he ate his usual supper of goats' milk and great hunks of heavy bread. Supper over, the boy sat on an old bench just outside the cabin, watching the evening shadows.

It was a warm summer evening, and so clear that Kobi could see the cows grazing on Schwarz Alp across the valley. He could even hear Sepp's dog bark.

Shadows slowly drowned each bright green Alp in gray, as night crept up and up along both sides of the valley. In a short time, only the tops of the mountains shone with the last rays of the sun. Soon the gray shadows covered them too, and the world faded into darkness.

Slowly stars came out. By the faint glow in the eastern sky, Kobi knew the moon would rise. As it grew still darker, a bird called sadly in the forest beyond the hut. It sang as if it had lost something it would never find again.

Kobi saw a light flicker in Sepp's hut. On Hoch Alp the cows grazed restlessly. Every few minutes they stopped in their feeding and looked around as if they heard someone coming. Blass the dog lay panting at Kobi's feet, his red tongue hanging from his mouth, for it was warm. Usually when the sun went down the night was cold, but this night Kobi thought the air very sultry.

The world outside was so unfriendly that Kobi went into the cabin and lit the lamp. Blass always slept in the barn, but on this strange night Kobi called him into the hut for company.

But even with the light shining in the old lamp on the rough table and Blass panting beside him, Kobi still felt the world was unfriendly. Earlier than usual he put out the light, and crawled into bed. But it too was lonely, without Uncle Jacob.

Kobi lay thinking about the day that had just gone: the edelweiss he had picked high on the top of the mountain; the chamois that crept along the cliffs; Grittli, Mother, Aunt Marie.

It was so hot, Kobi threw off the goose-feather pad. The wind rose. A shutter banged. Kobi heard a stick of wood slip from the woodpile outside. An ax leaning against the hut fell to the ground with a soft thud.

Kobi would never have heard these little noises if Uncle Jacob had been there. But tonight they made him afraid.

He thought of Franzli in the story Grandfather had told so often, the old story of "The Boy Who Wanted to Yodel." That boy had slept all alone in an Alpine hut too. What if a giant should come to this cabin tonight and give to him, Kobi, the gift of yodeling like Uli the cheesemaker? Everything seemed possible tonight.

The wind whined louder as it rose. Kobi heard the goats bleating outside. Even Blass was restless. He could not find a comfortable place to sleep. He walked around the cabin from spot to spot, never quiet.

Suddenly the door blew open. Blass growled. Kobi was so startled he jumped out of bed to bolt the door. But before he did this, he peered out of doors. The sky was overcast with clouds. The stars were gone. Was a storm coming?

Hurriedly he climbed back into bed. But he did not stay long, for drops of rain began to fall gently upon the roof. Through the window Kobi saw a bright fork of lightning flare and disappear.

Grandfather had told him many a story from his own boyhood of storms that came and disappeared in an hour, leaving behind them ruined bridges, dead cattle, broken barns.

He knew how suddenly the weather changed in the mountains. Animals felt it before people did. Kobi thought of the panting dog, the restless cows, the sad bird in the forest. He must drive the cows into the barn at once.

He jumped out of bed and lit the lamp. He pulled on his heavy woolen trousers, his hobnailed shoes, and a warm coat. By the time his black leather cap was on his head, the rain was pouring down.

He unbolted the door and ran into the storm; it was so dark he could see only when the lightning flashed. When he reached the barn he pulled open the door, and the cows and goats piled in pell-mell, happy for a roof. Kobi lit a lantern. Each cow stood in her own stall. But thirteen stalls were still empty. Thirteen cows were missing. He must find them.

When Kobi, followed by Blass, raced once again into the night, the rain was coming down so hard he was soon wet to the skin. His feet sloshed about in his soggy shoes as he ran here and there over Hoch Alp, looking everywhere for the lost cows. The thunder was deafening. Each peal bounded back from the sides of the mountains, echoing time and time again. Before one died away another peal of thunder had taken its place. The noise was earsplitting. Lightning flashed every second. Kobi could see everything clearly, but he did not see any cows.

Then he remembered Uncle Jacob had told him never to let cows stand under trees during a storm. He said lightning often hit the trees.

There was but one tree on Hoch Alp. That was the crooked old pine tree on the north side, near the steep cliffs. It's a long way to the old tree, thought Kobi as he slipped through the wet grass. Once he fell headlong on his face. But he struggled up and on. He was so worried about the lost cows that he had no time to fear the wind, the thunder, the lightning.

When at last he reached the tree, Kobi saw a dark mass of animals huddled together under it. Cows! He yelled and called; Blass barked; each tried to make himself heard above the storm. Boy and dog ran this way and that, chasing the frightened animals toward the distant barn. It took a long time, but when at last each cow stood in her stall, Kobi saw by the light of the flickering lantern that one stall was still empty. It was Roslie's stall—Roslie, the fine prize heifer he had promised Mrs. Bach to guard so carefully and bring back to Wolfram's Castle in September. Where could Roslie be?

Once more the boy and his dog went into the storm. It was even worse than before. Peals of thunder boomed against the rocks like giant cannon. Kobi and Blass raced from one end of the Alp to the other, looking everywhere.

Perhaps I have missed her near the tree, thought Kobi, and he ran on and on until he could hardly breathe and his heart beat wildly.

He was near the old tree when suddenly a sheet of living white fire dropped out of the sky and struck the ground before him. Kobi fell on his knees. He covered his eyes with his hands. He smelled burning wood.

He was helpless, afraid, trembling all over. His ears hurt and he could not see—he could not get to his feet.

Strangely enough this last fierce blinding stroke of lightning was the last to flash that night on Hoch Alp. Kobi heard the thunder die slowly away, growing fainter and fainter, as the sound of the great bells died in the church tower on feast days. The wind drove the sullen clouds before it like an army beaten in battle. The rain stopped. The moon looked through a clear bit of sky.

Kobi could hardly believe the world had not ended. As he looked around, his trembling stopped. He saw where the lightning had struck. It had split the tree in two. One great gnarled limb lay across the fence, breaking it down. The old pine had lost its last battle with the storm.

In the strange calm that followed, Kobi heard a faint sound. It seemed to come up from between the canyon walls. He ran to the tree and leaned over the broken fence, peering down into the dark canyon. He heard a soft sad "moo." As he looked into the darkness, he thought he saw something move. He called:

"Roslie, Roslie!" and another "moo" came out of the canyon.

Kobi knew the cliff wall as well in the darkness as he knew it in the daylight. Many an afternoon he had sat there and studied its rocky forms from the edge, the cliff sloped gently down and ended in a narrow shelf of rock in the side of the canyon wall. Then it plunged straight down for over a hundred feet to meet the noisy stream far below.

Roslie must have been knocked over by the broken limb. Or she might have jumped over in fright. "Be still, Roslie." He slid down the incline and landed beside the heifer. She licked his hands.

"Don't move, Roslie," Kobi whispered to her. "Don't move." And with these words the boy clambered up the cliff and raced with all his strength toward the distant barn, to get a rope. Fear lent him wings.

When Kobi returned to the edge of the canyon, and once more slid down to the rocky shelf, Roslie was still there. He tied the rope around her neck and fastened it to a stout root that stuck out of the rocks. Then he said to her: "Roslie, I'm going away. But I'll be back soon and pull you up. Stay here, Roslie, I'll be back."

As Kobi had raced to the barn for the rope, he had thought of a plan. He would go down into the valley, cross the river, climb up to Schwarz Alp, and get Sepp. Sepp was strong. He and Sepp together could pull the heifer out of the canyon.

The moon shone so brightly as Kobi hurried down the muddy trail into the valley that he could hardly believe death had walked on the Alp only a few minutes before. The creek in the bottom of the valley roared, swollen into a river. The foot bridge seemed to hang by a thread.

Kobi crossed it carefully. As he climbed up toward Schwarz Alp Sepp saw him coming.

"Come and help me!" cried Kobi to his friend, and then he hurriedly told him the story of Roslie. "Hurry up," he cried, plucking at Sepp's sleeve. "Of course I'll come," Sepp said. He ran to the barn, and came back with a thick heavy rope curled over his shoulder.

When the boys arrived on Hoch Alp a half-hour later, Roslie was still there. They could hear her chewing her cud on her little haven of rock.

"Imagine that," laughed Sepp, out of breath with the steep climb, "chewing her cud! She's not hurt at all."

Kobi grabbed one end of the rope, and slid down the embankment. He put the rope around the heifer's neck, and threw the other end to his friend on the bank, who wound it around the old tree-trunk, which was still standing. Then Sepp called: "Steady, Kobi. Push!"

Kobi pushed, Sepp pulled on the rope. Roslie did her best. She knew the boys were trying to help her, but the rocks were slippery and she always slid back. The boys tried time and time again until they were both out of breath.

"We may have to wait until Uncle Jacob comes," cried Kobi.

"Let's try once more," argued Sepp. "If she doesn't come up then, I'll go and get Father."

So once more they pushed and pulled Roslie. The bank was full of holes, washed out by the storms that had fallen on the Alp in many years. By accident Roslie put a hind foot in a hole just as Kobi pushed her from behind. Suddenly, almost without knowing how it happened, Roslie walked up the cliff and stood safely on the Alp.

The faint gray of dawn was pouring over the mountains as the tired, sleepy boys drove the heifer into the barn. "Come and have something to eat," said Kobi to Sepp, putting his arm over his shoulder in affection.

"No, sorry, Kobi. I've got to get home and help Father milk. But tonight I'll come over." Sepp hurried down the trail.

Kobi could hardly drag himself into the cabin, he was so tired and hungry.

He took off his muddy shoes and his wet coat; he poured himself a bowl of milk and cut a thick piece of bread. Then he sat down on a bench, his back to the door.

Kobi did not hear the quick footstep, until he felt a pair of strong arms around him, holding him tight. And Uncle Jacob's voice was saying: "Kobi, Kobi, my brave herder."

Uncle Jacob had met Sepp as he crossed the broken bridge in the valley, and Sepp had told him about the long fight to save Roslie. But Kobi was so tired he could not say a single word. He burst into tears as Uncle Jacob patted him on the shoulder and said: "Never mind, Kobi. You are a brave boy! I woke up when I heard the thunder and saw lightning flash on the mountain. I came as fast as I could, my boy, but the roads were rivers of mud. Many of the bridges were washed away. In all of my life in the mountains I've never seen a storm like this. Many a cow was lost, I know. I prayed for you, Kobi, all alone with those cows in such a storm. Your mother will be proud of you. You are a real cowherd now, Kobi, as good as any man!" But the real cowherd was fast asleep, worn out with the work and the excitement.

Early in September, a snow storm fell over the Alps. In the morning when Kobi woke, everything was white. When the sun came out, the snow melted. But it was a warning to the herders that autumn had come.

Uncle Jacob told Kobi: "If we have another snow storm like this, we must go home. The grass is short now. When snow covers it for a few hours, the cows don't get enough to eat."

The grass was very short. Only a few fall flowers still bloomed in the pastures. On a clear day Kobi could see the beech trees, in the valley below, turned red.

Then another snow storm came, covering the roofs of the barn and hut. The snow did not melt quickly.

"Kobi," said Uncle Jacob as they were milking that morning, "I think we must go home, and go today. Bring down the big bells. We will start as soon as the hut and barn are in order."

So without any more talk, Kobi and Uncle Jacob drove the cows down the trail toward home. When they reached the lowlands, everything seemed new to Kobi. The villages were so crowded. There were so many people everywhere. He had lived for three months in a world of only Uncle Jacob, Sepp, Uli, the cows, Blass, the goats; he had forgotten how crowded the villages were, how close to each other the farmhouses were, and how tiny the fenced pastures of the lowlands.

As he and Uncle Jacob went through the villages they saw many other processions of cattle. The snow storm had driven the wise herders from the mountains that September day.

When they reached Uncle Jacob's house, Kobi did not stay long enough to eat. He wanted to get home. He wanted to see Mother, Grandfather, Father. He wanted to play with Grittli, and he wanted to eat fried potatoes covered with caraway seeds, and hot sausage.

It was late afternoon when he saw his old brown house far in the distance. The red geraniums were not in the windows. The fields were shaved close by the mowers. The leaves were falling from the pear trees. There were late apples still clinging to the apple trees.

Kobi ran the last half mile, he was so anxious to get home. He pulled open the heavy kitchen door, and rushed through the house, calling: "Grittli, Mother, where are you? I'm home! It's me—Kobi!"

Then he saw his mother. She was very beautiful, for she wore her fine dress that she wore only on Sundays and feast days. But this is not Sunday, thought Kobi.

As the boy hugged her, he cried: "Mother, you have on your Sunday dress; this is not Sunday. And how beautiful you are, Mother!"

Mother smiled down at him, tears in her eyes, as she said: "Brave Kobi, I heard all about that night in the storm. Do you remember that Aunt Marie told you we had a surprise at home for you? It is upstairs in my room. Come, Grittli, we'll show him."

Up the rickety stairs Kobi followed his Mother. Grittli danced on ahead of them both. The three entered Mother's bedroom. Beside her bed was the old wooden cradle. Kobi's grandfather had slept in it when he was a baby; so had Kobi's father, and Kobi himself. There were roses painted on the headboard, and between the roses it read: "1842."

Kobi's mother lifted a white cloth. Kobi peered inside as she said:

"This is the surprise for you, Kobi. This is why I have on my best dress. We have just come from the christening. This is your baby brother —Conrad Tobler."

from PEDRO'S COCONUT SKATES

Esther Wood

Esther Wood has the knack of re-creating the work and play, longings and achievements, the sadness and fun of children of other lands. Pedro's Coconut Skates *is the tender story of a little Filipino boy's desire to have a house for his grandmother.* Great Sweeping Day, *house cleaning in Japan, and* Silk and Satin Lane, *a charming story of an unwanted Chinese girl who makes some grave blunders in her efforts to be indispensable, are two other fine books by Esther Wood.*

Singing Souls

Hundreds of little candles twinkled in the darkness of All Saints' Eve. They looked as if the stars might have fallen, and, just for one night, snuggled down against the earth.

Aunt Valentina dressed herself in her best clothes. She put on a long skirt, tucking the train up neatly to show her embroidered petticoat and her green velvet chinelas. Her blouse was thin and crisp with big, bell-like sleeves. When she had tied on her best black apron, she called to Uncle Manuel that she was ready.

He finished the song he was singing and tucked his guitar under his arm. "Time for bed," he called to the children, who were playing tubigan in the moonlight.

Pedro stamped out the water marks they had made in the road for their game and followed the three little girls into the house. Great Aunt Trinidad had spread their mats on the floor, and hung up the mosquito nets around each bed. In no time at all the four of them were in bed; even Magellan was tucked in, much against his will.

"Well," said Great Aunt Trinidad, "you never know about children. It's always trouble, trouble, trouble, putting them to bed; and now on All Saints' Eve they're asleep almost before I get the mats on the floor." She held the lamp high that Aunt Valentina might see her way down the ladder and out the gate.

"They're too good to be true," she said, holding the lamp to look at the children, who already seemed to be sound asleep. With that she blew out the light, and leaned back against the wall where her eyes were shaded from the moonlight coming through the door. In a few minutes she was asleep and snoring softly.

Pedro raised his head. "Are you ready?" he whispered.

Three black heads popped out from under three mosquito nets, and nodded. Three little girls slipped on their dresses and quietly stole down the ladder to the gate where Pedro waited for them.

"Where is Magellan?" asked Pedro. "I thought you had him."

Magellan scampered out from under the house. He was carrying Pedro's coconut skates.

"Oh, Magellan," cried Pedro, "I don't want them now." He put the skates back of the fence and picked up the monkey. "But—" he said, "you're a smart monkey. You gave me a good idea."

Juana stopped. "I forgot the coconut shell," she said. "Singing souls always carry a coconut shell."

"And the candle," said Marciana.

"And the bell," said Nene.

Juana climbed back into the house and presently came out with a bell, a candle, and half a coconut shell. She gave the bell to Nene and the candle to Marciana, keeping the coconut shell for herself.

Pedro led the way down the dark street, staying well in the shadows that no one might see them. Instead of crossing the moonlit plaza, they slipped around its edge where the houses cast deep, black shadows. Past the old stone church they crept and across the market place, until they came to the big house of the landlord.

"Do you think they'll hear us?" whispered Nene.

"Perhaps they aren't at home," said Juana.

The shell windows had been closed and the house looked quite dark.

"Well, sing as loudly as you can," said Marciana. She started the song, for she was the only one who knew all the verses of the long ballad that told of the travels of the Singing Souls from heaven to earth. Nene rang her bell, and they all sang very loudly when Marciana came to the parts they knew.

The door was opened a crack, and someone looked out at them. Then it was opened wider. A servant in a long, white apron shuffled out and put five centavos in Juana's coconut shell.

Juana excitedly poked Marciana. "Look!" she whispered. "Five centavos!"

The man shuffled back into the house, but just as he was about to close the door, he popped his head out again. "Is that Magellan?" he asked, peering at the monkey in Pedro's arms.

"Yes," said Pedro. "I found him, and I am bringing him back to the Señor."

Magellan jumped to the ground, bounded through the man's outstretched arms, and ran into the hall.

"Oh, Magellan!" cried a woman's voice from inside. "Where have you been?"

"The Señora was very sad to lose that little monkey," said the servant to the children. Then he whispered behind his hand, "As for myself—" He shrugged.

"Bring the children inside," said the Señora, coming to the door, with Magellan sitting on her shoulder. "And, Vicente, bring my purse to me."

The servant ran down the hall, the wooden soles of his shoes clattering on the floor.

"Come in." The Señora smiled at them.

The four children followed her down the hall and out into the patio. The moonlight made everything look white in the little garden, surrounded by the four walls of the house. They climbed the stairs and crossed the balcony to a sitting room where the Señor sat reading.

"Look! Here is Magellan home again!" cried the Señora.

Magellan bounded across the room and jumped on the Señor's shoulder, where he snuggled his head against the man's collar.

"Where did you find him?" the Señor asked, as he stroked the monkey's back. His stern face softened, and he smiled.

The three girls said nothing. They were afraid of the landlord.

"In—the haunted house," stammered Pedro.

"That old house by the river?" asked the Señor.

"Yes," said Pedro.

"What were you doing there?" asked the man sharply.

"I—I just wanted to see what it was like," explained Pedro. "I didn't touch anything."

The Señora interrupted, "Oh, I know you didn't," she said. "It's such a tumble-down house, anyway." She took the purse the servant had brought her.

"Weren't you afraid to go there?" asked the landlord.

"No. It's just like any other house," said Pedro, "only old."

"What's your name?" asked the Señor.

"Pedro."

"Well, Pedro, I like you," said the Señor. "You're one boy who doesn't believe the old women's stories."

The Señora slipped five centavos apiece into the coconut shell. "For the Singing Souls," she said. "And now," she said to her husband, "what about a reward for bringing back Magellan?"

"Good," said the man, turning to Pedro. "What do you want?"

"Well—" said Pedro, "I don't want a reward. But, you know, that little, old house by the river is just the kind of house my grandmother has always wanted."

"Yes?" said the Señor.

"It's very old," said Pedro, "but she wouldn't mind. We could mend it."

"Yes?" said the Señor.

"Well—it's like this," said Pedro. "I haven't any money, but I could work for you. I'm a good houseboy; I could bring my coconut skates and polish your floors every day."

The old servant poked the Señora and vigorously nodded his head. She smiled and nodded to her husband.

"I could come every day on my way to school," said Pedro.

"It seems to me," said the Señor, "that would be enough rent for the little old house."

"Do you mean it?" cried Pedro. "Could we really have it?"

"Yes, of course," said the landlord, "but don't let it fall down on you."

"Oh, thank you, Señor," said Pedro.

The man laughed and patted his head. "I like you, Pedro," he said. "Do whatever you want with the little old house."

The children went down the stairs and across the moonlit patio to the hall, where the servant held the door open for them. Pedro saw nothing. He was too excited. Christmas was coming, and maybe—! Perhaps it was too much for a little boy to do, but it wasn't too much for a little boy to think about.

Mending the Nipa House

Early the next morning the Cruz family went down to the bamboo grove to see Pedro's house. Even Great Aunt Trinidad left her sunny doorway and stomped along with her cane. She took a special interest in the house, for wasn't it she who had told Pedro to find out about things? And if it had not been for Pedro's curiosity, he would not have had the little house.

Pedro was proud to show them his house, old and wornout though it was. To be sure, it was very small, but Grandmother Paz had always wanted a wee nipa house. There were four windows, one on each side, and a door. In the open space beneath the house, Grandmother Paz could keep her chickens.

"It's a bit dilapidated, to be sure," said Uncle Manuel, shaking the old ladder by the front door.

"And there are holes in the roof," said Aunt Valentina, peering up at the ceiling.

"And the floor sags a little," said Great Aunt Trinidad, poking through the cracks in the bamboo floor with her cane.

"Oh, but we can fix it!" cried Pedro. "We can mend the holes and make a new ladder."

"Well, you children go to work," said Uncle Manuel. "There's plenty of bamboo and nipa palm around."

"There's a nice mango tree out there," said Aunt Valentina.

Pedro looked out the door. "Grandmother Paz likes mangoes," he said.

"And Pedro can have his bananas," said Great Aunt Trinidad, poking her cane into the banana tree by the window.

Uncle Manuel took down the shutters, the worn and sagging shutters that all but fell apart when they were touched. The house looked bare, but much neater without them. They made a great bonfire and burned up all the rubbish they could find.

With great enthusiasm Pedro and the three girls started mending the house for Grandmother Paz. Before they knew it, the bamboo grove had become the most popular place in the village. It was like a new game; after school everyone raced down to the river to see who would be allowed to help the Cruz children that day.

Even the older boys and girls came to help, for building a house by themselves was fun. The boys borrowed their fathers' bolo-knives and cut down the bamboo shoots in the yard. The girls brought mangrove leaves and mended the holes in the walls. With the help of Uncle Manuel they made four new shutters, weaving strips of bamboo into mats and tying them tightly with rattan. Each one they hung by rings on a bamboo pole, so that it could be slipped back along the wall, or propped out to make a window shade.

Finally, the parents had heard so much about Pedro's house, that they, too, came to the bam-

from Budapest." Then, unable to keep from gossiping like womenfolks, he blurted out his news: "She had the measles and is delicate and her name is Kate! She'll live with us!"

Father came down the store steps, stuffing his pipe. Jancsi prayed for a miracle. If the boy would only go away or if Father would only let him drive . . . !

The miracle came. Father walked around the wagon and, getting up next to Jancsi, said: "Let's see how you handle wagon and four!"

So they left the boy staring after them open-mouthed. Jancsi drove through the village like a king in a golden coach. The clouds of white dust around the horses' hoofs were like stardust to him. The glittering hoofs were made of diamonds. Everything looked new and beautiful to him today. The endless rows of snow-white houses with their gayly painted doors and shutters were like pearls in a row. The geraniums in the windows were a brighter red than ever. The church seemed taller, the grass greener. He flipped his whip impatiently at the barking dogs and almost rode over a flock of honking geese slowly plodding across the street. Then they were in the open country again. It was almost noon; the spring sun beat down on the shimmering fields. They passed a long fence. Horses were grazing placidly in the pasture.

"Good horseflesh," remarked Father. "See how meek they look now, but it's a man's job to stay on one of those beasts."

"I can get on one and stay on it, Father. Those aren't worse than your own horses."

"Think you can, Son?"

"I *know* I can!" asserted Jancsi hastily, forgetting that this would call for explanations. He was not yet allowed to ride unbroken horses.

"You *know* you can?" said Father, reaching for his pocket knife. Jancsi watched him in shocked silence. He knew he was in for it, but somehow he didn't mind. After the pocket knife came a little round stick of wood with many cross-marks cut into it. It was the score pad. One notch was cut in for each sin Jancsi committed, and after a while it was crossed out. But the "after a while" usually included moments Jancsi didn't like to remember. Holding knife and stick in his hands, Father looked at Jancsi. Jancsi looked far, far ahead. Suddenly Father laughed and, putting away the "score," slapped Jancsi on the back.

"You're no worse than I was at your age, Son. You'll make a good rancher."

Jancsi heaved a sigh of relief. This was a man's world, and he was accepted!

Father pointed ahead. "See those houses and chimneys? That's the town and the station." Jancsi was all eyes and ears now. Soon the wagon was rattling on the cobbled street. They passed lots of buildings, and there were a great many people walking around. Father told him where to stop and, after the horses were hitched to a post, said: "Well done, boy!" This made Jancsi feel still better. Praises from Father were few and far between, but they were all the more satisfying.

Walking through the station building, they came to the platform. "Those long shiny snakes are rails, Son; the train travels on them. It'll be here soon now."

Jancsi heard a great rumbling, snorting, and pounding in the distance. He felt the platform shake under his feet. Casting a frightened look at his father, he saw that Father wasn't afraid, so it must be all right. Then he saw a black monster rushing around the curve. It must be the dragon. It had an immense eye glittering in the sunshine. Vicious-looking black teeth, close to the ground. And black smoke poured out of its head. Then it gave a shrill scream, blew white smoke out of its ears, and came to a groaning halt. Men jumped down, opened the doors of the funny little black houses. Jancsi waited with eyes round and shiny like big black cherries. He expected to see people in silks and velvets, glorious people. But not one of them had good clothes on; they were just everyday people dressed in drab grays and browns. Then he heard someone shouting: "Márton Nagy! Is Márton Nagy here?"

Father yelled back: "Here! Márton Nagy!" A man hurried toward them, dragging a little girl with him. Just any kind of little girl, with plain black hair, a smudgy face, and skinny legs.

"Well, thank goodness you're here," said the man, wiping his forehead. "Here, take this—this imp, this unspeakable little devil—take her and welcome." He pushed the girl to Father. "Never again in my life will I take care of girls. I'm a self-respecting railroad guard. I handle anything from baggage to canaries, but I'd rather travel with a bag of screaming monkeys than her, any time." He gave her a final push. "Here's your uncle, he'll take care of you now. G'bye and—good luck to you, Mister Nagy!"

All this tirade left Jancsi and Father speechless. Here was Kate, looking as meek as Moses, but evidently something was wrong with her. Father bent down and said: "Well, Kate, I am your Uncle Márton and this is Jancsi, your cousin. We'll take you home now."

Cousin Kate looked up. Her dirty little face broke into a grin. "Oh, but you look funny!" she cried. "And I thought my cousin was a boy, and she's nothing but a girl!"

"But, Kate," said Father, "can't you see he's a boy?"

"I only see that she has skirts on and an embroidered blouse. Nobody's wearing embroidered blouses this season, they're out of style!"

Jancsi just began to realize that this dirty, skinny little girl in the plain blue dress was his cousin. He felt cheated—that was bad enough—but she called Father "funny" and said he was a *girl*—that was really too much! With fists clenched, chin stuck out, he advanced toward Kate. "I am a girl, am I? . . . I'm funny, am I? . . . I'll show you!"

Kate was ready. She dropped her bag, took a threatening step toward Jancsi. They were face to face now, tense, poised like two little bantam roosters, ready to settle the argument on the spot. Suddenly Father's hearty laugh broke the tension. "You two little monkeys," he cried, "now I'll tell you that you are both funny! Stop this nonsense, both of you. Jancsi! Gentlemen don't fight girls. Come on, we'll go home."

He grabbed their hands and, still laughing, walked to the baggage-room. Jancsi and Kate had no choice, they had to go, but at least they could make faces at each other behind his back. The fight was not over, it was just put off for the moment.

When they reached the wagon, there was more trouble. Kate declared that since the wagon had no top, she'd get a sunstroke. It didn't have cushions on the seat, so she'd break to pieces. She told Father to "phone" for a "taxicab."

"I'll wash your mouth out with soap, if you swear at *my* father!" cried Jancsi. "Phone" and "taxicab" sounded like swearing to him.

"She wasn't swearing, Jancsi," said Father; "she is just talking city language. 'Phone' is a little black box, you can talk into it, and people many miles away hear you. 'Taxicab' is a horseless wagon city people travel in." He turned to Kate. "We haven't any taxicabs here, Kate, so come on, hop on the seat."

Kate shook her head. "I will not. Ride in this old wagon indeed! Why, everybody will laugh at me."

Father's patience was wearing out. He just grabbed Kate under the arms and lifted her into the seat before she knew what had happened. "Come on, Son, we can't waste the whole day. You sit on the outside so she won't fall off." They both got on the wagon. Kate almost disappeared between them. Father was a very big man, and Jancsi a big husky boy for his age. But what Kate lacked in size, she made up in temper. When she realized what had happened, she turned into a miniature whirlwind. She kicked and screamed, she pinched Jancsi, she squirmed like a "bag of screaming monkeys."

"Father, the man was right, she's a bag of screaming monkeys!" said Jancsi, half angry, half amused, holding on to Kate.

Father was busy holding the horses in check. They were respectable farm horses, not used to the unpleasant sounds Kate managed to make. Soon they left the town and were traveling at a fast clip on the country road. Little by little Kate subsided. The long trip in the train and all the excitement were beginning to wear her out. She looked around. She saw the great Hungarian plain unfold before her eyes. Something in her was touched by the solemn beauty of it. Its immense grassy expanses unbroken by mountains or trees, shimmering under the spring sun. The dark blue sky, cloudless, like an inverted blue bowl. Herds of grazing sheep, like patches of snow. No sound, save the soft thud of the horses' hoofs on the white dusty road, and now and then the distant tinkle of sheep's bells, or the eerie sound of a shepherd's flute, the tilinkó. At times these plains, called the "puszta," are the very essence of timeless calm. At times the puszta wakes up and resembles an ocean in a storm. Clouds, so low it seems you can reach up and touch them, gather above. Hot winds roar over the waving grass. Frightened herds stampede,

"So forgive me, Márton, and try to put a halter on my wild colt.

"Your loving brother,

"Sándor."

There was a long silence. Everybody looked at Kate. She, with her eyes cast down demurely, was the very picture of innocence.

"My poor little motherless lamb," cried Mother, gathering Kate in her arms. "I don't believe a word of it. Why, look at her, Father, isn't she like an angel?"

Jancsi felt gooseflesh creeping up his spine. He had seen this angelic expression before—his uncle was right, it was a danger signal. He looked at Father and caught his eye. Father was actually winking at him. Then he stood up, and said:

"Jancsi and I are going to look after those 'wild horses,' Mother; you watch our new angel. See that she doesn't fly away."

The horses were a sorry sight indeed, caked with dust. Father and Jancsi worked hard for a long time. Under the currycomb and brush the black coats of the animals were glossy once more. After the cleaning Father gave them their rations. The stable was spick and span, the wagon put in the shed. "Time for our supper, Jancsi. Let's see what Mother is doing with the 'angel.' "

"There's Mother calling now," cried Jancsi, "but she's calling Kate."

Mother was running toward them, flushed, with all her numerous petticoats swaying around her.

"Kate! Where is Kate? Have you seen Kate? She was in the kitchen one minute, making the most awful faces at the bowl of milk I gave her for supper. Then she disappeared in thin air while I went out for water!"

They looked high and low. No Kate. No sign, no sound, of Kate. In the sheep house, the chicken coop, pigsty, cowbarn—no Kate. They looked up the roof and down the well. Back to the house, maybe she was just hiding. She wasn't in the house.

Utterly exhausted, Father sank into a kitchen chair. "If she's still alive, she's going back to the city tomorrow, so help me! I wasn't made for this sort of thing, it gives me a pain in my side," he said.

"Send the poor little motherless lamb away, Father? You couldn't," cried Mother. "Her very own father calling her names. I just know her poor little heart is broken. And you two looking at her as if she were a bug. It's enough to kill the child!"

"Tee-hee!" a sound came from the rafters. "Tee-hee!"

"Mice or rats after the sausages again. Light a candle, Jancsi," said Father. He was very fond of sausages. Mother made quantities of them in the winter. Thin long ones with lots of paprika, short fat ones with liver; she made head cheese, smoked hams. When they were ready, Father hung them on the rafters in the kitchen. He hung long rows of peppers and strings of corn on the cob. He kept bacon on one rafter, his carving tools on another. Even Jancsi wasn't allowed to touch anything stored up there.

When the candle flared up, Father was ready with a broom. Rats were his personal enemies.

"Tee-hee!" came the sound again. There sat Kate, straddling the smoky beam, skinny legs dangling, munching one end of a long sausage. Gulping down a huge mouthful, she volunteered an explanation to her thunderstruck relatives. "She gave me milk for supper. Hate milk! I like sausages!"

As long as Jancsi lived, he never forgot the uproar that followed the discovery of Kate. He wanted to laugh, but didn't dare, Father was too mad! Grasping the broom, Father roared: "Come down!" Kate shook her head. "COME DOWN!" Kate moved like lightning, out of the path of the swinging broom. Mother was wringing her hands, trying to calm Father, and imploring Kate to come down, all at once. There was a cascade of assorted sausages, pepper, and corn. Father got red and redder in the face. Kate was scurrying like a monkey from one beam to the other, screaming like a tin whistle. It went on and on. It was Father who gave in first. He sank into his chair, wiping his forehead. "Angel . . . motherless lamb," he panted. "Look at her now. Her little heart is broken." And with utter contempt: "Delicate! Devouring yards of sausages!"

"Come down, my lamb, he won't hurt you." Mother held out her arms to Kate.

"Can't," was the laconic answer.

"How did you get up there anyway? If you

went up, you can come down," growled Father.

"I climbed on that big white beehive in the corner, but it's hot now, she made a fire in it," said Kate. She meant the stove. It did look like a beehive, squatting in the corner. There was a bench around it. Jancsi loved to cuddle on the bench, propping his back against the warm side of the "kemence."

"Well, now you'll stay there until the 'beehive' cools down. Jancsi! Mother! I forbid you to take her down. She can stay there all night!" said Father. And no amount of Mother's begging and crying softened him. There she was, and there she stayed.

Mother began to serve supper. They ate in silence. Jancsi was grinning secretly. Once he looked up. Kate was peering down, her face black, her dress smoky, her stockings torn, but she grinned back.

Suddenly Father began to laugh. "Screaming monkey! Poor kitten! Colt! Motherless lamb! Why, she's a whole menagerie! You always wanted to go to a circus, Jancsi; now the circus has come to you!"

"I'm thirsty," announced Kate unexpectedly.

"Anybody would be after eating two yards of sausages. If you want a drink, come down and get it!" was Father's answer.

She tried "I'm sleepy," "I'm tired," without any satisfactory results. In fact, they were going to bed, actually leaving her perched on the rafters, and the "beehive" still too hot. She began to whimper. Jancsi felt sorry for her, but orders were orders.

Mother prepared the beds. The guest bed for Kate. This was seldom in use, all the fancy embroidered pillows were piled up to the ceiling on it. Mother carried them to a chest, put down two huge featherbeds for mattresses, and a lighter featherbed for a cover. She was shaking her head, looking at Kate, looking at Father, but he wouldn't soften. Finally they put out the candles and silence settled upon the house.

Jancsi fell asleep. The sound of soft footsteps woke him up. Then he heard whispers and a giggle. He tiptoed to the kitchen door. There was Father, holding Kate in his arms, stroking her hair.

Something made Jancsi feel all shaky inside —he felt like crying, but he was happy.

He crawled back to his bed. A little later he heard Father's voice whisper: "Good night, little screaming monkey."

Dozing off to a contented sleep, Jancsi's last thought was: "I'm glad she isn't a golden-haired princess—she's almost as good as a real boy!"

AT THE GRANDFATHER'S

Johanna Spyri

College girls have frequently said that Heidi *was one book they brought with them when they first came to college. It is easy to see why. Heidi is the homeless, forlorn child trying to make a place for herself. Like* The Wind in the Willows, *this is a reassuring book, and the gallant spirit of that little girl is unforgettable.*

After Dete had disappeared, the uncle sat down again on the bench and blew great clouds of smoke from his pipe, while he kept his eyes fixed on the ground without saying a word. Meanwhile Heidi was content to look about her. She discovered the goats' shed built near the hut and peeped into it. It was empty.

The child continued hunting about and came to the fir trees behind the hut. The wind was blowing hard, and it whistled and roared through the branches, high up in the tops. Heidi stood still and listened. When it stopped somewhat she went round to the other side of the hut and came back to her grandfather. When she found him in the same place where she had left him, she placed herself in front of him, put her hands behind her, and gazed at him. Her grandfather looked up.

"What do you want to do?" he asked, as the child continued standing in front of him without moving.

"I want to see what you have in the hut," said Heidi.

"Come along, then!" and the grandfather rose and started to go into the hut.

"Bring your bundle of clothes," he said as he entered.

"I shan't want them any more," replied Heidi.

The old man turned round and looked sharply

From *Heidi* by Johanna Spyri, translated by Helen B. Dole. Used by permission of the publishers, Ginn and Company.

at the child, whose black eyes shone in expectation of what might be inside the hut.

"She's not lacking in brains," he said half to himself. "Why won't you need them any more?" he asked aloud.

"I'd rather go like the goats, with their swift little legs."

"So you shall, but bring the things along," commanded the grandfather; "they can be put into the cupboard."

Heidi obeyed. The old man opened the door, and Heidi followed him into a good-sized room, which occupied the whole hut. In it were a table and a chair; in one corner was the grandfather's bed, in another the fireplace where hung the large kettle; on the other side, in the wall, was a large door, which the grandfather opened; it was the cupboard. There hung his clothes, and on one shelf lay his shirts, stockings, and linen; on another were plates, cups, and glasses, and on the topmost a loaf of bread, smoked meat, and cheese. Everything the Alm-Uncle owned and needed for his living was kept in this closet. As soon as he had opened the door, Heidi came running with her bundle and pushed it in, as far back of her grandfather's clothes as possible, that it might not be easy to find it again. Then she looked carefully round the room and said:

"Where shall I sleep, grandfather?"

"Wherever you like," he replied.

This was quite to Heidi's mind. She looked into every nook and corner to see where would be the best place for her to sleep. In the corner by her grandfather's bed stood a little ladder, which led to the hayloft. Heidi climbed this. There lay a fresh, fragrant heap of hay, and through a round window one could look far down into the valley below.

"This is where I will sleep," Heidi called down; "it is lovely! Just come and see how lovely it is up here, grandfather!"

"I know all about it," sounded from below.

"I am going to make a bed," called out the child again as she ran busily to and fro in the loft; "but you must come up here and bring a sheet, for the bed must have a sheet for me to sleep on."

"Well, well," said the grandfather below; and after a few moments he went to the cupboard and rummaged about; then he drew out from under his shirts a long, coarse piece of cloth, which might serve for a sheet. He came up the ladder and found that a very neat little bed had been made in the hayloft; the hay was piled up higher at one end to form the pillow, and the bed was placed in such a way that one could look from it straight out through the round open window.

"That is made very nicely," said the grandfather; "next comes the sheet; but wait a moment,"—and he took up a good armful of hay and made the bed as thick again, in order that the hard floor might not be felt through it; "there, now put it on."

Heidi quickly took hold of the sheet, but was unable to lift it, it was so heavy; however, this made it all the better because the sharp wisps of hay could not push through the firm cloth. Then the two together spread the sheet over the hay, and where it was too broad or too long Heidi quickly tucked it under. Now it appeared quite trim and neat, and Heidi stood looking at it thoughtfully.

"We have forgotten one thing, grandfather," she said.

"What is that?" he asked.

"The coverlet; when we go to bed we creep in between the sheet and the coverlet."

"Is that so? But supposing I haven't any?" asked the old man.

"Oh, then it's no matter," said Heidi soothingly; "we can take more hay for a coverlet"; and she was about to run to the haymow again, but her grandfather prevented her.

"Wait a moment," he said, and went down the ladder to his own bed. Then he came back and laid a large, heavy linen bag on the floor.

"Isn't that better than hay?" he asked. Heidi pulled at the bag with all her might and main, trying to unfold it, but her little hands could not manage the heavy thing. Her grandfather helped, and when it was finally spread out on the bed, it all looked very neat and comfortable, and Heidi, looking at her new resting-place admiringly, said:

"That is a splendid coverlet, and the whole bed is lovely! How I wish it were night so that I could lie down in it!"

"I think we might have something to eat first," said the grandfather. "What do you say?"

In her eagerness over the bed, Heidi had forgotten everything else; but now that eating was suggested to her, a great feeling of hunger rose within her, for she had taken nothing all day, except a piece of bread and a cup of weak coffee early in the morning, and afterward she had made the long journey. So Heidi heartily agreed, saying:

"Yes, I think so too."

"Well, let us go down, since we are agreed," said the old man and followed close upon the child's steps. He went to the fireplace, pushed the large kettle aside and drew forward the little one that hung on the chain, sat down on the three-legged wooden stool with the round seat and kindled a bright fire. Almost immediately the kettle began to boil, and the old man held over the fire a large piece of cheese on the end of a long iron fork. He moved it this way and that, until it was golden yellow on all sides. Heidi looked on with eager attention. Suddenly a new idea came to her mind; she jumped up and ran to the cupboard, and kept going back and forth. When the grandfather brought the toasted cheese to the table, it was already nicely laid with the round loaf of bread, two plates, and two knives, for Heidi had noticed everything in the cupboard, and knew that all would be needed for the meal.

"That is right, to think of doing something yourself," said the grandfather, laying the cheese on the bread and putting the teapot on the table; "but there is something still lacking."

Heidi saw how invitingly the steam came out of the pot, and ran quickly back to the cupboard. But there was only one little bowl there. Heidi was not long puzzled; behind it stood two glasses; the child immediately came back with the bowl and glasses and placed them on the table.

"Very good. You know how to help yourself; but where are you going to sit?"

The grandfather himself was sitting in the only chair. Heidi shot like an arrow to the fireplace, brought back the little three-legged stool and sat down on it.

"Well, you have a seat, sure enough, only it is rather low," said the grandfather; "but in my chair also you would be too short to reach the table; still you must have something anyway, so come!"

Saying which he rose, filled the little bowl with milk, placed it on the chair, and pushed it close to the three-legged stool, so that Heidi had a table in front of her. The grandfather laid a large slice of bread and a piece of the golden cheese on the chair and said:

"Now eat!"

He seated himself on the corner of the table and began his dinner. Heidi grasped her bowl and drank and drank without stopping, for all the thirst of her long journey came back to her. Then she drew a long breath and set down the bowl.

"Do you like the milk?" asked her grandfather.

"I never tasted such good milk before," answered Heidi.

"Then you must have some more"; and the grandfather filled the bowl again to the brim and placed it before the child, who looked quite content as she began to eat her bread, after it had been spread with the toasted cheese soft as butter. The combination tasted very good, with frequent drinks of milk.

When the meal was over, the grandfather went out to the goat-shed to put it in order, and Heidi watched him closely as he first swept it clean with a broom and then laid down fresh straw for the animals to sleep on. Then he went to his little shop, cut some round sticks, shaped a board, made some holes in it, put the round sticks into them, and suddenly it was a stool like his own, only much higher. Heidi was speechless with amazement as she saw his work.

"What is this, Heidi?" asked the grandfather.

"It is a stool for me, because it is so high; you made it all at once," said the child, still deeply astonished.

"She knows what she sees; her eyes are in the right place," remarked the grandfather to himself as he went round the hut driving a nail here and there; then he repaired something about the door, and went from place to place with hammer, nails, and pieces of wood, mending and clearing away wherever it was needed. Heidi followed him step by step and watched him with the closest attention, and everything he did interested her very much.

Evening was coming on. It was beginning to blow harder in the old fir trees, for a mighty wind had sprung up and was whistling and moaning through their thick tops. It sounded so beautiful in Heidi's ears and heart that she was quite delighted, and skipped and jumped under the firs as if she were feeling the greatest pleasure of her life. The grandfather stood in the doorway and watched the child.

A shrill whistle sounded. Heidi stopped her jumping, and the grandfather stepped outside. Down from above came goat after goat, leaping like a hunting train, and Peter in the midst of them. With a shout of joy Heidi rushed in among the flock and greeted her old friends of the morning one after the other.

When they reached the hut, they all stood still, and two lovely slender goats—one white, the other brown—came out from the others to the grandfather and licked his hands, in which he held some salt to welcome them. This he did each evening. Peter disappeared with his flock. Heidi gently stroked first one goat and then the other and ran round them to stroke them on the other side; she was perfectly delighted with the little creatures.

"Are they ours, grandfather? Are they both ours? Will they go into the shed? Will they stay with us always?" asked Heidi, one question following the other in her delight. When the goats had finished licking their salt, the old man said:

"Go and bring out your little bowl and the bread."

Heidi obeyed, and came back at once. The grandfather milked the goat and filled the bowl and cut off a piece of bread, saying:

"Now eat your supper and then go up to bed! Your Aunt Dete left a bundle for you; your nightgowns and other things are in it. You will find it downstairs in the closet if you need it. I must attend to the goats now; so sleep well!"

"Good night, grandfather! Good night—what are their names, grandfather? what are their names?" cried the child, running after the old man and the goats as they disappeared into the shed.

"The white one is named Schwänli[1] and the brown one Bärli,"[2] answered the grandfather.

"Good night, Schwänli! good night, Bärli!" called Heidi at the top of her voice. Then Heidi sat down on the bench and ate her bread and drank her milk; but the strong wind almost blew her off her seat; so she finished hastily, then went in and climbed up to her bed, in which she immediately fell asleep and slept as soundly and well as if she had been in the loveliest bed of some royal princess.

Not long after, even before it was entirely dark, the grandfather also went to bed; for he was always up with the sun, and it came climbing over the mountain very early in the summer time. In the night the wind blew with such force that its blasts made the whole hut tremble, and every rafter creaked. It howled and groaned down the chimney like voices in distress, and outside in the fir trees it raged with such fury that now and then a bough was broken off.

In the middle of the night the grandfather rose and said half aloud to himself:

"She may be afraid."

He climbed the ladder and went to Heidi's bedside. The moon outside shone brightly in the sky for a moment and then disappeared behind the driving clouds, and everything grew dark. Then the moonlight came again brightly through the round opening and fell directly on Heidi's couch. Her cheeks were fiery red as she slept under the heavy coverlet, and she lay perfectly calm and peaceful on her little round arm. She must have been dreaming happy dreams, for a look of happiness was on her face. The grandfather gazed long at the sweetly sleeping child until the moon went behind a cloud again and it was dark. Then he went back to his own bed.

[1] Schwänli = little swan.
[2] Bärli = little bear.

FOUR SILVER PITCHERS

Ann Weil

The Silver Fawn, *from which this selection is taken, presents an excellent picture of the skillful craftsmen of Mexico and the beautiful things they make. It is also a moving story of one boy's achievement.*

Señor Bill was right. With the coming of the weavers, more and more Mexicans found their way to the little shop in Taxco. First they came only to buy the *serapes,* but it was not long before they were buying the silver, too. The months passed quickly, and with their passing the shop grew both in size and popularity.

And as the months passed Chico, too, grew rapidly. Now, when he was almost sixteen, he had the clear bright eyes and steady hands of a real silversmith. The other workmen in the shop saw his work grow better and better. They began to admire his well-formed pieces and his clear-cut designs. All of the beautiful things that Chico had dreamed of making—these, one by one, were becoming real. Now Chico worked beside Alfonso, Alfonso who was the most famous silversmith in all of Taxco. True, Chico was only Alfonso's helper, but the very fact that he worked beside him every day made Chico happy. Chico watched this fine artist while he modeled and soldered and formed the silver. "Someday," Chico whispered to the fawn, "someday I, too, will be an artist." When such ideas popped into his head these days, Chico did not shake them impatiently away. It was nice to dream again as he had when he was a little boy. It was nice to know that much of the hard work was well behind him. It was nice to know that his fingers had learned how to obey his commands—that they no longer behaved like ten useless sticks.

So the shop and Chico grew and grew, and it was not long before the dry season came again bringing with it the tourists. By the time the shop was two years old, it was one of the show places of Taxco. Tourists asked to see it as they asked to see other places of interest. They wanted to see the parrots who walked round the shop and talked to the customers. They wanted to see the kid and the fawn who were always there to be petted. They watched the weavers carding, spinning, weaving. They watched the silversmiths molding and hammering. They looked at the beautiful things on display. Certainly it was a workshop, a museum and a zoo all rolled into one.

And then one day a very important woman came into the shop. She was a Mexican from Mexico City. Señor Bill recognized her at once as Donna Gamanio who was known all over Mexico for her interest in art. She had helped and encouraged many young artists. She had helped revive the interest in Indian art. At her home all artists were always welcome. Certainly her presence in the shop was a thing to be proud of.

"I wish to order four pitchers," she said to Señor Bill. "A small one for cream and a larger one for milk. A fat, round one for chocolate and a tall one for water. They are to be given as a wedding present," she said as she left. "I must have them in two weeks."

Four silver pitchers! Everyone in the shop was excited about the order. Certainly it was exciting for two reasons. First, the order was big. Never before had one person ordered so much. Second, if Donna Gamanio was pleased, she would probably tell her friends, and her friends were the most important people in Mexico City.

Señor Bill could not hide his delight with the order. Donna Gamanio did not spend her money carelessly. If she had not heard good things about the shop, she would never have come all the way from Mexico City to give an order. Her coming was an honor he had not expected.

The whole shop seemed to work on the pitchers. True, only one workman, Alfonso, did the actual work, but everyone was interested; everyone wanted to help. Chico watched each step, fascinated. He saw the silver bars melted. He saw the pitchers taking form beneath the hands of Alfonso. Finally three were finished. They stood in a row in a place of honor.

Everyone who came into the shop saw and admired them. "They are for Donna Gamanio," the workmen whispered to the customers. "*The* Donna Gamanio?" the people answered. "No wonder, then, they are so beautiful." Yes, everyone in Mexico knew that Donna Gamanio accepted only the best.

And then, with three pitchers finished, an accident happened! Alfonso was all ready to start on the fourth and last pitcher. The soldering pot stood before him, boiling and bubbling. Everything was ready. That was *one* second! The *next* second Alfonso's foot slipped, and he fell against the table. But that was not all! In falling he upset the soldering pot, and the hot lead ran all over his fingers. Certainly the pain from the burns was great, but as Alfonso looked down at his blistering fingers, he thought only of the one unfinished pitcher. He had only three days in which to finish it. He shook his head sadly. He

"On Chair-Makers' Way."

"My family lives on Chicken Street, but I, of course, share the coppersmith's roof. You will sleep next me, I suppose."

"No, my mother is alone and this morning she asked the master if I might return to keep her company each night."

"That is not the custom." Small Li's eyes were wide with surprise. "But then Tang's payments to the Brassworkers' Guild are so large that it is easier for him than for most to arrange things to his own liking." He sighed. "I am sorry. Den is a poor companion. He wishes to forget he is still an apprentice and his ears are only for the men."

Young Fu thanked him for this friendly advance. He was moved to frankness, "Den, I think, will not regret my absence."

Small Li threw him a questioning glance. "So this early he vented his bitterness, did he? A member of his house, a cousin, wished to become Tang's apprentice. The coppersmith would not consider him. It was bad fortune enough to have one in his shop like Den; he did not wish a second. I myself heard him say it. Den will not soon forgive you for filling the place."

When they reëntered the store late that afternoon, Young Fu felt braced to meet anything. One in this place was his friend, the others did not matter. As they appeared, Tang called out, "Did you enjoy yourselves playing about this afternoon? Or can it be that the customer has moved?"

Small Li bowed with a grin. Noticing his companion's confusion, he waited until they had reached the rear, then told him, "Tang is always like that. His tongue is sharp and his wit worse than Old Tsu's, but he does not beat his apprentices, and that is a great blessing. My cousin who works for a tanner bears scars from the bamboo's strokes—and for no reason but that he placed a skin with a tear on a pile of perfect ones."

That Tang had another side to his character, Young Fu discovered later. At dusk the coppersmith beckoned to him. "You need not remain to finish tonight. The ways of this city are new to you, and your mother will carry a heavy heart until you return. Do you know the direction to Chair-Makers' Way?" The youth nodded. "Then follow it without delay." His eyes held a kindly expression, and through the devious turns that led him home, Young Fu remembered it.

The light was still dim when he arrived at the shop next morning. Lanterns suspended from the ceiling softened the brasses to a satiny sheen, and Young Fu was held for a moment by the beauty on display. His pride increased; these objects were the work of men who had at one time started as apprentices. In time he, too, would be permitted to do something more than tend fires and run errands. Small Den's challenge broke the spell, "Did you never see a piece of brass before, countryman?"

Young Fu's countenance hardened. This morning was not yesterday! Coolly he faced his antagonist, "If I have not, is it your affair?"

"Ai!" exclaimed Den turning to the accountant for appreciation, "his temper is easily fired!"

Tang, suddenly appearing, took the conversation into his own control. "As is mine, when I see the dust still thick where you have left it."

Small Den began to whisk furiously at the offending tables, and the other boy lost no time in applying himself to the fire. Twice his enemy had lost face in his presence. This would be something to remember for future consolation. Also, his first opinion that the coppersmith missed nothing was being momentarily proved. Wherever Tang was needed at the moment, there he was to be found. No smallest detail of the work escaped him, and he gave the impression of being in all three rooms at once. There was nothing he did not know about his craft. A hint from him saved a sheet of metal from an unnecessary degree of heat; a stroke of his thumb nail hastily corrected a weak line in a design. Under his suave influence, customers whom the clerk was unable to interest would invariably buy.

When Tang was in the store, Old Tsu would chuckle: "There is no better bargainer in this city than the master. Never does he follow a patron into the street; always they tug at their moneybags before they leave this place. I have seen his competitor, Wu, a half li from his shop trying to persuade a reluctant buyer to return and purchase." And the men would acknowledge the truth of these statements.

Tang, though he demanded the utmost in effort and artistic achievement from his workmen, held their respect. He wasted none of his suave manner on them, he was blunt and his tongue could flay like a whip, but Young Fu soon recognized the fact that the coppersmith was just in all of his dealings, and no artisan in Chungking gave better quality of work for value received.

From sunrise to nightfall, the new apprentice had no free minutes except those stolen from errands. The workrooms were a bedlam of noise—hammers beating against anvils, chisels screeching their way into designs, voices calling out, tongs clattering beside the fire. And the oven, stretching out long tongues of green and gold flame, added its contribution of soot to the blackened figures of the journeymen and recalled to Young Fu's mind pictures he had seen of the realms in which evil spirits dwell.

His thoughts of evil spirits became vividly real one afternoon as he squatted in the middle room and polished a brazier which a workman, named Dsen, had just finished. Through the doorway he watched coolies lower an open sedan chair from which a tall, strangely dressed person stepped out. The apparition sauntered into the store and Young Fu stopped his work and gazed open-mouthed. It was a foreigner. In the weeks of living in Chungking, he had not yet been close to one. Occasionally he saw them at a distance, but they were usually so well hidden by the inquisitive crowds that always accompanied their appearance, that he still had no idea what they were like. Tang took immediate charge of the stranger, and the clerk and Den rushed about displaying goods.

Young Fu turned to the journeyman beside him. "Is that a man?"

Dsen laughed. "Truly you are from the country. Have you never seen a foreigner before?"

"Not so close. And if it is a man, even you will agree that he wears the jacket and loose trousers of a woman."

"All of their men dress in this fashion, and their women clothe their bodies in men's skirts. Everything they do is the opposite of accepted custom. The women all have feet as large as coolies', and they go about, even the young ones, in open chairs that expose their faces to the gaze of the world. The shoes they wear have thin pegs under the heels, to make them taller, I suppose, though High Heaven knows they are ungainly enough by nature. And their hair flies loosely about their faces and they laugh and talk as freely as a man. But they are as all other barbarians: they have no polite rules of conduct, and we of the Middle Kingdom can feel pity."

The boy listened attentively, but his eyes never left the figure in the store. The foreigner moved restlessly about the room, pointing out objects with a long stick and refusing to sit down and drink tea, which was what any Chinese gentleman would have done in the same circumstances.

"I like not his face," Young Fu told the journeyman. "The skin is white with bristles and resembles a poorly plucked fowl, and his nose is twice the size it should be."

Dsen went on with his work. "I felt the same about the first one I saw. When he opened his mouth to smile, he was so ugly I thought it would kill me. But I am used to them now, and while I see no good in them, I do not believe

with the women that they cause bad fortune. Indeed, they are too stupid for any sensible man to fear. With money they are fools, paying coolies for every service twice what they ought to receive. But they are rich, and silver means nothing to them. They have meat every meal, it is said, and the choicest vegetables and fruit. Even the poorest among them lives like a Mandarin."

The foreigner, who showed no particular interest in the objects before him, was attempting to explain his dissatisfaction to Tang. Young Fu strained to hear, but nothing reached him above the usual uproar of the room.

"What language does he speak?" he asked Dsen.

"English, and some few words of Chinese, I suppose."

"Does Tang understand English?"

"No, but what the fellow cannot say in Chinese, the coppersmith will guess."

Tang came swiftly toward them. "With such industry in an apprentice, my fortune is made already," he remarked wryly in passing.

Old Tsu called out, "Does nothing suit your rich customer?"

"Nothing in the store. He wishes a finer piece to send as a gift to his friend in America. He shall see the best that we have." The master moved to a large chest, pulled a key from his belt, inserted it in the triangular hanging lock, and lifted the lid.

Young Fu's hands moved rhythmically over the surface of the brazier, but stolen glances told him everything. He had noticed that chest many times but he had paid it little attention. That shopkeepers did not show their finest stock in the open store, was news to him.

Tang beckoned. "Wipe your greasy hands and carry these to Den."

At the partition to the outer room, the youth halted. Fu Be Be's warnings about foreigners returned to him in full force. Suppose evil should fall on him as a result of being close to this creature. His skin prickled; then he moved forward. Evil was certain to follow if he made Tang angry by not obeying orders, and the unknown seemed the lesser of the two. He gave the articles carefully to Small Den. On his third return to the inner room, a voice called after him, "Tell your master I wish to hurry."

Startled, Young Fu glanced over his shoulder. That had been the foreigner speaking. He could not believe his own ears. He himself knew no English, so the man must have used Chinese words. In a daze he repeated the message to Tang.

"Always these foreigners must hurry," remarked the coppersmith. "They waste good time studying their watches. They hasten to earn money and hasten to spend it. Why then trouble to gain it? Careful spending increases riches."

Old Tsu was now helping Tang to choose from the hidden treasures. "His hurry will be to your advantage," he said. "He will not linger over the bargaining."

Carrying a tray and a jar, Tang and the apprentice strode toward the customer. In a moment the latter had selected the tray and asked its price. Young Fu was amazed at the stupidity of such a course. Even a child knew better than to let a merchant guess which purchase pleased him most. One pretended interest in everything else and asked the price only after the storekeeper had, himself, centered attention on the article desired. Tang mentioned a sum at which Young Fu caught his breath. The foreigner looked up quizzically, then offered half the amount. Tang raised it to three fourths of the original and the other man met this compromise with one of two thirds. He accompanied the last figure with action. His hand drew from a slit in the side of his trousers—a queer place, indeed, to keep money!—several silver dollars. They were accepted. Small Den wrapped the gleaming tray in tissue paper and carried it to the chair. With a nod, the foreigner was gone.

That night on Chair-Makers' Way, Young Fu told his mother, "Today a foreign man bought a tray in our store."

"He did not see you, I hope!"

"He did. Tang told me to carry brasses into his presence. Also, he spoke to me." At his mother's exclamation of fright, he reassured her, "Do not fear! He was ugly, but harmless."

"When did you acquire so much wisdom? Already you copy these city people. You are like a man who sits at the bottom of a well and boasts about his knowledge of the world. No one now is wise save those within the walls of the brass shop! But in the country we still know a few things, and one is that foreign barbarians should be avoided."

"But do you wish me to disobey Tang's orders?"

No reply came, and rolling in his pu-gai, her son fell asleep.

THE SNOWSTORM

Steingrimur Arason

An Iceland farm and the continual struggle of the farmers against the short season and violent weather are the setting for this story. This chapter gives a picture of the people and their quiet fortitude. To make the excerpt easier to follow, it helps to know who the characters are. Erik and Helga are master and mistress of the farm; Nonni is their son, Skuggi his dog and companion; Sigga and Gudda are maids, and Snorri and Thor are farmhands.

Everyone seemed uneasy all day. Nonni noticed first when he dropped his spoon on the floor during breakfast and Sigga looked at him too quickly, with startled eyes. His mother went about her work absent-mindedly, in an unusually silent mood, and when he called to Skuggi the dog refused to leave his warm corner by the fire and only thumped his tail.

By afternoon Helga stated her worry. "I don't like that whistling sound up in the mountain pass," she said, with a frown.

Erik got up and went to the window. "I wonder if the farmhands have gone for the sheep?"

Gudda chimed in, shaking her head dolefully. "I had a bad dream last night. I spilled a whole pail of milk on the dairy floor."

Nonni laughed, but Sigga looked up with interest. "That was bad, to spill the milk, Gudda. What do you think it means?"

"It means a terrible storm is sure to come. I have never known it to fail."

Nonni looked at her quickly. She was making it all up, of course.

And yet, when he went over to the windowpane, he was not so sure. "The frost roses are all turned down!"

Sigga swung around at his shout, her face bright with excitement. "Go, Nonni, and find out how the bladder is!"

Storms were frequent enough, but one that had announced itself beforehand in Gudda's dream was certainly out of the ordinary. When Nonni reported that the sheep's bladder, hung up to serve as barometer, was very hard, she stared at Gudda with fascinated eyes.

Erik had paid no attention to the chatter in the room, but now he turned from the window and began getting into his sheepskin coat.

"I must go and help the farmhands before it gets quite dark," he said.

Gudda smiled and nodded her head, but Helga took alarm at his tone.

"Please be careful, Erik. It is bad enough knowing the sheep and the farmhands are out in a storm without being afraid for you too."

"Oh, I'll be in no danger."

He put on his storm cap while Nonni watched enviously. It came way down and completely covered his head, all but his eyes and nose. Then he took his walking stick, six feet high and tipped with sharp steel, and left.

Nonni watched at the window. It was really growing steadily darker; and every now and then Gudda would shuffle up behind him and peer out with a satisfied air, as though she were cooking up the storm by a special recipe. Half an hour after Erik had gone, the snow began. In a few minutes the air was full of fine, driving flakes, and a little later the house began to shake as though it were pummeled by giants' fists.

"God help all those who are outside now," Helga said softly.

She had her embroidery in her lap, and in the light from the kerosene lamp she appeared peaceful in contrast with the nervous Sigga. But Nonni saw the knotted frown between her eyes and noticed that her hands lay frequently idle on the embroidery frame.

Sigga could not sit still. She walked up and down, and shivered with each onslaught of wind.

"I am afraid the house will be blown away."

Nonni laughed. "No danger of that," he assured her. "It is frozen too solidly into the ground!"

He was enjoying the storm, and wished he

might have gone with his father into the arctic darkness. With a cap like Erik's, to keep his neck and ears warm, and a staff in his hand, he would have felt equal to anything. He was sorry his mother could not see it that way.

Gudda looked up from her spinning and listened to the wind.

"In all my eighty years I have never seen weather like this," she said with evident pride. "Well, once it was like this. That was when the brothers from Bakki died. They were coming from town just before Christmas, and they lost their way on the lowland. They had heavy burdens on their backs, and they kept walking through the night. In the morning they were found far up the valley, dead, stiff, and frozen."

Helga got up abruptly, letting her sewing fall to the floor.

"Let's put lights in all the windows," she said. Her voice was quick and frightened. "Sigga, you go put one in the guest-room window, and fasten a mirror behind it. There may be someone out on the lowland now, coming from the town. Nonni, you put one in the south window, facing the highland."

Three long hours passed, during which they were all unwillingly conscious of the storm and the angry knocking of the wind. It sounded so sharp and insistent that Nonni wondered how they dared refuse it. Each knock sounded angrier than the one before. He could not think of the storm as just wind and weather swirling impersonally about the farmhouse. He saw it now as a huge giant towering over them in a purple cloak; tossing his head in a fury and kicking his boots against the little house; roaring that he would come and get them anyway, so they had better open the door.

Suddenly the outer door was opened. A sharp cold wind with snow in it rushed through the long hall and came right into the *badstofa*. Nonni jumped up, his heart leaping with unreasonable fear. Helga caught up a lamp and rushed out, followed by Sigga and Nonni. The hall was already white with fine snow. Two men, looking unnaturally large in their storm coats and so covered with snow that they were almost unrecognizable, stood there, beating themselves free. Snow fell in showers all about them. They were Snorri and Thor.

"Where is Father?" Nonni called.

"Where is Erik?"

They stopped beating away the snow and stared as though they had not heard correctly.

Then, "Isn't he here?" Snorri asked.

Thor said, "I saw him over two hours ago. Some of the sheep were missing, and he said he would go up to the mountains to look for them. It wasn't bad then," he ended lamely as he saw the look on Helga's face.

There was a short stillness. Then Snorri turned back to the door.

"Come on. We'll go look for him."

Helga caught his arm. "No, you don't." Her voice was small and determined. "If you go, you will not find him; and you will be of no help to any of us, lost yourselves. Erik can take care of himself and come home as soon as it's possible to do so."

There was so much truth in this that they could not deny it, and they were soon warming themselves at the fire and drinking hot coffee while their outer clothes were hung up to dry. Their coffee finished, they brought some harness out of the storeroom and went to work mending it. Everyone was busy at something and everyone worked silently, listening for the door to open once more and trying not to show the anxiety they felt.

The storm kept hammering on the house. Helga went into her bedroom once and closed the door. Nonni knew that she went to read the Bible. After a time she came out again, seemingly calmer.

"Your father has been out in bad storms before this," she told Nonni. "He will be able to stand this one just as he stood those."

Surprisingly, Gudda lifted her wrinkled face.

"Yes, I know," she said. "He has the warmth of a bear in him. Anyone who has that has a gift from God."

They all felt vaguely comforted after that. It was so seldom that Gudda had anything good to say. Nevertheless, the night passed very slowly. They lay on beds in the *badstofa* and seldom spoke. Nonni slept a little and roused at times from a light slumber to hear Gudda chanting some dreary rhyme and the storm still beating its drum.

He awoke the next morning aware of a great

stillness. The storm had worn itself out and the sky was clear, with all the stars shining. The windows were coated with frost, and Nonni blew his warm breath on the glass until a round, clear spot appeared. Through this he looked into the dim, snow-covered farmyard and immediately gave a glad shout.

"Father is coming!"

Everyone ran eagerly to open the door for him. Helga's wan face was shining with relief and joy. Erik came in walking heavily, too tired to scrape the snow from his heavy boots. He tracked it straight into the *badstofa* and sank onto a bed, clothes and all. Helga helped him out of his coat.

"Where have you been all the night?" Nonni demanded.

"I have been walking all night, my boy."

"Oh, your poor toes!" Helga cried, struggling with his boots. "Aren't they frozen?"

Erik roused enough to smile at her. "I should say not. I was warm enough." Then he looked grave as he added, "The worst of it all is I did not find the sheep. It was not easy to look for them. I never could see a yard from me. Every hollow is filled up. They must be under the snow, or I would have found them. Ah, well, I will have to go out again, later, to see what I can do."

Helga had pulled off the boots and now began brushing the snow from his clothes.

"Go to the kitchen, Sigga, and heat a quart of milk," she said. "You, Erik, no more talking about going out again. You must get in bed and go to sleep, right away."

Erik started to protest, but at that moment there was a loud knocking at the outer door. Helga hurried to open it, and was astonished to see Karl, the postman, standing on the threshold.

He smiled at her. "I am in poor condition to enter your house," he said, glancing down at his wet, half-frozen clothes. "I have been sleeping under the snow. Could you give me dry clothing?"

"Of course, Karl. Come in," Erik cried. He had left his bed at the sound of Karl's voice and now stood in the hallway in his stocking feet. "You and I are a fine pair. I have been out all night, too, but not sleeping."

"Oh, Erik, get in bed! And you, too, Karl—you must get into dry clothes and rest a while."

But Helga's solicitude was wasted. Tired as the men were, they wanted to talk about the storm more than they wanted to sleep. When Karl had changed into some clothes of Erik's, much too large for him, the two sat at the table and ate a hearty meal.

"How did it happen that you were out last night?" Erik asked.

"I was caught on the mountain, coming from Reykjavik, when the storm broke out. When I became aware of it I did as I always do, stopped and stood still for a long time."

"Why did you do that?" Nonni asked curiously.

Karl was long-winded and could make a story out of almost anything. It was not often he had such good material as this to work with.

He leaned back in his chair and prepared his explanation slowly. "When the blizzard is just beginning, the wind is blowing from all directions at once. Then people are apt to get confused and lose their way. It is necessary to think hard at that moment. When the wind has grown very strong and the blizzard is well under way, it seldom changes direction until it clears up. After that it is all right to plot your course. Just so, last night. When the wind was blowing steadily, and I had made sure of the direction, I noticed that it was blowing straight against the outer end of my left eyebrow."

Nonni giggled, but Karl's face was grave.

"After that," he continued, "I kept on walking, keeping the wind always on that spot—except where there were windings on the road and, after traveling that same road ever since I was a lad of eighteen, I guess I know those pretty well. I wasn't really lost once. When I had walked about three hours, I said to myself, 'Karl, you have walked far enough. If you can't find Fairdale here, you will not look for it any farther.' "

"And you did not find it!" Nonni said.

Karl nodded. "And I did not find it. It was about the darkest dark I have ever met with. You couldn't have seen your hand five inches from your eyes. And the storm was sweeping over me so fast that I could not stand on my feet at times."

"What did you do?"

"Well, there was only one thing I could do. I

lay down in a little hollow at the south of a hill. I put the mailbag under my head and turned down the flap, to be sure the letters wouldn't get wet. In no time at all the snow had covered me as snug as your mother would, with an eider down quilt, if I would let her."

He cackled as Helga smiled in spite of herself and gave an impatient shake of her head.

"I don't care what becomes of the two of you," she said. "Out all night in a storm and then sit there talking your heads off all day!"

"Never had a better sleep in my life," Karl assured her gravely, though his blue eyes twinkled.

"You must have been very hungry," Nonni said, thinking what it would be like to go to bed in the snow and deciding it would be a lot of fun.

"Oh, no," Karl cried quickly. "I forgot to tell you I had some sandwiches in my pocket. Never travel without them. When the snow had covered me all up, I moved around so as to hollow out a little elbow room for myself; and I made space enough to get out those sandwiches."

"So you had a comfortable night out there in the blizzard after all." Erik smiled.

"Yes, yes, a very fine night," Karl said. "The trouble did not start until I climbed out of bed this morning. Then it occurred to me that I was all dripping wet. The frost was so hard that I thought I would freeze all through in a moment. You may believe that I walked fast to this house. And, surprisingly enough, I was only a few yards from your house all the time!"

Everyone laughed, but Sigga gave a little shudder and said, "I would go crazy right now if I were buried like that!"

"I wouldn't!" Nonni cried.

It was very exciting to think that Karl, the postman, had been sleeping only a few yards from them under the snow all night!

Nonni's thoughts turned to the sheep, still out in the snow. Karl had dug himself out, little the worse, but the sheep were too foolish to do that. They would freeze to death if they were not found soon. He remembered how the ewes had behaved during sudden windstorms in the summer. They had huddled together in little groups, in the lee of a big rock. He rembered the ravine where Halli had found Flenna. The sheep would be sure to go to some such place as that when the storm broke. Perhaps they had not been able to reach it and were snowed under on the way. Suddenly he wanted to be out over the unbroken pastureland.

"Mother, let me go skiing!"

"Yes, do that," she agreed. "The snow must be good. But put on your hood. I don't want you coming back with your ears frozen."

He went into the storeroom for his skis. As an afterthought he took a shovel with him. He called to Skuggi, put on his skis, and climbed up to the pastureland. The skis left a clean herringbone track behind him. When he had gone a long way and was approaching the place where the sheep usually grazed, he brushed the snow from a rock and sat down to rest. Skuggi came to him and sat in front of him. He found it hard work, floundering through the snow, and was glad for once to stop when Nonni did. Nonni took the dog's head in his hands and looked into his eyes.

"You have a good sense of smell, Skuggi. I want you to find the sheep that are buried somewhere near here. You must try your very best!"

Then they went higher up into the hills. Skuggi really was sniffing and running about as though vigorously searching for something. Sometimes the snow got into his nose and made him sneeze. The two of them searched the snow all around for a long time. They had covered nearly all the pastureland, and Nonni, tired and hungry, was ready to turn back in disappointment when Skuggi commenced to scratch at the snow and bark furiously.

Nonni's spirits rose at once, and he rushed to Skuggi's aid with the shovel. It was no easy task. The snow was heavy, and wherever he shoveled it away more tumbled in from the sides. At last he discovered that it was better to make big blocks of the snow and push these away down the hillside. Even though this involved more work, it was the only way he could make any progress. He worked hard for a long time; then, panting and damp with perspiration, he sat down to rest. Even now, it seemed, after all his work, he would have to make the hole much wider or there would not be room enough, as he got down deeper, to wield the shovel. If only Skuggi had not been barking and scratching merely in play! He looked sharply at him, but the dog was nosing eagerly at the snow and scratching it away with his claws.

Nonni picked up the shovel and went to work again, standing in part of the hole while trying to enlarge it. Suddenly, without even a crack to warn him, the snow under his feet gave way, and he fell into a dark cave. At the same time he heard the bleating of sheep! He was so happy he shouted; and above him he saw Skuggi, waving his tail and barking. Several sheep lay close together in the darkness, in a little room. The heat from their bodies had melted the snow from the ground around them, leaving a roof of snow over their heads. They appeared warm and comfortable.

How to get them out was a problem. Nonni looked at the gaping hole through which he had tumbled. It was too steep for sheep to scramble through. He looked at his shovel, which his fall had brought down with him. He had had enough of that for a while. But it was the only way. He took it up and once more bent his aching back to the task of digging. He had to make a great many steps, close together yet on a gradual slope away from the sheep, before he was through. At last the animals could climb out of the cave, and Nonni was surprised to count ten of them.

Even now the work was not over. The sheep were heavy and sank too far into the snow with every step. He would have to walk slowly, dragging his skis behind him by a piece of string luckily found in his pocket, and try to beat some sort of solid path in front of the sheep so they could follow him.

It was quite a procession that came into the farmyard an hour later. Nonni tramped slowly along. Behind him came the sheep in single file; and bringing up the rear was Skuggi, carrying his plumed tail proudly. Erik, who had just opened the door to start out after the lost sheep, could hardly believe his eyes. He stared for a moment at the little figure stamping toward him through the snow, and then he gave such a shout of joy, pride, and sheer amazement that all inside the house rushed out.

Nonni came carefully forward, and the sheep crowded as close as the skis would allow. He could not keep the delighted grin from his face, although he would have liked to hide it.

"Now you can go back to bed, Father," he called.

"What a wonderful thing!" said the farmhands, marveling. "Who would have thought he could find them!"

Helga only smiled from the doorway, her face rosy with pleasure, but Erik went over to Nonni and led him into the house almost as though he were an important guest.

"Let's have food for this shepherd, Helga," he said. "What do you have extra fine in the storeroom?"

Nonni noticed, as he entered the door, that Sigga put out her foot to bar the way to the dog.

"No, no! Let Skuggi come in," he said, and Skuggi jumped over the outstretched ankle. "I did not discover the sheep," he said stoutly. "It was Skuggi who did that, and I want him to have the best supper he has ever had."

from DOBRY

Monica Shannon

Dobry *won the Newbery Award in 1935, and it still remains one of the finest books in the list of Newbery winners. Beautifully written, rich in unique characters, this is a slow-moving story that does not make an immediate appeal to children. Reading it aloud, discussing the people and Dobry's problem will help. Should Dobry do what his mother expects him to do, stay on the farm, or go away to study art as he yearns to do? Grandfather helps Dobry to find the answer.*

Dobry ran to a window, slid back its windowpanel carved with buffalo heads. "Snow! Why, it's snowing, Grandfather! The courtyard is white already." Snow was never rare in a mountain village of Bulgaria, but nobody, not even Dobry's grandfather, had seen snow coming down to hide red apples on the tree, late corn on the stalk, ripe peppers in the field, grapes on the vine. The golden-leaved poplar tree in the courtyard of Dobry's peasant home was completely hushed with snow. Wool, too, from the autumn shearing was hanging out to dry. The wool grew thicker, the thickest wool imaginable as more and more snow came down. Without making a sound, the sky itself seemed to be coming down bit by bit.

"Nobody has ever seen a happening like this one," Dobry's grandfather said, and followed the little boy to the window. "Snow already, even before the gypsy bear gets here! My back, my legs complain of getting in the grass and the early corn. They wanted a good rubbing before snow set in. Snow? To the devil with gypsies! They should be here with the massaging bear!"

Dobry hung out of the window as far as he could. The rickety outside stairway going down to the ground floor where their two oxen lived had a carpet of snow, immaculate, and the oxen looked up from their stalls each wearing a furry hat of new snow.

Dobry shouted, "Look! Sari and Pernik are surprised too. Look, Grandfather, they wear white fur hats like royalty!"

The grandfather leaned out. "It's true." He shook his head instead of nodding because in Bulgaria you shake your head for "yes" and nod your head for "no." "They do look like royalty," the grandfather said. He drew in his head, shivered, muttered, "You feel the first cold. Anyway, you feel it when one day is like summer and the next day like winter. Come in out of that."

Dobry pulled his head in, turned around. His hair and eyelashes had gone completely white.

"St. Nicholai, the Miracle Maker, bless us all!" The grandfather stared at Dobry. "You look just like me with all that white on you. Snow is blowing in! Close that window tight."

"Wait, wait," Dobry begged and cupping his hands he put them out for snowflakes. "Look, they are beauties," he told the grandfather. "Look at the shapes! Flowers from the sky."

The grandfather shook his head vigorously instead of saying, "Yes, yes." "Each flake is a different one. Perfect! All white flowers—little, new, and no two alike."

Dobry asked him, "And why aren't the snowflakes alike, Grandfather? Different, each one different?"

The grandfather said, "Everything is different, each leaf if you really look. There is no leaf exactly like that one in the whole world. Every stone is different. No other stone exactly like it. That is it, Dobry. God loves variety." Grandfather found it hard to say exactly what he meant. "God makes better icons than those in the church. He makes a beautiful thing and nothing else in the whole world is exactly like it. That is it, Dobry. Something for you to remember."

"Why?" Dobry asked him.

"Well, it's as good a thing to remember as anything. I never went like you do to the school but I know it. No two things are exactly alike. In odd days like these—snow comes too early, the gypsy bear too late—people study how to be all alike instead of how to be as different as they really are."

Grandfather slid back the window-panel, threw a log on the open fire, pushed it in farther with his foot, and sat himself down on the three-legged stool under the fireplace hood reaching far out into the room.

Dobry, his mother Roda, his grandfather, all of them called their fireplace a "jamal" and a jamal it really was. It stood out from the wall, tiles green, yellow, blue, glimmering in the firelight, and its big yellow chimney was stuccoed to make a picture of quail hiding in ripe grass.

Dobry squatted on the hearth. Above his head under the jamal's hood dangled copper pots, copper kettles, and copper pans, tarnished now because the gypsy cleaner had not yet come to brighten them up for the winter. He looked at the flames, content to watch their colors, their motions, and listen to their chat, but his grandfather interrupted.

"Ours is the most beautiful jamal in the whole village," he said. "No other like it. It knows its work, too. Never smokes. Heats up the whole house instead of trying to change the weather outside. Only Maestro Kolu could have made a jamal like this one."

"Couldn't you make a jamal like this one? You could, couldn't you, Grandfather? And the blacksmith could make one too, couldn't he?"

Grandfather said very loud, "Pff! Pff! Not Pinu, the blacksmith. That fellow! Maestro Kolu is a Macedonian and almost a magician besides. He puts little pipes into a chimney the way God puts blood vessels into our bodies. Perfect! The heat goes around but stays in the house. Maestro Kolu knows the secret and that secret has been growing up for centuries. He knows how to make a jamal as no other man knows it—tiles colored up like our stony earth, the chimney a picture like one of our fields. I tell you, if Maestro Kolu lives to be five hundred years old he'll never have time enough to make the jamals people ask him to make. And——"

Realizing all of a sudden that he was roaring instead of talking, the grandfather stopped to laugh at himself. "Some day you will see Maestro Kolu, maybe, and then you will know for yourself what he is."

The old man got a pipe out from the sash winding seven times around his middle and, his pipe filled, going, he felt around in his sash for a red pepper and gave it to Dobry to nibble. Dobry never could guess at all the things his grandfather tucked away in that broad red sash making a middle for his blue homespun suit. Pipes, coins, red peppers, cheese, bread, garlic, wooden boxes of spices to brighten up his bread in the fields, a painted flute—Dobry often saw these things come out and always asked himself, "What else may be in there?"

Dobry's mother hurried in from the kitchen fetching a bucket of water to heat in the cauldron hanging from big iron chains over the open fire. She added to the brightness the firelight made in this room of plain wooden walls and carved wooden panels—there was so much color to Roda that in the summer field bees often sought her out. Her cheeks and black eyes glowed, her white lace petticoat swirled below a sunflower-colored dress and an apron woven over with roosters just about to crow. A white kerchief topped her head and her hair danced behind her in two long braids.

"What is this?" she asked them. "A boy thinks of everything except going to bed. A big, sleepy boy and long after his supper time! A boy grows big enough to down four bowls of buttermilk at a sitting and he can't tell bedtime yet! We must be up and out before the sun is up and out tomorrow. Peppers to come in and be dried, corn to come in and be husked! When are the roads going to be cleaned up for hauling? There is too much to do now that it snows when it shouldn't. Pop yourself into bed, Dobry!"

Dobry said, "Everybody expects me to go to bed the way bread goes into the oven. Pop! Am I bread? Mother, you should see the way Sari and Pernik go to bed. You should see it! Close one eye, eat a little more, open that eye, close the other, and eat a little more. Very slow. And Grandfather said they were good beasts fit to wear tall fur hats like royalty. Didn't you, Grandfather? You should see their hats, Mother. Snow, very new. Perfect!"

His mother said, "There it is! A boy can think of everything except going to bed. Bread, ovens, fur hats, royalty even. Go to bed!" She stooped and kissed Dobry. "The whole world taken by surprise! All these snowflakes dancing the horo outside—and this boy! Well, I must go and look after the bread. The bread is growing up now."

Dobry said, "Good-night, Grandfather," and kissed him.

The grandfather told him, "Don't forget to pray to St. Triffon about the gypsy bear, will you now? How late those gypsies are and the snow early! Ask St. Triffon to bring the gypsies soon with the massaging bear."

"Do your back and legs complain much tonight?" Dobry asked him.

"Yes, always a little. Ever since I weeded tomatoes when the fields were wet."

"Do we eat the tomatoes now, Grandfather? We always eat tomatoes after the first snow comes."

The grandfather nodded his head emphatically to say, "No, no. It's not winter yet. Tomatoes are for winter. Later snows will cover them just right. Then we'll have tomatoes, a few at a time, and a whole vineful of tomatoes for Christmas Day—the way we always do."

Dobry's grandfather alone of all the villagers knew how to make snow take care of his tomatoes for him. He picked the tomato vines with their ripe fruits, wove them together in a weaving dense enough so that not the smallest chink was left for frost to get through. Snow covered his pyramid of tomatoes on their vines and all winter long he had only to dig down into the snow to bring up tomatoes as fresh but crisper than the morning they first ripened.

"But can't I eat some tomatoes right away?" Dobry begged. "This snow will make them crisp. You said all summer, when I helped you weed the tomatoes, you said to me, 'When snow comes you will be very happy, Dobry, for all this work. When snow comes we will both be warmed to red inside with tomatoes.' Don't you remember,

nature and relationship of father and son. The trial scene which has been chosen for this book is handled in the same way. So, in these fictionalized biographies we are permitted to know the thoughts, motives, and conversations of the heroes, although these are not to be found in the historical record.

The worth of fictionalized biography depends upon the honesty of the author in utilizing verifiable historical facts and in his ability to write his imaginary scenes and dialogue in the spirit of the times and the characters involved. This form of writing is so popular with children today that it is bringing an unprecedented increase of fictionalized biographies for the youngsters to enjoy.

Good adult biography tries to give its readers the whole man, with his faults, weaknesses, and failures and his ability to conquer or rise above them to greatness. This practice is not as true of juvenile biographies as it should be. The biographies of musicians in the series by Opal Wheeler and Sybil Deucher follow a pleasant pattern—the child musician displays the qualities that are to make him notable as a man, there are a few childish pranks or mistakes which are amusing but not serious, and life flows along with a series of successes and never a hint of the grueling struggle and toil or the handicaps and tragedies. It is too neat a pattern; life does not move like that as some of the more recent biographies are beginning to show. To be sure, these biographies are for children of nine or thereabouts, and most of them are as delightful as they are popular. But even at that level, life should not look too easy and too smooth. Carl Sandburg in his *Abe Lincoln Grows Up,* for children of eleven years old and older, gives the sorrows, the privations, and the limitations of Lincoln's early years. His was not a normal, joyous childhood but quite the reverse.

Some authors of juvenile biographies disregard the childhood of their heroes, and boldly present the man. In MacKinley Kantor's *Lee and Grant at Appomattox,* for example, children read about the failures and the drinking which clouded General Grant's early manhood. These, in contrast to Lee's honor and nobility, actually increase the reader's respect for Grant's achievements later and for the generous and noble heights to which he rose in the hour of the surrender.

George Washington has always seemed a mythical and nebulous figure to most children because biographies have made him a stereotype for honesty and courage. Now, recent lives of Washington present him as a bad speller and a backwoods boy who had to learn both spelling and good manners, but rose to greatness in spite of his limitations. To try to minimize or omit the tragedies of George Washington Carver's early days and to turn him into the figure of a normally happy boy is to falsify the records. Perhaps young children cannot bear all the tragic facts, but the shadows over Carver's childhood point up the brilliance of his achievements later on.

Most juvenile biographies do give rich details of life in other days which help children to relive the past and feel close kinship with their heroes. These lives of great men are unusually well written on the whole, with a sense of pattern and style in the narrative and of unity in the life described. Publishers are selecting eminent writers to produce the new biography, and this has resulted in a decided swing away from the all-sweetness-and-light school of writing to a sensible and truthful realism. Indeed historical facts are so competently and conscientiously handled that the popularity of these juvenile biographies is something to be thankful for and to be encouraged.

Children find qualities in biography that are lacking in other types of literature. It carries the convincing weight of reality and so stirs emulation. The child identifies himself with the hero and begins to think to himself— "If he did that, maybe if I try hard enough, I too can do what needs to be done." Reading about his hero's difficulties and achievements the child gets a clearer picture of his own problems and goals or lack of them. Many distinguished men have testified to the impact of biography on their own lives. Because of its reality it gives courage and helps to clarify or even focus youthful ambitions.

Finally, both historical fiction and biography can re-create a period or a crisis for young readers as factual narratives can rarely do. In the dramatic impact of world events on individual people the conflict takes on meaning and emotional color which historical records lack. If children have discovered the charm of Washington's peaceful, luxurious life at Mt. Vernon, the great parties at the mansions, the pleasant visiting back and forth between the big plantations, they sense at once the sacrifice it must have been to give up this life. For after all, Washington had to turn his back on his best friends, the Tory Fairfaxes, and line up with the ragged colonists in their hazardous rebellion against tyranny. Or the bloody Indian massacres are seen in a new light when a young reader follows Crazy Horse through the hard disciplines of his childhood to his mature decision to save the land for his people. And through an amusing and slight incident, life on the old canals becomes real when children read about two little girls hastily exchanging greetings as the boats pass briefly in opposite directions. It is the concrete episodes and the individual human being that bring the past to life for children. But these juvenile books, good as they are, are not the final word—they are only a beginning. When they make great men and stirring events forever memorable to children they serve as introductions to the wider and richer field of adult history and biography.

from THE VOYAGES OF CHRISTOPHER COLUMBUS

Armstrong Sperry

Here is the first chapter from the first of the Landmark Books, a distinguished series about famous men and events in American history. They may be read in sequence or singly, but every one of the thirty volumes will add to the reader's understanding and appreciation of our national ideals and the men who helped to mold them. Armstrong Sperry, author and artist, won the Newbery Award in 1941 for his exciting adventure tale Call It Courage. *His record of the glories and tragedies of Columbus' life is just as well done.*

Refuge

"Courage, my son. Are you very weary?"

"Yes, Father," the child answered. "Have we a long way still to go?"

The man pointed up the hill. There a massive building crouched like a watchdog above the seaport of Palos. Its painted walls were flushed with the afterglow of the sun. A sound of vesper bells drifted across the still air.

"We are almost arrived," the man said. "Look! The monastery of Our Lady of La Rabida. For tonight, it is the end of our journey."

The little boy's fingers tightened on the man's. "And we will find rest there?" he demanded hopefully. "And food?"

"For certain," the man reassured him. "The good Franciscans never close the door to one who hungers."

But it was a steep climb up the hill. Long before the two travelers reached the monastery, the man was forced to carry his son. They had covered many miles since dawn. The dust of Spain lay like a powder on their boots and clothing. The day had been unbearably hot, even for that summer of 1491, and the heat had pulled at their muscles, drained their limbs of strength.

With a sigh of relief the man set the boy down upon the doorstep. Then he lifted the silver knocker and let it fall against the ancient worm-bored panel of the door. The noise of the summons echoed through the silence.

As he stood waiting, the man cast a backward glance down the hill whence he and his small son had come. Across the vineyards and beyond the tiled rooftops of Palos, the masts of many ships could be seen on the darkening waters of the Rio Tinto.

Beyond the bar of Saltes, a magnificent galleon was standing out to the open sea. Her sails were dyed blood-red by the Andalusian sun, her flags and pennants whipping on the wind. The man's heart quickened. What would he not have given for such a ship! She was on a westward tack, but her captain would change that soon enough. Men didn't sail into the Sea of Darkness that lay at the western edge of the earth! They sailed south to Guinea, or east to the Golden Horn, or sometimes north as far as Iceland; but never into the unknown West.

"Fools!" the man muttered. "Why won't they listen to me?"

There came a sound of sandals flapping on a

"Brother Sebastian has already told me your name and that you come from Portugal. But I do not know your way of life." The Prior remained standing, as if undecided whether to encourage this stranger or put a speedy end to his visit.

"I am a mariner, Father, and a maker of maps," Columbus answered.

At once Father Perez took seat on the opposite side of the table. His interest had been immediately caught; for the learned Prior of La Rabida had long been a student of astronomy and geography. "So!" he echoed, "A maker of maps. I myself have given much thought to the mysteries of the heavens and the earth." As he spoke, he smiled and laid a hand lovingly on the model of the caravel which Columbus previously had noted. "But now and again I play a little," he confessed. "This ship-model is one of my playthings. Tell me—as a mariner you have voyaged far?" There was a hint of eagerness in the grave voice, a glimmer of youthful light in the dark eyes. This elderly man, garbed in the sober habit of Saint Francis, spoke of ships and the sea as only one could who yearned for them.

Columbus warmed to his host. For so long he had been treated with ridicule that now he expanded in the glow of the Prior's interest. "For thirty years, as man and boy, I have followed the sea," he said. "I have crossed the Mediterranean times without number and touched all its coasts. I have been to the English islands, to the Portuguese Azores, to Iceland, and to the Spanish archipelago of the Canaries."

For a second, doubt flickered in the Prior's eyes. "That means you have touched the very boundaries of the whole world, señor."

"Of the known world, yes," Columbus replied. "But not of the whole world. I believe there are still other lands, perhaps continents, to be discovered."

"Indeed! How can you state that so surely, since you have never seen them?"

A sudden smile robbed Columbus's answer of its edge. "How can you state that there is a Heaven, Father, since you have never seen it?"

"Because I believe in it," the Prior answered quietly.

"Exactly! And I share that belief. But to it I add—mathematics."

Father Perez nodded his head thoughtfully. "It is possible," he admitted. "After all, the Canaries were only discovered in my father's time."

From within his shabby doublet, Columbus drew a folded parchment carefully wrapped in waxed silk. He spread it on the table.

"Look you, Father," he explained, eagerly. "The only chart the Portuguese didn't get away from me! It is a map I have drawn of those unknown regions. Although I have not seen them, I know from the facts we already have what those far-off lands must be like."

"Of what facts do you speak?" And Father Perez' tone was cautious. This stranger, he felt uneasily, might be either a lunatic or a genius.

Columbus warmed to his subject. "Gales blowing from the west have washed ashore on Porto Santo timbers of unknown wood, carved without the touch of iron!" he exclaimed. "What hand carved them? And bamboos, too, so thick that one section could hold gallons of wine; and trees, the like of which do not grow in the Azores. Whence did they come? The Governor of Flores himself reported the bodies of two men cast up by the ocean—men with yellow faces and straight black hair, like the people of Asia. What of all this?"

For a second the Prior was silent, touched by a sense of wonder and of awe. Hesitantly, he said: "But who could be found to face such monstrous perils on an unknown ocean? The very thought is terrifying."

A rare smile lighted Columbus's somber face. "He who would make sure of dying in bed should never go to sea," he answered. Suddenly he picked an orange from the bowl on the table. "Consider for a moment, Father, that this is the world," he pleaded. "This point we shall call Lisbon. And here—" he marked another point on the fruit, "is the uttermost region of Cathay: a distance of fourteen thousand miles. Now, instead of voyaging east by land, suppose we sail west by water. What will happen? We shall reach Cathay by traveling only four thousand miles. Think of it! Four thousand miles by sea rather than fourteen thousand by land."

A wry smile twisted the Prior's lips. "You have, it seems, an answer to all objections. But tell me —to what good end do you desire to prove your theory?"

Proudly Columbus's answer came back: "To find the shortest route to the continent of Asia, and to bring to its people a knowledge of the true Faith." There was no mistaking the ringing sincerity of the words. "I believe, good Father, that God has called me to this mission—in giving me, since childhood, a love of far places. He has taught me the secrets of the stars and the sea. He has granted me wisdom for mathematics and skill for making charts. Until I cease to breathe, I must follow His bidding."

The man broke off, made a gesture of helplessness. "And what do I ask for this great venture? Only three ships. Three small ships. Is that so much to ask?"

The Prior sank his chin in thought while the tapers burned low. In his mind the belief was growing that this man called Christopher Columbus, this stranger who had chanced to knock at the doors of La Rabida, had pierced to the heart of the truth.

Conscious now of a great fatigue, Columbus arose and pushed back his chair. That sense of failure which had weighed upon him so heavily and so long had returned. "I have taxed your kindness unduly, Father," he said in a low tone; and folding the chart, replaced it in his doublet. "If you will show me to the chamber where my child sleeps——The hour is late and we must be off at dawn."

"Off?" The Prior roused himself. "To where?"

"I seek a ship to France. To offer this empire of which I speak, this great glory, to the French King."

"But——"

"I have lost too many years already!" the man cried bitterly. "Fourteen of them I gave to Portugal. And for what? They stole my calculations, promising to study them and give me a decision. But secretly they sent out the ships they refused to give me. Now their fleets creep along the coasts of Guinea, getting here a bit of gold and there a Negro slave. But I shall secure for the French Crown a direct route across the western ocean to the vast wealth of Asia."

"But why for the French King?" the Prior objected. "Why not for King Ferdinand and Queen Isabella, when already you stand on the soil of Spain?"

"There is no sovereign I would more gladly serve than Isabella of Castile," said Columbus heavily. "But how should I ever command the ear of Her Majesty?"

"It is not beyond possibility," the Prior answered slowly, "though this is scarcely the moment to petition Their Majesties for ships and funds. The war with the Moors has drained the Treasury. Still, a thought presents itself to me——"

"And that, good Father?"

"It occurs to me that this port of Palos is under sentence of the Royal Council to furnish two ships for any service the Crown may appoint. With two provided, the cost of a third ship might not seem so formidable to the Queen."

Such a hope surged in Columbus's breast that he could not trust himself to speak; for he remembered that the Prior had once been father-confessor to Queen Isabella herself.

Father Perez was saying: "I shall show you now to your chamber. We will sleep on the notion. Sleep brings wise counsel." And then for a second his thin old body stiffened. He stared into the other's eyes, probing deep. What he discovered must have satisfied him, for he said: "It takes courage to be the first to do a thing which the world needs. The little men turn back and the cowards never start. In me you have found a friend. I believe in you, Christopher Columbus. And remember that the longest day, however hard, has an evening; the longest journey, an end. Go with God, señor."

Columbus bowed his head. Tears stood in his eyes. "God bless and keep you, Father," he whispered.

THE TRIAL

Elizabeth Janet Gray

Elizabeth Janet Gray (Mrs. Vining) won the Newbery Award in 1923 for her story of medieval life in England, Adam of the Road. *Later, she was chosen to go to Japan to undertake the education of the Japanese crown prince. She has written a fascinating account of her experience in Japan, called* Windows for the Crown Prince. *Mrs. Vining is a Quaker, so her interest in William Penn is understandable. England's illustrious admiral, Penn, was bitterly disappointed*

have asked but one question, and you have not answered me; though the rights and privileges of every Englishman are concerned in it."

"If I should suffer you to ask questions till tomorrow morning," replied the Recorder huffily, "you would never be the wiser."

And young Penn could not resist the temptation to retort: "That is according as the answers are."

That was too much for the judges; they turned purple with rage.

"I desire no affront to the court but to be heard in my just plea. . . ."

The Mayor and the Recorder both broke out in indignant shouts: "Take him away! Take him away! Turn him into the bale-dock."

The bale-dock was a sort of pen at the far end of the courtroom, open at the top but enclosed by high palings so that the prisoners could not see or hear what was going on. Before he was dragged off to this coop, William Penn delivered a ringing challenge:

"Is this justice or true judgment? Must I therefore be taken away because I plead for the fundamental laws of England? However, this I leave upon your consciences, who are of the jury and my sole judges, that if these ancient fundamental laws which relate to liberty and property (and are not limited to particular persuasions in the matter of religion) must not be indispensably maintained and observed, who can say he hath a right to the coat upon his back?"

"Be silent there."

"I am not to be silent in a case wherein I am so much concerned, and not only myself but many ten thousand families besides."

Roughly they pulled him off to the bale-dock. Mead had his turn, stood his ground well, quoted a Latin tag, defined a riot, and was also consigned for his pains to the bale-dock.

There, stuck away in the dimness, they could not hear what was going on in the court, but one of the officers whispered to them that the Recorder was charging the jury. It was absolutely against the law to charge the jury in the absence of the prisoners. Penn flung himself on the palings and pulled himself up so that he could shout over the top of them:

"I appeal to the jury who are my judges!" Loudly as he could, he quoted the law, and he called to the jury to take notice that he had not been heard in his own defense.

"Pull that fellow down, pull him down," bawled the Recorder.

The people in the galleries craned their necks and rustled and buzzed.

"I say these are barbarous and unjust proceedings!" shouted Penn, clinging to the side of the bale-dock.

"Take them away to the hole," commanded the Recorder.

To the hole they went, a sort of dungeon in the Sessions House, a stinking hole, Penn said, and one that the Lord Mayor would not consider a fit sty for his swine. There they stayed while the jury deliberated.

They were a long time at it. After an hour and a half, eight of them returned to the court, and four who disagreed remained in the jury chamber above. The four, of whom Edward Bushell was recognized as the leader, were brought down and scolded and threatened by the court. All twelve of them were then sent back to reach a conclusion, and this time, after more deliberation, they brought the unanimous verdict that William Penn was guilty of speaking in Gracechurch Street.

This of course was equal to an acquittal. There was no law against speaking in Gracechurch Street. The Mayor tried to make them say "speaking to an unlawful assembly," but they refused. Determined to have a different verdict, he ordered them back to the jury chamber, and they asked for pen, ink, and paper to take with them.

In a little more than half an hour they returned, Penn and Mead were brought back to the bar, and the jury handed in its verdict again, this time written and signed. "We do find William Penn to be guilty of speaking or preaching to an assembly met together in Gracechurch Street, the fourteenth of August last, 1670, and that William Mead is not guilty of the said indictment."

Whereupon the Mayor called Bushell "an impudent, canting fellow," and the Recorder told them all:

"Gentlemen, you shall not be dismissed till we have a verdict the court will accept; and you shall be locked up without meat, drink, fire, and tobacco. You shall not think thus to abuse the court; we will have a verdict, or by the help of God you shall starve for it."

Before the jury departed again, Penn got his word in, and the voice of this young man of twenty-five, whom the Lord Mayor later called "that wild, rambling colt," was the only calm and authoritative voice in the whole amazing, hysterical courtroom.

"My jury, who are my judges, ought not to be thus menaced. Their verdict should be free and not compelled. The bench ought to wait upon them but not forestall them."

But the court was ready to break up for the day and "huddle the prisoners to the jail and the jury to their chamber." As the second day of the trial ended, Penn turned to the jury and said:

"You are Englishmen; mind your privileges, give not away your right."

To which Bushell stanchly made reply: "Nor will we ever do it."

And that night the jury was shut up without "meat, drink, fire, nor any other accommodation."

The next day was Sunday, and it was illegal to hold court. Nevertheless, at seven, the court sat.

The foreman of the jury read the verdict again: "William Penn is guilty of speaking in Gracechurch Street."

The Mayor prompted him: "To an unlawful assembly?" and Edward Bushell answered for him: "No, my lord, we give no other verdict than what we gave last night; we have no other verdict to give."

Another of the justices, Sir Thomas Bludworth, commented gloomily: "I knew Mr. Bushell would not yield," and the Recorder threatened again: "I will have a positive verdict, or you will starve for it." After the night they had just spent, the jury could not look on this as an empty threat.

Penn desired to ask one question: Did the court accept the verdict "Not guilty," given of William Mead?

"It cannot be a verdict," said the Recorder, "because you are indicted for a conspiracy; and one being found guilty and not the other, it could not be a verdict."

Penn's answer was quick. "If not guilty be not a verdict, then you make of the jury and Magna Carta a mere nose of wax. . . . And if William Mead be not guilty, it consequently follows that I am clear, since you have indicted us of a conspiracy, and I could not possibly conspire alone."

But for the third time the verdict was rejected and the jury sent back to find another. Again it returned with the one answer it had to give.

The court was well-nigh beside itself with rage. It threatened to set a mark on Edward Bushell, to have an eye on him, to cut his nose. And now Penn's voice rings out:

"It is intolerable that my jury should be thus menaced. Is this according to the fundamental law? Are they not my proper judges by the great charter of England? What hope is there of ever having justice done, when juries are threatened and their verdicts rejected? I am concerned to speak and grieved to see such arbitrary proceedings. Did not the Lieutenant of the Tower render one of them worse than a felon? And do you not plainly seem to condemn such for factious fellows who answer not your ends? Unhappy are those juries who are threatened to be fined and starved and ruined if they give not in their verdicts contrary to their consciences."

The Recorder had nothing to say in answer but: "My lord, you must take a course with that fellow."

"Jailer, bring fetters," commanded the Chief Justice, "and stake him to the ground."

"Do your pleasure," replied Penn superbly, "I matter not your fetters."

And now the Recorder's rage did what Penn was later to tell his children anger always does: it threw him into a desperate inconvenience. He made a speech that echoed around London and that he bitterly regretted afterwards.

"Till now," he said, "I never understood the reason of the policy and prudence of the Spaniards in suffering the Inquisition among them. And certainly it will never be well with us till something like the Spanish Inquisition be in England."

It was a dreadful thing to say. The torture and terror of the Spanish Inquisition were fresh in men's minds—Penn's grandfather, Giles Penn, had suffered from it—and in England Popery was more feared and detested than non-conformity.

For the fourth time the jury was ordered to go find another verdict; this time they refused to go, saying there was no other verdict. The Recorder in a passion left the bench, sputtering: "I protest I will sit here no longer to hear these things," but the Mayor called to him to stay while he uttered a few more threats, had the sheriff take the jury up to their room, and adjourned the court.

The prisoners were sent back to Newgate, where at least they had more freedom and comfort than the jury.

At seven o'clock on the morning of Monday, September fifth, the court sat again. The jury staggered in, wan, white, hungry, thirsty, and disheveled.

"Look upon the prisoners," said the Clerk. "What say you, is William Penn guilty or not guilty?"

"Not guilty."

"What say you? Is William Mead guilty, or not guilty?"

"Not guilty."

It was plain and definite this time. There was nothing the Bench could do except to call the roll and make each juror give his verdict separately. Everyone answered firmly: "Not guilty."

The people in the galleries were pleased, so pleased that they "made a kind of hymn about it." All over the courtroom there were little murmurs of satisfaction.

But the affair was not over. The Recorder had his last word. "I am sorry, gentlemen, you have followed your own judgments and opinions rather than the good and wholesome advice which was given you. God keep my life out of your hands: but for this the court fines you forty marks a man, and imprisonment till paid."

They had been threatened with fines and imprisonment, they had faced the ugly temper of the Bench, they must have known this was coming. But forty marks was a lot of money, about twenty-six pounds sterling, in a day when a lieutenant in the Plymouth colony, for instance, got an annual salary of twenty marks, and women worked in the hayfields for a penny a day.

Penn then stepped up toward the Bench and demanded his liberty. He was told that he too was in for fines—the forty mark fine imposed at the beginning of the session for wearing his hat. He began to quote the Magna Carta again, but the Recorder had had all he could stand. "Take him away," he implored, "take him away, take him out of the court."

But before he went young William Penn had one thing more to say. He said it. "I can never urge the fundamental laws of England but you cry: 'Take him away, take him away.' But it is no wonder, since the Spanish Inquisition hath so great a place in the Recorder's heart. God Almighty, who is just, will judge you for these things."

So the prisoners who had been acquitted, and the jury who had acquitted them, went together to Newgate prison.

That night Penn wrote to his father. "Because I cannot come, I write." He told him the story of the trial, ending: "I am more concerned at thy distemper and the pains that attend it, than at my own mere imprisonment, which works for the best."

The next day he wrote: "I entreat thee not to purchase my liberty. They will repent them of their proceedings. I am now a prisoner notoriously against law."

And the next: "I am persuaded some clearer way will suddenly be found to obtain my liberty, which is no way so desirable to me as on the account of being with thee. . . . My present restraint is so far from being humor that I would rather perish than release myself by so indirect a course as to satiate their revengeful, avaricious appetites. The advantage of such freedom would fall very far short of the trouble of accepting it."

To pay the fine would be to admit its justice. What he wanted was either to be released by the court, or to bring suit against the judges for illegal imprisonment. In this way a principle could be established. This was the course the jury was taking. Every six hours they demanded their freedom, and when at length they were released on bail, they brought suit against the judges—and won their case. The whole body of judges in the King's Bench Court decided that no jury could be fined for its verdict. So it was that as a result of the trial of William Penn the sacredness of trial by jury was established for all time.

But that was nearly a year later.

The Admiral could not wait. He was dying, and he wanted to see his beloved son William again. He secretly paid his fine, and Mead's too, and they were set free.

LONG AFTERNOON

James Daugherty

James Daugherty's biographies Daniel Boone, Poor Richard, *and* Abraham Lincoln *portray the men and the spirit of the times with fidelity and zest. He writes with the same swing and verve to be found in his pictures. But the last part of this last chapter in his life of Daniel Boone is slow moving, suited to the tempo of the old man whose stormy days have run into a quiet twilight. Even so, the reminiscences provide glimpses of the lusty young Daniel, who hunted, pioneered, and gave a droll twist to a story, even as the old Daniel does as he talks to the young artist. You must read the whole book and enjoy the narrative, the poems, and the vigorous pictures. Then, if you like* Daniel Boone, *read Mr. Daugherty's other biographies and John Mason Brown's* Daniel Boone, *one of the finest of the Landmark Books.*

At last the river voyage was ended and the Boones were crossing the Mississippi, the Father of Waters, into the little easy-going town of St. Louis. Boone was treading on the same spot where the great La Salle had built the first fort so long ago. He, too, had been a wilderness explorer of the farthest reaches, with his head full of great visions for a French empire of the Mississippi. And even before La Salle, at a point farther down the river, on a moonless night they had dropped into the dark waters the worn body of another seeker of far horizons, the Spaniard De Soto.

But on that July day in 1800 it was De Lassus, the Spanish Commandant of St. Louis, who welcomed Boone with a graciousness and respect that he had not known among the thankless Kentuckians. Here was an easy grace and gaiety of living that were foreign to the bleak Kentucky cabins. The French and Indians lived together on friendly terms and the Spanish and Americans were drawn together in their common antagonism to the British who had been a constant menace to the territory.

De Lassus knew a man when he saw one. He commissioned Boone as a government official or syndic. Besides the usual grant to a settler of one thousand arpents of land, he gave Boone a tract of ten thousand arpents with his office. The syndic was the government representative who administered law and justice in a lawless land. Boone administered primitive justice according to his own rules of common sense. He knew when a rogue deserved a lashing and he saw to it that he got it well laid on. There was no appeal from his decisions, so everybody had to be satisfied. The Femme Osage country was no place for claim jumpers under the Kentucky syndic. His duties as a judge were light in this simple and honest community. In the whole town there were only two locks, one for the government house and one for the calabozo.

So there was plenty of time for hunting and exploring trips up the Missouri to where the beaver and big game were plentiful. Jesse and Nathan Boone with their families had come to the Missouri country. Daniel Morgan, of course, was there and later came Flanders Calloway and his wife, Boone's beloved Jemima of the Boonesborough siege. They all lived within a half-day's journey of Daniel's cabin. Rebecca was happy amid friends, her children and grandchildren. It was almost another Boonesborough.

Mr. Peck, the traveling preacher, came to the Kentucky colony in Missouri and visited the old hunter. In his fine *Life of Daniel Boone* he describes him. "His high bold forehead was slightly bald and his silvered locks were combed smooth; his countenance was ruddy and fair, and exhibited the simplicity of a child. His voice was soft and melodious. A smile frequently played over his features in conversation. At repeated interviews, an irritable expression was never heard. His clothing was the coarse, plain manufacture of the family; but everything about him denoted that kind of comfort which was congenial to his habits and feelings, and evinced a happy old age."

He was the especial hero of a numerous race of grandchildren for whom he relived with zest his adventurous youth. They swarmed upon his knees and gazed wide-eyed into the fire as he told of the great siege of Boonesborough. These full years of overflowing happiness passed too quickly. History was moving on and dreamy Spanish St. Louis lay directly in her path. The nineteenth century was a husky pioneer baby that had climbed out of its cradle and was wading across the Mississippi. History was always catching up with the Boones.

In 1803 the tall red-headed Virginian, President Thomas Jefferson, bought the Territory of Louisiana for the United States from the little Corsican dictator who ruled Europe with artillery. The price was twelve million dollars; it was a big bargain for a westward-marching democracy.

In the crowd of cheering Americans who watched the stars and stripes raised at St. Louis were two young Americans, Captain Meriwether Lewis and his friend William Clark, younger brother of Clark of Vincennes. They had been personally appointed by the President to head an expedition into the West across the Rockies to the Pacific. On May 14th, 1804, "they proceeded under a gentle breaze up the Missouri," wrote Clark.

The old eagle stood looking into the West at the end of the trail as the young men started on a new enterprise that would blaze the path of empire to the Pacific. Boone had cut a path for history from the Yadkin to the Mississippi and he was ready to roll back the years and ride off into the Far West. But Rebecca and his sons and grandchildren said no, and so he stayed in Missouri. He went on long trapping trips, alone or with a Negro or Indian for a companion.

Now his broad Spanish acres were slipping away. Again he had forgotten under the easy Spanish Commandant to sign the papers. The American commissioners were genuinely sorry but there was the law. The Louisiana Purchase that had doubled the area of the new republic and enriched it with untold wealth left Daniel and Rebecca landless and penniless.

But beaver skins were worth nine dollars apiece and Daniel was planning a big winter's work with the traps. He paddled alone up the Missouri River and made a snug camp well hidden in the bluffs. It was good beaver country and he cunningly set his traps. One morning when he was making the round of his traps he saw smoke rising near his camp. A little cautious scouting showed him the hunting camp of a large body of Indians. It was hostile country for white men; Daniel concealed his tracks as he made for camp and kept out of sight till nightfall when he could safely build a fire and cook food. Next morning there was a blessed blanket of new-laid snow which had covered his traps from the Indians. For a week he lay low and watched the Indian camp, praying that the prowling savages would not stumble on some sign of his presence. One never could tell how luck would break in the wilderness. He had enough dried meat to last a long time. It was twenty days before the snow melted and the Indians packed their camp on the poles of their travois and rode away. He told Mr. Peck he "never felt so much anxiety in his life for so long a period, lest they should discover his traps and search out his camp."

He came back in the spring to the Osage settlement with a big winter catch of fine beaver fur. Saying good-by to his family he packed up the bales on his horses and departed, saying only that he was going to Kentucky on business.

John James Audubon was a young Frenchman who had just come to Kentucky from Philadelphia with his lovely wife, Mary Bakewell, to make his fortune as a merchant. Instead, he was out in the woods studying and drawing birds. He was gaily letting the business go to the dogs. When Daniel Boone came back to Kentucky and sold his furs for a bag of silver dollars to pay his debts, John James Audubon was glad to meet him. They went squirrel barking together and sat up late at night while the old hunter told of Indian escapes and perils, and then lay down on the floor and went to sleep. Audubon thought he had met the rarest bird in all America.

They both had the curious mind to see and to know about America. They shared an enormous zest for living. They wanted to enjoy all of it first-hand, and were not satisfied to settle down and own a few thousand acres with a fence around it. They were a pair of shiftless traipsers, poor as Job's turkey most of the time, walking and riding and flatboating up and down the trails and rivers of America. The rougher and tougher it was the better they liked it. Audubon went everywhere from Labrador to Florida, from Boston to Missouri. He lived with Osage Indians and spoke their language. When he needed money he drew human birds for five dollars a portrait. He drew pen portraits, too, of the strange human birds he met everywhere. His keen eyes missed no detail of the roaring pageant of democracy marching westward.

Here is John James's own story of how he went squirrel barking with Daniel Boone: "Barking off Squirrels is delightful sport, and in my opinion requires a greater degree of accuracy than any other. I first witnessed this manner of procuring Squirrels whilst near the town of Frankfort. The performer was the celebrated Daniel Boone. We walked out together, and followed the rocky margins of the Kentucky River, until we reached a piece of flat land completely covered with black walnuts, oaks, and hickories. As the general mast was a good one that year, Squirrels were seen gambolling on every tree around us. My companion, a stout, hale, and athletic man, dressed in a homespun hunting-shirt, bare-legged and moccasined, carried a long and heavy rifle, which as he was loading it he said had proved efficient in all his former undertakings and which he hoped would not fail on this occasion as he felt proud to show me his skill. The gun was wiped, the powder measured, the ball patched with six-hundred-thread linen, and the charge sent home with a hickory rod. We moved not a step from the place, for the Squirrels were so numerous that it was not necessary to go after them. Boone pointed to one of these animals which had observed us, and was crouched on a branch about fifty paces distant, and bade me mark well the spot where the ball should hit. He raised his piece gradually, until the bead (that being the name given by the Kentuckians for the sight) of the barrel was brought to a line with the spot which he intended to hit. The whip-like report resounded through the woods and along the hills, in repeated echoes. Judge of my surprise when I perceived that the ball had hit the piece of the bark immediately beneath the Squirrel, and shivered it into splinters, the concussion produced by which had killed the animal and sent it whirling through the air, as if it had been blown up by the explosion of a powder magazine. Boone kept up his firing and before many hours had elapsed we had procured as many Squirrels as we wished." It was fun for everybody but the squirrels.

A mid-October afternoon. The oak and the maple were still in full leaf, but the oaks had turned to a crimson that burned in the mellow sunshine. Little yellow leaves were spiraling down from the maples that were blazing in a burnished splendor. Autumn was a parade of blood and gold, proud and splendid.

An old brown hound snuffed among the fallen leaves. The old hunter leaned lightly against a shell-bark hickory. His face under his broad hat-brim was a noble bronze mask fringed with silver hair. Under his arm he carried the long-barreled Kentucky rifle. He was tossing a silver half-dollar in his hand. Through his mind drifted the memories, gold and crimson. Long memories of Rebecca and Squire and Jamie Boone lingered and touched hands and drifted on. Kentucky was a pageant of leaf memories. The figures of Clark of Vincennes and Robertson of Watauga, Nolichucky Jack and Simon Kenton rode down the years, tough-fibered men of action who had been gallant companions. The solemn chieftains—his Shawnee father, Black Fish, and his friend, Logan, Cornstalk and Dragging Canoe, standing by the council fires—rose up out of the past. They had fought it out man to man. They had been great enemies and he, too, was a disinherited son of Kentucky.

He had sold the heavy bales of thick beaver skins for nine dollars apiece and with a fat bag of carefully-guarded silver dollars he had sought out old friends who had lent him money and forgotten, or merchants who had advanced him supplies for which he had never turned in barter or skins. Warm Kentucky hearts glowed to see the old man again. And he paid over the counter every dollar asked on past accounts. He said: "No one can say when I am gone that Boone was a dishonest man."

He was square with Kentucky, Kentucky for which he had given so much and taken so little, and he still had four bits. He felt rather rich. The rambunctious American eagle on the half-dollar gleamed in the late sunlight as he tossed it in the air.

He hummed the old tune that he used to sing in the Kentucky canebrakes.

He whistled to the brown hound and shouldered his long rifle. He would go back to Missouri now. His grandchildren would be waiting for him, waiting to swarm into his lap or to lie on their stomachs on the floor and gaze at the burning hickory logs as he told them the old stories. He would tell them about Black Fish, his Indian father, and how he lived when he was captured by the Shawnees and they made him into an Indian and washed his white blood away in the smoky huts of Chillicothe. They would laugh and say that he was still an Indian.

He had written a memorial to Congress telling them how it had been in the old days and what he had done for Kentucky. He explained how the Spanish Commandant De Lassus had said he wouldn't need the papers signed in New Orleans in order to hold his Spanish lands in Missouri. He should be allowed the lands by the American government. The memorial had got to Washington after a time and the committees had investigated and considered and recommended. So by an Act of Congress the government in Washington put it down on paper that the land which the Spanish government in Missouri had given him was really his after all. They said it was the right thing to do because "it was unjust as it was impolitic that useful enterprise and eminent services should go unrewarded." He didn't understand what that meant about its being "impolitic," but he remembered that his friend Mr. Henderson had been given four hundred thousand acres for his eminent services in getting Daniel Boone to build the Wilderness Road. So he figured that everybody was square.

It didn't much matter anyhow, now that Rebecca had gone on to the Promised Land. But that would be all right, too, for he would be going to get her soon. It would be just as when he had always come back from the wilderness and she would be waiting in the cabin door. They would be moving on together into the happy valleys.

He roused himself and went to the fire where he was roasting a venison steak on the ramrod of his gun. Some friends were coming and he rose to greet them. "Mr. Harding, the painter, has come all the way from St. Louis to take your likeness," they explained. He didn't quite know what it was all about. The next day the young man came and asked him to sit very still while he painted his picture on oil-cloth. So he sat and talked of old memories and answered the young man's foolish questions. Had he ever been lost? He, Daniel Boone, lost! He thought back a while, shook his head, and said very slowly: "No, but I was right bewildered once for three days."

They were laying the corner-stone of a brand new state in St. Louis in September 1820. The Constitutional Convention was meeting in St. Louis to build a great new state for democracy right in the middle of the continent of America. When the news came that the mighty hunter had gone beyond the borders, beyond the ranges, the Constitutional Convention adjourned that day to remember Boone—of Missouri, of Kentucky, of Carolina, of Virginia and Pennsylvania. Boone—Trail-breaker for destiny for a free people marching on.

So they took a day off for remembrance about humble, great-hearted men whose lives were a strong invisible substance for enduring cornerstones for these United States of America.

from AWAY GOES SALLY

Elizabeth Coatsworth

Elizabeth Coatsworth is a versatile author. Many of her lovely poems, some of which are reprinted in Time for Poetry, *are tucked away between the chapters of* Away Goes Sally *and other books. Her fanciful tale,* The Cat Who Went to Heaven, *won the Newbery award. Whether she writes prose or poetry, she writes with rare distinction.* Away Goes Sally *is the first of a series of four historical stories about Sally. Sally's uncles, Joseph and Eben, wanted to move the whole family to Maine, but Aunt Nannie vowed "I will never leave my own fire nor sleep in any but my own bed." Sally and her young Aunt Esther were as disappointed as the uncles. They gave in, but not Uncle Joseph.*

Aunt Nannie's House

They drove home quickly. When Dorcas stopped at the back door it was still light, but there was no sign of the uncles, or of Jehoshaphat Mountain. Then, as Sally started to take the mare to the barn, she was stopped by several voices coming down the wood-road, men's voices gee-hawing oxen, and the screech of heavy runners on snow. The three aunts paused on the doorstep and Sally jumped from the sleigh to watch, as out of the darkness of the last pine thicket appeared the strangest thing she had ever seen. First came Peacock, Uncle Joseph's big horse, with Uncle Joseph on his back, and then six yoke of oxen, led by the red pair from their own farm, treading through the heavy snow in a slow procession of swaying heads and thick necks. Beside them walked Uncle Eben and Jehoshaphat Mountain with long poles, and behind them—wonder of wonders!—came a little house on runners, a house with windows whose small panes sparkled in the late light, with a doorstep, and a water-barrel under the drip of the roof, and a chimney pipe from which smoke was actually rising.

Sally jumped up and down, clapping her mittened hands, Aunt Esther uttered a cry of delight, and Uncle Joseph stood up in his stirrups and waved. But Aunt Nannie made no motion, and uttered no sound.

Slowly the line drew to the step and stopped. "Nannie," said Uncle Joseph in a solemn voice, "here is a house I have built for you and which I give you with all my heart, so that you may travel to the district of Maine and yet never leave your own fire."

He paused and they all waited, Peacock pawing the snow.

But Aunt Nannie's face was still blank with surprise, and did not show her thoughts. She felt behind her for the door to support herself, and once she tried to speak but could not. In the long silence Sally heard her own heart pounding like a colt galloping over a frozen meadow.

"Thank you, Brother Joseph," said Aunt Nannie at last in a small gentle voice, "thank you, my dear, I shall go willingly."

Sally let her breath out in a gasp of joy, and Uncle Joseph jumped from the saddle and kissed Aunt Nannie, who cried a little, mostly from relief because he had made it easy for her to give in and yet keep her word.

"Dorcas will take herself to the barn, Sally," Uncle Joseph called. "Come and see Aunt Nannie's house," and they all crowded in together. It was small, of course, but bright with windows, and warm with the Franklin stove which had a little fire burning in it. Two big beds stood in two corners of the room, covered with the blue eagle woven quilts. There was a smooth wooden sink and several chairs, and china in racks on the walls. Behind the larger room was a small room with two bunks in it for the uncles.

"There will be sleds for the rest of the furniture, Nannie," went on Uncle Joseph. "I have hired some men and their teams from down the road. You will, I imagine, wish to take our own cows, and Dorcas and the sleigh will bring up the rear, so that you may all take an airing when you grow tired of being in the house. And here, Deborah, are your seeds for a new garden, and we will carry some of your bulbs and roots on the sleds."

"And Aunt Esther will be a bride before the leaves turn yellow in Tuggie Noyes' woods!" cried Sally.

"Sally!" protested Aunt Esther laughing a little.

"I may come back and fetch someone to take your place, if it's not too much trouble," said Uncle Eben.

"Eliza is worth a good deal more trouble than that, Brother Sit-by-the-fire!" exclaimed Aunt Esther indignantly.

"How soon do we flit, Brother Joseph?" Aunt Nannie asked as she hung up her cloak on a peg and seated herself in her own chair, taking out her go-abroad sewing which she had brought back with her from Great-aunt Colman's.

"It's a picture to see you," said Uncle Joseph, smiling at her. They looked at each other and made their peace without a word being spoken. "I wanted this to be a surprise for you like the doll's house I made when you were a little girl. That's why I packed you all off to Quincy to have you out of the way while we furnished the house. But you asked when we would leave, Nannie. In a week, if you can be ready, my dear, so that we may have the advantage of the snow. The neighbors will help you."

"It doesn't matter what else you take," said Uncle Eben, "so long as you have plenty of meat-pies and apple-pies, baked beans, doughnuts, chocolate cake, pound cake, roasted chickens, hams——"

"Here, here," said Aunt Deborah, affectionately putting a hand across his lips, "you must not sound so greedy, Brother." She took her hand quickly away, for he had nipped it.

"Only a nibble," he joked her. "I've always said you had a sweet hand, Debby."

Meantime Jehoshaphat Mountain had been unyoking the oxen and taking them yoke by yoke to their quarters in the barn.

"I've been building the house for weeks in the wood lot," went on Uncle Joseph. " 'Twill be a good way to carry our goods and ourselves without having to put up at the ordinaries, which they say are sometimes poor and dirty. And when we reach our land we shall have this to live in until we can build better. A new home, Nannie, on wider acres."

It was Sally who discovered the six little pots steaming in the rack that had been made for them on the stove. Uncle Eben, always ready to help in any matter of food, showed Sally where a pine table let down from the wall. She found the cloth and silver spoons and a jar of cookies, and soon six cups were filled, Uncle Joseph's with coffee, Uncle Eben's with chocolate, Aunt Nannie's with old Hyson, Aunt Deborah's with new Hyson, Aunt Esther's with Souchong, and Sally's with milk and chocolate. And so they shared their first meal in the house that was to carry them to a new land.

The Start

Uncle Joseph rode Peacock to the head of the procession, a dark figure in the early dawn. The men shouted, the oxen strained, and the little house shivered, then jerked forward with a screeching of runners, and the long journey was begun.

"They're off!" shouted Captain Dagget, waving his red muffler.

"They're off!" cried old Mrs. Captain Dagget, her white kerchief thrashing up and down in her mittened hand.

"Hip, hip, hurrah!" piped little John Hale from Sweet Brook Farm, running beside the oxen, waving his stocking cap.

"Good-bye, good-bye! Write me, my dearest Esther!" called Mrs. Caleb, beginning to cry.

All the neighbors were gathered at the doorstep to see them go, although the sun had not yet fully risen, and the snow seemed dark and grave against the pale yellow sky.

Sally stood in the doorway of the little house in her red cloak, with her aunts behind her. She could see the broad strong backs of the twelve oxen straining as they started on their road, and beyond them rose the farmhouse, the only home she had ever known. It looked so low and strong, with its wide chimney and a dark sparkle on the little panes of glass in the windows, and their friends standing on the doorstep! Her cheeks stung with cold and tears, and she felt suddenly a great hollow inside her. Then they came to the road and Uncle Joseph turned in his saddle and waved to her. Peacock was pulling at the bit, prancing, impatient to be off.

"To Maine!" called Uncle Joseph, making a gesture northward. "To Maine!"

The oxen quickened their pace on the beaten highway. Jehoshaphat Mountain shouted cheerfully at them. The sunlight caught the tops of the trees and the church weathervane in the distance. Sally heard a cow low behind her and knew it was old Brindle.

"We're off! We're off!" she thought, her mind turning to the future. "At last, we're off!"

"Come in, child, and shut the door," said Aunt Nannie, and Sally came in. Did ever a little girl go traveling like this before, in a doll's house on runners, seeing everything go by! She hung up her cloak and sat looking out of one of the little windows, watching how astonished people looked at seeing them. Whenever she waved, she did it stiffly, and she pretended she couldn't move her head at all.

"What *is* the matter, Sally?" asked Aunt Deborah, looking up from her sewing. "Have you caught rheumatism, child?"

"No, I'm being a doll," said Sally. "We're all dolls and this is our home."

Aunt Esther jumped up and did a doll's dance. Her eyes were shining, her curls bobbed up and down. Even Aunt Nannie smiled above the stocking she was knitting.

"Now, have we forgotten anything?" asked Aunt Deborah. "Where's Dinah's basket?"

Dinah was the black cat. She was shiny black all over, except for her paws and a star in the hollow of her throat, and a little white chin that always made her look as though she had just been drinking milk.

"Dinah, Dinah," called Sally.

"Mew," said Dinah, answering dismally from under one of the big beds.

Sally got down on her knees and pulled out the covered basket in which Dinah was imprisoned. When she took the cover off, Dinah jumped out, but she paid no attention to any of her mistresses. Round and round the room she went, with her nose extended, smelling everything, her tail stiff, her ears a little flattened. She smelled the pipe from the sink, she went into the corners, she disappeared under the beds, she sniffed at the furniture. She pushed open the door into the little room and investigated that. Then when she had thoroughly looked over every inch of this new home, she exclaimed, "Prrr!," stopped looking wary, and neatly jumped onto one of the beds, in the exact spot where the sunlight from the south window met the warmth of the stove. Kneading the place for a moment with her little white paws to make sure that it was soft, she turned round once, and went to sleep, as though traveling to Maine were something she had done all her life.

"Well, I declare, Dinah," said Aunt Nannie, "you *do* know how to make yourself comfortable! I suppose with all of us cooped up here together you'd best go where you've a mind to, but once in Maine I'll thank you to keep off the beds."

Getting dinner was great fun.

"We can't all be turning round in here like a lot of tops," said Aunt Nannie. "Deborah, you and Esther sit where you are and Sally and I will get things ready."

Sally gave her aunt a grateful look. And Aunt Nannie's ear-drops jingled back at her as Aunt Nannie nodded. They both had to learn to fit their walking to the movement of the house, especially when it jerked over a rut, but soon the potatoes were poked deep into the ashes, and the little table was laid with dishes taken down from the wall. Sally hung onto the doorstep while she dipped water from the barrel outside, breaking the thin skim of ice across it. It felt good outdoors in the cold, sunny air with the oxen pulling solemnly at their yokes and Peacock settled down to a slow walk, and the caw of a crow and the creak of snow for sound. Sally jumped down and ran along beside Jehoshaphat Mountain. An ox rolled his eyes at her, and she put her hand on his spotted white shoulder. It felt warm and muscular to her touch.

At noon they pulled the house to one side of the road, and all the horses and cattle were given feed. The hired men built a fire and ate around it, but Uncle Joseph and Uncle Eben had their dinner in the little house.

"There's no room for me at the table," said Uncle Eben, "but I know where the warmest place in the room is. Scat, Dinah!" And he made himself comfortable where she had been. Dinah blinked her yellow eyes at him, stood up, stretched one leg after another, yawned so that her pink tongue showed stiff and curly, and then lay down again out of his way farther up on the bed.

"Dinah and I understand each other," said

Uncle Eben, scratching her under the chin. "Don't we, Dinah?"

Dinah caught his finger between her two front paws and pretended to bite it, purring in gusts which, with her mouth open, sounded almost like growls.

"Careful, old girl," said Uncle Eben. "You must set an example of good behavior to all the cats in Maine."

That evening they stopped at a farm on the outskirts of Boston where they could find shelter for their animals in the big barn. The teamsters slept in the loft, but Sally and her family made themselves snug in the little house. It was drawn up in a barnyard, across which Sally could see the lighted kitchen windows of the farm, and the dim outlines of its roofs. A man came to see them, holding a lantern, but it was too late for visiting. By candlelight they had their supper of bread and cheese and warm milk just drawn from the cows.

"Twelve miles—a good journey for the first day," said Uncle Joseph, contentedly, after supper. "And now to bed, for we must be up early in the morning."

"Read us first the promise to Joseph, Brother Joseph," said Aunt Deborah, and Sally jumped up and brought the heavy Bible from its box and laid it on Uncle Joseph's knees. He drew the candle near and, after thumbing the pages until he found the place, read in his warm quiet voice:

"'Blessed of the Lord be his land, for the precious things of heaven, for the dew, and for the deep that coucheth beneath, and for the precious fruits brought forth by the sun, and for the precious things put forth by the moon, and for the chief things of the ancient mountains, and for the precious things of the lasting hills, and for the precious things of the earth and the fulness thereof——'"

"That is God's blessing upon farmers," said Aunt Nannie.

"It makes me feel warm inside," whispered Sally to Aunt Esther. And then when the uncles had gone into the back room, they all raced one another to bed. Aunt Nannie and Aunt Deborah shared one bed, Aunt Esther and Sally the other. It was Sally who jumped in first, and she was asleep almost as soon as the blankets were under her chin. But once in the night she woke up to find the room growing cold and Dinah beside her—the cat had jumped up and now, rubbing against her cheek before she slipped in under the clothes, she curled up against Sally's chest, her black head on the pillow beside her mistress's.

WINTER

Rachel Field

A number of Rachel Field's poems from Taxis and Toadstools *are to be found in* Time for Poetry. *They are always favorites, but* Calico Bush, *a historical novel, is one of the finest things she ever wrote. The heroine, Marguerite Ledoux, a French orphan, was bound out to Joel and Dolly Sargent. She traveled with them to a new settlement in Maine and although she loved them and shared all of their hardships without complaint, they never made her feel that she was one of them. This excerpt has about it a poignant loneliness.*

It was a fairly warm day for December and she went out with Debby to watch him split the wood. It was pleasant to see his ax come down so swift and sure each time, and sometimes when he paused to rest he would talk to her for a minute or two. The baby was so well wrapped in a woolen shawl that she looked like a brownish caterpillar with a pink nose and tufts of light hair showing at one end.

"What time of year is it now?" Marguerite asked as Ira stopped to draw his sleeve across his streaming forehead.

"Let's see," he answered going over to the post where he still made his daily notches, dividing the months by means of long horizontal strokes. "Well, I declare, if it ain't got to be the middle o' December! Yes, tomorrow's the seventeenth, time I finished that beaver cap I promised Abby."

"Is it for Christmas?" asked Marguerite.

But he shook his head. "No," he said. "Our folks don't hold with such foolishness. We went to meetin' back in Marblehead on Christmas, I recollect, but there was a Dutch boy I knew told me how they had all kinds o' doin's where he come from."

"You mean, it will be no different from other days?" Marguerite's eyes grew wide with disappointment. "No carols, and no cakes, and no gifts from one to another?"

"I guess that's about right," he told her and went on with the chopping.

If Ira gave her no encouragement in Christmas festivities she knew it would be useless to expect more of Dolly and Joel Sargent. She tried to put the thought from her mind, but as each day came bringing it nearer she found herself remembering more and more the happy preparations for it she had helped to make at home. She dreamed of the Christmas cakes Grand'mère had always baked with such pride, of the seeded raisins and the picked nut-meats stirred ceremoniously in the rich batter. And then there were the carols, with the Sisters in the convent beating time and making sure that not a single "Noël" was left out when all their pupils' voices were lifted together. She tried to tell the children of the tiny carved statues of the Virgin and Joseph and the little Christ Child in the manger, with cattle and sheep and shepherds all painted as perfectly as life, that were brought out on Christmas Eve in the candle-lit chapel. Unfortunately Dolly had overheard part of this recital and had chided her roundly.

"I'll thank you to keep your Popishness to yourself," she had told her. "We may be in too God-forsaken a spot for a meetin' house, but that's no reason to put ideas in the children's heads."

And so it came to be Christmas Eve in the log cabin on Sargents' point with no smell of spice cakes, or incense, or candles, and none to feel the lack of them but Marguerite Ledoux.

She had been out to the post herself that noon, counting the month's notchings to be sure. There could be no doubt—tomorrow would make twenty-five. She would not have missed the holiday preparations so much, she thought, if she might have gone over to see Aunt Hepsa; but she knew there was no chance of this with such a high sea running and snow left in patches from last week's fall. It was rare, Joel had said, to have much fall near the sea. A bad winter ahead, Seth Jordan had predicted, and it looked as if he were right. Frost had covered the little square panes of glass with such feathery patternings, it required much breathing and scratching to make even a little hole to see out. Marguerite was tired of doing this. The room was almost dark, but she knew that outside there was still half an hour or so left of twilight. She went over to the pegs behind the door and took down the brown cloak and hood.

"What are you doin'?" Dolly asked her as she had her hand on the door.

"I'm—I want to bring more cones," she hazarded, grasping at the first idea that came into her head. "There are not so many left in the basket."

"Well, all right, then," Dolly told her, "only don't fetch in the wet ones that make the fire smoke. Pick 'em from underneath. No, Jacob," she added at a question from the child, "you can't go along—it's too cold."

Marguerite buckled on the shoes Aunt Hepsa had given her, tied on her cloak, and went out basket in hand. Once she shut the door behind her some of the depression which had weighed upon her spirit all day left her. It was impossible to feel so sad out in the snow with the pointed trees and all their shiny dark-green needles. They smelled of Christmas to her. There had been branches of evergreen in the chapel sometimes. Perhaps if she hunted at the edge of the tall woods behind the spring she might find some red partridge berries to bring back to the children. It was bad luck if you gave nothing on Christmas, and they need not know the reason for such a gift.

As she turned into the wood path behind the house she looked across the water to Sunday Island. White places showed on the cleared field round the Jordan house where the snow remained, and the trees above it on the upper pasture where she and Aunt Hepsa had gathered bayberry looked more dark and bristling than ever in the winter twilight. She was glad that a curl of smoke rose from the chimney. Aunt Hepsa must be cooking supper, she told herself, and she paused to send her a Christmas wish across the water.

"I wonder if she's begun her new quilt yet?" she thought as she struck into the wood path. "She had the indigo dye Ethan brought her all ready to make a blue pot."

There were no red berries under the snow in the clearing by the spring where she had hoped to find them, so she went on farther along the blazed trail. It was very still there, with only a light wind stirring the spruce and fir boughs overhead. The light stayed longer there than she had expected, for the snow helped prolong the winter afternoon. Sometimes she stooped to gather cones, taking care to shake off the snow as Dolly Sargent had bidden her. The cold was intense, but her blood was quick and the old homespun cloak and hood enveloped her warmly. There was no sound except her footfalls in the snow. A sudden impulse came upon her to sing one of the carols which she knew the Sisters in the convent must even then be teaching other voices to raise.

She set down the half-filled basket of cones, folded her hands piously under the cloak, and began the first simple little chant that she had ever learned.

"Noël—Noël—Noël!"

Her own voice startled her in the stillness. Then at the sound of the familiar words she grew confident and began the one that had been Grand'mère's favorite because she also had sung it when she was a girl in the little village where she had lived.

"J'entends le ciel retentir
Des cantiques des Saints Anges,
Et la terre tressaillir
Des transports de leurs louanges.
C'est l'Oinct qui devoit venir,
Il est déjà dans ses langes.
Miracle! prodige nouveau,
Le fils de Dieu dans le berceau!
Mais plus grand prodige encore,
Ce grand Roi, que le ciel adore,
Doit expirer sur un poteau.
Noël! Noël! Noël!"[1]

[1] This old carol may be freely rendered as follows:—
I hear the heavens resound
To such angelic song
That trembling stirs the ground,
While rolls the news along—
The Heavenly Child is found,
To Whom all praise belong.
Oh! wondrous miracle,
A God in his cradle!
Yet must we wonder more,
This King the heavens adore
Must die upon a cross.

As she sang there in the deepening twilight, she felt strangely comforted. The French words that had lain so long forgotten welled up out of her mind as easily as if she had been with the Sisters in the candle-lit chapel and not alone these thousands of miles away in a snowy wood.

"Noël! Noël!" she cried once more to the ranks of spruces, and then as she turned to retrace her steps something dark and swift moved towards her from behind a tree trunk.

There was not time enough to run away. The words were hardly cool on her lips before he stood beside her—a tall Indian in skins, with a musket that went oddly with his fringes and bright feathers. So silently did he come that not a twig snapped under his foot. He seemed not to dent the snow as he moved over it. His eyes showed bright in the copper of his skin, and a deep scar ran crookedly across one cheek. He came so close that she saw it plainly, and yet she could not move so much as an inch. Her feet seemed rooted in the snow, and if her heart continued to beat, she could not feel it. For what seemed like ages he continued to regard her fixedly with his black, unblinking eyes, while she waited for him to seize the tomahawk from his belt and make an end of her. But he did not move to do so. Instead, his lips parted in a queer smile.

"Noël!" he said, pronouncing the word carefully in a deep, guttural voice. "Noël!"

Marguerite felt her heart begin to beat again, though her knees were still numb and she continued to stare at him incredulously. Surely this must be a miracle, more extraordinary than any bestowed on Saint Catherine or Saint Elizabeth! A savage had come out of the woods to greet her in her own tongue on Christmas Eve! She forced herself to smile back and answer him.

His words were meager and hard to catch, but she made out from them and his signs that he had lived with the French in Quebec. He was bound there now, or so she guessed from his pointing finger. She could not tell how many of her words he understood, but whenever she said "Noël" his eyes would brighten with recognition and he would repeat it after her. "Les Pères Gris," he told her, had cured him. He touched the scar as he spoke and crossed his two lean forefingers to make a cross.

It was almost dark now; only a faint light lingered between the spruces. Pumpkin barked in the distance and Marguerite knew she must hurry back lest they grow alarmed. What would they think, Joel and Dolly Sargent and the rest, if they should come upon her there in the woods holding converse with an Indian? Prompted by an impulse she pulled the cord out from under her dress and jerked off Oncle Pierre's gilt button. It glittered in her hand as she held it out to the tall figure before her.

"Pour un souvenir de Noël," she said as she laid it in his hand before she turned and sped off towards the clearing.

Her heart was still pounding as she came out of the woods and in sight of the log house. Pumpkin bounded to meet her as she paused to put back the cord and its only remaining treasure. She had not thought to make such a Christmas gift, but surely she could not have done less. She could not but feel that somehow it was a fortunate sign, this strange meeting. Perhaps Le Bon Dieu had Himself arranged it that she might be less lonely on Christmas Eve. But she knew there must not be a word of it to the rest. She would never be able to make them understand what she scarcely understood herself. As for Caleb, she could well guess what he would say and that he would think ill of her ever after.

Dolly Sargent scolded her roundly for staying away so long.

"I declare you deserve a beatin'," she told her hotly, "strayin' so far at this time o' night. I vow Debby's got more sense 'n you show some times."

There was no mention made of Christmas next day save that Joel asked a lengthier blessing over their breakfast cornmeal than was usual with him. But Marguerite no longer minded. Had she not had her miracle the night before?

from RIVER OF THE WOLVES

Stephen W. Meader

Every book Stephen Meader has written is a thriller, and River of the Wolves *is one of the best. It shows the results of the careful historical research which goes into Mr. Meader's historical stories and accounts for their convincing realism. This excerpt begins after Dave has been captured by a band of marauding Indians who massacred his relatives and took their scalps. Yet in the hard days that followed, Dave shared the work of the march in good spirit and began to feel some liking for his captors, especially Nequanis, whose prisoner he was. The results of Dave's behavior are evident in this chapter. You will want to read the book to find out whether or not Dave remains in captivity.*

[*Captured by the Abenaki*]

The southwest wind held, and when the tide turned, just before sunset, the canoes put out once more. They paddled until late in the evening and covered another ten or fifteen miles before they camped.

It was not yet dawn when Nequanis shook Dave awake. "We go soon," he told the white boy. "When the sun rises the water will run toward the sea."

Dave built a fire and Nequanis made johnny-cakes of corn meal, which he baked on a flat stone, heated in the coals. Matawassie meanwhile had caught several small fish, of a kind unfamiliar to Dave, and they had a more elaborate breakfast than usual.

There was hardly any breeze when they got into the canoes, but the tide was past the flood and they were soon driving along at four or five miles an hour. More wooded islands appeared to the north. Every few miles there was a glimpse of low, white houses on the mainland shore.

From one of these French villages, late in the morning, they saw two big canoes shoot out. There were four men in each, paddling hard and singing lustily as they skimmed along. They passed within a hundred yards, heading northward toward a gap between two islands. Dave could not understand the words of their song, but the rollicking lilt of it and the bright colors of their costumes gave him a feeling of excitement and adventure.

Their blanket-cloth shirts were vivid blue, and they wore red sashes and red knitted caps with tassels that swung rakishly at the side. Their canoes were loaded deep with provisions and duffel.

Around his naked upper body he wrapped his blanket, following the example of his companions.

About the time they were dressed, Bemokis and Josh Boles came out of the sweat-house. Josh was stubborn about plunging into the river. When he refused to dive, the bent-backed Indian seized him by the hair, dragged him down the bank and ducked him in the chilly water.

Josh sputtered and struggled but was finally persuaded to swim a few strokes. Nequanis watched him, scowling.

"He is a bad prisoner," the young warrior told Dave. "He will make trouble for himself."

They went up through the village, Dave feeling somewhat conspicuous in his Indian dress. But nobody paid much attention to him. The braves were squatted in the doorways of their cabins renewing their warpaint. The squaws had gone back to their work in the little corn and pumpkin patches that lay between the houses and the edge of the woods.

Nequanis and Matawassie led the way to the smallest and most dilapidated hut in the town. It was at the farther end of the row, only a few yards from the chapel and the priest's house. Dave gathered from the Indians' talk that this was one of several cabins used as bachelor quarters by the younger braves.

"You will live here with us," Nequanis told him. "You will do the squaw work—getting wood, making fires, cooking and washing. That is for now. Afterward, if you prove yourself strong and brave, perhaps the chief will let you become a hunter, as we are."

Dave took the new order of things with good grace. After all, he reflected, the chores he was expected to do were just what any white boy did in the settlements—all but the cooking, which he didn't mind. After the hard, constant labor of the journey northward, his present lot seemed an easy one.

Since he had nothing else to do while the young braves were decorating themselves, he took an ax and followed the path into the forest. In an hour he had cut up half a dozen dead trees and brought back the wood to stack behind the cabin. Then he started to build a fire, but Nequanis told him it was not needed.

"There will be a big campfire tonight," said the Indian, "and much eating. Our chief, Maranoquid, the father of Cochequa, has been on a hunt with the other men of the town. Soon they will come back with meat. If they have made a good kill, some of the meat will be smoked and dried for winter. But there will be enough left over for a feast."

It was about two hours before sunset when a high-pitched Indian war whoop came from the river above the town. The dogs began barking furiously and everybody in the village hurried toward the landing.

Dave saw six canoes coming swiftly downstream. There were four Indians in each one, and they shouted, waved their paddles and pointed to the carcasses of deer and moose that loaded the birch-bark craft deep in the water.

The first man ashore was a stalwart six-foot redskin with mighty shoulders. He wore three eagle feathers in his scalplock, and a long necklace of bears' claws about his neck. Dave did not have to be told that this was Maranoquid, the chief.

Neither the older man nor Cochequa, his son, gave any special sign of joy as they greeted each other. Each had the grave and courteous manner expected of a leader. Maranoquid asked no questions about the war party, nor did Cochequa inquire as to the success of the hunt. Indeed, no one would have needed to ask. The heavily loaded canoes spoke for themselves.

The braves carried the bodies of four deer, a moose, a black bear and some smaller game to the top of the bank, where the squaws immediately set to work with their skinning knives. No rules of behavior governed their tongues and they kept up a running fire of talk and laughter while they ripped the hides off the animals and cut up the meat. The hearts, livers, tongues and other Indian delicacies were put in one pile for immediate cooking. The tougher parts of the carcasses were saved for winter food. But nothing seemed to be wasted. The sinews and intestines—even the hoofs and claws—were carefully removed. Dave knew that they would be used later for stitching clothes, making bowstrings, bags and ornaments.

He went back to the cabin where Nequanis and Matawassie were waiting. They sat cross-legged, wearing such finery as they owned and looking proud and satisfied. The bright new stripes of pigment on their faces made them extra hideous—extra handsome, Dave supposed, to Indian eyes.

"When the feast starts," Nequanis told him soberly, "if you are wise you will not eat too much. You may have to do some running afterwards, and it will be better for you if you can run fast."

The young brave glanced at Matawassie, and Dave thought he caught the flicker of a grin under the streaks of paint.

As darkness crept over the town the great drum began to beat. Dave heard the throb of it and looked out to see what was happening. A dozen squaws were busy around a big cook-fire, stirring kettles and roasting meat on spits. Beyond the immediate circle of light made by the fire, everything looked unreal and shadowy, but an occasional gleam fell on the drum and the strange figure standing behind it. Dave made out the shape of a man, his face painted with weird vertical stripes of yellow. Above his eyes was the grinning head of a wolf, the long white teeth glittering wickedly when the firelight touched them. The wolfskin hung over the man's shoulders but his bare arms moved up and down in rhythm as he struck the taut hide with the flat of his hands.

"That," Nequanis said, from the darkness at Dave's elbow, "is the M'teoulin—the medicine man. He is very old and very wise, and familiar with all the spirits."

The throb of the drum quickened and grew louder. One by one the warriors came out of their houses and went toward the fire. When Maranoquid, the chief, arrived, he dipped his hand in the huge stew kettle, drew out a piece of meat and began eating it. After that they all fell to without further ceremony.

Mindful of Nequanis' advice, Dave did not gorge himself, good as the food tasted. He tried to warn Josh Boles, who was stuffing himself with fat chunks of bear and raccoon meat, but the other boy merely scowled and ate faster.

For nearly an hour the feast went on. At last, when the braves were full almost to bursting, they seated themselves in a circle around the fire and the chief lighted a stone pipe. The pungent smoke of tobacco and kinnikinnick drifted in a wreath above his eagle crest. When he had taken two or three puffs he passed the pipe to Cochequa and it went on around the circle.

The squaws and the prisoners sat in an outer ring, and still farther from the fire the dogs sniffed and trotted back and forth, scavenging for scraps. Father Pierre was not there. A beam of candlelight, coming from the window of the little church, showed where he knelt at his prayers. The medicine man, on the other hand, was much in evidence. He had left the drum when the feasting began and now he strutted about near the fire, calling on various spirits, gesturing with his skinny arms and doing small feats of magic. He would hold a birch twig in one hand, make a pass over it and cause it to disappear. Dave was not impressed, for he had seen more than one white man who was better at such tricks than the old Indian.

After a while Maranoquid rose and began to speak in the measured sing-song cadence that was typical of the Abenaki ceremonial language. As his deep voice rolled out the sentences, Dave realized it was a kind of poetry.

The chief described the hunt in detail, telling how they had gone up the river; how the first deer had been sighted by such-and-such a warrior; how so-and-so had fired and missed because Lox, the evil one, had turned the bullet in midair. The tale ran on and on till all the game was accounted for and loaded in the canoes.

When Maranoquid finished he turned politely to his son and asked for an account of the war party's experiences.

Cochequa was not the orator his father was, but he spoke well. Dave heard for the first time that the raiding band had attacked two other small settlements near the Connecticut before they reached the Contoocook. As each incident was told, the proper scalp or prisoner was trotted out for inspection. The young chief was fairly modest about his own deeds, but he played up the exploits of Bemokis, making the Indian with the twisted back the principal hero of the expedition.

When Cochequa held up the red scalp and told the story of the looting and burning of the Foster farm, Dave had to hold himself tense to keep from shaking. Then the chief's son turned in his direction and he was seized and led into the circle by his two young captors. He walked stiffly, his back straight and his lips tight. Several of the older warriors grunted their approval of Nequanis and Matawassie for taking him prisoner, and he felt the whole ring of beady eyes centered on him for a long moment. Then he was hustled out again and the narrative continued.

It was now well along toward midnight and there was a chill in the air. The fire had been kept up, but it gave little warmth beyond the inner circle of braves. The squaws and prisoners wrapped their blankets tightly around them and sat shivering while Cochequa was winding up his oration.

The older chief rose, when his son had finished, and complimented all the members of the party on their courage and skill. Then shorter speeches were made by Bemokis and some of the other veteran warriors. And finally the M'teoulin pronounced a few incantations, whirled about in a fantastic dance and appeared to vanish in a puff of smoke.

Dave stared at the place where the sorcerer had stood. Most of the Indians seemed as mystified as he was, but the older braves chuckled and applauded. After a moment the big drum, back in the darkness, began to rumble. Peering behind him, Dave was not surprised to see the wolf mask of the medicine man bobbing above the drumhead.

As the throb of the beat grew faster, the young bucks leaped up and began to prance. Bending from the waist and throwing their knees high, they picked up the rhythm of the drum with their pounding moccasins. One by one other warriors jumped to their feet, until only Chief Maranoquid and a dozen of the more venerable men were left seated.

The booming of the drum quickened in tempo, and the dancing grew wilder as the young braves shouted hoarsely and flung their arms above their heads. Dave caught the fierce excitement. He felt his blood beat faster, in time with the drum's thunder. At the climax, he even wished he could get up there and join in the dance.

At last the warriors had enough. Panting, their copper bodies glistening with sweat, they flung themselves down on their blankets. The pipe went around the circle again. When it reached Bemokis he got to his feet and pointed the reed stem toward the prisoners. Dave could not hear clearly what he said, for his words were drowned out by gleeful whoops and cheers.

All the younger braves sprang up and ran toward their houses. When they came back, each one was carrying a kind of flattened club, three or four feet long.

Dave caught his breath. He understood now what Nequanis had been talking about before the feast. The prisoners—or at least Josh Boles and he—were going to have to run the gantlet!

Ever since he was a child he had heard tales of how the Indians put their male captives to this form of torture. Boys, and even grown men, had been beaten to death in the gantlet, according to stories told in the settlements. The clubs appeared brutal enough, but he could tell by the way the young men swung them that they were lighter than they looked. Probably they were made of spruce.

The braves lined up in a double row, a dozen on a side. Nequanis and Matawassie came toward Dave and another pair of Indians approached Josh Boles. The two boys had their leggins stripped off and were led toward the head of the lane of yelling braves.

Bemokis was the first Indian in line, and he brandished his long club, his cruel face grinning with anticipation. Dave, standing there shivering in his breechclout, set his teeth and waited. Bemokis pointed at him.

"Let that one run first!" he shouted, and the others greeted his words with a cheer.

Dave felt himself pushed forward. A sudden desperate resolve took form in his head. He had been afraid, but now his fear was gone in a surge of bright anger. He started running at top speed. Then, just as he flashed abreast of Bemokis, he swerved straight at him.

The Indian with the twisted back had both arms lifted high, ready to strike a mighty blow. Dave's shoulder caught him squarely in the stomach and doubled him up with his wind knocked out. The boy was lucky then. As the club flew out of Bemokis' fingers he caught it in mid-air. It felt good in his hands—smooth, well-balanced, heavy enough to do damage if it landed in the right places. He whirled the club around his head, parried a glancing blow from the Indian across the way and struck savagely at the next brave in line. Then he raced down the alley, whaling away to right and left as he ran.

He was hit solidly half a dozen times before he reached the other end, but he was still on his feet. Fully expecting the angry mob to follow him, he dashed on another fifty yards before he came to a panting stop. Nobody was near him. He turned and saw the whole crowd roaring and rolling on the ground with laughter.

Nequanis had left the line and was hurrying to meet him. The young Indian had a lump over one eye but he grinned broadly as he slapped Dave on the back.

"You did what I hoped you would do, my Brother," he said. "Even Bemokis must agree now that you have courage."

As they walked back the lines were forming again. The bent-backed Indian had picked up another club and was waiting in his place, crouching a little and wearing a ferocious scowl. Dave felt sorry for Josh Boles.

The stocky white boy was plainly scared. He hung back till a pair of braves caught him by the arms and threw him into the opening between the rows. Stumbling, he put up his arms to protect his head and started to run. The clubs rose and fell like flails—*thwack—thwack—thwack*—landing heavily on his back, shoulders and elbows. The poor lad fell twice but staggered up again and went on. He was blubbering like a baby when he passed the end of the line, and he dropped in a heap, blood oozing from half a dozen bruises on his body.

The Indians turned away from him contemptuously but Dave picked him up, wiped off the blood as best he could and helped him over to his blanket.

"Here," he said, "just lie still and they won't bother you any more. I'll get some water and fix you up the best I can."

Dave brought a kettle from the cabin and ran down to the river. Carrying it back full of cold water he washed Josh's head and body, then wrapped his blanket around him and left him sitting there in the shadows.

It was close to midnight now but the gathering showed no signs of breaking up. Cochequa was standing before the elders of the village, making another harangue. This time he was briefer. Dave paid little attention to what he was saying, but suddenly he saw the young chief stretch out one muscular arm and point directly at him. Nequanis, too, was beckoning. Hesitantly the boy stepped forward and in a moment he was standing inside the circle of warriors, his back to the fire.

"You have seen what this young paleface has done," Cochequa chanted. "He is strong and his heart is brave. On the trail he carried his pack and did not grow weary. In the canoes he worked hard with the paddle. He is of an age when he can be taught to hunt with the skill of an Abenaki.

"Already he speaks a little in our tongue. Our young brother, Nequanis, will vouch for him and teach him. I, Cochequa, ask that you take this white youth into kinship with our tribe."

The faces of the older Indians were as expressionless as blocks of wood. Maranoquid refilled the pipe and it went the rounds while Dave stood uncomfortably in the middle of the ring. The young chief's words had taken him completely by surprise. He felt a thrill of pride when he realized that a real compliment had been paid him, but there was no telling how the warriors would react. He wasn't even sure whether he wanted to become a member of the tribe, for he recalled all too clearly the terrible scene in his uncle's clearing.

Fifteen or twenty minutes dragged by. Then Maranoquid rose slowly and with great dignity.

"Cochequa, my son, has spoken," said he. "Our numbers are few, for many of our men have fallen in battle. If this young paleface is strong and brave, as we have seen and as Cochequa has told us, he may become a true warrior of the Abenakis."

Scattered nods and grunts came from the assembled elders. Finally Bemokis stood up.

"You know me," he said. "I have hated the English since I was a boy. I have killed many and taken many scalps. But I believe this young Bostonnais has courage. I have felt the weight of his blows on my body. I, Bemokis, say he is ready to be taken into the tribe."

Those words seemed to swing the decision. One after another the warriors voiced their approval. As the last one finished speaking, the M'teoulin stalked into the center of the ring. He lifted both thin arms and uttered a scream so sudden and so piercing that Dave leaped back, startled. Then he found Nequanis beside him, steadying him.

"Do not be afraid," the Indian boy whispered. "What comes now will make you a man and an Abenaki."

The medicine man shuffled forward, muttering mysteriously. Out of his robe he whipped a slim, shining knife, and with his other hand he seized Dave's left wrist. The white boy clamped his jaws hard to keep from shivering, for the needle-like point of the knife was poised just above his open hand.

With a quick, careful movement the M'teoulin pricked the end of Dave's middle finger. Then he turned toward Nequanis, took his left hand and went through the same performance.

Mumbling more incantations the old Indian took a drop of Dave's blood on his finger and placed it on Nequanis' tongue. In a moment Dave tasted the Indian lad's blood, warm and salt, in his own mouth.

"Say these words," the medicine man commanded. "He is my brother. I am his brother."

Together the two boys repeated the Indian words.

"At all times and in all places," the M'teoulin continued, "until the squirrel again grows greater than the bear."

"At all times and in all places," they murmured in unison, "until the squirrel again grows greater than the bear."

Dave had a queer feeling, as if he were outside his body and listening to someone else speaking. Then the sorcerer leaped into the air and gave that bloodcurdling scream, and the spell was broken.

"Welcome, Brother," said Nequanis with a grin, and threw his arms around him.

from BENJAMIN WEST AND HIS CAT GRIMALKIN

Marguerite Henry

Benjamin West, America's first distinguished artist, in this entertaining biography is only a little boy with a remarkable friend and ally in his cat Grimalkin. Here we find Benjamin trying to draw for the first time and fearful of his Quaker father's reception of his efforts. The cat plays an important part in father West's decision to let his son draw and the book tells how Grimalkin's tail became even more important to Benjamin than his eloquent "mee-ows." Marguerite Henry writes with rare humor and a tender understanding of both animals and people. No wonder her books are popular with children.

There was a kind of magic in the way Grimalkin grew. His fur began to fluff out, soft and black and shining. His tail became thick and uncommonly long. His body waxed strong and very nimble.

And it was like magic the way he took possession of Door-Latch Inn. Almost as soon as Elmira and her kittens were returned to the barn, he began to look after things.

Indoors and out, he set his own tasks. If one of the hound dogs so much as showed his nose in the parlor, Grimalkin cuffed him smartly and sent him yammering out the door. If the chickens got into Mamma's kitchen garden, it was Grimalkin who chased them out. He also took care of the ground hogs and rabbits and snakes. There were the mouse holes to watch too. And the cows to bring in. He not only helped round them up; he also thought it wise to be on hand during the milking. No matter who did the milking—John or Thomas or Samuel or Joseph, or even Papa—he would squirt some of the fresh milk right into Grimalkin's mouth. Grimalkin had to be there to catch it!

Never was a cat so busy. Nor so independent. He slept where he pleased—on the candle shelf, or in a drawer atop Mamma's newly spun cloth, or on Papa's basket-bottom chair. But if the weather was cold, he liked to toast his bones before the fire or crawl into bed with Benjamin. Often, in the dead of night when the moon was full, he would take it into his head to go hunting. And being as clever as he was independent, he asked no one to let him out. With one paw he could lift the door latch as neatly as if he had four fingers and a thumb.

In no time at all Grimalkin was everyone's pet. Papa and Benjamin's four brothers liked him because he was a great ratter and mouser. Mamma and Benjamin's four sisters liked him because, as Mamma so often said, "A more mannerly cat thee would not find anywhere. What other cat in all the Province wipes his paws on the doormat before entering the kitchen? Polite and tidy!" she added with a bright nod.

Even Nanny Luddy, Papa's big mare, liked Grimalkin. She would sleep standing if Grimalkin chose to lie on her bed of straw. Yet Grimalkin treated Nanny Luddy as if he were a king and she his slave. If he leaped upon her back to warm his paws, one would have thought, by the airs he put on, that he was doing her quite a favor.

As for the guests who came and went, Grimalkin openly disapproved them. After investigating them with his nose he left them strictly alone. And when their carts rattled out of the innyard, he helped chase them on their way and then flew back to the inn as if to say, "At last! At last! I have The Family all to myself!"

But if he felt this way toward The Family, he treated Benjamin almost as if he knew that Benjamin had saved his life.

There was nothing he would not do for Benjamin. He would jump through a barrel hoop for him. He would roll over when told. He would box. He would play hide and seek, and a fairly good game of catch and toss. But, more than all this, he was a partner in everything that Benjamin did. And such an understanding grew up between them that strangers would remark on it. "I vow and declare!" they would say. "Grimalkin's tail twitches with excitement and he begins purring at the mere sound of Benjamin's voice."

What these strangers did not know was that Benjamin and Grimalkin could talk to each other almost as person with person. Grimalkin would prick his ears forward and listen gravely to each word of Benjamin's. Then he would make eager little mewing replies, his talk growing louder and louder until he felt certain that Benjamin understood.

There was the day that Benjamin and Grimalkin were left alone to mind Sally. Sally was Benjamin's baby niece.

It was a day made for fishing. Sky overcast. Winds gentle. For a whole hour Benjamin had been sharpening a long pole. He was going to try spearing for trout the way his friends the Indians did.

He had already promised Grimalkin a fishing trip, with all the minnows he could eat.

But just as Benjamin was tucking an apple and some johnnycake into his shirt, he heard the *cloppety-clop* of a horse's hoofs. And then such a hubbub! Rachel, Benjamin's married sister, came flouncing into the house, carrying baby Sally.

"Oh, Mamma!" she cried. "I have been homesick for thee and Benjamin—and everyone."

Benjamin tried hard to look pleased, but in his mind's eye he saw a trout jump out of the water with a silver splash.

Mamma made little cooing noises to the baby. Then she hung Rachel's hood and cloak on a peg as if she were company.

"Benjamin!" she said. "Run up to the front bedchamber and fetch down the cradle we let the little Scotch baby sleep in last night."

With Grimalkin at his heels, Benjamin took the stairs two at a time. He returned breathless with a basket which looked like a great bird's nest on rockers. Grimalkin sat inside it, looking enormously pleased with himself.

"Come, Grimalkin," whispered Benjamin, as he set the cradle down and began edging toward the door.

"Thee, Benjamin!" called Mamma. "Please to fetch thy sisters. They will want to see our dear Sally."

"Where are they, Mamma?" asked Benjamin in despair.

"They are gathering wild mint by the creek!"

"Oh, Benjamin," cried Rachel in her most pleading manner, "I long to be out there with them. If thee were to mind Sally, Mamma and I could have a little outing."

Benjamin bit his lips. He did not mind fetching wood or water. He did not even mind cleaning out the hen house—very much. But minding the baby on a good fishing day!

At a sharp look from Mamma, however, he sat down quickly.

"Oh, thank thee, brother," smiled Rachel. "Here is the flytrap. Please to keep the flies away from Sally's face."

Before Benjamin could say a word, he found himself face to face with the wailing Sally.

"Why, she's mostly mouth!" he said with disgust.

Grimalkin's ears were thrown backward in disapproval. "Can't thee *do* something about this noise?" he seemed to ask.

"Why, of course, I can," replied Benjamin. "I can rock the cradle."

The wailing stopped at once.

The room grew so quiet that Benjamin fancied he could hear the bread rising.

The minutes seemed like hours. The day was going to waste! Benjamin kept tiptoeing to the door to watch for Mamma and Rachel.

"Poor Grimalkin," he sighed, "I promised thee some minnows. And here we are, caught like insects in a web."

He looked about the room. Suddenly his eyes fell on the wells of red ink and black ink on Papa's counter. Beside them lay a goose-quill pen, a sand box for blotting the ink, and a fresh sheet of paper. How smooth and clean the paper looks! thought Benjamin. Then he turned to see if the flies were bothering Sally. And at that precise moment, the baby happened to smile in her sleep.

"Why, Grimalkin!" Benjamin cried. "Sally is less funny-looking when she smiles. She is quite fair." His fingers reached for the goose-quill pen. "I could draw her picture!" he said in amazement. "I believe I could!"

Grimalkin smoothed his whiskers against Benjamin's leg. Then he gazed up with mischievous green eyes. "Well, why doesn't thee do it?" he purred, as plainly as words. "Who is to stop thee?"

Only a Piece of Paper

Benjamin had to work rapidly. Sally's pleasant dream would not last forever. Besides, Mamma and the girls might walk in any minute.

He placed the clean sheet of paper and Papa's ink wells and sand box on a bench beside the cradle. He knelt down on the floor. He dipped the goose-quill pen into the black ink.

Scratch! Scratch! went the pen. With quick strokes he sketched the outline of Sally's head. Then, very lightly, he drew her features. The faint eyebrows. The closed lids. The rounded nose. The smiling lips.

His eyes darted back and forth from Sally's face to his drawing. He forgot about the spear he had made. He forgot about the beautiful red-bellied trout. He forgot everything in the excitement of making his first sketch.

There! He could try the red ink now. He wiped the pen in his hair as he had seen the travelers do. Then he dipped it in the red ink and gave Sally an orange-red mouth. With round-and-round lines he sketched her silken curls. "Why, the color nigh matches her own!" he exclaimed.

Just then Grimalkin leaped on his shoulder and patted his cheek with a gentle forepaw.

"Can thee see any likeness to our Sally?" Benjamin asked of him.

Grimalkin seemed to gaze fixedly at the picture. Then he opened his wide pink mouth. *"Mrr-aow,"* he said, in complete approval.

Benjamin laughed out for joy. But his laughter was cut short. There, in the doorway, stood Mamma and Rachel and Sarah and Hannah and Mary and Elizabeth.

Benjamin sprang to his feet, upsetting the sand box, and almost upsetting the ink wells. He hid his drawing behind him. He could almost hear Mamma say: "If the world's people wish to draw, well and good. But *thee* is a Quaker, son. Thy grandfather was chief councilor for William Penn himself!"

Mamma stood rigid, holding bunches of bright green mint in her hands. Behind her clustered the girls, their eyes questioning.

At last Mamma came toward Benjamin with slow, measured steps.

"Benjamin!" she said crisply.

"Y-y-yes, Mamma."

"What is thee hiding?"

"Only a piece of paper, Mamma."

"I would see it."

Benjamin winced. He handed her the picture and waited for the shocked, hurt look to cross her face. He watched Rachel and Sarah and Hannah and Mary and Elizabeth gather around the picture. He heard their little gasps of surprise.

Then something happened which Benjamin did not in the least expect. Mamma clapped her hand over her mouth as if to smother an outcry of pleasure. Her eyes grew big with wonder.

"Why, 'tis our Sally!" she exclaimed. "An excellent likeness of our dear Sally." And then she smiled down at Benjamin. "How would thee and Grimalkin like to go fishing now?" she asked. "Papa ever was fond of fresh trout. But what he will say to picture-making, I do not know."

Benjamin's face grew as red as a coxcomb. Why, Mamma had not minded at all!

"What did I tell thee?" Grimalkin seemed to say as he reared up on his hind legs and put his forepaws into Benjamin's hand.

Benjamin's heart danced. He picked up his spear, his apples and his johnnycake, and turned to go.

"We'll be back in time to bring home the cows," he sang out.

Grimalkin lifted the latch, and together the boy and the cat set off across the innyard.

"Oh-ho!" laughed Benjamin. "Thy tail is a weather vane, Grimalkin. It stands straight as a poker whenever thee is happy."

Grimalkin led the way, and the sound of his purring was like the gladness in Benjamin's heart.

Weeks went by before Papa saw the picture of Sally. By day he was busy planting Indian corn and pumpkins. By night the guests hovered around him like bees after honey. They hung on his every word, for while Papa was a man of few words, each one counted.

By the time he had a moment to spare, there was not only the picture of Sally to show him. There was a whole stack of pictures, done on poplar boards, on birch bark—on *any*thing that would hold a pen stroke or a smudge of charcoal.

It was midmorning of a bright May day when Papa first heard about the pictures.

"Benjamin!" he called out as he came into the kitchen, bringing the smell of rich black earth with him. "Nanny Luddy has lost a shoe. See if the smith can attend her at once."

"Oh, yes, Papa," replied Benjamin quickly. He grinned at the thought that now Sarah or Hannah or Mary or Elizabeth would have to come down from her bedmaking and take over his job. He was doing a hot and tiresome chore at the time. He was sitting on the hearthstone, turning the crank handle that turned a joint of meat before the fire. And every now and then he had to baste the meat with the brown gravy that dripped into the pan beneath.

Grimalkin sat watchful at Benjamin's feet. Memory told him that sometimes the gravy spattered on the hearthstone, and all of the spatters belonged to him.

"The sun has great power this morning," Papa remarked. "It is pleasant and cool inside."

Cool! thought Benjamin as he wiped the beads of perspiration from his upper lip.

Papa sat down at the table. He began sampling the wild strawberries that Mamma was putting in a pie. Then, looking as sheepish as a boy, he reached over and scooped up on one finger some of the floating island pudding that stood cooling in a bowl. He smiled up at Mamma. "The pudding is exactly to my taste," he observed.

"Benjamin," said Mamma, "this would be the time to show Papa thy pictures."

At the word *picture* Papa coughed and sat bolt upright. His hands tightened on his whip handle until the knuckles stood out white and big. His face went redder than the strawberries. He fixed his hat more firmly on his head.

Oh, oh! thought Benjamin. How quickly Papa can change!

Grimalkin rolled over and over to attract attention, but Papa took less notice of him than if he had been a fly.

"Ho, ho! Look at Grimalkin!" laughed Benjamin nervously.

A heavy silence was the only answer.

Slowly Benjamin got up and walked over to the pine dresser. If only John or Thomas or Samuel or Joseph would come to get Papa! But Door-Latch Inn was as still as a meetinghouse. Only the hens clucked beneath the windows.

With trembling hands, Benjamin took the stack of pictures from the bottom drawer of the dresser. He handed Papa the one of Sally.

It was as if Papa hated even to touch it. Gingerly he laid it on his lap. He reached into his pocket and took out his square-rimmed spectacles. Slowly he adjusted them under his beetling brows. Then he brought the picture up close.

For a long moment he said nothing. Grimalkin lowered his tail at the awful stillness. Mamma's spoon dropped out of her hand with a loud clatter.

Finally Papa placed the drawing on the table. "The image of Sally should be carried in our hearts," he said, as he looked up over the rims of his spectacles. "Not on a piece of paper. Pictures fade; memories remain green forever."

"Green!" shouted Benjamin. "How I long to put green into my pictures! I tried to draw a hummer bird yesterday, as he dipped his beak into a flower. I wanted to paint his shiny green head. But all I had was red and black ink."

Papa shook his head, as he looked at the pictures of redheaded woodpeckers and swamp roses and bushes with scarlet berries.

"It would be better to study cabbages and turnips. Or even gooseberries," he said with a sniff. "These are gay and gaudy. Pride in pictures shows a worldly spirit."

"But, Papa! I am *not* proud of these pictures. I aim to do better. Much better. If only I had more colors!"

At this Papa gave up. "Tell me why it is that thee must draw?" he asked.

Now Benjamin was at a loss. How could he explain the need for putting things on paper? How could he explain that?

"Was it that Sally's smile is fleeting and thee wished to hold it?" asked Mamma.

"That's it, Mamma. That's it! The hummer bird, too, is gone in winter. Yet I could capture him on paper."

Now Grimalkin stretched his muscles and looked up at Papa as if he wished to add a few remarks. First he uttered a little sneeze to attract attention, as people sometimes clear their throats. Then he started talking.

"Yee-oo, mrr-aow, mee-aw-oo, ye-ah-oo." Louder and louder he talked until finally he flung back his head and opened his mouth so wide it showed all the black ridges inside.

Papa sat silent and thoughtful for a moment. Then his eyes twinkled. "Grimalkin is right," he said. "To preserve *good* actions on paper can do no harm. Benjamin is but a lad, Mamma. He will outgrow this." Then turning to Benjamin he said, "Thee may continue with thy drawing —*if* it does not interfere with chores."

Benjamin wanted to scoop Grimalkin up in his arms and dance in circles like a whirl beetle. He wanted to toss Papa's hat to the sky. He wanted to hug Papa until they both gasped for breath. But all he said was, "Thank thee, Papa. Now I shall see about Nanny Luddy's shoe." And he frisked Grimalkin's whiskers for pure joy.

from GEORGE WASHINGTON, LEADER OF THE PEOPLE

Clara Ingram Judson

Washington's boyhood has had a mythlike quality for most children. This selection re-creates the period, the customs, the family, and above all young George Washington and his idolized older brother, Lawrence Washington. Clara Ingram Judson's biographies can be relied upon for their careful historical details. Her many books about American immigrants (They Came From Sweden, They Came From Scotland, *etc.*) *and her exciting story about Chicago's Chinatown*—The Green Ginger Jar—*illustrate her appreciative understanding of widely different people and her profound concern for everything that goes to make our American culture rich and sound.*

By the Rappahannock

The farm by the river was the lush green of June in Virginia. The air was warm, fine for growing things. A mocking bird sang in the linden tree and the chatter of wrens mingled with domestic noises of roosters, hens, and ducks in the chicken yard.

A house, high above the Rappahannock, had a comfortable look against a line of tall trees. Nearby, a barn, the kitchen, poultry house, storeroom, smithy and quarters for the slaves made a little settlement such as was usually found on prosperous Virginia farms in that year 1739.

At the horse lot a boy tugged at the heavy gate bar, while his pony, Whitefoot, pawed impatiently, eager to be gone.

"Want help?" Tim, the stableman, called.

"No, I can do it myself," George Washington said quickly. As he tugged again, he noticed that Whitefoot was suddenly still, ears cocked as though he heard a new sound.

"Someone coming, Whitefoot?" George asked, listening. The rhythmic sound of hoofbeats came from far down the lane leading to the main road to Fredericksburg.

George climbed onto the fence for a look. He was sturdy and tall for a boy in his eighth year. Freckles sprinkled his straight nose, and his hands were tanned from long hours out of doors. Now he brushed a lock of sandy-colored hair from his forehead and squinted his gray-blue eyes down the lane.

"It's *Lawrence!*" he cried excitedly. "Whitefoot! Lawrence is coming!"

George jumped down from the fence, pulled out the gate bar, which suddenly seemed lighter, threw himself onto his pony and dashed off down the lane.

A visit from George's twenty-one-year-old half-brother was a thrilling surprise. Lawrence Washington had been home from England only a few months. George admired this tall, handsome brother and saw him far too little.

Lawrence waved as George drew near and grinned with amusement when the boy pulled Whitefoot up short with a flourish that sent pebbles flying.

"Oh, Lawrence! I am so glad to see you!" George cried breathlessly. "I didn't know you were coming today!"

"I started early; I have meant to come for several days," Lawrence said. "Is Father here?"

"No," George told him. "I think he is at the iron works. Maybe you had better ride over and see him?"

"No, my errand is here," Lawrence said. "And I doubt if your mother would let you ride over with me in any case. Where are you bound now?"

"To school," George told him in a bored tone. "That Master Hobby is a tiresome man, Lawrence. He teaches the same thing over and over."

"Perhaps it is a good thing that I came today," Lawrence remarked as they rode along toward the house.

"Did you come about *me?*" George was astonished. But Lawrence merely shook his head and laughed mysteriously.

"I must talk to your mother now," he said. "And you should shut that gate, George. You will be in trouble if a colt gets into the field."

Reluctantly George stopped to close and fasten the gate while Lawrence rode to the hitching post near the house.

George turned Whitefoot into the lot, fastened the gate and called to a stableboy to care for Lawrence's mount. But his manner was absent-minded; his thoughts were on Lawrence. Something was up, that was certain, something that concerned George. But what could be important enough to bring Lawrence on a thirty-mile ride from Hunting Creek farm? In June, too, when a farmer had work to oversee.

Shouts of small children and the bark of a dog guided George to the lawn in front of the house. There, on the high bank Lawrence had joined Mrs. Washington and the younger children, Betty, Sam, and Jack. They had been watching their father's scow as it crossed the river.

"It is a good thing you came today, Lawrence," Mrs. Washington was saying to her stepson as George came near. "While you are in Fredericksburg about George, you can attend to the delivery of my boxes. I saw the ship from England arrive yesterday."

"Am I going to Fredericksburg?" George exclaimed. Many times he had looked toward the white steeple of the church across the river and wondered what was beneath the thick trees. "I have never been to a town," he added.

"That is not surprising," Lawrence said casually. "Virginia has few towns. But you shall see Fredericksburg today, for my errand there is for you. Father thinks it is high time . . ."

"George! Run to the house and put on your best coat," Mrs. Washington interrupted. "Lawrence can explain your father's plan while you are on the ferry. It comes now." The scow had reached the landing at the foot of the ravine.

George glanced down at his shirt and kneepants. The garments were clean and good enough for Hobby's little school. But he did look shabby compared with Lawrence's elegant coat and breeches, trimmed with shining buttons and buckles. He hurried into the house, brushed his hair and put on his best coat and the shoes with buckles. Lawrence was strolling toward the ravine when he returned and together they hurried to the wharf.

"Lawrence! Tell the captain to have a care for my boxes," Mrs. Washington called after them. "The last time your father ordered goblets, every one was broken on the way."

"I shall see to it," Lawrence promised. "Come, George!"

The children left behind began to fuss.

"I want to ride on the ferry," six-year-old Betty teased.

"I want to go!" Sam planted his feet wide apart and yelled.

Jack was too young to understand but he yelled too.

"Quiet, all of you!" Mrs. Washington commanded. "Better be gone quickly, Lawrence," she called over her shoulder, "or these children will be heard in Fredericksburg."

Laughing, Lawrence and George hurried away. In a few minutes they were aboard the clumsy ferry.

As they pulled away, George looked expectantly at Lawrence.

"So you want to know what this is about?" Lawrence said. "The last time Father came to

Hunting Creek, he told me that he was not pleased with Hobby's teaching. A one-room neighborhood school is good for a time. It is convenient and gives you a start. But Father heard that a better school might be opened in Fredericksburg. He wants to know if the rumor is true. We shall not count on it until we see."

The crossing was brief. Before George had time for many questions, the ferry tied up near the sailing ship from England. Lawrence went at once to attend to Mrs. Washington's boxes.

George marveled that Lawrence knew exactly what to say and do as invoices were checked and boxes marked "Fragile" were moved to the ferry under his watchful eye.

"I am lucky to have a brother as wonderful as Lawrence," George thought humbly. "I wonder if I can ever be as smart and as handsome?" It seemed doubtful.

"Now we can leave," Lawrence said in relief. And the two climbed the steep cobblestone road to the town.

George looked around with keen curiosity. He saw the church with the familiar steeple, many houses, a stone jail with iron-barred windows, shops, and people strolling about.

Lawrence inquired of one of these for the residence of the Reverend James Marye and was directed to the parsonage, by the church. The rector was at home, and Lawrence introduced himself and George and accepted the invitation to come inside.

"My father had hoped to call upon you, sir, about the education of my young brother," he explained as they all sat down. "But because of his many duties at his iron works and the task of managing his three plantations, the matter has been postponed. My father has heard that you may open a school. If this is your intention, we would like to enroll my brother."

The Reverend Marye had looked keenly from one Washington to the other while Lawrence was speaking.

"Where did you receive your education?" he asked.

"At Appleby in England," Lawrence told him. "My father lived in England and attended Appleby. Others of our family went to that school and my brother Augustine, Jr., who is near my age, is there. At the proper time my father plans to take George to England, too. Meanwhile, my brother needs good preparation which my father hopes you can give him."

"Have you had any schooling, George?" Marye asked.

"Yes, sir. Master Hobby teaches me reading and writing and sums," George answered respectfully.

Marye turned to his desk and selected a bit of paper and a quill pen.

"Let me see your writing," he said.

George sat down, took the quill, and wrote his name in his best style. The result was not remarkable. Marye eyed it, frowning.

"Those field schools," he began. Then he paused and rubbed his chin thoughtfully. It was plain he was not favorably impressed with George's instruction. The term "field school" which he used was often applied to a small one-room schoolhouse erected by a group of neighbors. One gave a part of his field, others labor, materials, or tobacco for buying books. The great problem was to find a suitable teacher; the colony of Virginia lacked such men.

"I do better with sums," George ventured to speak up when the silence grew long. "I like arithmetic."

"I hope we are not too late to enter my brother," Lawrence remarked, now a bit anxious at the turn the interview was taking.

"On the contrary, you are too early," Marye answered more cheerfully. "I shall not open my school before autumn, perhaps not until next year. Um-m-m, I wonder if your father has considered the cost of textbooks as well as tuition?"

"My father will not object to any proper charge," Lawrence answered, with due caution about committing his father's purse. "Perhaps you will be good enough to send Father word when your school is about to open?"

"You may count on that," Marye said, now reassured. "Meanwhile, have the boy continue his studies."

The visitors bowed out politely. As they walked down the street, George sighed with relief.

"The Reverend Marye must be a *very* learned man," he said. "He is so very solemn."

"Never mind!" Lawrence answered. "You have to be prepared for Appleby, and Hobby could never do it. Where shall we go now? The ferry can wait."

"I would like to go to the Apothecary's Shop, Lawrence," George said, eagerly. "Our smith has told me about it. The window has two big urns, one red, one green. Candy is for sale," George added hopefully.

Lawrence was willing, and soon they saw the small but enchanting window. Inside, the shop had a luscious fragrance.

"We have some excellent sugar which has just arrived from England," the apothecary told them. He opened a case and took out a shallow wooden bowl in which hunks of a taffylike substance were piled. George's mouth watered as he admired the rich caramel color and watched Lawrence expectantly.

"I shall take two pounds," Lawrence ordered. The apothecary reached for his iron sugar clippers; he used them like tongs to cut off individual portions and place them on the scale.

"Two pounds," he repeated.

"Can you direct us to a baker's shop?" Lawrence asked as he paid for the sugar and handed the sack to George.

"Down the street by the corner there is a good place," the man said.

At the baker's, Lawrence bought caraway comfits. George ate two on the ferry and found them delicious.

"I shall take the rest home for a treat," he decided.

The dining table was set in the wide hall. The stone fireplace was empty this June day, but the hearth was cheerful with bright brasses and an embroidered fire screen. A gold-framed mirror hung on one wall and opposite a handsome floor clock ticked off seconds. Leather-bottomed chairs were set up to a large table covered with a linen tablecloth and set with china and pewter. The children stood by their chairs as their mother entered.

"We saw the ferry coming so we waited dinner," she said. "George has learned to say grace, Lawrence. We are ready, son."

They stood with bowed heads while George recited: "God bless us for what we are about to receive." Then they sat down.

A young serving maid hovered over the children, tying bibs, while an older woman brought food from the kitchen. In Virginia this was often a separate building; the danger of fire was less and flies, drawn by cooking, were kept from the dining room.

The woman set a large platter before Lawrence, who carved the two roast chickens. Then she brought sliced ham, a bowl of greens cooked with bacon, blackberry jam, butter, hot cornbread and handleless cups of hot tea. Later she passed wheat bread and a large bowl piled with fruit picked that morning; early plums, cherries and red currants.

As they were finishing the meal, Lawrence winked at George, who promptly produced the comfits and the sugar.

"I shall persuade Father to take *me* to town soon," Betty announced as she found the last crumb and plunked it into her mouth. George chuckled. They both knew their father had no time for shopping journeys.

The other children drifted out of doors. George sat quietly as Lawrence talked with Mrs. Washington about the school and left messages for his father. Until last winter the Washingtons had all lived at Hunting Creek farm and Mrs. Washington was interested in the place.

"Perhaps your father will come to Hunting Creek soon," she remarked as Lawrence rose to leave.

"I wish he would bring George with him," Lawrence said. "That is, if you can spare him?" George's face brightened and Mrs. Washington half promised.

Striding along by Lawrence, George went to the horse lot where he mounted Whitefoot to ride as far as the main road.

"I wish you could stay longer, Lawrence," George said.

"And who would do my work at Hunting Creek?" scoffed Lawrence. "Lucky for me the day is long so I can get home before dark. But you will be coming to visit me, George. Don't tease Father. Better be surprised when he mentions a visit. Then you may say that I will teach you farming and care of the stock. He will like that, and you will enjoy it more than school." Laughing, Lawrence touched his horse lightly and was on his way.

George rode back to the barn. The Washingtons had slaves to do the work at Ferry farm, but Mr. Washington had told George that a boy old enough to have his own horse must take care of it. That was no hardship; George liked keeping Whitefoot's stall clean, bedding the pony with fresh straw, and measuring out the feed. Usually he talked as he curried and cared for his pony. But today his thoughts were with Lawrence. The prospect of a visit at Hunting Creek farm was far more interesting than a new school.

. . . .

Many Changes

After months without word from the West Indies a letter that Lawrence had written in Jamaica arrived. George was astonished that Lawrence wrote more about smallpox and yellow fever than about glorious battles. After more months word came that the war had turned to Georgia; the fleet was not needed, and Virginians were coming home.

Lawrence arrived late in 1742 and was received with honor by the colony. Later the governor appointed him military adjutant in recognition of his war service, an office that gave him charge of the militia of Virginia.

The returned warrior found changes at Ferry farm. The baby sister had died. Austin, Lawrence's brother who had expected to study law in England, had come home to help his father. He was learning to manage the farm at Pope's Creek.

"I had George visit me for a time," Austin told Lawrence. "He is good company." Lawrence saw that the two got on well.

But George soon showed his family that no one took Lawrence's place in his affections. Now his hero was more fascinating than ever; he had seen foreign places and could tell tales of ships and battles. Lawrence had served on the flagship and was the friend of a real admiral. George followed his brother around and begged to be allowed to go back with him to Hunting Creek.

"And leave school?" Lawrence exclaimed. "Are you failing?"

"Oh, no, Lawrence!" George was shocked. "But I could learn more with you."

Lawrence grinned understandingly. But George stayed in school.

After gay holidays with six sons and daughter Betty crowding the modest house, the older sons went back to work. At Pope's Creek, Austin was trying to set up a business of raising fine horses, much needed in the colony. Lawrence, at Hunting Creek, planned to erect a few needed buildings and clear more fields for growing tobacco. He had told his father that he hoped to marry Anne Fairfax in the spring. As for Gus Washington, he continued his heavy round of duties at his Accokeek Iron Works, Hunting Creek, Pope's Creek, and Ferry farm.

The iron business had first been successful in America in 1717, with a Maryland furnace owned by an English firm. There Gus Washington learned how to take ore from the ground, smelt it, and ship it to England. Colonists were not allowed to make durable goods; that profitable business was reserved for England.

Washington built furnaces, prepared wood for charcoal from his own forest and built ships for transport. All this required scores of laborers who must be housed and fed. Wagons, tools, and all sorts of supplies were needed, and craftsmen, too; wagonwrights, blacksmiths, millers, sawyers, carpenters, and others. Slaves could be trained to work under a skilled manager, but this last was a hard job to fill. Gus Washington had to be his own manager much of the time.

As for George, he did so well in school that his father planned an Easter vacation for him—a visit to his cousins in another county. George was there, in the midst of a day of sports, when a messenger arrived from Ferry farm.

"Your father is ill—very ill!" the man cried as he slid from his exhausted horse. "You are to come home at once."

George dashed for Whitefoot. The messenger was loaned a fresh mount and the two galloped home. George arrived in time to see his strong father stretched flat on his bed, too ill to know his son or to speak. Mrs. Washington let him stand there a few minutes, then she motioned him away.

Soon Lawrence came into the hall. "Father is dead."

"Dead!" George exclaimed incredulously. His strong handsome father, the man who had more energy than any person George had ever known—dead? But it was true. This sad loss came a few weeks after George's eleventh birthday.

During those next sad days George thought

often of the ride with his father nearly four years before. He was glad to have had that trip and their talk to remember.

After Augustine Washington had been buried in the family burying ground a mile from Pope's Creek, his will was read. George's father had thought of the future of all his children.

Lawrence, the oldest son, was to have the largest plantation, Hunting Creek farm. That was still the custom in the colony. Austin inherited Pope's Creek farm. George was to have Ferry farm when he was twenty-one and also some other land. Sam and Jack and Charles were each given tracts of several hundred acres and Betty's inheritance was in money. The forty-nine slaves were divided among the heirs, and each child and the mother were given shares in the iron company. Mrs. Washington was to hold and manage her children's property until they became of age.

When this legal business was finally settled, Lawrence and Austin went back to their homes, and life at Ferry farm settled down. George missed Lawrence more than ever because now he had no father.

In July of that year, 1743, Lawrence married Anne Fairfax and the family reassembled for the wedding. The event, so soon after Mr. Washington's death, was not as festive as it might have been, but George thought it very grand. The social life of Virginia was the most elegant of all the colonies.

This marriage brought many changes in George's life. Lawrence's bride invited him for a long visit; she told him to call her Nancy, as Lawrence did. George's mother was willing to have George stay at Hunting Creek now that Lawrence had a bride of distinction.

Nancy's father, Colonel William Fairfax, continued his liking for George. Fairfax was one of the richest and most distinguished men in Virginia; he was a burgess, then a member of the higher body, the Council, and a year after the wedding was made President of the Council. Next to the governor's palace, his home, Belvoir, was the meeting place of the greatest men in the colony.

George was now eleven and a half and naturally quick to observe people and manners. This association with the Fairfax family had taught him fine manners and habits of graciousness; in a measure, it took the place of the training his father had intended him to have in England.

Lawrence and Nancy lived in the story-and-a-half house that was probably built by Gus Washington before he moved there in the seventeen-thirties. It had a center hall and four rooms downstairs and rooms with dormer windows above. They added furniture and hangings, and Nancy had handsome silver and other choice things. George thought the place very elegant, though, of course, it was not large and handsome like Belvoir.

When the pretty things were all in place, Nancy told George they were giving the place a new name.

"This is no longer Hunting Creek farm, George," she said. "We call it Mount Vernon; Mount for the high bank above the river, Vernon for Lawrence's good friend the admiral."

"Mount Vernon," George repeated the words, testing the sound. "That is a good name, Nancy. I like it."

A few days later the Lawrence Washingtons gave a dinner party as a housewarming. The slaves worked early and late with the preparations. They polished silver, washed and ironed linens, and washed the china and every window in the house.

George wondered if a boy going on twelve would be allowed at the table. Nancy soon relieved his mind about that.

"Lawrence thinks this is a good chance for you to learn about grown-up affairs," she said. "Wear that new suit Lawrence ordered from London. Better try it on today, George, and let Lawrence see if it needs any changes. And, George, will you tell Chloe that I shall be out to inspect every duck myself when she has finished cleaning them? Everything is to be perfect at my first party!"

She bustled about happily, keys clicking at her belt like an experienced housewife. George did the errand and then ran upstairs to try on the suit. It had come only that morning.

The guests were very fashionable. The dinner was delicious, George thought, though he was so excited he could not eat as much as usual—well, not quite as much. When the ladies retired to the drawing room to talk of fashions and house-

hold matters, Colonel Fairfax motioned for George to sit by him. The men were talking, at the moment, about war.

"You must feel a satisfaction, Lawrence," a guest across the table remarked, "to know that you could serve the king when he needed you." Lawrence nodded and bowed modestly.

"His majesty needs service in peacetime, too," a man in a green satin coat said. The others looked at him.

"I am thinking of the land west of the mountains," he explained. "Your relative, Lord Fairfax, owns vast acreage. I believe you manage it for him, Fairfax?"

"If you can call it managing," Colonel Fairfax waved his hand casually. "Actually wilderness land has little value. King Charles the Second would not have given it away, years ago, if he had thought well of it."

"You speak of the Fairfax Proprietary, I take it?" a guest in a bright-blue coat and stylish periwig inquired.

"Yes." Fairfax smiled. "An elegant name for a wild, unsurveyed stretch of country. I had a letter from Lord Fairfax the other day—he asks whether there is a demand by settlers for his land. I do not know what to tell him."

"No demand at all, I'd say," some one spoke up. "Not with Indians only a short journey away. Now if the Indians could be persuaded to move west of the Allegheny Range a lively trade in land might open up."

"At great profit to us all," Fairfax laughed and raised his glass. The talk went on until the guests' carriages arrived.

That was only the first of many dinner parties at Mount Vernon. How much of the talk—business, military, and political—a boy of twelve could understand, George himself could hardly have told. But he was a thoughtful lad. He turned men's words over in his mind and began growing up.

Occasionally George rode with Lawrence to see Austin at Pope's Creek. This brother urged George to live with him.

"You like to work with horses, George," he said. "And there are boys your own age nearby—the Lee family, and others." But though George did go for one or two visits, he was always glad to return to Mount Vernon. He loved that place.

When he stayed at Ferry farm he found that life very different from either brother's. There, small children, school, and daily tasks under his mother's supervision kept him busy.

Mrs. Washington had considerable help, both slaves and indentured servants. Still, the mother of five children and manager of a farm had a great deal to do. She must guard the children from daily hazards: poison ivy on the river slope, measles, warts, croup (the terror of those days), and chicken pox. She was also the doctor, and she made her own medicines from herbs grown in her garden or searched out in the forest.

The blacksmith was the dentist, though of course the mother pulled "baby teeth." She tied a string from tooth to doorknob and held the child while some one slammed the door—and pulled the tooth. The blacksmith was called in when a "second tooth" ached. Mother held the patient flat on the table while the smith, with a dramatic flourish of black pincers and sheer strength, yanked out the tooth—and often some bone along with it.

The children all rode horses, too. So the mother must be ready to tie red meat over bruises or set broken bones. It was a busy life, full of surprises.

At school, George studied the classics, writing, algebra, and geometry. Reverend Marye was most particular about writing. He had George copy one hundred and ten rules from an old English volume called *The Rules of Conduct.*

"Write each rule over and over until you have it perfect," the master ordered. "I shall accept no carelessly made letters."

So George wrote in his copybook:

"Mock not, nor jest at anything of importance; break no jests that are sharp biting, and if you deliver anything witty or pleasant, abstain from laughing at it yourself.

"When you see a crime punished, you may be inwardly pleased; but always show pity to the suffering offender.

"Labor to keep alive in your breast that little spark of celestial fire called conscience."

This chore of copying over and over to satisfy his teacher taught George the easy, flowing handwriting that was to be so important to him later.

One Saturday his mother set him at the tedious task of cleaning the storehouse. This was a small building, near the kitchen, where countless articles were put when not in daily use. He moved boxes and bundles. He scrubbed and sorted under her keen eye until someone called her away. While alone, George rummaged in a dark corner. There he found an odd thing made up of iron rods and chains. As his mother returned she heard the sounds he made examining the thing.

"Now what have you there?" she demanded.

"I don't know, Mother," George said. "Do you?"

When she saw what he was holding, she laughed. "Of course I know! That's your father's surveying chain; did you never see it before? His compass is in the desk. Your father always surveyed property he bought to make sure of the boundaries."

"Father knew everything, didn't he?" George said quietly.

Something in the lad's tone caught his mother's attention. She put her hand on his shoulder in a rare gesture of affection.

"Not everything, son," she answered kindly. "But he was a fine man. He had more knowledge than most men in the colony. But a chain is no good to us now. Take it to the smith; he can use the metal." Mary Washington was her practical self again.

"May I keep it because it was Father's?" George asked.

"Oh, yes, if you like. After you have scrubbed the floor, put it in the corner, there. It does not take much room."

She bustled away, the keys at her belt jingling. "He will soon forget," she thought. "Then the smith can have it."

George finished the scrubbing and put the brush and bucket away. As he laid the long chain in the corner he made a promise to himself.

"Monday I shall begin to learn surveying."

from **BENJAMIN FRANKLIN**

Ingri and Edgar Parin d'Aulaire

This is a selection from one of the D'Aulaires' beautiful picture-biographies for young readers 8 to 10. If the text seems a bit stiff, the bright, powerful pictures give their books a color which the narratives lack. However, even in this selection, the sturdy, intelligent Ben comes to life. All the picture-biographies of this husband and wife team are worth looking up: George Washington, Abraham Lincoln *(Caldecott Medal),* Leif the Lucky, *and* Pocahontas.

[*Boy into Man*]

At the time when the King of England ruled over the American colonies there stood a small house on Milk Street in Boston.

In this house there lived a candlemaker whose name was Josiah Franklin. He was a good and pious man, and the Lord had given him a virtuous wife and a blessing of seventeen children, all counted.

Three times each Sunday he led all his children to church and he taught them to be honest and hard-working and satisfied with little.

"He who knows his trade does not have to stand except for kings," said Josiah Franklin. He looked proudly at his ten husky sons and hoped that someday they would all be good tradesmen.

The youngest of his sons was Benjamin. He was born in 1706. He was different from his brothers. He was only knee-high to a grasshopper when he first learned to read and he wondered and asked questions from morning till night. He was a merry little fellow with stocky legs and a bright mind, busy with flights of fancy and practical ideas. He thought it was a pity that his father, who was so busy working to keep them all in food and clothes, should waste so much time saying a long grace every time he ate.

"Father," he said one day as they were sitting down to table, "think of all the time you could save if you would thank the Lord, once and for all, for the whole larder."

His father was pious and serious but he could not help smiling, and when he told his friends what a clever young son he had, they laughed with him and agreed that Benjamin was so bright he might even become a minister. And on the next holiday one of the friends filled Benjamin's little coat pocket with copper pennies. Benjamin had never had a penny of his own before and joyfully he ran to a toy shop, where he offered all his money for a whistle he had set his heart on. He ran home and marched through the house shrilly blowing it while the rest of his family stopped up their ears.

When his sisters and brothers found out that he had spent all of his pennies for the whistle, he was the one who stopped up his ears. They teased him and called him a spendthrift till he wept. He had spent four times as much as the whistle was worth. That was the only time Benjamin ever spent a penny unwisely.

Benjamin lived near the sea, and he early learned to swim and sail. He never grew tired of watching the wind carry the boats over the water, just as it carried his kite up into the sky. One day, while he was swimming, he fastened the kite to himself as if it were a sail and he were a boat. It carried him gently over the water while his friends, who were kicking and splashing, looked on in astonishment. Because he had so many ideas like this, he was usually the leader among his playmates.

Like any boy, he sometimes led them into mischief. Once he got all of his playmates together at the shore where they liked best to fish. The ground was swampy, but near by Benjamin had found a big pile of stones that were to be used for building a house. He and his friends took these stones and built a fine wharf. But when the workmen came and found the stones gone, it helped Benjamin little to plead the usefulness of their work.

After he had been soundly spanked by his father, Benjamin was convinced that nothing is useful that is not honest.

When Benjamin was eight years old, his father sent him to grammar school. He rose to the head of his class in reading and writing, and he read every book he could lay his hands upon. But he was poor in arithmetic. His father began to think that perhaps Benjamin should be a tradesman like his brothers. So, when Benjamin was ten years old, he was taken out of school to learn his father's trade of candlemaking.

Benjamin hated dipping candles and cutting wicks the whole day long. He read and he dreamed. More and more he dreamed about ships and voyages to faraway ports. His father began to fear that his son might become a sailor and be lost at sea. Hoping to find Benjamin a trade that he would really like, he took him to call on joiners and braziers and cutlers and bricklayers in their workshops. Benjamin learned much about these trades but he did not want to follow any of them. At last his worried father persuaded him that, since he was so fond of books, he should become a printer's apprentice. Then he could look at the printed word all day long.

His older brother James had a printing shop and, when Benjamin was twelve, he moved from his father's house and bound himself to be his brother's apprentice for nine years. In return, James was to teach him to print and to give him him his board and clothes.

James was a strict master. When his young brother answered back with his quick wit and ready tongue, he boxed his ears severely. Benjamin had to sweep the floor, wash the type, and do all the dirty work while he watched his brother and his helpers print pamphlets and books. By and by James taught him to set type and print.

Benjamin was a hard-working boy and he learned fast. In a few years he was his brother's best worker. He would have liked life in the printing shop very much if he had had more time to read all the books around him. One day he had one of his practical ideas. He asked his brother to give him half of the money he paid for Benjamin's board so he could get his own meals and eat them in the shop when the others went out. James did not mind. He saved money. And Benjamin was happy. Now he had time to read books in peace while he ate his gruel and munched an apple. He did not care much what he ate as long as it was cheap and wholesome. He soon found that he could save half of the money his brother gave him for food. With that he bought books.

Benjamin wanted very much to become a writer himself. When he read something he liked especially well, he rewrote it in his own words. And sometimes he would be hanged if he didn't think that he was better than the author.

One of the things James printed was a newspaper. Benjamin's fingers were itching to write for it, for who does not want to see his own words in print? But he knew that his brother would only laugh and say he was getting too big for his breeches and give him a whack into the bargain. So he kept his writing secret.

One morning his brother found under his door a letter to the newspaper signed Widow Dogood. James did not recognize Benjamin's writing, for he had disguised it. Benjamin chuckled and was very pleased with himself when not only his brother and his friends but also the readers of the paper highly praised the widow's good sense and learning. His brother had many letters from the virtuous lady and printed them all before Benjamin confessed that he was the widow.

James was angry. After that he was stricter than ever with Benjamin. In his eyes Benjamin was a fresh little sprout who believed he could both print and write better than his master.

Benjamin thought he was now too big to be thrashed by his brother. He had been his apprentice for five years and had become a very good printer. Yes, he had even run the printing shop alone while his brother was away. He asked his brother please to let him go so that he could find work for himself elsewhere. But James said no, he must stay till his nine years were up.

Then Benjamin made up his mind to run away. He knew it was wrong but he could no longer stand his brother's harsh treatment. He sold some of his cherished books to get a little money, and late one night he secretly boarded a ship bound for New York. He stood at the rail watching his native town vanish into the night. He felt small and lonesome. His parents would be sad and his brother would be angry. He was only seventeen and he did not know a soul in New York who might help him.

The winds were fair, but even so the trip to New York took three days. During a lull the sailors fished and made a big haul of cod. They invited Benjamin to eat with them, but Benjamin said no, thank you, he ate neither flesh nor fish, for he had read in a book that it was murder to kill and eat creatures that had done him no harm. But he loved codfish and, when the fish was cooking and the good smells reached his nose, he began to hunt about in his mind for a reason to share the sailors' meal. He remembered that when the codfish were cut open he had seen small fish in their stomachs. If big fish ate small fish, why should he not eat big fish? Then he ate heartily and thought to himself how lucky he was to be a thinking creature who could find a good reason for doing what he wanted to do. After that Benjamin always ate what was set before him.

Benjamin liked the sea voyage. When he arrived in New York, he stood at the wharf for a while and thought. He could go to sea if he still wanted to, but he had become a printer, and a printer he would be.

New York was a very small town in 1723 and there was but one printer. He had no work for Benjamin and advised him to go to Philadelphia. Philadelphia was a larger town.

So Benjamin set off for Philadelphia. He had very little money left and could not afford to travel all the way by ship. He stuffed what he could into his pockets and shipped the rest of his belongings. A few pennies paid his passage on a ramshackle old boat that was about to cross to the Jersey shore.

Halfway across, a gale blew up and the rotten sails went to pieces. In the storm a Dutchman fell overboard, Benjamin quickly grabbed him by the hair and pulled him back into the boat. The dripping Dutchman pulled a book out of his pocket and asked Benjamin to dry it for him.

It was the most beautiful book Benjamin had ever seen. It had been printed in Europe with fine type and many pictures. That was the kind of book he would like to print.

He had plenty of time to enjoy the book, for the boat pitched and tossed in the bay of New York for thirty hours. At last the crew managed to bring her to port on the Jersey shore and, cold and wet, Benjamin started to walk. It was a long way on foot, for it is a hundred miles from New York to Philadelphia.

For days he trudged through ruts and mud, in rain and storm, and he began to be sorry he had ever run away. When he reached the Delaware River, he was lucky. A small boat came sailing downstream and the crew took him on board. But soon the wind died down. Benjamin had to help row the boat till his hands were covered with blisters. He looked so bedraggled and forlorn, it was a wonder he was not sent home as a runaway bound boy.

That is the way he arrived in Philadelphia early on a Sunday morning. People in their Sunday-go-to-meeting clothes were walking through the streets, Benjamin walked along with them, looking this way and that till he came to an open bakeshop. He was very hungry and went in and asked the baker for three pennies' worth of bread. To his surprise, the baker handed him three huge buns, for bread was very cheap in Philadelphia. It was three times more than he could eat! The people turned their heads to hide their smiles when they saw Benjamin walking up Market Street with his pockets stuffed with clothes and his arms full of bread. A pretty girl standing in a doorway snickered and giggled out loud.

He followed the people in the street until he came to a Quaker meetinghouse, which he entered. He was so exhausted that he fell asleep the moment he sat down. He had come to the city of brotherly love, so nobody woke him till the meeting was over. Then a kind Quaker showed him to an inn where he could rest and eat.

Scrubbed and refreshed, Benjamin went out the next morning, and soon he found work as a printer's helper. Nobody laughed at his looks any longer, but everybody laughed at his jokes. It was not long before the people of Philadelphia were telling one another how lucky it was that such a good printer and fine young fellow had settled in their town. Many of them made friends with him. The governor of Pennsylvania came to see if Benjamin was really as clever as people said. He asked him out to dine with him and was much taken by his good sense. He advised Benjamin to go back to Boston and ask his father's forgiveness for running away and his help in setting up a printing shop of his own. Then he, the governor, would help him to get printing to do. That sounded like good advice to Benjamin.

Eight months after he had run away, he sailed back to Boston for a visit. He was dressed in a fine new suit. He had a watch, and silver coins jingled in his pocket. His parents were happy that he had done so well, and readily forgave him. But his father thought he was still too young to have a shop of his own and told him to return to his well-paid work as a printer's helper. His brother would not forgive him and it was not till many years later that the two brothers were friends again.

TOM JEFFERSON CLIMBS A MOUNTAIN

Frances Cavanah

"Will dinner time never come?"

Tom Jefferson did not dare to say the words aloud; he was in school. It was a very little schoolhouse—built especially for the use of his cousins, his sisters, and himself—on the grounds of Tuckahoe, the beautiful estate in Tidewater, Virginia, where they lived. Though Tom was only five, he was already learning to read and write and cipher. But today he found it very hard to keep his mind upon his sums. Outside the birds sang. Inside there was only the squeak of slate pencils.

Tom was getting hungrier every minute. "I can't stand it any longer," he decided. And, getting up very quietly, he tiptoed from the room.

Once outside, he didn't know just what to do. The air was fragrant with roses and bridal wreath in bloom. In the distance the James River shone like a bright twisted ribbon. On the brow of the wooded hill sprawled the manor house, beyond the avenue of beautiful elms. If the dinner bell would only ring! Perhaps if he said his prayers, it would help the time to pass.

"Our Father, which art in heaven—" Tom knelt beside the schoolhouse on the ground. He finished the Lord's Prayer. Again he said it, and again, and again. He loved the sound of the slow, beautiful words.

Clang-clang! Clang-clang!

"Dinner!" someone shouted, and the little schoolhouse seemed to rustle with excitement. Jane and Mary Jefferson came bursting through the door. Tom's cousins, Judith and Mary Randolph, followed with their little brother, Thomas. Tom jumped up, and the six children raced through the English garden to the manor house. When Tom, his hands carefully washed and his sandy hair smoothed down, took his place at the long dining-room table, he sighed blissfully. There at its head sat his tall father, carving a big ham. He placed a pink slice on a plate, which a grinning colored servant placed before the hungry boy. Tom took a deep breath, cut a piece of the delicious ham, and sank his fork into a fluffy sweet potato. It was worth waiting for!

Tom's real home was Shadwell, in the wild farm country farther to the west, but he was living at Tuckahoe so that his father could look after the orphaned Randolph children, Tom's cousins. Here the two families of children had wonderful times together. The girls played house at the foot of the big oak tree. The boys flew kites and went swimming. There were orchards where they played tag and "thread the needle." There were horses to ride, stables to visit, and fascinating places to explore. There was the smokehouse where ham was cured, the soaphouse where fat was saved, and then put into big copper kettles to be boiled down and made into soap. In the tobacco houses the leaves of the tobacco plant were stripped and dried, ready to be loaded on the ships that would sail down the river and away to England. Most interesting of all, perhaps, were the slave quarters, where the cousins often played with the little colored boys and girls.

But life at Tuckahoe was not all play. When Tom was six, he began to learn to be a gentleman. On special occasions he wore a dress suit exactly like his father's, with velvet breeches and coat, a flowered waistcoat, and a cocked hat. And sometimes he had to wear a stiff steel-and-canvas corset like his mother's. Tom took dancing lessons, and acted as the host at the children's balls held in the big two-story room that connected the two wings of the house. At such times, the great chandelier, brightly lighted with candles, shone down upon the boys and girls of the neighborhood as they danced the minuet or the Virginia reel.

One day, when Tom was nine, Colonel Jefferson said to him, "I have news for you, my son. I have decided to go back to Shadwell."

Tom's long, freckled face lighted up with pleasure at the thought. At heart he was a pioneer, just as his father was, and he knew that when he returned to Shadwell he would have bears and otters to hunt, buffalo to shoot, rivers to ford, and mountains to climb.

"I have arranged for you to live with Rev. William Douglas a few miles from Shadwell," his father went on. "He will instruct you in Latin, Greek, and French, and many other subjects which I am unprepared to teach you. You are to have the education that I missed. I want you to be a scholar, Son."

"Oh!" Tom sounded disappointed. He had hoped to live at Shadwell. Still, he did want to be a scholar. He had known how to read since he was five, and he had read every book in his father's library. But his mind was still full of questions. Perhaps, under his new teacher, he would find many of the answers.

"I shall like that, Father. But may I spend my vacations at Shadwell?"

"Indeed you shall." Colonel Jefferson smoothed back the sandy hair that grew in bushy masses about his son's temples. "We shall hunt and ride and fish together, and I shall take you on some of my surveying trips. Perhaps you may see the great Cherokee warrior, Ontassete."

Tom learned rapidly under Mr. Douglas. He studied Greek and Latin, and he read the classics. He became very good in mathematics. He was learning new things every day. When he went home to Shadwell, he kept right on learning—only here he learned from the outdoors instead of from books. Vacations at this simple home in the wilderness were everything that his father had promised.

"It is the strong in body who are both strong and free in mind," his father often said, and he taught his son to swim and ride and shoot. Tom liked to explore the high hills near his home. Often he looked across the Rivanna River to his favorite hill, which he called *Monticello,* the Italian word for "little mountain." It was on Colonel Jefferson's land, and Tom knew that some day it would belong to him. Somehow it seemed more beautiful than any of the surrounding mountains. The pine trees looked more majestic, and the dogwood blossoms bloomed with a sweeter fragrance in the spring. Often he rode his horse down to the river's edge, forded the stream, and followed the path that led to the wooded summit. From here he could look down at the town of Charlottesville and out over a great expanse of green valley to other mountains half lost in a blue haze. In all the world he did not believe that he could find a scene more beautiful.

Another favorite haunt was a deserted Indian town, where Tom sometimes dug for arrows and stone hatchets. The Indians were his father's friends. Several times the chiefs had stopped at Shadwell on their way to Williamsburg, where they had gone to make treaties with the whites. Tom was especially thrilled to see Ontassete, the famous Cherokee warrior, and to listen to his fascinating tales of Indian lore. His English was slow and halting but Colonel Jefferson said that when he spoke in his own language he was a great orator.

One day when Ontassete stopped at Shadwell on his way back from Williamsburg, he had news. "Ontassete go to country across the water to make treaty with white men. Ontassete tell red men farewell when the moon shines in the forest." With a glint of a smile in his dark eyes he glanced at Tom, leaning forward in his chair, his big knuckled hands clasped about his knees.

"Colonel Jefferson good friend to Ontassete. Come to farewell campfire and bring the tall papoose."

Tom's heart was racing with excitement the night that he rode to the Cherokee village with his father. It was almost as light as day when they dismounted and walked under moon-drenched trees to the Indian campfire. There in a solemn circle sat the Cherokee braves, their faces ruddy in the glow, but showing no hint of the grief they felt at saying farewell to the great Ontassete. In the background, among the shadows, hovered the women and children.

Tom and his father walked past them to take their places among the warriors. A huge log, licked by an orange flame, fell apart with a soft crackle, but there was no other sound. The thin gray smoke curled upward and grew thinner in the moonlight, but there was no other movement. To Tom it seemed as though he sat there for a long, long time.

Then, just as he was beginning to wonder if anything was going to happen after all, there was a slight stir in the circle. Ontassete arose and held out his arms to the moon that hung like a great golden ball in the sky. The warriors lifted their faces toward him, waiting, waiting. The chief's words, now that he was speaking in the

Cherokee language, were no longer slow and halting, but came in a full, rushing, golden stream of sound. Tom could not understand a word, but a cold chill ran up his spine. He knew that the Indian warrior was praying that the Great Spirit would grant him a safe voyage and bring him home again to his own people.

Tom remembered that evening all his life. He remembered, too, many happy evenings that he spent at Shadwell. In the summer time the family gathered together under the trees, in the winter around the fire. After the three younger children were tucked in bed, the four older girls —Jane, Mary, Elizabeth, and Martha—helped their mother sew, and Colonel Jefferson read aloud or taught Tom to keep accounts. Then Jane, Tom's favorite sister, would sit at the harpsichord, and Tom would pick up his fiddle. *Squeak—squeak—squeak!* Perhaps the younger children stuffed their fingers in their ears. But Tom did not realize that other people did not always enjoy his playing as much as he did. He practiced three hours every day. When he tucked his violin beneath his chin, he forgot everything else. As he drew the bow across the strings, the dreams in his heart were reflected in his eyes.

Colonel Jefferson died when Tom was fourteen, and Tom went to live and study with Rev. James Maury, who held his classes in a log-cabin schoolhouse. It was rather lonely when he came back to Shadwell for vacations, now that his father was no longer there. But Jane was always ready to play for him on the harpsichord and to listen to his glowing plans for the future. And there was still the little mountain that he loved. Tom shared it with his friend, Dabney Carr, a boy about his own age in the neighborhood. Often they rowed across the river to visit it.

"I have something new for us to read, Dabney —Anson's *Voyage around the World,*" Tom said one day, as he stepped into their boat. He placed the book carefully on the seat beside him as though it were a treasure, and picked up the oars.

"Faith, I am glad," Dabney replied, his eyes lighting up with interest. "Let us take it up to our favorite oak tree and read it there." The oak tree stood at the top of the blue-green mountain, and the boys loved it so much that they had made each other a strange promise. Whoever died first, the other was to bring back his body and bury it beneath the friendly shade. Somehow, beneath the tree's tall branches it was easier to talk of their ambitions, and all things seemed possible.

"That's what I want to do, Dabney," Tom confided eagerly. "I want to travel like Captain Anson. Then I want to come back here and build a beautiful home on top of this mountain."

On and on the boys talked, telling each other of their secret dreams. For hours they sat there, looking down on the bright valley at their feet. It was a valley of pioneers, where every man was free and each had an equal right to carve out for himself the kind of life that he wished to live. It was the way that all Americans should live, thought Tom. Somehow, the freedom and the right to govern himself that the pioneer had found in the wilderness should belong to all men everywhere.

"All men are created equal."

Was that what the wind whispered through the branches of the oak tree? And did the leaves murmur softly, "The right to life, liberty, and the pursuit of happiness"?

Tom stirred restlessly. A shaft of sunlight glinted through the branches and lay across his face. He had no words as yet for the exciting ideas surging through his brain—ideas which later would find expression in the Declaration of Independence. Years of thought and study were to pass before he was to find those ringing phrases that would announce the birth of a new nation and a new way of living to the world.

But already the dream was stirring in his heart.

PATRICK HENRY

Sonia Daugherty

Sonia Daugherty has the knack of making people and scenes from the past as real to young readers as their everyday companions. In this selection, notice how Patrick Henry's actions and his words reveal two different sides of his character.

"I know not what course others may take; but as for me, give me liberty, or give me death!"

It was early morning. The sun was shining and birds were singing in the gnarled old oak tree on the bank of the river. The water ran so smoothly and quietly, you could hardly hear it. A man in a coonskin cap was sitting under the oak tree fishing. He listened to the birds and to the river, and watched the silver trout under the water, but his thoughts were far away. His tall shaggy horse nibbled at the grass nearby and waited patiently. He was hungry and the grass was mostly weeds, but he was used to that and he seemed not to mind it.

An old wagon rumbled down the road and slowed up. The man in the wagon looked around and waved his hand. But the fisherman was not looking in his direction and did not see him. The man in the wagon shook his head, and clucked to his horse to go on. He was in a hurry to get to the store, to trade the pelt of the fox he had trapped on his mountain farm, for nails he needed to fix his roof.

"I saw Patrick Henry fishing," he told the storekeeper, later.

"I thought Patrick went to Williamsburg to sit in the House of Burgesses," exclaimed a wiry little man sorting seeds he wanted for his garden.

"So did I," said the farmer. "But there he was sitting on the bank of the South Anna fishing."

"Maybe Louisa County made a mistake to elect Patrick to the House," said the little man.

"Maybe so," said the farmer. "Patrick failed as a storekeeper and he failed as a farmer. He may fail as a politician."

The storekeeper shook his head. Everybody in Hanover came to his store to buy and to trade, and stayed to talk about this one and that one. "Folks think well of Patrick," he said at last. "Patrick is a good lawyer."

"Patrick studied law only six weeks," laughed the little man.

"He is a mighty good lawyer," said the storekeeper again. "He won that 'Parson's Cause' case right over lawyer Lyons' head. People are expecting big things of Patrick."

A rider in buckskin breeches and a coonskin cap over his tousled red hair, pulled up his horse at the door at this moment, and entered the store, carrying a fishing basket over his shoulder. "Good morning," he called out in a friendly voice.

"Good morning, Patrick Henry," said the storekeeper. "We thought maybe you went to Williamsburg."

"I should be on my way there now," admitted Patrick. "But there isn't a better place to think things over than sitting with a fishing rod in your hand and a fish nibbling at the bait."

The men crowded around the newcomer to examine the silvery trout shining against the sides of the basket.

"I'll trade you a new rod for the catch," offered the storekeeper.

"I guess Sally will want half of it," smiled Patrick. "And you take the rest."

The storekeeper went to fetch a basket to transfer his share of the fish while Patrick scanned the shelf. "It isn't a fishing rod I want this morning, but a little present to leave with my wife and the children while I am away to Williamsburg," he said after a while. His eyes fell on a crock of wild honey on the counter, as he spoke. "That's just the thing," he nodded.

"Jim Hastings found a honey tree the other day. It's the best honey I've had in a long while," said the storekeeper, measuring off a generous chunk of golden honey into a container.

Patrick fitted the small crock of honey into the pocket of his hunting jacket, flung the basket of fish to his shoulder and rode away as suddenly as he had come. Humming a tune and weighing in his mind the things he had been thinking about when fishing, he hardly noticed how his horse galloped to get home to breakfast.

"Father is coming, Mother!" Little Martha ran shouting into the house where Sally was preparing her spinning wheel for the day. Sally and her two younger daughters, Ann and Betsy, came out on the porch where Billy, the young terrier was barking a wild welcome at his master. Patrick lifted his little daughters, one after the other, for a swing high above his shoulders. They screamed and laughed, and asked to do it again.

"What?" he cried, pretending to be angry. "Away with you. You are making me work too hard." But they knew he was only pretending and that he would swing them again. They laughed and danced about him and hung on to his hunting jacket.

"I nearly forgot to tell you in this commotion," said Patrick, "I bumped right into a honey tree."

"A honey tree?" shouted little Martha.

"A honey tree, a honey tree," sang the little girls reaching for the crock of honey.

"Help, help," cried Patrick capturing the crock, and handing it to Sally. "The honey tree sent it to you with compliments."

Sally laughed, and took the honey jar. "We were waiting breakfast for you," and she led the family to the belated breakfast.

They gathered around the table and listened wide eyed to Patrick's account of his adventure —"Shandy, the horse, found a four-leaf clover in the weeds. The birds were so pleased they began to sing a dance tune, and would you believe it, the trout in the brook danced to the tune." The little girls shouted with delight. They were used to his stories. But suddenly he stopped talking, got up from the table and began to pack a bundle, to take with him to Williamsburg: a homespun coat and a fresh shirt to wear to the House of Burgesses. "They will be elegant folks there," he said to Sally, pointing with pretended disapproval at the hunting shirt he was wearing.

"They may be dressed in elegant coats, but you'll measure up to the best of them," said Sally with confidence.

"Play us a tune, father," begged little Martha.

"Yes, yes, play us a tune," chimed in Ann and Betsy.

"Who ever heard of it, a tune so early in the morning?" Patrick pretended to look outraged.

"A good-by tune," said little Martha.

"I'll play you a weepy tune then," said Patrick, brushing away imaginary tears.

"A dance tune, father, a merry tune," cried the little girls clapping their hands.

"So? A dance tune? Very well," he said, still pretending to weep. His fiddle in his hands now, he began to play one tune after another. The children danced around him in circles, singing the tunes to keep time. Then his face became stern. He stopped playing, laid the fiddle in its case and tied it into his bundle.

Jack White, his young Negro servant, brought the shaggy horse to the door now.

"There," cried Patrick, "Jack knows I should be on my way."

"Must you go? Do you have to go away?" The little girls clung to his legs and to his arms.

"Be good, be extra good while I am away." He lifted each one for another high swing and a kiss.

Sally walked beside him to where the impatient horse was pawing the ground, eager to be off.

"There will be important questions to decide," said Patrick quietly.

"You will be equal to whatever comes up," Sally assured him.

He leaned over, kissed her good-by, and jumped on his horse. The young terrier ran barking after him as the horse trotted away.

The sun was high in the blue sky, the air was sweet with honeysuckle and wild orange. It was a beautiful morning. Patrick Henry sat on his horse, lost in thought. He had not been in Williamsburg since the day he went there to ask Wythe and Peyton Randolph to sign his license to practice law. He smiled now as he remembered it all—Wythe, the learned scholar, refused even to listen to his arguments.

"You say you studied law alone, and only for six weeks?" asked Wythe with a frown. "Go to college, young man, and study with proper teachers," he told him.

It was a great good fortune for him, mused Patrick, that the venerable Peyton Randolph became interested in his arguments and consented to sign his license to practice law. And two other lawyers did likewise. They believed in him. Why? wondered Patrick, gratefully. He promised them that he would continue to read and to study. But that was not the reason they believed in him; he understood it better now. They were convinced he could be a lawyer by the way he argued his own case with them. "Yes," he cried aloud, and the lean horse under him bounced forward to a quicker pace, raising a cloud of red dust on the bumpy road. "I proved it, I proved I am a good lawyer."

The sun was hot on his shoulders. Patrick took off his cap and mopped his forehead. He felt excited and happy and a little uneasy at the same time. He was going to sit in the House of Burgesses. It was an honor, but more important, he thought soberly, was the opportunity he would now have to help shape events, make changes for the better for the people in the colonies.

It was dusk by the time his horse turned into Duke of Gloucester Street. After Hanover, Williamsburg seemed very elegant to Patrick. Fashionable ladies in silks and velvets passed him by in elegant carriages. Patrick galloped down the entire length of the street from William and Mary College at one end, to the Capitol at the other. He turned about to trot back to the Raleigh Tavern. The uncurtained windows of the tavern sparkled with candlelight. Patrick reined his horse, and watched the parade of gentlemen in powdered wigs, frilled shirts, velvet coats and knee breeches, coming and going in and out of the wide doors of the tavern. It would be a pleasant place to stay the night, but as he jingled his meager purse in his hand, he decided he must find himself a cheaper place. He thought of Sally and his little daughters snug at home. He felt lonely now, wondering where he could find a bed to sleep.

Two men came out of the tavern talking and laughing, and stopped to try a new dance step on the green in front of the tavern. Patrick pulled his violin out of his bundle and started to play a dance tune. A horseman galloped by, and came back presently. A tall slender young man with sandy red hair leaned forward from the saddle—"Patrick Henry," he called out in a surprised voice. "I was wondering who it could be, playing like that."

"Thomas Jefferson," exclaimed Patrick in a delighted voice.

"What are you doing in Williamsburg?" asked Jefferson.

"I guess you haven't heard I've been elected to the House of Burgesses from Louisa County," said Patrick with a slow smile.

"Then you've come to Williamsburg to sit in the House of Burgesses. Stay the night at my house," invited Jefferson.

"Thank you," said Patrick with a wide smile. "I was just wondering where I'd sleep this night."

"I'll hurry and tell Caesar there will be company, and you come along," Jefferson called over his shoulder as he galloped away in the dusk.

Patrick finished playing his tune, and went to find a stable to put his horse away for the night.

Caesar, Jefferson's young slave, was waiting for him at the door when he arrived, the bundle under his arm. "Come right in, sir, come right in." Caesar beamed a wide smile as he led the way into Jefferson's bachelor apartment. It was a pleasant room to come into out of the night. Candles were lit on the fine mahogany table. The white cloth and the silver sparkled in the candlelight. Book shelves crowded with books lined the walls: law books, histories, poetry. Patrick put his bundle on the sofa, took off his coonskin cap, and went to wash the dust from his hands and face.

Jefferson came in from an inner room now, his sandy hair freshly combed, his white face shining with a genial smile. He was seven years younger than Patrick, and he was still a student, studying law at William and Mary College, but already he was a finished gentleman. "You are just in time," he exclaimed gaily. "Caesar is waiting to give us our supper."

The cold meat and hot corn bread tasted good to Patrick after his long ride. There were many things to talk about, pleasant things they both remembered as they sat in the soft candlelight—"Do you remember the first time we met?" asked Jefferson in his slow genial voice. "Twas a house party at Captain Daindridge's house."

"Ay, at Hanover, at Captain Nathaniel West Daindridge's house. It was Christmas holiday," reminisced Patrick with a wide smile.

"I still remember the dance tunes you played," smiled Jefferson. "But I hear you have become a great lawyer now," he added, shortly.

"I wouldn't claim that." Patrick looked very serious now, and pleased at the same time, that Jefferson had heard a flattering report of him.

"The learned lawyers, here in Williamsburg, talk with much wonder of the way you pleaded that 'Parson's Cause' case," said Jefferson.

"The lawyers are surprised I won the case, because they know I studied by myself, and only for six weeks," grinned Patrick.

"Well, yes," admitted Jefferson. "It's a wonder to us all; and what's more to wonder at is that you win every case you take."

"The 'Parson's Cause' case was my first case," said Patrick. "I was mighty anxious to win that case for my clients. I read and studied in the law books, and prepared my case carefully to make sure my arguments would be correct. But first I made sure I was in the right. When I know a thing is right, I plead from the heart."

"From the heart, I like that," exclaimed Jefferson. "Maybe you didn't need to read law books as long as we all do at college."

"As to that, I promised Peyton Randolph when he signed my license that I would read and study, and I do," said Patrick.

"When you are not fishing and hunting," laughed Jefferson.

"It is true, I'd rather fish and hunt," confessed Patrick with a wide smile. Caesar came in now to clear the table. Jefferson took his violin from the top shelf of his bookcase and began to tune it.

"That 'Parson's Cause' case," said Patrick, "gave me a chance to show the Parliament in England that they can't tell us here in the colonies, what we should pay our clergy. The Parliament in England is running us high handed, what with taxes and trade regulations."

"That's true," Jefferson nodded, his face clouded now. "But we can't deny that England has a right to tax her colonies and that's what we are, a colony to England."

"Nevertheless, they go too far, and now there is that Stamp Act. It's not only a nuisance, but a hardship," cried Patrick, with such heat that Jefferson stopped tuning his violin, and stood waiting to hear what he had on his mind. "We'll have to pay for a stamp every time we use a legal paper, and every time we buy a newspaper or sign a document. Are we going to submit to that?"

Jefferson scratched a few notes on his violin, his face grave and thoughtful. He felt embarrassed that he had not given the question much thought. Patrick seemed to know and to understand things he had hardly thought about. "No one likes the Stamp Act, but what can we do about it?" he asked after a while.

Patrick fumbled in his bundle for his violin and struck up one of the tunes they had played together at the Christmas house party in Hanover. It was a merry tune; they broke out into a song, and began to dance. Another tune came to their minds, and then another. They forgot England, and the tax and law books. Their voices

rang out through the windows into the starlit night. Suddenly there was a loud banging on the door. Jefferson stopped playing and went to the door still holding the fiddle in his hand. A man in a nightshirt and a night cap over his head was shivering in the night air on the doorstep.

"Sir," he cried indignantly. "The whole neighborhood is waiting for you to stop fiddling. It is long past midnight. No one can sleep with such noise going on."

"I am right sorry, sir," apologized Jefferson. "I had no idea it was that late."

"Look at the clock, look at the clock," roared the man, as he turned to go to his house.

Jefferson tiptoed back into his rooms and went to bed. Patrick took off his dusty boots and curled up on the sofa to sleep.

The sun was just rising when Patrick wakened. This was the *day,* he remembered instantly, his first day to sit in the House of Burgesses. He tiptoed noiselessly into the dressing room to wash and dress himself with particular care.

When Jefferson wakened a little later, he saw Patrick sitting at the window dressed in the new homespun coat he had brought with him, his red unruly hair carefully groomed. He was too engrossed, writing on the flyleaf of an old book, to notice Jefferson standing in the doorway.

"I hope you don't mind," he called out when he looked up presently and saw Jefferson watching him with an amused smile.

"Not in the least," Jefferson assured him. "The book is in tatters."

"I didn't want to waken you to ask for paper," explained Patrick, as he tore the leaf from the book, folded it carefully, and put it in his pocket.

Caesar came in with breakfast now, and Jefferson wondered what Patrick had to write down in such a hurry that he couldn't wait to ask for paper. But Patrick Henry didn't offer to tell him.

The Capitol building was crowded to the door for there were many people in Williamsburg who were anxious to hear the debate on the Stamp Act. The law students from William and Mary College were obliged to stand in the doorway to listen to the discourses in the House of Burgesses. Patrick lingered in the entrance for a parting word with Jefferson before he pushed his way through the crowd into the courtroom. Speaker of the House Robinson, was already in his place at the front. The leaders of the House, wealthy plantation owners in powdered wigs and broadcloth coats, were talking in little clusters, laughing at each other's pleasantries.

They didn't seem at all preoccupied with the important question that was to be discussed, marveled Patrick Henry. He was glad to recognize George Johnston, of Fairfax County, standing near by. Here was someone he could sound out—"What will be done about the Stamp Act, sir?" he asked Johnston.

"Nothing more can be done about it," Johnston shrugged his shoulders. "The Stamp Act's been passed. We don't like it, but what can we do about it?" he demanded.

"We can protest," cried Patrick hotly.

"Protest?" Johnston looked surprised.

"If we accept the Stamp Act without a protest it's a sign we've no spirit. That's what they'll think about us in England, and they'll be right. And they'll levy more taxes on us. We'll be taxed and taxed and taxed again and again."

"We have no redress. We can't stop them taxing us. We're subject to the crown," reasoned Johnston.

Patrick pulled out a folded paper from his pocket and handed it to Johnston. "I've written out seven resolutions, sir, if you would care to read them. You might be willing also to second them."

Johnston took the paper and read it slowly. An excited look came into his eyes. "I'm with you, sir, I'll second your resolutions," he cried.

Speaker Robinson was now pounding the table with his silver mace. Patrick slouched into his seat on the long wooden bench with the other burgesses. Two men on the bench beside him were talking in low grumbling voices. "We force the soil so as to grow bigger crops of tobacco so as to pay taxes to England," one of the men was saying.

"Ay, and if we keep on forcing the soil, there'll be no life left in it," said the other man. "It's getting poorer all the time."

"That's it," exclaimed a man in a nearby seat. "Can't raise crops on poor soil."

"I've no glass in my windows, but I must pay taxes to the crown before I spend money on window glass," broke in a third man.

"If we spent some of that tax money on fixing our roads—" mumbled another burgess from the up country.

"The meeting please come to order," cried the clerk.

A gentleman in a powdered wig and a handsome coat, stood up now and began to talk. He looked very imposing as he stood there, talking in a loud voice—"The Stamp Act seems to have caused much talk," he measured every word carefully. "The fact is, this tax is so small it is but a trifle. I see it more as a nuisance rather than a hardship to complain about."

"The cost of the stamp may be small, but it's an extra tax, and it's a tax too much," cried a voice from the back seat in the row of benches.

No one paid attention to the interruption. A stout man with many ruffles of fine lace on his shirt stood up now and began to explain the reason why the colonies should pay the tax with good grace—"The English Parliament deems it necessary to fix the Stamp Act, therefore we, the loyal subjects to the crown, are willing to obey."

"The two gentlemen hold the welfare of the crown before the welfare of the colonies, it seems to me," Patrick whispered to Johnston.

"Governor Fauquier is a Tory as you may have heard, and he has many admirers in the House," Johnston whispered back.

Patrick listened to the speeches of the leaders of the House with a frown, and shifted uneasily in his seat. Suddenly he stood up and began to talk. His voice sounded frightened at the first few words:

"The English Parliament is interfering with the affairs of the colonies," he exclaimed. "The misrule of the English Parliament has brought great hardships to the colonies," Patrick's voice grew louder and firmer.

"Who is this buckskin gentleman, giving his views?" cried an indignant voice from the front.

"An ignorant fellow from the backwoods," said one of the lawyers with a shrug.

Patrick went on talking as if he had not heard them. He was talking about something he understood and treasured. He was talking about liberty, the right of men to govern themselves. His eyes glowed, his voice rang. A spell fell on the assembly as they listened to his arguments—"We submit to taxation without representation," he cried in a challenging voice.

Peyton Randolph frowned. He was a proud Virginia gentleman, and he was also attorney general to the king of England.

"This thing must be stopped," he said to Pendleton. Wythe shook his head. A debate started up now as leaders of the House rose to interrupt Patrick at every word—"Is this new member from Louisa County claiming Virginia has a right to make laws to resist the English Parliament?" demanded an indignant voice.

In answer Patrick unfolded the piece of paper he was holding in his hand and began to read what he had scribbled there early that morning:

"The first adventurers who settled in America brought with them the right of franchise," Patrick pronounced each word in a high fiery voice.

"What's that?" interrupted an angry man at the front. Patrick straightened his shoulders and went on reading from his paper, explaining the rights of the colonies.

"Two royal charters were granted by King James the First that entitled the colonies to all privileges, liberties and immunities . . . as if they were living within the realm of England . . ."

"Patrick Henry may be from the backwoods," called out a burgess from the benches, "but it's Patrick Henry, this man from the backwoods, and not our learned lawyers who is saying what we need to know."

"Yes, that's true," said Wythe to Peyton Randolph. "I now wish I had signed his license to practice law."

Peyton Randolph frowned, his face red and angry.

"Resolved therefore," Patrick went on—"Resolved that the general assembly of this colony have the only sole and exclusive rights and power to lay taxes and impositions upon the inhabitants of this colony."

"This is sedition," cried out a Tidewater gentleman.

"Sedition, sedition," cried out several leaders of the House.

"No person that is not in the general assembly of the colonies has a right to impress taxation on the people of the colonies; such a person should be considered an enemy. Caesar had his Brutus and Charles the Second his Cromwell and George the Third—"

"Shame, shame," interrupted the Speaker of the House, pounding his mace on the table.

"Treason," cried an indignant voice. "Shame, treason, treason," resounded from all sides.

Patrick looked around him slowly, noting the frightened faces. His eyes flashed—"And George the Third may profit by their example." His voice rang and echoed in the ceiling. "If this be treason, make the most of it."

The whole House buzzed with excited voices now. The burgesses crowded around Patrick to congratulate him, clapping him on the shoulder, shaking his hand.

"Who was Caesar?" a farmer was asking.

"Caesar was a dictator in olden times in Rome. He ruled the people of Rome without their consent exactly, and Brutus killed him. And Charles the Second tried to rule England without Parliament; Cromwell and his army beheaded him," explained a more informed burgess with a knowing wink.

At the front of the House, Tidewater gentlemen were talking in troubled voices. Many of them agreed with what Patrick said, but they were not ready to say aloud what might bring on war.

Patrick listened to the buzz of many voices all talking at once. There was to be a vote. They were going to vote on his resolves. The burgesses from the back country were in high spirits, making jokes and laughing. They gave their vote fearlessly; come what might, they were ready for it in their own minds. Patrick listened to the vote as it was taken— Some of the burgesses had gone home to their mountain farms to look after the spring plowing, but there were enough left who would vote for his resolves. "We'll win by a small majority," he whispered to Johnston. He looked very sober now. Virginia must not lose this chance to stand up, and show the English Parliament that the colonies had a spirit in them to resist oppression.

The clerk cleared his throat and announced the vote. The resolves had passed. That meant that the colonies would offer a protest based on what they knew was their right.

The House adjourned. The burgesses could go home now to their plowing. They lingered a while to talk— This was an important day. They all only dimly guessed how important it was. They left the Capitol at last. There was a lot to think about on the way home. This day, May 29, 1765, was a day to remember.

Patrick went now to find his bundle which he had left in a corner of the entry.

"You spoke with courage and with wisdom." Jefferson came up now to press his hand warmly. "From today, I shall take note of the affairs in the colonies."

"You spoke for all Virginia," one of the leaders of the House stopped to say to Patrick as he was leaving the Capitol.

"I hope so, sir," Patrick bowed. He could bow with as much grace as any Tidewater gentleman when he chose. But now he was thinking of going home. He went to get his horse. He could go fishing with an easy mind now, and he might hunt in the woods, and trap a bear, as he once did— But his foremost thought would remain with meetings in Louisa County, and in the Hanover Courthouse, where he would raise his voice to challenge men's minds to think of freedom as a gift already theirs to claim.

His lean horse trotted briskly over the red clay road. Patrick clicked his tongue to spur him on. He was in a hurry to get home to share his happiness with Sally. He had spoken for Virginia. He felt proud of that, but in the back of his thoughts was the hope that all the other colonies might hear of it, and arise to speak for their rights.

from JOHNNY TREMAIN

Esther Forbes

The first episode given here reveals the patience of the British soldiers with the rebellious colonists and the deadly earnestness of the rebels. The second provides a glimpse of the plotters, their ideals, and activities.

["*That a Man Can Stand Up*"]

Along down Old Country Road, marching through the meager, half-light of the new day, came a company of Minute Men up and out early, drilling for coming battles before it was yet the hour to get to their chores. Left, right, left, right, left . . . they did not march too well. A boy no bigger than Dusty Miller had put a fife to his lips, was trying to blow it. He made awkward little tootles. The men marched on past the defaced gates of the Lytes' country seat, never turning to look at them or Doctor Warren's chaise with Cilla and Johnny under the hood.

Oh, God help them, thought Johnny. They haven't seen those British troops in Boston. I have. They haven't seen the gold lace on the generals, those muskets—all so alike, and everyone has a bayonet. They haven't seen . . .

The chaise overtook and passed the marching farmers.

That musket which Rab did not have bothered Johnny. However, the soldiers never carried them while loitering about alehouses and wharves, or the stables of the Afric Queen. They stood guard with them. They drilled with them. They practiced marksmanship (very badly, Rab said), and now and then over at the foot of the

Common they executed a deserter with them, but never, not once, as far as Johnny could make out, did they leave them about. Drilling, shooting, marching over, they stacked them at their barracks and there was always at least a sergeant guarding these stacked guns.

Johnny and Rab dropped their voices, even in the privacy of their attic, when they discussed these muskets. The Yankee gunsmiths were working from dawn to dusk preparing guns, making new ones, but as long as Rab had a weapon and was, after all, little more than a boy, he believed he had no chance for a modern gun unless he got it for himself from the British.

"How soon," Johnny whispered, "before they march out . . . and the war begins?"

"God knows," Rab murmured. "God and General Gage. Maybe not until next spring. Armies always move in the spring. But before then I must have a good gun in my hands. A man can stand up to anything with a good weapon in his hands. Without it, he's but a dumb beast."

Johnny had never seen Rab so blocked by anything. Apparently he went through every situation without friction, like a knife going through cheese. Now he was blocked and it made him restless, possibly less canny. One day he told Johnny that he had a contract with a farmer from Medway who was making a business of buying muskets from the British privates and selling them to Minute Men. Rab did not like to ask his aunt for so large a sum. She had little enough to buy food. But she had said, "Weapons before food."

One morning Johnny knew Rab was meeting the farmer at market. He knew that the soldier, returning from guard duty, was going, absent-mindedly, to leave his musket on a pile of straw. It had all been worked out. But when he heard yells and shouts from the market-place and the rattle of British drums calling up reserves, he tore over to Dock Square. He had a feeling that the turmoil was over Rab's gun. He was right.

A solid block of redcoats faced out, presenting their muskets at the market people and inhabitants. The Captain was yelling to the churning hundreds. "Get back, stand back, good people of Boston. This is our own private affair."

"What's happened?" Johnny asked an old hen-wife.

"They've caught one of their own men selling a musket to a farmer."

"Happens he comes from Medway?"

"So 'tis said."

"Happens they caught more than the farmer and the soldier?"

"They caught three in all. They are taking them over to the Province House—for General Gage."

"Gage is in Salem."

"For some colonel, then."

No mob gathered to rescue the two Yankees. All, by now, felt a certain confidence in the British way of doing things. A general, or even a colonel, had the right to punish a soldier caught selling his arms, and also anyone who tempted him.

Johnny tagged the marching soldiers, but it was not until they turned into the Province House that he saw the three prisoners. The British soldier was grinning, and Johnny guessed that he had been put up to this game merely to snare "the yokels."

The farmer was in his market smock. He had long, straight gray hair and a thin, mean mouth. You could tell by looking at him he had gone into this little business for the love of money, not for the love of freedom. Rab had been shaken out of his usual nice balance between quick action and caution by his passionate desire for a good gun. Otherwise he would not have mixed himself up with such a man. Rab himself was looking a little sullen. He was not used to defeat. What would they do to him? They might imprison him. They might flog him. Worst of all, they might turn him over to some tough top sergeant to be taught "a lesson." This informal punishment would doubtless be the worst.

The Province House was a beautiful building and as Johnny hung about the front of it he had a chance to admire it for over an hour. It stood well back from the rattle and bustle of Marlborough Street, with its glassy-eyed copper Indian on top of the cupola and its carved and colored lion and unicorn of Britain over the door. Behind the house he heard orders called and soldiers were hallooing—but worst of all they were laughing. And that was Colonel Nesbit's boy bringing around the Colonel's charger. There was a large group of people still standing in the street. The hilarity of the British soldiers did not ease their fears as to the fate of the prisoners. Johnny could hear the rattle of the men's muskets as they came to attention, and then, all together, four drummers let their sticks fall as one.

Out onto Marlborough Street, with the drummers in black bearskin caps first, and then Colonel Nesbit on horseback, came almost the entire Forty-Seventh Regiment, surrounding a cart. In the cart sat a hideous blackbird, big as a man, shaped like a man, with head hung forward like a moulting crow. It was a naked man, painted with tar and rolled in feathers. Three times already the Whigs had tarred and feathered enemies and carted them through the streets of Boston. Now it was the British turn. The redcoats marched. The Colonel's horse pranced. The cart with its shameful burden bumped over the cobbles. One glance had convinced Johnny this was not Rab. The hideous blackbird had a paunch. Rab had none.

Before the Town House, Colonel Nesbit ordered a halt, and an orderly came forward and read a proclamation. It merely explained what was being done and why, and threatened like treatment to the next buyer of stolen weapons.

Then (Colonel Nesbit was evidently a newspaper reader) the regiment went to Marshall Lane and stopped before the office of the *Spy*. The threat was made that the editor of that paper would soon be treated like the bird in the cart. Then they were heading for Edes and Gill's office. Johnny guessed the *Observer* would come next after the *Boston Gazette,* and ran to Salt Lane to warn Uncle Lorne. He jumped into the shop, slamming the door after him, looking wildly about for the printer. Rab, in his printer's apron, was standing at his bench, quietly setting type.

"Rab! How'd you do it? How'd you get away?"

Rab's eyes glittered. In spite of his great air of calm, he was angry.

"Colonel Nesbit said I was just a child. 'Go buy a popgun, boy,' he said. They flung me out the back door. Told me to go home."

Then Johnny laughed. He couldn't help it. Rab had always, as far as Johnny knew, been treated as a grown man and always looked upon himself as such.

"So all he did was hurt your feelings."

Rab grinned suddenly, but a little thinly. Johnny told of the tar-and-feathering of the farmer and also that he expected in a short time the Forty-Seventh Regiment would come marching down Salt Lane and stop before the door to read that proclamation about tar-and-feathering seditious newspaper publishers.

"And here they come—those dressed-up red monkeys. But they don't dare do anything but stop, read a proclamation, and move on."

When this was over and the troops moved on down the lane to Union, Johnny and Rab stood in the street and watched them.

"Luckily," said Rab, "I didn't give my money in advance. I'll return it to Aunt Jenifer."

But he still stood in the street watching the stiff rhythm of the marching troops, the glitter of their guns and bayonets, the dazzle of the white and scarlet disappearing at the bottom of the lane.

"They'll make good targets, all right," he said absent-mindedly. "Out in Lexington they are telling us, 'Pick off the officers first, then the sergeants.' Those white crosses on their chests are easy to sight on . . ."

His words frightened Johnny a little. Lieutenant Stranger, Sergeant Gale, Major Pitcairn . . . Johnny could not yet think of them as targets. Rab could.

. . . .

It was fall, and for the last time Sam Adams bade Johnny summon the Observers for eight o'clock that night.

"After this we will not meet again, for I believe Gage knows all about us. He might be moved to arrest Mr. Lorne. He might send soldiers to arrest us all."

"I hardly think they would hang the whole club, sir. Only you and Mr. Hancock."

Johnny had meant this for a compliment, but Sam Adams looked more startled than pleased.

"It has been noticed that every so often many of us are seen going up and down Salt Lane, entering the printing shop. We must, in the future, meet in small groups. But once more, and for the last time . . . And make as good a punch for us as you can."

. . . .

It would be a small meeting, for of the twenty-two original members many had already left town to get away from the threat of arrest by the

British. Josiah Quincy was in England. Of the three revolutionary doctors, only Church and Warren remained. Doctor Young had gone to a safer spot. James Otis was at the moment in Boston. Johnny had not notified him, although he had founded this club in the first place. Ever since he had grown so queer, the other members did not wish him about, even in his lucid periods. He talked and talked. Nobody could get a word in edgewise when James Otis talked.

This, the last meeting, started with the punch bowl on the table instead of ending with it. There was no chairman nor was there any time when the two boys were supposed to withdraw. They were talking about how Gage had at last dared send out a sortie beyond the gate of Boston and, before the Minute Men got word of their plans, they had seized cannon and gunpowder over in Charlestown, got into their boats and back to Boston. Not one shot had been fired and it was all too late when the alarm had been spread and thousands of armed farmers had arrived. By then the British were safe home again. Yet, Sam Adams protested, this rising up of an army of a thousand from the very soil of New England had badly frightened General Gage. Once the alarm spread that the British had left Boston, the system of calling up the Minute Men had worked well indeed. The trouble had been in Boston itself.

"In other words, gentlemen, it was our fault. If we could have known but an hour, two hours, in advance what the British were intending, our men would have been there before the British troops arrived instead of a half-hour after they left."

Johnny had been told off to carry letters for the British officers, to keep on good terms with their grooms and stable boys over at the Afric Queen. Somehow he had failed. He hadn't known. Nobody had known that two hundred and sixty redcoats were getting into boats, slipping off up the Mystic, seizing Yankee gunpowder, and rowing it back to Castle Island for themselves.

Paul Revere was saying, "We must organize a better system of watching their movements—but in such a way that they will not realize they are being watched."

. . . .

There was a heavy footstep across the floor of the shop below. Rab leaped to the ladder's head.

"James Otis," he reported to the men standing about Adams.

"Well," said Sam Adams, a little crossly, "no one needs stay and listen to *him*. He shot his bolt years ago. Still talking about the natural rights of man—and the glories of the British Empire! You and I, John, had as well go home and get a good night's sleep before leaving at dawn tomorrow."

Otis pulled his bulk up the ladder. If no one was glad to see him, at least no one was so discourteous as to leave. Mr. Otis was immediately shown every honor, given a comfortable armchair and a tankard of punch. Seemingly he was not in a talkative mood tonight. The broad, ruddy, good-natured face turned left and right, nodding casually to his friends, taking it for granted that he was still a great man among them, instead of a milestone they all believed they had passed years before.

He sniffed at his punch and sipped a little.

"Sammy," he said to Sam Adams, "my coming interrupted something you were saying . . . 'We will fight,' you had got that far."

"Why, yes. That's no secret."

"For what will we fight?"

"To free Boston from these infernal redcoats and . . ."

"No," said Otis. "Boy, give me more punch. That's not enough reason for going into a war. Did any occupied city ever have better treatment than we've had from the British? Has one rebellious newspaper been stopped—one treasonable speech? Where are the firing squads, the jails jammed with political prisoners? What about the gallows for you, Sam Adams, and you, John Hancock? It has never been set up. I hate those infernal British troops spread all over my town as much as you do. Can't move these days without stepping on a soldier. But we are not going off into a civil war merely to get them out of Boston. Why are we going to fight? Why, why?"

There was an embarrassed silence. Sam Adams was the acknowledged ringleader. It was for him to speak now.

"We will fight for the rights of Americans. England cannot take our money away by taxes."

"No, no. For something more important than the pocketbooks of our American citizens."

Rab said, "For the rights of Englishmen—everywhere."

"Why stop with Englishmen?" Otis was warming up. He had a wide mouth, crooked and generous. He settled back in his chair and then he began to talk. It was such talk as Johnny had never heard before. The words surged up through the big body, flowed out of the broad mouth. He never raised his voice, and he went on and on. Sometimes Johnny felt so intoxicated by the mere sound of the words that he hardly followed the sense. That soft, low voice flowed over him: submerged him.

". . . For men and women and children all over the world," he said. "You were right, you tall, dark boy, for even as we shoot down the British soldiers we are fighting for rights such as they will be enjoying a hundred years from now.

". . . There shall be no more tyranny. A handful of men cannot seize power over thousands. A man shall choose who it is shall rule over him.

". . . The peasants of France, the serfs of Russia. Hardly more than animals now. But because we fight, they shall see freedom like a new sun rising in the west. Those natural rights God has given to every man, no matter how humble . . ." He smiled suddenly and said . . . "or crazy," and took a good pull at his tankard.

". . . The battle we win over the worst in England shall benefit the best in England. How well are they over there represented when it comes to taxes? Not very well. It will be better for them when we have won this war.

"Will French peasants go on forever pulling off their caps and saying 'Oui, Monsieur,' when the gold coaches run down their children? They will not. Italy. And all those German states. Are they nothing but soldiers? Will no one show them the rights of good citizens? So we hold up our torch—and do not forget it was lighted upon the fires of England—and we will set it as a new sun to lighten a world . . ."

Sam Adams, anxious to get that good night's sleep before starting next day for Philadelphia, was smiling slightly, nodding his gray head, seeming to agree. He was bored. It does not matter, he was thinking, what James Otis says these days—sane or crazy.

Joseph Warren's fair, responsive face was aflame. The torch Otis had been talking about seemed reflected in his eyes.

"We are lucky men," he murmured, "for we have a cause worth dying for. This honor is not given to every generation."

"Boy," said Otis to Johnny, "fill my tankard."

It was not until he had drained it and wiped his mouth on the back of his hand that he spoke again. All sat silently waiting for him. He had, and not for the first time, cast a spell upon them.

"They say," he began again, "my wits left me after I got hit on the head by that customs official. That's what you think, eh, Mr. Sam Adams?"

"Oh, no, no, indeed, Mr. Otis."

"Some of us will give our wits," he said, "some of us all our property. Heh, John Hancock, did you hear that? *Property*—that hurts, eh? To give one's silver wine-coolers, one's coach and four, and the gold buttons off one's sprigged satin waistcoats?"

Hancock looked him straight in the face and Johnny had never before liked him so well.

"I am ready," he said. "I can get along without all that."

"You, Paul Revere, you'll give up that silvercraft you love. God made you to make silver, not war."

Revere smiled. "There's a time for the casting of silver and a time for the casting of cannon. If that's not in the Bible, it should be."

"Doctor Warren, you've a young family. You know quite well, if you get killed they may literally starve."

Warren said, "I've thought of all that long ago."

"And you, John Adams. You've built up a very nice little law practice, stealing away my clients, I notice. Ah, well, so it goes. Each shall give according to his own abilities, and some—" he turned directly to Rab—"some will give their lives. All the years of their maturity. All the children they never live to have. The serenity of old age. To die so young is more than merely dying; it is to lose so large a part of life."

Rab was looking straight at Otis. His arms were folded across his chest. His head flung back a little. His lips parted as though he would speak, but he did not.

"Even you, my old friend—my old enemy? How shall I call you, Sam Adams? Even you will give the best you have—a genius for politics. Oh, go to Philadelphia! Pull all the wool, pull all the strings and all the wires. Yes, go, go! And God go with you. We need you, Sam. We must fight this war. You'll play your part—but what it is really about . . . you'll never know."

James Otis was on his feet, his head close against the rafters that cut down into the attic, making it the shape of a tent. Otis put out his arms.

"It is all so much simpler than you think," he said. He lifted his hands and pushed against the rafters.

"We give all we have, lives, property, safety, skills . . . we fight, we die, for a simple thing. Only that a man can stand up."

With a curt nod, he was gone.

Johnny was standing close to Rab. It had frightened him when Mr. Otis had said, "Some will give their lives," and looked straight at Rab. Die so that "a man can stand up."

Once more Sam Adams had the center of attention. He was again buttoning up his coat, preparing to leave, but first he turned to Revere.

"Now *he* is gone, we can talk a moment about that spy system you think you can organize in Boston."

Paul Revere, like his friend, Joseph Warren, was still slightly under the spell of James Otis.

"I had not thought about it that way before," he said, not answering Sam Adams's words. "You know my father had to fly France because of the tyranny over there. He was only a child. But now, in a way, I'm fighting for that child . . . that no frightened lost child ever is sent out a refugee from his own country because of race or religion." Then he pulled himself together and answered Sam Adams's remarks about the spy system.

That night, when the boys were both in bed, Johnny heard Rab, usually a heavy sleeper, turning and turning.

"Johnny," he said at last, "are you awake?"

"Yes."

"What was it he said?"

"That a man can stand up."

Rab sighed and stopped turning. In a few moments he was asleep. As often had happened before, it was the younger boy who lay wide-eyed in the darkness.

"That a man can stand up."

He'd never forget Otis with his hands pushed up against the cramping rafters over his head.

"That a man can stand up"—as simple as that.

And the strange new sun rising in the west. A sun that was to illumine a world to come.

LOST IN THE APPLE CAVE

Carolyn Sherwin Bailey

There are many stories, books, and poems about Johnny Appleseed, but this story gives a long-range picture of the man from the standpoint of one of his beneficiaries. Look up the poem, "Johnny Appleseed," in The Book of Americans *by Rosemary and Stephen Vincent Benét. Carolyn Bailey has written many books for children including her unusual fairy tale* Miss Hickory, *which won the Newbery Award in 1947.*

Swinging her worn shoes from the steps of the covered wagon whose great canvas top had been her only roof for months, Rose looked back along the wilderness road. At its beginning lay the mountains. Where the road ended was a wide river. Rose and her father and mother were on their way from New England to that great unknown place beyond the Ohio River called the West. Everything they owned was packed in the great clumsy wagon, camped now on the banks of the Ohio until a flatboat should come to ferry it across. Rose had loved everything about the trip: the slow movement along strange roads, the tinkle of bells on some peddler's mule, the glimpse of a passing wain full of barrels of maple syrup or of raw hides and raw wool, the evening's camp beside some brook with a supper of cornmeal mush and salt pork cooked over an open fire.

The big wagon was like home to the twelve-year-old girl. In a corner crowded with pewter plates, patchwork quilts, sacks of cornmeal, and gourds of milk, Rose had a family of dolls made of great pine cones she had gathered on the road. She had dressed them in bits of her own calico frock as it had become torn. The little heads of these dolls, made of small wild apples, wore sunbonnets like Rose's own, or hats made of plaited rushes gathered by the brooks. The pine-cone dolls had a set of dishes made of acorns.

Kicking her heels against the wagon step, feeling the warm harvest sun on her bare legs, Rose wished that she knew what lay within those deep woods at the right of their camp. She was sometimes lonely, for they had not happened to meet any other girl of her age all summer. She watched her mother bending over the knitting she was trying to finish before the sun dipped down into the river in flaming crimson. Her father was trying to catch some fish for supper. Rose stood up at last, swinging a little hand-made basket over her arm.

"I am going for a walk, Mother," she said. "Perhaps I can find some berries in the wood to eat with our porridge tonight."

"Do not go too far, Rose," her mother warned. "Your father saw a big brown bear quite close this morning."

"I will be back by suppertime," Rose said.

In five minutes from the time she left the wagon camp, Rose was out of all sight and sound of it. The faint stir of a passing snake among the fallen leaves in the forest, the rustle of a chipmunk's little feet, the flapping of a crow's wings or an owl's, were the only sounds. Rose hurried, remembering the bear. She never thought that she could lose the trail, but soon it seemed as if she were going round and round, each moment straying deeper into the wilderness. Her arms and legs were scratched by the bushes, each step was less sure. Rose ran. She clung to the little rush basket for comfort. It broke the force of her fall as she stepped down, tumbled, and found herself imprisoned in a cave. The entrance had been carefully screened by leafy boughs and bushes. When she got up and looked about, Rose could not believe her eyes.

The cave smelled deliciously of apples. Eating apples were a new fruit in those days, and rather rare. But here, in a roomy cave that had a little bubbling spring at the back to keep the fruit moist, was shelf upon shelf of wonderful apples such as Rose had never seen, stored away for the winter. There were August apples, the delight of harvesters. There were great golden pippins which made Rose think of the big bell on the church at home that had rung for their courage when the covered wagons started out; hard little russet apples that would keep all winter and be sweeter in March than they were now; and great red spicy apples, grown by grafting a shoot from a wild-apple bough into a bough of a sweet orchard-apple tree. Rose selected one of these apples and sat down in content on the mossy floor to munch it. This might be a bear's cave, she thought, but it was the pleasantest place she had seen in a long time.

Bright skin, delicious juice, crunchy pulp, Rose ate her apple down to its nest of big black seeds. She was just cupping her hands to drink from the spring, when a shadow darkened the door of the cave. Could it be the bear of whom her mother had warned her? Rose was dumb with terror as she saw a dark form closing the cave entrance. But a voice reassured her.

"Don't be afraid, little girl. It's only Appleseed Johnny. Welcome to my orchard!"

The man, strange indeed with his long hair, ragged clothes, and feet bare save for Indian moccasins, held out his hand to Rose.

"Come and see my trees, little girl," he said. "Many of the people of the covered wagons make this orchard of mine their halfway house before they cross the Ohio River. Come and see my house, too, and then I will show you the way to the camp again."

As the man led Rose out of the cave and into a clearing where grew more apple, cherry, peach, and plum trees than she had ever seen before, he talked about himself. He was still a young man, but he said that he had traveled on foot to Pittsburgh all the long way—across mountains, fording streams, and breaking trails through the wilderness—from Springfield in Massachusetts. His name was John Chapman. He was called Appleseed Johnny because he was the only orchardman of the pioneers. He loved apples, and he knew how much the West needed fruit. The rich soil was fairly aching to nourish the seeds that he had begged from farmers in Pennsylvania and planted there on the banks of the Ohio River.

Appleseed Johnny showed Rose the shed where he sorted and washed apple seeds, started shoots for new trees, and kept his spade and pruning shears. Then they went into the big comfortable cabin he had built for himself of forest wood, lusty logs of oak, chestnut, and pine. An apple bough, gnarled and crooked into the shape of a forest gnome, was perched on the ridge of Appleseed Johnny's cabin for its roof-tree. The nails that held the cedar planks of the door were handmade. So was the star-shaped iron latch that Appleseed Johnny lifted as he opened the heavy door and led Rose inside.

In the light of the big stone fireplace the girl thought that Appleseed Johnny looked like an Indian, as brown, sharp-eyed, and slender. He gave a low call, and down from a shelf near the roof fluttered a fluffy sleepy little owl and nestled on his shoulder.

"I came too far away from our wagon," Rose explained. "Folks say there are bears in these woods."

Appleseed Johnny laughed. He went to the door and made an odd growling sound. Fascinated, Rose saw a shaggy brown animal lumber out of the gathering darkness, sniff at Appleseed Johnny, and then pass by.

"All the wild creatures love this appleman," Rose thought.

Appleseed Johnny came in and filled a big pewter mug with milk for Rose. He put a comb of golden honey and three red apples in her basket. Last, he gave her a little apple tree, no taller than her pine-cone doll, and a small deerskin bag of seeds.

"Now I will guide you to the edge of the woods," he said. "And when you come to your new home in the wilderness, set out this young apple tree in the sunshine, and water it and build a little fence of brush about it to keep off the deer.

"In this bag are precious seeds of other apples, of berries, pears, cherries, grapes, plums, and peaches. Plant them and tend them, for there is no fruit in the wilderness. Your mother will want berries and fruits for her autumn pies, and jellies and preserves for the winter. Your new home in the West will need grapevines growing over it, and a pink cloud of orchard blossoms in the spring."

As Appleseed Johnny talked, he led Rose safely through the darkening forest until she could see her own campfire and smell the fish her mother was cooking.

"Good-by, and thank you," she said.

"Good-by, Little Pioneer," he said. "Remember Appleseed Johnny and plant your trees."

"I will!" she called as she ran over to hide her little tree and the seeds. She ate supper in a dream and in her sleep smelled apples under the canvas top. A flatboat was waiting for them in the morning, and they drifted, wagon and all, over the Ohio River and into the wild lands beyond.

Season after season Appleseed Johnny tended his trees, harvested his fruit, and sorted his seeds. He kept cows and had a row of beehives. Season after season the covered wagons carrying hundreds of pioneers West stopped by his cabin. The travelers were fed apples, honey, and milk and given little bags of Appleseed Johnny's precious seeds.

Rose's covered wagon rolled on into the untilled, wild country of Ohio. Her father told her about Appleseed Johnny. "He was only a boy when he left his home in Massachusetts and tramped out to Pennsylvania," he said. "He took apple seeds in payment for work for the farmers, and he built his house and planted his orchards with his own hands. Hundreds of covered wagons stop at his door, rest, and go on, carrying his bags of seeds."

On, on went the wagon until Rose's father found a farm site. The seasons passed quickly, with so much work to be done. The land was cleared and a cabin built in two years. That was the year that Rose picked berries from the bushes that grew from Appleseed Johnny's seeds. In four years roads were built, the cabin made larger, and Rose's dresses were longer. That was the year that she picked peaches, cherries, and plums from the trees planted from Appleseed Johnny's seeds. In six years Rose was a young lady. It was another October, and the apples from the little tree that Appleseed Johnny had given her were harvested and waiting in the kitchen to be made into apple butter for the winter. Rose would trust no one but herself to do this.

In the sunny kitchen she had set out empty pans, tubs, sharp knives, and a great basket of juicy red apples. On linen thread, hanging from the beams of the kitchen were strips of apples drying. The strong crane in the open fireplace held a brass kettle filled with pared apples, sweet and sour in proportion, the sweet ones at the bottom, with quinces and molasses added for flavor. She had put straw in the bottom of the kettle to keep the cooking apples from burning. Rose would spend days preserving the apples for the winter. Down cellar, tubs of apple sauce would freeze and keep through the winter as sweet as when it was made. The dried apples would be made into pies.

Rose stirred the apple butter, her back to the open door. Suddenly she heard a low call, like that of a little screech owl. She turned and saw a surprising figure.

The man was as tall and straight as an Indian, keen-eyed, and on his back he carried a great sack. He was as ragged as a beggar, his hair had grown to his shoulders and he wore Indian moccasins. He gave his bird call again, and smiled at Rose. "You have grown, my child," he said.

"Appleseed Johnny!" she cried.

"Yes, I am Appleseed Johnny, still planting orchards in the wilderness. I gave away my house, filled this sack with seeds, crossed the Ohio River in a dugout canoe, and have been wandering for many years, scattering seeds, and teaching the pioneers how to plant and tend orchards."

"Come in," Rose begged. "Spend the night with us, and let us feed you as you fed me when I was a covered-wagon girl. These are your apples that I am cooking. Your little tree lived, and every one of your seeds grew and gave us fruit."

An old letter tells us the rest of the story: how Appleseed Johnny, pioneer nurseryman of the early nineteenth century, spent the night in the Rice cabin, made welcome by Roselle Rice and her family who had passed his door many years before. Many covered-wagon children knew Appleseed Johnny, but Rose was the only one who wrote about him. In the morning he started on again. He carried a Bible in the sack with his seeds, and left one leaf of it with Rose. Then he tramped off into the woods farther West and she never saw him again.

But Appleseed Johnny walked for forty years, leaving his little buckskin bags of seeds and his Bible pages at lonely cabins, planting the orchards that now cover acres of the West, sleeping outdoors, making friends with bears, wolves, and foxes, looked upon by the Indians as the Great Spirit. Pioneers went on with his work. Today skilled orchardmen cultivate the vast tracts of fruitland of our West. Following the trail he started, great freight trains return now to the East carrying barrels of Jonathan, Winesap, Spitzenburgh, Northern Spy, Delicious, King, Greening, and Golden Pippin apples for hungry boys and girls. The wild hardy stock poured into the spiced sap of the cultivated growth still gives us new, larger, tastier apples. The sturdy covered-wagon people, going West, gave us our beautiful Western cities, our fertile farms, our fine schools. And every pink apple blossom of the spring is scented with Appleseed Johnny's kindness to little Rose, and every bite of a rosy October apple tastes as sweet as those he laid away in his cave.

"His name is Tom!" shouted Harriet, but the *Red Lion* was too far along the canal for the pink child to hear. This was just as well, for never in the world could she have owned a kitten with the plain name of Tom.

It was Sunday morning when next the *Red Lion of the West* passed the *Blossoming Bough.* The sound of church bells came faintly across the fields. It was very quiet on the canal. The boats slipped silently along, for on Sundays they were not allowed to blow their horns. Harriet stood as close to the edge of the deck as she dared. Alice stood close to the edge, too. Each little girl was wearing a Sunday dress. Each dress was white, with white pantalettes. Alice's hair was blowing in the breeze, but on Harriet's head there was a bonnet, a dainty straw bonnet with pink roses and pink ribbons tied under the chin.

"Look at my Sunday dress!" screamed Alice.

"Look at mine!"

"Why, Harriet, you have a pink bonnet!"

"Yes, isn't it beautiful?"

There was quite a long silence while Alice took in all the glory of the pink bonnet.

"It's the most beautiful bonnet I ever saw."

Harriet turned around to show the back of the bonnet.

"Did your mother give it to you?"

"No, I got it from a little girl in exchange for a kitten."

"For *what?"* The boats had passed each other.

"For a kitten!"

But the *Red Lion of the West* was now too far away from the *Blossoming Bough.* There was nothing to do but wait until they passed again, then Harriet and Alice could finish their conversation. It was often like that!

THE EARNED NAME

Shannon Garst

This exciting and tragic story of Crazy Horse, who led the Sioux in their last stand against the white invaders of their territory, is one of the few books which tell the story from the Indians' point of view. The early chapters record the rigorous training of an Indian boy, and show Crazy Horse to have been a highly intelligent and resourceful youngster.

As the hunters rode into the Oglala village, laughing and jabbering, the Indian women came out to meet them and ran beside their horses. Has-ka's sister, Laughing One, and his stepmother, Gathers-Her-Berries, ran beside his horse chattering like magpies over his kill.

Reaching camp the women seized the meat and threw the hunks onto beds of leaves while they deftly sliced it into strips which they threw over pole racks to dry, out of reach of the dogs.

That night the campfires sputtered and blazed as the buffalo fat dripped onto them. The air was savory with fine smells of roasting hump and ribs. The Oglalas ate until they were stuffed. Never had food tasted so good to Has-ka. The fact that he had helped in providing meat for the camp made him feel pleasantly important and he was still elated over the fact that Hump had singled him out.

He purposely walked through the camp to see if he would be noticed. He was. Men pointed to him and said, "There goes Has-ka. His arrow brought down a buffalo. He was the youngest one on the hunt."

It was very agreeable to be pointed out and noticed this way. He almost forgot that Hump had to come to his rescue just in time.

When the Oglalas had eaten so much that they could not cram down another mouthful, they danced to the throbbing drums until the food was jounced down enough so that they could eat some more. Has-ka ate and danced with them. He was aware of No Water's glowering, envious glances upon him but this only increased his feeling of triumph. The older boy had gone along on the hunt, but only as one of the boys who led a pack horse on which to bring back the meat. He had had no part in the kill and no one after the hunt had pointed him out as he walked through the village.

Has-ka gorged himself and danced until he grew so sleepy that he crawled off to his sleeping robes. However, he was up at dawn the next morning, eager for more excitement.

Mock buffalo hunts were always a favorite pastime of Sioux youngsters. After one of the real hunts there were often buffalo calves left behind on the plains, which had been unable to keep up with the herd after it had been stampeded. It was the delight of the boys to chase these calves, shooting at them with the blunt arrows they used in their games.

Has-ka, filled with elation over his first buffalo hunt, joined in the noisy horseback chase of one of these young calves. Strongheart was the first to catch up with it. With a yell of triumph the boy shouted, "I, Has-ka the buffalo hunter, will ride this calf!"

Leaning over, he grabbed a handful of the woolly hair of the hump and threw himself onto the calf's back. More frightened than ever by this new terror, the young buffalo increased his speed so that the Indian boys' ponies could scarcely keep up. But what they lacked in speed, they made up for in yelling as they gave chase.

The calf suddenly stopped running and tried by bucking to rid itself of the strange and frightening thing clinging to its back. Has-ka found this change of pace not at all to his liking. His head was rammed down between his shoulders. With each jump that jounced him first to one side, then to the other, he thought he could not stick on, but he righted himself and managed. His companions were not going to be given a chance to laugh at him. He must not lose the importance he had gained. Most of all he dreaded giving No Water another opportunity to ridicule him. Once he was tipped clear over to the side of the calf. It was only the realization of how his comrades would whoop with glee if he were thrown that gave him the determination to right himself and hang grimly on.

Gradually the bucking eased off, then ceased, when the calf became tired.

"I, Has-ka, did ride the buffalo calf," he cried, raising his hand in triumph.

"Has-ka did ride the buffalo calf," his companions chanted.

"I, Has-ka, will ride the buffalo calf into the village," he shouted.

"Hoka hey! Hoka hey!" his friends cried, crowding their ponies close to the buffalo calf and driving it toward the Oglala camp. The riderless Strongheart trotted at the rear of the yelling horde.

Drawn by the shouts of the boys the people came from their tepees to see the procession led by young Has-ka riding the buffalo calf.

"Has-ka did ride the buffalo calf!" his friends shouted.

The warrior Hump stood in front of his lodge laughing at the sight. "The buffalo calf seems too tame a mount for you, my friend," he said.

"He was wild enough out there on the hills," young Hump said. "You should have seen Has-ka ride. I thought the calf's bucking would snap his head off as we snap off the head of a grouse."

"It was easy," Has-ka said modestly. A new hope, however, was born within him that his people would now give him a man-like earned name such as Rides the Buffalo Calf instead of the one he so detested.

But the next day he was still called Has-ka.

The incident, though, did reawaken Hump's interest in him and the warrior made him his adopted son, according to the Sioux custom, and taught him the lore of his people, the best way to make weapons and the secrets of warfare, finding in the eager boy an apt pupil.

His own son, young Hump, was restless and had not Has-ka's ambition to become a leader and his father often lost patience with him. The warrior and his pupil, however, were so often together that their tribesmen spoke of them as the "grizzly and his cub."

Was ever another boy so fortunate, Has-ka wondered, as to have so fine a teacher? In every way he strove to make himself like his hero. Yet he never found courage to speak to Hump of his high ambitions for fear of being laughed at. The man, however, at times possessed an uncanny ability to sense what was in the boy's mind.

One day they were returning from a hunt, jogging along in silence. Has-ka had been completely lost in his thoughts, imagining himself leading a band of Oglala warriors against the Crow tribe.

Suddenly Hump said, "To be a leader of your people you must listen often and in silence to the Great Holy Mystery. The day is not too far away when you will go alone to the hills for the Vision Quest."

Has-ka looked startled. He was surprised that Hump knew what was in his mind, and it pleased him that his teacher considered him worthy of the test which would prove whether or not the *Wakan Tanka* would guide him to leadership.

"You think—I may someday be a leader?" Has-ka's tone was hopeful.

Hump gave him a long, strange look, and for a moment did not speak. Finally he said, "The desire for prominence among our people is always in your heart. Why?"

Has-ka met his friend's glance with a questioning look.

"Why?" Hump asked again. "Why is the wish for greatness always with you?"

"Because—" Has-ka floundered for words. "It is a good thing to be great. To be pointed out. To be a leader—"

It was not easy to put into words the reasons for his deepest desire. A shadow of disappointment crossed the warrior's face and Has-ka saw that he was not pleased.

"Your reasons are selfish ones," Hump's tone was harsh. "Leadership is a gift from the *Wakan Tanka.* To be used for the good of the people —not because one would be pointed out."

Has-ka felt humbled. "How does one know if he is singled out for leadership—to serve his people?" he persisted.

"At the time of the Vision Quest," Hump repeated. "It is time you were thinking about getting ready."

As the preliminary step of training for the sterner ordeal ahead, Hump one day ordered him to do without food for an entire day. The warrior blackened Has-ka's face with charred wood as the sign that he was fasting. His comrades pranced about him, tantalizing him by holding juicy chunks of savory buffalo meat close to his mouth, or by offering him *wasna,* dried ground buffalo meat mixed with ground-up plums—a favorite food of the Indians.

He wore a solemn expression on his blackened face as he went about the camp. The holy, set-apart feeling he had today was very pleasant—not like the old set-apart feeling he used to have because of his light complexion and his lack of sureness in himself. In those days the feeling had been so painful and unbearable sometimes that he had wanted to crawl off like a wounded animal.

He kept to himself the entire day, not being in a mood to join the other boys in their rough fun. He wandered along Lodge Pole Creek, then lay on the warm grass with his hands under his head, staring at the lazy clouds floating above him until he drifted off into deep sleep. In his dreams he saw himself single-handed driving off the pony herds of the enemy—slaying enemy chiefs—saving his hero, Hump, from the scalping knife. He saw himself being called upon to stand up beside the campfire to tell of his remarkable coups. Saw his record being painted upon a white buffalo robe. Saw the feathered crown of a chieftain being placed upon his head.

When he awoke he struggled to recapture those pleasant dreams, but now he was wide awake. He got to his feet and strolled along the stream, then wandered to the top of a hill. By now the sun was dipping beyond the western horizon in a blaze of brilliant colors. Light-headed from hunger, Has-ka stretched his hands toward the sinking sun. "A vision, *Wakan Tanka*," he murmured. "Grant me a vision of greatness. Show me the path I must take."

In his dizzy, elated state he fully expected the golden clouds to part, revealing the *Wakan Tanka*.—Or the Holy Mystery would send one of His animal spirits with a message telling Has-ka that he was truly destined for greatness and that he would be powerful among the Sioux. All of the men who were leaders among Has-ka's people had received such visions or messages at some time or other—usually following a fast.

He stood until his outstretched arms ached—and his soul ached, too, with the waiting. But no vision—no message came. The sun sank. A veil of darkness fell over the world, and Has-ka's spirits sank with the sun. Perhaps he was not destined for greatness after all! His arms fell to his sides and he walked slowly back to the village.

Two sleeps following Has-ka's fast, No Water raced through the village shouting, *"Che-hoo-hoo! Che-hoo-hoo!* All who are brave and strong, line up for *che-hoo-hoo."*

This was a wrestling game in which the Sioux boys chose sides, each boy picking his own opponent. When a wrestler's shoulders were forced to the ground, he was "dead."

Young Hump was one of the leaders; No Water, as usual, was the other. Hump chose Has-ka to be on his side. Has-ka looked over the "enemy" line to pick out someone about his own size and weight to challenge.

He was startled when he heard No Water shout his own name.

"I, No Water," the enemy leader yelled, "do challenge the One Who Cries When the Wasps Sting Him."

The older boy could not have chosen a surer way of arousing Has-ka to anger than with this almost-forgotten taunt. Sudden fury boiled through his veins, yet he was no fool. No Water was larger and heavier—had every chance of winning. But, of course, he had to accept the challenge or be disgraced in the eyes of his comrades.

Soon enemy was upon enemy and the ground was covered with writhing, struggling pairs. Has-ka braced himself as No Water seized him. He fought with every ounce of strength that was in him and when his breath rasped in his throat and he was so exhausted that every muscle felt limp, he gritted his teeth and kept on struggling and straining until unknown reserves of strength came to his help. But grit and determination were not sufficient against superior strength and weight.

At last when many shoulders were pinned to the ground, the victors pretended to take the scalps of those whom they had defeated. It was not until most of the pairs had ended their struggles that No Water managed to throw Has-ka and leap upon him to pin his shoulders to the ground. According to the rules of the game that was supposed to be the end of it, except for the pretended scalping, but No Water knelt on Has-ka's shoulders while his thumbs pressed the beaten boy's windpipe.

Has-ka's breath came out with a gurgling groan—almost a cry. His good friend, He Dog, pulled No Water off.

The *che-hoo-hoo* winners danced the victory dance about the defeated enemy who hunched sullenly in the center of the ring. No Water pointed triumphantly to Has-ka and shouted, "*Hopo!* I, No Water, did beat my enemy He-Who-Cries-When-the-Wasps-Sting. And I did make him cry out again. Has-ka has not the brave heart! Has-ka is a girl!"

The beaten boy's spirits sank to his moccasins. He had thought he was making headway in gaining the respect of his comrades. Now, even though he had done his best, he had disgraced himself again. He had given his rival another chance to gloat over him. Why did the older boy hate him so? Why did he always try to belittle him before his companions?

Disgraced and unhappy Has-ka shunned his comrades until an exciting event made him forget his personal troubles.

An unknown disease had swept through the pony herd the previous winter and there was talk of the need of new horses. Has-ka listened eagerly. He hoped that a pony-stealing expedition was afoot.

The easiest method of acquiring new horses and the one the Sioux liked best because of the excitement it afforded, was to creep at night into some camp of their enemy, the Crows, and drive their tamed horses away. But now the Crows were far beyond the Big Horns, so the Oglalas must round up wild horses to replenish their herds. This method was harder work, for the horses so caught must be broken and the Sioux would be denied the sly pleasure of besting the enemy Crows.

An excited longing swept through Has-ka as he listened to the plans for the wild horse hunt. He made up his mind to go along.

Nearly all of the men, and some of the boys who were old enough, joined the wild horse hunt. Scouts rode out ahead toward the sand hills to see if they could locate a herd of wild horses and after riding for nearly half a sun they gave the blanket signal from a hilltop that they had discovered a herd in the valley below. The Indians scattered, circling the valley, but staying out of sight of the horses. Has-ka was riding Strongheart. He quivered with excitement as his group waited beneath the brow of the hill for the signal to advance.

When the surround was complete, several of the hunters on the south side rode over the hill yelling. The wild horses stampeded in the opposite direction, where Has-ka and his companions were waiting. Some of the hunters strung out across their path. The horses galloped in another direction only to have more hunters block their way. Finding every direction of escape closed to them, the frightened, bewildered animals started circling. When they were milling in a compact bunch, the hunters closed in on them and started thrusting their long sticks with hair rope loops over the heads of the horses they wanted to capture.

Has-ka caught sight of a pony the color of a red autumn leaf. It carried its small, well-shaped head high, nostrils distended. Its eyes were wide open but there was more a look of fight in them than of fear. The instant he saw the red stallion, Has-ka knew that it was a spirited and intelligent animal and he wanted it with all of his heart. So also did Lone Bear and he thrust out his loop trying to get it over the animal's head, but missed. Has-ka thrust out his loop, but he missed, too, for even though the red horse was frightened he was wise and wary.

Finally Lone Bear gave up with a grunt of disgust and concentrated his efforts on a less crafty animal, but no other would satisfy Has-ka. Already some of his comrades were riding toward home trailing their mustangs, which they called crazy horses, tied to the tails of their tame ponies.

At last his loop settled over the neck of the red horse and with a yell of triumph he jerked on the willow pole, drawing the loop tight. The animal reared and snorted, but could not rid itself of the thing around its neck that was fast choking its breath from it.

Has-ka edged Strongheart close to the wild pony and then he did a daring thing. He threw himself onto the red pony's back, with nothing in the world with which to control it but the hair loop around its neck.

With a shrill whinny of rebellion the red horse broke loose from the herd, galloped into the open, bucking, rearing, turning, twisting, omitting none of the tricks a wild horse knows in an effort to dislodge its rider. He sunfished and galloped, but Has-ka clung to his mane, tightening the noose around its neck when necessary, but giving the magnificent animal its head as much as possible. A wild sense of elation swept through the boy. He yelled and his heels pounded the sides of the wild horse. He would ride this horse and finally conquer him.

The hunters stopped trying to capture mustangs to watch the performance that went on all over the hillside between Has-ka and the wild horse, until it was flecked with foam and finally stood with drooping head and heaving sides, too spent to struggle longer. It recognized a master.

Has-ka was spent, too, yet a thrill of triumph swept through him. He had conquered this splendid beast. Loosening his noose he reached forward and grasping an ear he turned the pony's head, his heels pounding its sides. Slowly the red pony obeyed his master's will and stumbled in the direction Has-ka wanted him to go.

When Has-ka, astride the horse he had conquered, rode up to his companions, they shouted, "He has ridden a crazy horse! *Tashunka-Witko!* Crazy Horse! Crazy Horse! His name shall be *Tashunka-Witko!* Crazy Horse!"

The boy's heart beat faster. At last he had an earned name—and a splendid one. The name of his father, but one which he himself had earned. To the Indians the name meant an untamed, splendid horse of great spirit and courage. He could not have earned a finer name, ever if he had chosen it.

Crazy Horse made his rope into a halter and tied the horse to Strongheart's tail. Neither animal liked being tied to the other, but Strongheart was trained to obey and the wild horse was tired, so they got along well enough.

When the horse hunters reached their village, the first thing they did was to rope and throw the mustangs they had captured. The right fore foot was tied to the left hind foot and the horse allowed to struggle to his feet. Now the ponies could not kick and the process of taming them started at once.

Every day Crazy Horse went to the corral and roped this new horse he named Warrior. He stroked him and talked to him, breaking and training him as he had Strongheart, until finally the spirited pony yielded to the stronger will. Crazy Horse grinned with pleasure, for there were not two finer ponies in the Oglala camp than Strongheart and Warrior—and well he knew there wasn't a better horseman.

Never was there a day when the boys of Crazy Horse's band were not practicing riding in some form or other. There were races in the early evening, but Crazy Horse's favorite sport and the one he always wanted was the riding contest in which the boys chose sides. When Crazy Horse would gallop his stallion at its utmost speed, past his admiring companions, making it zigzag in its course, with just the tip of his heel showing over its neck, they would cry, "*Tashunka-Witko*—Crazy Horse rides without being seen!" "Crazy Horse was invisible to the enemy!" "Crazy Horse is the finest rider in the Oglala camp!"

"PECULIARSOME" ABE

Carl Sandburg

Carl Sandburg is both a poet and an authority on Lincoln lore. From the first volume of his Lincoln biography he made a cutting for children and young people called Abe Lincoln Grows Up. *It is a remarkable book as this selection shows. Here we meet the young, backwoods Abe, starved for books, starved for an education, and making the little reading he could lay his hands on food for long, long thoughts. Turn to* Time for Fairy Tales *and find some of the fables that caught Abe's young fancy. Turn to* Time for Poetry, *and read in the last section, "Wisdom and Beauty," some of the proverbs he brooded over. In that book also read the moving poem by the Benéts, "Nancy Hanks" and on the same page the answers two children wrote to Nancy's questions about her son.*

The farm boys in their evenings at Jones's store in Gentryville talked about how Abe Lincoln was always reading, digging into books, stretching out flat on his stomach in front of the fireplace, studying till midnight and past midnight, picking a piece of charcoal to write on the fire shovel, shaving off what he wrote, and then writing more—till midnight and past midnight. The next thing Abe would be reading books between the plow handles, it seemed to them. And once trying to speak a last word, Dennis Hanks said, "There's suthin' peculiarsome about Abe."

He wanted to learn, to know, to live, to reach out; he wanted to satisfy hungers and thirsts he couldn't tell about, this big boy of the backwoods. And some of what he wanted so much, so deep down, seemed to be in the books. Maybe in books he would find the answers to dark questions pushing around in the pools of his thoughts and the drifts of his mind. He told Dennis and other people, "The things I want to know are in books; my best friend is the man who'll git me a book I ain't read." And sometimes friends answered, "Well, books ain't as plenty as wildcats in these parts o' Indianny."

This was one thing meant by Dennis when he said there was "suthin' peculiarsome" about Abe. It seemed that Abe made the books tell him more than they told other people. All the other farm boys had gone to school and read "The Kentucky Preceptor," but Abe picked out questions from it, such as "Who has the most right to complain, the Indian or the Negro?" and Abe would talk about it, up one way and down the other, while they were in the cornfield pulling fodder for the winter. When Abe got hold of a storybook and read about a boat that came near a magnetic rock, and how the magnets in the rock pulled all the nails out of the boat so it went to pieces and the people in the boat found themselves floundering in water, Abe thought it was funny and told it to other people. After Abe read poetry, especially Bobby Burns's poems, Abe began writing rhymes himself. When Abe sat with a girl, with their bare feet in the creek water, and she spoke of the moon rising, he explained to her it was the earth moving and not the moon—the moon only seemed to rise.

John Hanks, who worked in the fields barefooted with Abe, grubbing stumps, plowing, mowing, said: "When Abe and I came back to the house from work, he used to go to the cupboard, snatch a piece of corn bread, sit down, take a book, cock his legs up high as his head, and read. Whenever Abe had a chance in the field while at work, or at the house, he would stop and read." He liked to explain to other people what he was getting from books; explaining an idea to some one else made it clearer to him. The habit was growing on him of reading out loud; words came more real if picked from the silent page of the book and pronounced on the tongue; new balances and values of words stood out if spoken aloud. When writing letters for his father or the neighbors, he read the words out loud as they got written. Before writing a letter he asked questions such as: "What do you want to say in the letter? How do you want to say it? Are you sure that's the best way to say it? Or do you think we can fix up a better way to say it?"

As he studied his books his lower lip stuck out; Josiah Crawford noticed it was a habit and joked Abe about the "stuck-out lip." This habit too stayed with him.

He wrote in his Sum Book or arithmetic that Compound Division was "When several numbers of Divers Denominations are given to be divided by 1 common divisor," and worked on the exercise in multiplication; "If 1 foot contain 12 inches I demand how many there are in 126 feet." Thus the schoolboy.

What he got in the schools didn't satisfy him. He went to three different schools in Indiana, besides two in Kentucky—altogether about four months of school. He learned his A B C, how to spell, read, write. And he had been with the other barefoot boys in butternut jeans learning "manners" under the schoolteacher, Andrew Crawford, who had them open a door, walk in, and say, "Howdy do?" Yet what he tasted of books in school was only a beginning, only made him hungry and thirsty, shook him with a wanting and a wanting of more and more of what was hidden between the covers of books.

He kept on saying, "The things I want to know are in books; my best friend is the man who'll git me a book I ain't read." He said that to Pitcher, the lawyer over at Rockport, nearly twenty miles away, one fall afternoon, when he walked from Pigeon Creek to Rockport and borrowed a book from Pitcher. Then when fodder-pulling time came a few days later, he shucked corn from early daylight till sundown along with his father and Dennis Hanks and John Hanks, but after supper he read the book till midnight, and at noon he hardly knew the taste of his corn bread because he had a book in front of him. It was a hundred little things like these which made Dennis Hanks say there was "suthin' peculiarsome" about Abe.

Besides reading the family Bible and figuring his way all through the old arithmetic they had at home, he got hold of "Aesop's Fables," "Pilgrim's Progress," "Robinson Crusoe," and Weems's "The Life of Francis Marion." The book of fables, written or collected thousands of years ago by the Greek slave, known as Aesop, sank deep in his mind. As he read through the book a second and third time, he had a feeling there were fables all around him, that everything he touched and handled, everything he saw and learned had a fable wrapped in it somewhere. One fable was about a bundle of sticks and a farmer whose sons were quarreling and fighting.

There was a fable in two sentences which read, "A coachman, hearing one of the wheels of his coach make a great noise, and perceiving that it was the worst one of the four, asked how it came to take such a liberty. The wheel answered that from the beginning of time, creaking had always been the privilege of the weak." And there were shrewd, brief incidents of foolery such as this: "A waggish, idle fellow in a country town, being desirous of playing a trick on the simplicity of his neighbors and at the same time putting a little money in his pocket at their cost, advertised that he would on a certain day show a wheel carriage that should be so contrived as to go without horses. By silly curiosity the rustics were taken in, and each succeeding group who came out from the show were ashamed to confess to their neighbors that they had seen nothing but a wheelbarrow."

The style of the Bible, of Aesop's fables, the hearts and minds back of those books, were much in his thoughts. His favorite pages in them he read over and over. Behind such proverbs as, "Muzzle not the ox that treadeth out the corn," and "He that ruleth his own spirit is greater than he that taketh a city," there was a music of simple wisdom and a mystery of common everyday life that touched deep spots in him, while out of the fables of the ancient Greek slave he came to see that cats, rats, dogs, horses, plows, hammers, fingers, toes, people, all had fables connected with their lives, characters, places. There was, perhaps, an outside for each thing as it stood alone, while inside of it was its fable.

One book came, titled, "The Life of George Washington, with Curious Anecdotes, Equally Honorable to Himself and Exemplary to His Young Countrymen. Embellished with Six Steel Engravings, by M. L. Weems, formerly Rector of Mt. Vernon Parish." It pictured men of passion and proud ignorance in the government of England driving their country into war on the American colonies. It quoted the far-visioned warning of Chatham to the British parliament, "For God's sake, then, my lords, let the way be instantly opened for reconciliation. I say instantly; or it will be too late forever."

The book told of war, as at Saratoga. "Hoarse as a mastiff of true British breed, Lord Balcarras was heard from rank to rank, loud-animating his troops; while on the other hand, fierce as a hungry Bengal tiger, the impetuous Arnold precipitated heroes on the stubborn foe. Shrill and terrible, from rank to rank, resounds the clash of bayonets—frequent and sad the groans of the dying. Pairs on Pairs, Britons and Americans, with each his bayonet at his brother's breast, fall forward together faint-shrieking in death, and mingle their smoking blood." Washington, the man, stood out, as when he wrote, "These things so harassed my heart with grief, that I solemnly declared to God, if I know myself, I would gladly offer myself a sacrifice to the butchering enemy, if I could thereby insure the safety of these my poor distressed countrymen."

The Weems book reached some deep spots in the boy. He asked himself what it meant that men should march, fight, bleed, go cold and hungry for the sake of what they called "freedom."

"Few great men are great in everything," said the book. And there was a cool sap in the passage: "His delight was in that of the manliest sort, which, by stringing the limbs and swelling the muscles, promotes the kindliest flow of blood and spirits. At jumping with a long pole, or heaving heavy weights, for his years he hardly had an equal."

Such book talk was a comfort against the same thing over again, day after day, so many mornings the same kind of water from the same spring, the same fried pork and corn-meal to eat, the same drizzles of rain, spring plowing, summer weeds, fall fodder-pulling, each coming every year, with the same tired feeling at the end of the day, so many days alone in the woods or the fields or else the same people to talk with, people from whom he had learned all they could teach him. Yet there ran through his head the stories and sayings of other people, the stories and sayings of books, the learning his eyes had caught from books; they were a comfort; they were good to have because they were good by themselves; and they were still better because they broke the chill of the lonesome feeling.

He was thankful to the writer of Aesop's fables because that writer stood by him and walked with him, an invisible companion, when he pulled fodder or chopped wood. Books lighted lamps in the dark rooms of his gloomy hours. . . . Well—he would live on; maybe the time would come when he would be free from work for a few weeks, or a few months, with books, and then he would read. . . . God, then he would read. . . . Then he would go and get at the proud secrets of his books.

His father—would he be like his father when he grew up? He hoped not. Why should his father knock him off a fence rail when he was asking a neighbor, passing by, a question? Even if it was a smart question, too pert and too quick, it was no way to handle a boy in front of a neighbor. No, he was going to be a man different from his father. The books—his father hated the books. His father talked about "too much eddication"; after readin', writin', 'rithmetic, that was enough, his father said. He, Abe Lincoln, the boy, wanted to know more than the father, Tom Lincoln, wanted to know. Already Abe knew more than his father; he was writing letters for the neighbors; they hunted out the Lincoln farm to get young Abe to find his bottle of ink with blackberry brier root and copperas in it, and his pen made from a turkey buzzard feather, and write letters. Abe had a suspicion sometimes his father was a little proud to have a boy that could write letters, and tell about things in books, and outrun and outwrestle and rough-and-tumble any boy or man in Spencer County. Yes, he would be different from his father; he was already so; it couldn't be helped.

In growing up from boyhood to young manhood, he had survived against lonesome, gnawing montony and against floods, forest and prairie fires, snake-bites, horse-kicks, ague, chills, fever, malaria, "milk-sick."

A comic outline against the sky he was, hiking along the roads of Spencer and other counties in southern Indiana in those years when he read all the books within a fifty-mile circuit of his home. Stretching up on the long legs that ran from his moccasins to the body frame with its long, gangling arms, covered with linsey-woolsey, then the lean neck that carried the head with its surmounting coonskin cap or straw hat—it was, again, a comic outline—yet with a portent in its shadow. His laughing "Howdy," his yarns and drollery, opened the doors of men's hearts.

Starting along in his eleventh year came spells of abstraction. When he was spoken to, no answer came from him. "He might be a thousand miles away." The roaming, fathoming, searching, questioning operations of the minds and hearts of poets, inventors, beginners who take facts stark, these were at work in him. This was one sort of abstraction he knew; there was another: the blues took him; coils of multiplied melancholies wrapped their blue frustrations inside him, all that Hamlet, Koheleth, Schopenhauer have uttered, in a mesh of foiled hopes. "There was absolutely nothing to excite ambition for education," he wrote later of that Indiana region. Against these "blues," he found the best warfare was to find people and trade with them his yarns and drolleries. John Baldwin, the blacksmith, with many stories and odd talk and eye-slants, was a help and a light.

Days came when he sank deep in the stream of human life and felt himself kin of all that swam in it, whether the waters were crystal or mud.

He learned how suddenly life can spring a surprise. One day in the woods, as he was sharpening a wedge on a log, the ax glanced, nearly took his thumb off, and left a white scar after healing.

"You never cuss a good ax," was a saying in those timbers.

MARTIN AND ABRAHAM LINCOLN

Catherine Cate Coblentz

The year before her death, Catherine Coblentz wrote a wonderful fairy tale, The Blue Cat of Castle Town, *which should be read aloud. It embodies her own spirit of service to the "bright enchantment" of "beauty, content and peace." She also wrote many fine historical stories for young readers*—The Falcon of Eric the Red, Blue and Silver Necklace, Sequoya, *and others. But this little story is one of the most touching.* Martin and Abraham Lincoln *is a true incident of the Civil War.*

"Flour and sugar and butter and eggs. Flour and sugar and butter and eggs." Martin Emery kept saying the words over to himself as he went slowly up the lane.

He had heard his mother whispering them again and again these past days. The words reminded him of the songs which his friend, Snowden, sang. Only Martin felt sure Mother's words were not a song but a prayer. For Mother needed so many things for Martin, for Maria, and Amanda, and Anna, the baby.

Martin gulped. When Father was at the Fort near by he had seen to it that Mother had these things. But he was gone. He would be gone for a long time. Somehow or other Martin felt he must take his place and help. After all he wore a new uniform now with shiny buttons. It was just like the one Father was wearing the last time Martin had seen him.

By this time Martin had come to the end of the lane. So he climbed up on the big rock by the roadside. Then he turned about and waved at the little gray house. Maria and Amanda and Anna, the baby, were standing in the doorway. They all waved back. Though Maria had to start Anna's hand going.

Then Martin looked up the road. It was Saturday and time for Snowden and Nellie to appear around the curve. Pretty soon he saw Nellie's long white ears. He heard the bell on Nellie's neck, and the jingle of her harness. He heard the creaking wheels on Nellie's cart. He saw the baskets of fresh vegetables in the back.

He saw Snowden, but Snowden didn't see Martin. Snowden was bent over on the front seat. In his hand was a stub of a pencil; on his knee a piece of paper. He kept frowning and looking at the paper. "I sure got to make a lot of money today," he said loud enough for Martin to hear him. "I sure got to. There's flour to get for Rosebell, and sugar and butter and eggs."

But if Snowden didn't see Martin, Nellie did. As soon as she came to the rock, Nellie stopped still. She looked at Martin. Then she turned her head and looked at Snowden. Then she flicked her ears.

When Nellie flicked her ears it was a sign. As soon as Martin saw it, he began scrambling over the wheel. He climbed up on the seat beside Snowden. Snowden blinked with surprise.

"May I go to Washington with you?" Martin asked.

Snowden started to nod. Then he stopped and asked, "Does your mother know?"

"She knows," said Martin. "That's why she let me wear my new suit." He stood up so Snowden could see the suit better. He stretched his shoulders as high as he could.

Snowden looked him up and down. He didn't miss a quirk of the soldier like cap or a single shiny button. "Hmm," he said. "Nice, Martin. Just like your father's."

"Father's regiment brought Mother the cloth," said Martin, "and the buttons."

"Snowden," began Martin, as the cart moved on toward Washington, "how do you get flour and sugar and butter and eggs?"

Snowden sighed, "Sometimes I declare I don't know myself, Martin. Rosebell and the children need so many things." He took up the pencil once more. When he put it down again, Martin asked another question.

"When the war is over, will my father come home, Snowden?"

Snowden drew a deep breath. "All the war prisoners will come home then, Martin. All those that the northern army has taken will go back south to their homes. And all those that the southern army has taken will go back to their homes."

Martin and Abraham Lincoln by Catherine Cate Coblentz, Childrens Press, Inc., 1947. Used by permission of the publisher

"I wish the war was over now," burst out Martin.

Snowden looked at him. "So do I," he said. "Abraham Lincoln does, too, I reckon."

Martin knew who Abraham Lincoln was. His picture was in the little gray house at the end of the lane. He never could decide which picture he liked better, that of his father or of Abraham Lincoln. His mother said they were both very important people. "Mr. Lincoln is the best president this country ever had, Martin," she said. "And your father is the best cobbler."

Best cobbler, best cobbler went Nellie's iron shoes, as they thumped, thumped across the bridge that led from Alexandria into Washington. Martin kicked his feet back to feel whether the empty basket was under the seat. It was. Martin knew why it was there. He knew, too, what would happen to that basket.

At the very first house, Snowden began his morning song. Martin waited to hear what the song was. It was a different one every week. This week it was a good song. Martin joined in after the first time. He sang as loud as he could:

Squash and beans and 'taters,
Garden fresh, garden fresh,
Beans and squash and 'taters.

After every sale, Snowden would put a scoop of beans or 'taters, or maybe a big squash into the basket under the seat.

The faster Snowden sold what he had, the bigger the gifts to the basket. And when everything else was sold that basket would be quite full. When Snowden and Martin and Nellie went home, Snowden would stop at the little gray house at the end of the lane.

"Got some left overs, Mrs. Emery." Snowden would say. "Thought maybe you'd help me out by using them." Then he always added, "Martin was a big help to me today, Mrs. Emery."

Had it not been for Snowden's left overs, Martin knew that he and Maria and Amanda and Anna would be hungry oftener than they were. Now, if they only had flour and sugar and butter and eggs, Mother wouldn't need to worry.

So on this Saturday Martin tried harder than ever to help Snowden as much as he could. He called:

Squash and beans and 'taters,

at the top of his lungs. Earlier in the season it had been:

Rhubarb and radishes, ripe and red.

Later there would be cabbages and parsnips and turnips, and Snowden would make up new songs for them to call.

"You are good at making up songs," said Martin as the cart rattled along the wide streets.

"And you are good at singing them," replied Snowden. "Words said over and over make a good song."

Words said over and over! That made Martin think of his mother, and the words she made into a prayer. He drew a long, quivering sigh.

"Wars, which put fathers in prison when they are needed at home, are a bad thing," Snowden said. He had been watching Martin closely.

Martin nodded. He swallowed the lump in his throat and called:

Squash and beans and 'taters,
Garden fresh, garden fresh,
Beans and squash and 'taters.

However, his voice didn't sound nearly as cheerful as it usually did. Toward the end of the morning it began trailing after Snowden's like a small echo.

Squash and beans and 'taters,

Snowden would sing.

Beans and 'taters,

would come Martin's echo.

Snowden glanced at Martin several times. It was very hot. Martin looked pale. Snowden made up his mind he would take him to a cool spot, while he went off to buy the groceries which Rosebell needed.

So a little before noon, Snowden turned Nellie about. And when they came to a big parklike place filled with shade trees, Snowden pulled the reins.

"Whoa, Nellie," he said.

"Now, Martin," he went on, "you just stay here in the shade and rest until Nellie and I come back. It's a good place for anyone in a uniform like yours. There's been lots of soldiers on this lawn, I can tell you. I've seen them sleeping here at night sometimes. And all over the place in the day. And I've seen them jump up and stand just as proud and straight when Abraham Lincoln came along."

"Came along here, Snowden? Abraham Lincoln?"

"Of course, Martin. See that building there? That's the Capitol, Martin—our Capitol."

Martin stood on the ground and stared. Snowden and Nellie started to leave. Then Nellie stopped and flicked her ears. That made Snowden remember something. He reached in his pocket.

"I most forgot," he said. "Rosebell gave me a sandwich for you, Martin. And an apple."

"I have a sandwich." Martin pointed to his pocket. He did not take it out, for he did not want Snowden to see how small and thin that sandwich was. There was no butter on the bread, only a smear of molasses.

"You'd better take this," urged Snowden. "Rosebell made it special."

"Thank you," said Martin, reaching for the thick sandwich and the apple. He would just take a bite or two out of the sandwich and save the rest for Maria and Amanda and Anna. He would save the apple, too, most of it.

When Snowden and Nellie were gone, and when the last sound of Nellie's bell, the jingle of her harness, and the creaking of the cart wheels faded in the distance, Martin wandered about for a little. Then he climbed on a bench. He ate his thin sandwich. He ate a little of Snowden's thick one. It was so good. Half of it was gone before he knew it. He re-wrapped it in the paper Rosebell had put about it, and laid it on the bench. When Martin wasn't looking a fat squirrel slipped up on the bench and grabbed at it. Martin felt the squirrel touch his hand. He jumped. The squirrel jumped. The sandwich fell and landed in a puddle.

Martin could have cried when he saw that. But he didn't. He would save all the apple, he decided, for Maria and Amanda and Anna. He would not take even a bite.

The sun was hot. Martin went over and sat down on the stone steps of the Capitol. The steps were clean and cool. His eyes closed a little as he leaned back, his head resting against the stone at one side.

Then, as always when he was alone and it was still, Martin began thinking about his father. The lump in his throat began to grow.

He heard someone coming down the steps in back of him. But there was plenty of room so Martin didn't move. He just sat there and watched dreamily as a long shadow moved over the step he was on, and went slither-sliding down the step ahead. And the next. And the next. And the next.

Then the shadow stopped still and stayed in one place. A voice just in back of Martin said, "Well, well! How's my little soldier?"

Soldier! When his father's friends said that, Martin had always done as his father had taught him, jumped to his feet and saluted. So, forgetting how tired and sad he had been, he sprang to his feet, flinging his head back and his hand up at the same time.

As his fingers touched the visor of his little blue cap, Martin's heart began to thud like a drum. For Abraham Lincoln was standing there looking down at him, his sad face losing its look of worry, and breaking slowly into a smile. Abraham Lincoln, himself!

"What is your name, soldier?" the great man asked, gravely returning the salute.

Martin told him.

"Where were you born, Martin?"

"In Vermont. In a log cabin."

The man nodded. "I was born in a log cabin, too."

"I know, Mother told me. She said some day I might get to be President like you."

"All mothers say that, Martin. What does your father say?"

"I don't know." Martin's voice slowed. "You see, he is away. He used to be a cobbler, but now he is your soldier."

"What regiment? And where is he now?"

The lump in Martin's throat was growing worse. It was difficult to make the words come. "The First Vermont—" he managed. And then the sobs had him. "He's in Andersonville Prison," he jerked.

But the great man was bending over. Strong arms were lifting Martin. In another moment the man had taken Martin's place on the steps. Martin was folded into his lap.

The boy's face was hidden now, in Abraham Lincoln's vest.

Abraham Lincoln just sat there, holding the little boy whose sobbing had been so long kept back. A great hand patted him gently and understandingly between the shoulders. When Martin grew quieter the man began to talk.

"So your father is a cobbler. Is he a good cobbler, Martin?"

Martin nodded his head so hard that his nose went up and down against Abraham Lincoln's ribs.

"Good cobblers are mighty important," said the man. "Never made a pair of shoes myself. But I saw a boy once that needed some mighty bad." The President settled his back a little more comfortably into the corner of the step and the wall.

"It happened when I was postmaster back in Illinois," he went on. "People didn't write many letters in those days, so I carried them in my hat. One cold day as I was going along with the letters in my hat, I saw Ab Trout. He was barefoot as the day he was born and chopping a pile of logs from an old barn that had been torn down. The logs were gnarled and tough. And Ab's ax kept going slower and slower.

" 'What do you get for this job, Ab?' I asked him.

" 'A dollar.'

" 'What do you aim to do with it?'

" 'Buy a pair of shoes,' he said.

" 'You'll never get one shoe at this rate, Ab,' I told him. 'Better go in and warm yourself and you'll work faster.' So he did. Funniest thing, Martin. When Ab came out, that wood was all chopped! Now, what do you think of that?"

Martin sat up and looked straight at Abraham Lincoln. "I think you chopped that wood," he said.

"Maybe you're right," smiled Lincoln. "After all, folks must help each other."

Martin nodded. "I help my mother all I can," he said. "I fix the rough places when they come in the shoes of Maria and Amanda and Anna. I can do it most as well as Father did. Mother says it helps a lot."

"I am sure it does." The President nodded.

"Vermont is a long way off," he went on. "Tell me, how do you happen to be here, Martin?"

Martin wiped the last tear from his cheek with the handkerchief Mr. Lincoln handed him. He could talk now. He wanted to.

"Father went to war," he began. "He was stationed at a fort near Alexandria. So, after a time he found a house near the fort, and sent for Mother and me and Maria and Amanda and Anna. We came on the train. At first we saw Father often. Then one night when some of the soldiers were sent out to take a railroad bridge, Father was captured. He was sent to prison."

"How does your mother manage to take care of you?" asked Abraham Lincoln.

"Well, it's like you said. Folks help. The soldiers—Father's friends—bring their mending to her. They ask her to cook for them. And sometimes they bring their washing for her to do. They pay as much as they can. The soldiers give us cloth for our clothes, too.

"And Snowden helps. Snowden is my friend. He sells vegetables and I help him call. Snowden fills the basket under the seat with vegetables and calls them left overs. He gives the basket to

Mother. But the vegetables aren't left overs. Not really."

Martin didn't tell about his mother's prayer for flour and sugar and butter and eggs. He didn't need to. For Abraham Lincoln seemed to know all about that prayer.

"Hmm!" he began. "It seems to me, Martin, that part of this job of helping belongs to the army—your father's army, and mine. I will speak to somebody, and I'm pretty sure there will be food from the army stores every week for your mother. Things that Snowden and the soldiers can't supply, like butter and bacon and other things."

There wasn't any lump in Martin's throat now. He felt wonderful. But for some reason the tears began to pour down his face.

The man pretended not to see. Instead, he raised himself to his feet, and a sudden frown grew deep between his eyes. "It's my shoe, Martin," he explained. "There's a nail sticking right into my foot. And I keep forgetting to have it fixed."

"Oh, wait," cried Martin. "I can help you." He darted off to a pile of stones by the steps. Luckily he found the kind he wanted right away. When he came back Abraham Lincoln sat on the steps with his shoe off, waiting to be helped.

Martin sat down beside him. He slipped one stone inside the great shoe. With the other he pounded hard on the sole.

"My father showed me how," he boasted between pounds. "He is a good cobbler."

Abraham Lincoln smiled. "I'd like to be a cobbler myself, Martin. A good cobbler."

"That's what I am going to be," nodded Martin.

Down the street he could hear the sound of Nellie's bell, the jingle of her harness and the creaking of the wheels on Nellie's cart. But he finished the shoe and gave it to Abraham Lincoln.

The man put on the shoe. He stood up and set the foot, where the nail had been, down carefully. He pressed harder, while Martin watched his face. There was no frown between Abraham Lincoln's eyes.

"It's a good job, Martin," he praised. "It feels just fine." He paused and looked over Martin's head far into the distance. The worry had gone now from the President's face. "You have helped me, Martin," he said, "more than you know!"

Martin said nothing. He only slipped his hand inside Abraham Lincoln's. They came down the steps together.

They were waiting when Snowden and Nellie arrived.

Snowden's mouth popped wide open. Nellie stopped. She flicked her ears and Snowden swept off his hat.

The man beside Martin lifted his gravely in return. Then he bent and raised Martin high in the air and put him on the seat beside Snowden.

"Good-by, soldier," he said.

Martin saluted. Snowden saluted. Abraham Lincoln saluted. Nellie started toward home.

from AMERICA'S ROBERT E. LEE

Henry Steele Commager and Lynd Ward

The author of this book is a historian who does not try to add glamour to his hero but lets the facts speak for themselves. Lee does not suffer from this treatment but comes out the noble human being he seemed to all who knew him. Lynd Ward's fine pictures add to the importance of this book.

[*Lee at West Point*]

Meantime there was the serious business of an education—serious indeed for a boy whose family standards were so high, and whose prospects were so poor. For a time Robert had gone to one of the Carter schools; the family connection was so large that they kept up one school for the Carter girls and one for the boys. When he was thirteen his mother sent him to the Alexandria Academy—General Washington had been one of the trustees—where a genial Irishman named William Leary drilled him in Greek and Latin and mathematics. This would have prepared him for college, but there wasn't enough money for college. Brother Sidney Smith had made himself a career in the Navy; why shouldn't Robert have a career in the Army? Clearly, if he was to be a

From *America's Robert E. Lee* by Henry Steele Commager and Lynd Ward. Reprinted by permission of and arrangement with Houghton Mifflin Company, the authorized publishers

soldier, the place for him was the Military Academy at West Point. And to West Point he determined to go.

The first problem was to get into the Academy. The requirements for admission were easy enough, ludicrously easy by modern standards. Applicants had to be between the ages of fourteen and twenty, at least four feet nine inches tall, free from physical defects, able to read and write, and competent in arithmetic! Robert could meet these all right. He was seventeen years old, almost six feet tall, in perfect health, and as well educated as almost any boy of his age.

The real difficulty was to get an appointment from the Secretary of War who, at this time, was John C. Calhoun of South Carolina. Competition was sharp, especially in the South, where it was a tradition that the sons of gentlemen go into the Army. Yet Robert's chances were good. It was not only that he was a handsome and likeable young man, well trained in the classics and in mathematics. That helped, of course. Rather it was that he had behind him the powerful Lee connection, and all their friends. And there were many who remembered Light-Horse Harry's services to his country, and who were eager to extend a helping hand to his son. So Robert was able to submit to the Secretary of War not only the usual recommendations from friends and teachers, but letters from no less than five Senators and three Congressmen! Whether it was these letters, or the Lee name, or young Robert himself, we do not know, but in March 1824 Robert E. Lee was informed that he had been appointed to the United States Military Academy at West Point.

On a warm June day in 1825 Lee stepped aboard a gleaming white paddle-wheeler—perhaps it was the *Chancellor Livingston* or the *James Kent,* or even the new *Richmond*—and steamed up the Hudson to West Point. It was only fifty-some miles from New York to the Point, but the trip took half a day, and there was plenty of time to admire the scenery, as lovely as any in the country. It was all new to Robert, yet not wholly strange, not unlike the upper Potomac, which he knew well—the broad blue river, on one side the steep Palisades, on the other trim lawn running down to the water's edge, and handsome mansion houses. The steamer stopped when it came opposite the Point, swinging back and forth in the current. A little skiff put out from the pier, and the lads who were going to the Academy climbed down the rope ladder and into the boat, and were rowed to shore, Robert among them.

Set in a great bend of the Hudson, the Point was as beautiful then as now. It was hemmed in on two sides by the Majestic river; to the south stretched the Highlands, while Storm King Mountain, its summit often hidden in clouds, dominated the north. The magnificence of the natural setting brought out in sharp contrast the shabbiness of the Academy itself. As Lee came up the steep path from the river pier, he saw a group of ugly stucco buildings, squatting on a narrow, treeless plateau. There were the North and South Barracks, which housed the four-hundred-odd cadets, the main Academy building, a long mess hall—also used as a hotel for visitors—and, scattered around the grounds, a group of smaller buildings almost as ugly as the main ones.

Living conditions, Lee quickly learned, were as meager as the buildings. In the summertime Lee and his fellow cadets lived in tents, in what was called—in honor of the President then in the White House—Camp Adams. The rest of the year Lee lived in the old barracks. His room was small, bare, and uncomfortable, heated only by a tiny fireplace, and he had to share it with two or three other lads. Here he studied, in such time as was allowed him, by the flickering light of candles; here he slept, unrolling his mattress on a cold floor. The food, too, as Lee soon learned, was very different from the rich and varied fare he was used to at home. The Academy chef, a thrifty soul, filled his victims up on porridge, bread, soup, and potatoes, with bacon and mutton and beef only on rare occasions. It was, all in all, pretty grim.

Plebe Lee fell quickly into the routine of the Academy. Reveille sounded at sunrise; then came drill and parade for an hour or so; breakfast; five hours of classes and study; an hour for dinner; two more hours of study; two hours for drill; supper, study, and inspection. Taps were sounded at nine-thirty, and lights out at ten. It was all quite strenuous, but once Lee got the hang of it, he managed easily enough. There was not much time for play, and no organized sports at all. Saturday afternoons and Sundays the cadets could swim in the Hudson, or walk to near-by Buttermilk Falls, or find a few hours for reading, and perhaps for visitors.

Life, as Lee soon learned, was hedged around with endless rules and regulations. Woe betide the cadet who forgot them—who was late for classes or forgot to polish his boots or his buttons, who talked out of turn or failed in proper respect to instructors or to upper-classmen, or ventured off ground in search for food or for forbidden entertainment. Colonel Thayer, the Superintendent who had really made the Academy, was a strict disciplinarian, and failure to observe the rules was punished with demerits. Too many of these, and out you went!

The academic requirements, too, were stiff. Colonel Thayer had already established the rule, still an Academy tradition, that every cadet recite in every subject every day. There was no such thing as falling behind in your work, and then boning up for examinations: if you fell behind, you fell out. The course of study was a narrow one. The first year was devoted to mathematics and French. Gradually other subjects were added—drawing, surveying, engineering, a bit of physics and chemistry, a smattering of history, geography, and "moral philosophy." There was also something called "the science of war"—a subject which Lee certainly mastered, whether at the Academy or elsewhere.

This was all theoretical, and you couldn't make a soldier by theory alone. Colonel Thayer knew that well enough: he was an engineer himself. So on top of all the book-study, there was constant drill, and practical training. The cadets learned how to handle artillery, how to build forts, how to lay out roads and build bridges, how to survey and make maps. They were trained in tactics, and in the command of small groups of soldiers. All this was fun for the cadets: it took them out in the open, gave them a chance to ride horses, to use surveying instruments, to fire off guns, gave them a feeling that they were learning things of practical use.

Many a promising career was wrecked on the shoals of rules or grades. Of Lee's class of eighty-seven, almost half failed to graduate. But Lee had no difficulties either with the regulations or with his marks. From the beginning he was up among the first two or three in his class, and he held this position through the four years he was at the Academy. In his second year Lee was named staff sergeant, and asked to teach mathematics to the Plebes; thereafter he was both instructor and student. In his last year he won the most prized of all Academy distinctions—the position of Adjutant of the Corps. When he graduated he was number two in his class, and what is more, he had come through four years without a single demerit! As a "distinguished cadet" he could choose his own branch of service, and, like so many others, he chose the engineers.

To his classmates Lee was known as the "Marble Model." He may have been a model, but he was far from marble, far from cold and aloof, and there was nothing about him of the prig. Joseph E. Johnston—his classmate and later his ablest general—describes him at this time.

> We had the same intimate associates who thought as I did that no other youth or man so united the qualities that win warm friendship and command high respect. For he was full of sympathy and kindness, genial and fond of gay conversation, and even of fun, while his correctness of demeanor and attention to all duties, personal and official, and a dignity as much a part of himself as the elegance of his person, gave him a superiority that every one acknowledged in his heart.

Here we have the Lee of the future!

A full-fledged officer now, wonderfully handsome in his gray and white uniform, Lee returned to Virginia to visit with family and friends before taking up his professional duties. He came not a moment too soon. For Anne Carter Lee, long an invalid, lay at the point of death. Lee was with her when, a few weeks later, she died. All in all she had not had a very happy life. Her marriage had been a failure, she had been much alone, she had known poverty and sickness. But she had seen all her boys launched in life—Carter in the law, Smith in the Navy, and Robert, now, a lieutenant in the Army. She was proud of them all, as well she might be, and especially proud of Robert, who had been closer to her than any of her other children.

THREE ADVENTURERS

Carol Ryrie Brink

Caddie Woodlawn, *for which "Three Adventurers" is the first chapter, won the Newbery Award the year it appeared, and several library research studies have placed it at the top in popularity with children throughout the country. Indian John called Caddie Woodlawn "Missee Red Hair," and their friendship was to stand the whole community in good stead, when the two of them were able to avert a bloody war between the Indians and the white settlers.*

In 1864 Caddie Woodlawn was eleven, and as wild a little tomboy as ever ran the woods of western Wisconsin. She was the despair of her mother and of her elder sister Clara. But her father watched her with a little shine of pride in his eyes, and her brothers accepted her as one of themselves without a question. Indeed, Tom, who was two years older, and Warren, who was two years younger than Caddie, needed Caddie to link them together into an inseparable trio. Together they got in and out of more scrapes and adventures than any one of them could have imagined alone. And in those pioneer days Wisconsin offered plenty of opportunities for adventure to three wide-eyed, red-headed youngsters.

On a bright Saturday afternoon in the early fall Tom and Caddie and Warren Woodlawn sat on a bank of the Menomonie River, or Red Cedar as they call it now, taking off their clothes. Their red heads shone in the sunlight. Tom's hair was the darkest, Caddie's the nearest golden, and nine-year-old Warren's was plain carrot color. Not one of the three knew how to swim, but they were going across the river, nevertheless. A thin thread of smoke beyond the bend on the other side of the river told them that the Indians were at work on a birch-bark canoe.

"Do you think the Indians around here would ever get mad and massacre folks like they did up north?" wondered Warren, tying his shirt up in a little bundle.

"No, sir!" said Tom, "not these Indians!"

"Three Adventurers" from *Caddie Woodlawn* by Carol Ryrie Brink. Copyright 1945 by The Macmillan Company and used with their permission

"Not Indian John, anyhow," said Caddie. She had just unfastened the many troublesome little buttons on the back of her tight-waisted dress, and, before taking it off, she paused a moment to see if she could balance a fresh-water clam shell on her big toe. She found that she could.

"No, not Indian John!" she repeated decidedly, having got the matter of the clam shell off her mind, "even if he does have a scalp belt," she added. The thought of the scalp belt always made her hair prickle delightfully up where her scalp lock grew.

"Naw," said Tom, "the fellows who spread those massacree stories are just big-mouthed scared-cats who don't know the Indians, I guess."

"Big-mouthed scared-cats," repeated Warren, admiring Tom's command of language.

"Big-mouthed scared-cats," echoed a piping voice from the bank above. Seven-year-old Hetty, who fluttered wistfully on the outer edge of their adventures, filed away Tom's remark in her active brain. It would be useful to tell to Mother, sometime when Mother was complaining about Tom's language. The three below her paid no attention to Hetty's intrusion. Their red heads, shining in the sunlight, did not even turn in her direction. Hetty's hair was red, too, like Father's, but somehow, in spite of her hair, she belonged on the dark-haired side of the family where Mother and Clara and all the safe and tidy virtues were. She poised irresolutely on the bank above the three adventurous ones. If they had only turned around and looked at her! But they were enough in themselves. She could not make up her mind what to do. She wanted to go with them, and yet she wanted just as much to run home and tell Mother and Clara what they were about to do. Hetty was the self-appointed newsbearer of the family. Wild horses could not prevent her from being the first to tell, whatever it was that happened.

Tom and Caddie and Warren finished undressing, tied their clothes into tight bundles, and stepped out into the river. The water was low after a long, hot summer, but still it looked cold and deep. Hetty shuddered. She had started to undo one shoe, but now she quickly tied it up again. She had made up her mind. She turned around and flew across the fields to tell Mother.

Tom knew from experience that he could just keep his chin above water and touch bottom with his toes across the deep part of the river. It would have been over Caddie's and Warren's heads, but, if they held onto Tom and kept their feet paddling, they could just keep their heads above water. They had done it before. Tom went first with his bundle of clothes balanced on his head. Caddie came next, clutching Tom's shoulder with one hand and holding her bundle of clothes on top of her head with the other. Warren clung to Caddie's shoulder in the same manner, balancing his own clothes with his free hand. They moved slowly and carefully. If Tom lost his footing or fell, they would all go down together and be swept away by the current toward the village below. But the other two had every confidence in Tom, and Tom had not the slightest reason to doubt himself. They looked like three beavers, moving silently across the current—three heads with three bundles and a little wake of ripples trailing out behind them. Last of all came Nero, the farm dog, paddling faithfully behind them. But Hetty was already out of sight.

Presently there was solid river bed beneath their feet again. The three children scrambled out on the other side, shook themselves as Nero did, and pulled on their dry, wrinkled clothing.

"Hurry up, Caddie," called Tom. "You're always the last to dress."

"So would you be, too, Tom, if you had so many buttons!" protested Caddie. She came out of the bushes struggling with the back of her blue denim dress. Relenting, Tom turned his superior intelligence to the mean task of buttoning her up the back.

"I wish Mother'd let me wear boy's clothes," she complained.

"Huh!" said Warren, "she thinks you're tomboy enough already."

"But they're so much quicker," said Caddie regretfully.

Now that they were dressed, they sped along the river bank in the direction of the smoke. Several Indian canoes were drawn up on shore in the shelter of a little cove and beyond them in a clearing the Indians moved to and fro about a fire. Propped on two logs was the crude framework of a canoe which was already partly covered with birch bark. The smell of birch smoke and hot pitch filled the air. Caddie lifted her head and sniffed. It was perfume to her, as sweet as the perfume of the clover fields. Nero sniffed, too, and growled low in his throat.

The three children stopped at the edge of the clearing and watched. Even friendly Indians commanded fear and respect in those days. A lean dog, with a wolfish look, came forward barking.

He and Nero circled about each other, little ridges of bristling hair along their spines, their tails wagging suspiciously. Suddenly the Indian dog left Nero and came toward Caddie.

"Look!" said Caddie. "It's Indian John's dog." The dog's tail began to wag in a friendlier manner, and Caddie reached out and patted his head.

By this time the Indians had noticed the children. They spoke among themselves and pointed. Some of them left their work and came forward.

In all the seven years since the Woodlawns had come from Boston to live in the big house on the prairie, the Indians had never got used to seeing them. White men and their children they had seen often enough, but never such as these, who wore, above their pale faces, hair the color of flame and sunset. During the first year that the children spent in Wisconsin, the Indians had come from all the country around to look at them. They had come in groups, crowding into Mrs. Woodlawn's kitchen in their silent moccasins, touching the children's hair and staring. Poor Mrs. Woodlawn, frightened nearly out of

her wits, had fed them bread or beans or whatever she had on hand, and they had gone away satisfied.

"Johnny, my dear," Mrs. Woodlawn had complained to her husband, "those frightful savages will eat us out of house and home."

"Patience, Harriet," said her husband, "we have enough and to spare."

"But, Johnny, the way they look at the children's hair frightens me. They might want a red scalp to hang to their belts."

Caddie remembered very vividly the day, three years before, when she had gone unsuspecting into the store in the village. As she went in the door, a big Indian had seized her and held her up in the air while he took a leisurely look at her hair. She had been so frightened that she had not even cried out, but hung there, wriggling in the Indian's firm grasp, and gazing desperately about the store for help.

The storekeeper had laughed at her, saying in a reassuring voice: "You needn't be afraid, Caddie. He's a good Indian. It's Indian John."

That was the strange beginning of a friendship, for a kind of friendship it was, that had grown up between Caddie and Indian John. The boys liked Indian John, too, but it was at Caddie and her red-gold curls that the big Indian looked when he came to the farm, and it was for Caddie that he left bits of oddly carved wood and once a doll—such a funny doll with a tiny head made of a pebble covered with calico, black horsehair braids, calico arms and legs, and a buckskin dress! John's dog knew his master's friends. Caddie had been kind to him and he accepted her as a friend.

He rubbed his head against her now as she patted his rough hair. Indian John left his work on the canoe and came forward.

"You like him dog?" he said, grinning. He was flattered when anyone patted his dog.

"Yes," said Caddie, "he's a good dog."

"Will you let us see how you put the canoe together?" asked Tom eagerly.

"You come look," said the Indian.

They followed him to the half-finished canoe. Grunting and grinning, the Indians took up their work. They fastened the pliable sheaths of birch bark into place on the light framework, first sewing them together with buckskin thongs, then cementing them with the hot pitch. The children were fascinated. Their own canoe on the lake was an Indian canoe. But it had been hollowed out of a single log. They had seen the birch-bark canoes on the river, but had never been so close to the making of one. They were so intent on every detail that time slipped by unheeded. Even the squaws, who came up behind them to examine their hair, did not take their attention from the building of the canoe. Caddie shook her head impatiently, flicking her curls out of their curious fingers, and went on watching.

But after awhile Warren said: "Golly! I'm hungry." Perhaps it was the odor of jerked venison, simmering over the fire, which had begun to mingle with the odors of birch and pitch, that made Warren remember he was hungry.

"You're always hungry," said Tom, the lofty one, in a tone of disgust.

"Well, I am, too," said Caddie positively, and that settled it. The sun was beginning to swing low in the sky, and, once they had made up their minds, they were off at once. As quickly as they had come, they returned along the river bank to their crossing place. The Indians stared after them. They did not understand these curious red and white children of the white man, nor how they went and came.

Soon three bundles, three dirty faces, and three fiery heads, shining in the red autumn sun, crossed the river with a little trail of ripples behind them. Safe on the other bank, the three hastily pulled on their clothes and started to take a short cut through the woods, Nero trotting at their heels.

from A SOUNDING TRUMPET

Louise Hall Tharp

The following excerpt gives two chapters from the biography of Julia Ward Howe. The spirited little redhead of the first chapter grew into a beautiful young woman as her father foresaw. She married a distinguished doctor and had a lively family of children, among them Laura Richards, many of whose nonsense verses you will find in Time for Poetry. *In the second chap-*

ter given here the mature Julia Ward Howe is in Washington with her husband during the Civil War. This chapter tells how she happened to write "The Battle Hymn of the Republic."

Independence Day

The brisk notes of a French clock chimed the quarter hour as Julia ran downstairs. To her delight, she found the door of the front parlor wide open. At the windows, the heavy silk draperies had been looped to one side, while lace glass-curtains fluttered in the breeze. Sunshine flooded this formal room which was usually kept closed and dim. Julia tiptoed inside.

A long mirror reached from floor to ceiling between the two windows. Julia inspected herself carefully. Yes—her rebellious red hair was as flat and smooth as a dampened hairbrush could make it. Her ears and neck were still pink from a hard scrubbing. She looked like a little girl who meant to be very good indeed on this holiday morning. Then her gray eyes began to twinkle. The laughter spread, and suddenly Julia Ward was a very imp of mischief!

A muffled footfall on the carpeted floor made Julia spin around. Here came William, the Negro butler, with a huge feather duster under his arm. "My, my, Miss Julia, aren't you up pretty early?" exclaimed William, reproachfully. "'Pears to me like you couldn't wait for nurse to come and dress you."

"Oh, who could sleep on a morning like this!" cried Julia, pirouetting gaily before the mirror. "Do you realize what day it is?"

"Shore do," sighed William. "The old gentleman goin' to come here today. Got to get my parlor all shined up for the Colonel. So don't you go dancin' the roses right off that carpet—even if it is the Fourth of July!"

Julia laughed and managed to stand still for perhaps half a minute. "Grandfather calls this 'Independence Day,' William. I thought I'd show my independence by getting up when I pleased. Are Sam and Henry back yet?"

William's solemn black face relaxed into a grin. "No, ma'am! Those boys goin' to show up missin' if they don't watch out. Hate to think what their father will say." With an expert twist of the wrist, William flecked the dust out of the deep carving on the mahogany sofa. "Don' know as I blame the boys," he confided. "Most run off to have a look myself."

"I was going," announced Julia, "but the boys just wouldn't take me."

Now William was really shocked. It was one thing for the Ward boys to see the sights of New York town on the Fourth of July, but the Ward sisters never stirred abroad save in their father's carriage, or with a nurse or governess. "Miss Julia," warned William solemnly, "there's limits to independence!"

Julia tossed her red head. "When I grow up, I'm going to do things and see things—even if I *am* a girl. If they ever again have anything as wonderful as a balloon ascension at Battery Park, I'll be there to see the balloon!"

But Julia knew perfectly well that this small declaration of independence of hers would do her no earthly good at the present time. If she saw anything at all now, it would have to be from the parlor window. Impatiently, she shoved aside the lace curtain and leaned out.

Directly across the way was a park, surrounded by a neat iron railing. This was Bowling Green. Long ago, in old New York, British settlers in white periwigs and knee breeches loved to roll the heavy bowling balls here on the grass, in sight of the broad Hudson. A gilded statue of King George the Third of England had looked down upon his loyal subjects from astride a gilded horse.

But now there was no statue to be seen from Julia's window. One night in 1776 an angry mob had surged over Bowling Green. "Give us Liberty," they shouted, as they tore down the gilded king. The statue proved to be made of lead, so men melted it down into bullets for the battle for freedom.

Grandfather had been a lieutenant-colonel under General Washington, and Julia had heard many stories of the Revolution. But even today, on the Fourth of July, it is likely that Julia Ward was not thinking about history. She was a very-up-to-date little girl, and this was 1828. Today Julia wanted nothing in the world so much as to see a gas balloon! She climbed on a chair in the hope of seeing past Bowling Green into Battery Park, but it was no use.

With a sigh, Julia resigned herself to watching the holiday crowd as it surged past her door.

An omnibus, drawn by four white horses, pulled up at the curb. It was already crowded. A huge barrel on wheels came lumbering along. It was a street sprinkler, and Julia laughed to see the pedestrians scatter out of the road. Now they scattered again for something else, and Julia craned her neck to see what commanded so much respect. A huge black and white sow came around the corner, followed by four little pigs.

The omnibus had started, but the pigs, serenely certain that they owned the right of way, continued across the street to a fine wilted cabbage which lay waiting for them in the gutter. The bus driver swore, but prudently pulled up. With a contemptuous flip of her left ear, Mrs. Pig acknowledged the courtesy while the babies marched in her wake, looking neither to the right nor to the left. "Mother will manage everything," they seemed to say. And the pig family settled down to its business of garbage collecting right in front of the town house of Samuel Ward, Esquire.

Julia giggled. Father had already written letters to the *Evening Post* suggesting that pigs be kept off the streets of New York. But of course they never would be.

Behind her, the mantel clock chimed seven quick strokes, as if hurrying to catch up with time. Julia began to feel anxious. She craned her neck, trying to see all the way down the street, but there was no sign of Sam or Henry. In the back parlor, William was arranging eight chairs. Each one faced Father's big armchair with the little table beside it. William reverently dusted the family Bible and placed it upon the table. With it went a small Episcopal prayer book.

Overhead, sounds of activity increased. A warning voice cried, "No, Francis Marion Ward, how many times do I have to tell you!" Aunt Eliza had been just in time to prevent Julia's younger brother from sliding down the banister.

The rustle of starched petticoats announced Julia's little sisters. They ran into the front parlor with cries of delight. But Aunt Eliza was close behind.

"Go to your seats, girls," she said. "There isn't time to look out of the window now." Dark-haired Louisa and five-year-old Ann Eliza obeyed. Their brother, Francis Marion, climbed into a haircloth-covered chair which pricked his legs.

Reluctantly, Julia started for the back parlor. Then she gave one last glance over her shoulder and stopped dead in her tracks. Over in Battery Park, a great golden sphere rose slowly among the trees. At about tree-level, it halted and swayed gently in the breeze. "The balloon!" cried Julia, her eyes bright with excitement. The younger children screwed around in their seats and would have dashed to the window but for Aunt Eliza's restraining hand.

The door from the hall opened, and an ominous sound brought Julia to herself with a start. Father was clearing his throat. She looked around quickly, and there he was, settling himself in the big chair and reaching in his pocket for his gold-rimmed glasses. Julia scuttled for the back parlor and slid into her seat. In summer, Father began family prayers at seven-fifteen sharp; in winter, at seven-forty-five. Sad was the fate of any child whose chair was empty at that moment. The parlor clock chimed its hurried notes.

For a moment Julia thought of nothing but her glimpse of the beautiful balloon. Then, with a sudden sinking of heart, she saw that there were still two empty places. Sam and Henry were late! Faithful William was hovering near the front door to let in the boys as quickly and silently as possible, but he could not help them now. The hour had struck.

Father reached for his Bible. He took a good look at the empty chairs, and Julia's throat hurt as she imagined how sad it would be for Sam and Henry to be punished on a holiday. Then Father paused and took a huge gold watch out of his pocket. "Those newfangled mantel clocks are unreliable," he exclaimed, getting up and going into the front parlor. "Give me a good tall clock, every time." He scowled at the clock's pretty enameled face and set the filigree gold hands back two and a half minutes.

While Father looked reprovingly at the frivolous little clock, the front door opened softly, and closed more softly still. Sam and Henry tiptoed to their seats.

"Did you see them put the gas in the balloon?" Julia whispered.

"Oh, yes," they gasped, badly out of breath. "Julia, you must get Father to let you go!"

Julia nodded as Father walked majestically to his seat. If he noticed that two previously empty chairs were now occupied by two very red-faced and breathless small boys, he made no sign. Father read aloud from the Bible, then he turned to the prayer book. The children bowed their heads.

After family prayers, the Wards trooped down another flight of stairs to breakfast. The dining room was below the street level and none too well lighted by barred windows looking out upon a stone areaway. Aunt Eliza took her place behind a massive silver coffeepot at one end of the table. Father barricaded himself behind his newspaper at the other. Among themselves the young Wards talked in low tones, taking pains not to disturb their elders. Children were supposed to be seen and not heard, Aunt Eliza would say.

"Did you get into the park?" asked Julia cautiously.

The boys nodded. "We paid our fee at the gate. At first we couldn't see any balloon, though, and we thought we'd been cheated," Sam replied.

"Where was it?" Julia demanded.

"Why, it was flat on the ground—just a huge piece of yellow silk all sewed together in squares," Henry explained. "On top was a mass of rope like a great fish net."

"And then the silk began to heave gently," added Sam. "You would swear the balloon was coming alive!" Sam had a poetic imagination.

"That was because the men from the gas company began filling the balloon with gas," said practical Henry.

Father cleared his throat and the children fell silent immediately. "It says in the paper that the gas company has agreed to install street lamps all the way up Broadway beyond Grand Street," he announced. "Now, that will be a fine thing. We'll have over a mile of well-lighted streets. New York is getting to be quite a city."

Seeing that Father was in a good mood, Julia boldly put a question. "Doesn't it tell in the paper about the Fourth of July celebration, Father? I wish we could go to see the balloon."

"Eh? Oh—that." Father rattled the pages. " 'Parade of military and firemen. Balloon ascension at Battery Park.' Well, I expect the proprietors of Castle Garden will make a mint of money out of the crowd."

"Please, Father, may we go?" Julia asked eagerly.

Named for her mother, who had died some years before, Julia was her father's favorite child. But Samuel Ward was so overcome with grief at the loss of his beautiful young wife that he had become stern and strictly religious. He expected Julia to be painfully good. Now, as he read further in the paper, he gave a snort of indignation. "Why, it says here that a woman is going up in that balloon! What are we coming to? No, indeed, Julia, you may not go to see such a shocking, vulgar sight."

"But Father," cried Julia, "what's wrong about it? I think she must be very brave, and I'd like to see her."

Father promptly began a lecture to the effect that all girls should stay at home and just be sweet and obedient. Julia listened in silence, thinking her own thoughts. That red hair of hers came from her mother's side of the family, and with it she inherited her warmhearted, independent nature.

One of Julia's ancestors on her mother's side was General Francis Marion, the "Swamp Fox" of revolutionary fame, who outwitted the British in South Carolina. Her little brother, Francis Marion Ward, was named for this hero, but Julia was the one who could outflank her opponents every time. When Father had finished, Julia quietly continued her campaign. "There will be patriotic speeches by some of the old soldiers at Battery Park, Father," she remarked. "Grandfather Ward told me so."

Mr. Ward smiled indulgently. "Father will be there, resplendent in his uniform, I expect. Probably he'll get to telling some of those old stories of his."

"Well, there aren't many Revolutionary heroes like your father left," remarked Aunt Eliza, stirring her coffee in a casual sort of way. "I expect he would like to have the older children come to hear him speak."

Samuel Ward glanced at Julia's pleading gray eyes. "Send for the carriage if you've a mind, Eliza," he said. "The older children may go, I suppose. Julia, pay close attention and try to learn something about your country. But mind you behave all morning, or you shan't go after all."

The look of forlorn hope on Julia's face changed instantly to joy. Her eyes shone with the glory of anticipation. "Oh, Father, I'll be good as gold!" she cried.

She'll grow up to be very beautiful, thought Samuel Ward, pride mingling with anxiety. "All right, all right," he said gruffly, as he left the room. "Mind you behave."

. . . .

"Mine Eyes Have Seen the Glory"

The city of Washington was seething with excitement by the time Julia got back to Willard's Hotel. Dispatch riders galloped through the streets. From time to time a detachment of infantry marched past the hotel with no sound save the rhythmic crunch of heavy boots and an occasional shouted command. Inside the hotel lobby, groups of half-hysterical people were trying in vain to make arrangements to get out of town.

Julia was not the kind of person to try to escape to the North while every road and railroad was needed to move troops. She could keep calm and, if need be, help her husband with the wounded. Meanwhile she was tired, so she went to bed and slept soundly.

About dawn, Julia awoke. Once more men were marching in the street below. As she lay listening, she thought about the men and boys on the road from Upton's Hill. The song she sang to them came back to her—but with new words. Julia lay perfectly still, while stanza after stanza sang itself over in her mind. Then she got up, and in the gray light of dawn she wrote down the words.

In the morning, Julia wondered if the whole thing had been a dream. She went to the desk and found a sheet of paper with her husband's Sanitary Commission heading. Her writing was hard to read because the light had been so poor. But here were the words which had come to her in the night:

"Mine eyes have seen the glory of the coming of the Lord;
He is trampling out the vintage where the grapes of wrath are stored;
He hath loosed the fateful lightning of his terrible swift sword;
His truth is marching on.

"I have seen Him in the watchfires of a hundred circling camps;
They have builded Him an altar in the evening dews and damps;
I can read His righteous sentence by the dim and flaring lamps;
His day is marching on.

"I have read a fiery gospel writ in burnished rows of steel:
'As ye deal with my contemners, so with you my grace shall deal;
Let the hero born of woman crush the serpent with his heel;
Since God is marching on.'

"He has sounded forth the trumpet that shall never call retreat;
He is sifting out the hearts of men before His judgment-seat;
Oh, be swift, my soul to answer Him! Be jubilant, my feet!
Our God is marching on.

"In the beauty of the lilies Christ was born across the sea,
With a glory in His bosom that transfigures you and me:
As He died to make men holy, let us die to make men free,
While God is marching on."

There was one more stanza, but Julia decided not to use it. She made one or two slight changes and showed the poem to Dr. Clarke and the other friends who had been with her the day before. "This is the song!" exclaimed Dr. Clarke. "I can just hear our boys singing these inspired words.

One of the ladies asked Julia for the original copy of the poem.

"Willard's Hotel
Julia W. Howe
to
Charlotte B. Whipple"

That is what Julia wrote on the other side of the sheet. Then she handed her friend what was, in time, to become a priceless historical manuscript.

After Julia got home to Boston she sent her

poem to the *Atlantic Monthly*. "What title would you like?" she asked the editor, and "The Battle Hymn of the Republic" was suggested. They paid her ten dollars, and she was pleased to see her "Battle Hymn" on the front page of the next number of the magazine. As far as Julia Ward Howe knew, she had merely written another poem. It was a good one, to be sure, but no one seemed to pay much attention to it.

However, the Rev. Charles Cardwell McCabe, who was known as the "singing chaplain" of the 122nd Ohio Regiment of Volunteers, read the *Atlantic Monthly*. When he saw the "Battle Hymn" he was so struck with it that he learned it by heart before he got up from his chair. He went right out among the soldiers and began to teach them the new song. It took, and it spread like wildfire.

In 1863, Chaplain McCabe was taken prisoner and sent to Libby Prison. The gaunt old building on the bank of the James River had once been Libby's ship chandlery. Now it was packed with prisoners of war who slept on the floor at night and took turns watching at the window by day, hoping that the armies of the North would soon come marching to their rescue.

Down in the cellar of the building, some men had recently tunneled their way to freedom. Now the dirt floor had been covered in with masonry, a bloodhound patrolled the prison along with the guards and discipline was very strict. Chaplain McCabe found the prisoners in a mood of desperate discouragement. They asked him eagerly for news of the war, but there was little he could tell them that afforded any comfort. The fortunes of the North were still at a low ebb. But he had a new song to sing—and Chaplain McCabe cheered his fellow prisoners with "The Battle Hymn of the Republic."

"Two of your officers are to be executed because of the escape of the men in the cellar," the prisoners were told. "Draw lots and see which of you are to die." There was nothing to do but obey. Chaplain McCabe's fine voice was heard singing, and the prisoners joined in:

"In the beauty of the lilies, Christ was born across the sea,
As He died to make men holy, let us die to make men free."

The officers chosen for execution marched away.

Next day, the two officers were brought back again, to everybody's surprise and joy. The order of execution had been countermanded. They were not to die after all.

The prisoners were given food only once a day. For a while they got bean soup and corn bread. They complained, for the soup was terrible. Soon they longed for some of that soup again, for now they got only the corn bread and not very much of that. Corn husks were ground up and added to the meal to make it go farther. Sometimes a cockroach was found, firmly baked into a prisoner's small square of bread. "He's probably very nourishing," joked Chaplain McCabe. "Cheer up, men. The reason we have so little food is plain to see. Our army must have cut off Confederate supplies. We are winning the war at last."

It was an up-hill job for the chaplain to encourage the prisoners. General McClellan, the little Napoleon, was discredited now. He had organizing ability, but in the field he was a hopeless procrastinator. General succeeded general, but the results were always the same—disaster for the North.

News came to Libby Prison that the North had been defeated once and for all—at Gettysburg! Then a Negro servant, old Ben, slipped in with the news that a flood on the Potomac had swept away Lee's pontoon bridge, and Gettysburg was a Northern victory. Chaplain McCabe led the prisoners as they sang:

"Mine eyes have seen the glory of the coming of the Lord."

Before the Civil War was over, Chaplain McCabe was released from Libby Prison. He was asked to speak to a large audience in Washington and tell about his experiences. He told what "The Battle Hymn of the Republic" meant, both to the Ohio Volunteers and to the prisoners of war.

"Who wrote this hymn, anyway?" people began asking each other.

Julia Ward Howe was still blissfully unconscious that she was famous. She went right on raising money for the war, taking care of the children and making her home a happy place for family, friends and neighbors. Then one day came a letter from the Hon. George Bancroft, famous historian. Would Mrs. Howe attend a celebration at the Century Club in New York in honor of the poet Bryant's seventieth birthday? Would she read a poem?

"Good gracious, the whole thing must be a mistake!" cried Julie. "Why, the best poets in this country will be there!" But she sat right down, anyway, and wrote some lines for Bryant's birthday. Julia really admired Bryant, and had no trouble thinking of pleasant things to say about him.

When she got on the train for New York, there was Oliver Wendell Holmes, bound for the same celebration. "Mrs. Howe, I will sit beside you, but you must not expect me to talk," he said. "I must spare my voice for the evening, when I am to read a poem at the Bryant celebration."

Julia's eyes twinkled. "Let's both keep quiet," she suggested. "I have a poem to read at the Bryant celebration, as well." Holmes, who had a good opinion of himself, stared at Julia in astonishment. He had supposed she was just a pretty woman he happened to know who was bound for New York on a shopping tour. In a few minutes he had forgotten all about saving his voice, for Julia was immensely clever in a battle of wits. The great Dr. Holmes couldn't help showing off a bit for such an attractive woman.

The celebration was a brilliant affair. Emerson spoke and Holmes read his poem, of course. But it was Julia Ward Howe who sat on the platform between Mr. Bancroft and Mr. Bryant.

"This is the poet who has written the most stirring lyric of the war," said Mr. Bryant. The people clapped and cheered. They also stared at Julia, for somehow they had imagined that the writer of "The Battle Hymn of the Republic" would be an elderly lady in a lace cap, or else a very strong-minded-looking female in spectacles.

A photograph, taken at this time, shows that Julia was an unusually beautiful woman. Her hair was parted and drawn smoothly down to accent the delicate oval of her face. Her mouth was sensitive and sweet, while her shadowy gray eyes were full of sympathy and imagination. She loved fashionable clothes but chose them with taste, so that now they seem quaint but not grotesque. Most Civil-War-time photographs were far from flattering. If Julia looked so lovely in her picture, it was no wonder that her New York audience sat up and applauded.

When she got home, Julia wrote all about how wonderful people had been to her. "I want to leave a record for my grandchildren," she said, laughing. "Such a thing could never happen again." But she was wrong, for this was only the beginning—the first recognition of the author of the "Battle Hymn." From now on, Julia Ward Howe was a famous woman and she led more and more of a public life.

. . . .

INDEPENDENCE DAY

Laura Ingalls Wilder

Farmer Boy *is the one book in the Wilder series devoted to the Wilder family. The other seven, beginning with* Little House in the Big Woods, *are concerned with the adventures of the Ingalls family as it pioneers westward into new country. In the last three books, beginning with* The Long Winter, *the Ingalls family and Almanzo Wilder meet and share the same vicissitudes and adventures. Laura marries Almanzo, and later writes this wonderful series of books, a saga of pioneering in this country. The Fourth of July described in the following episode must have been about 1867. One of the important things Almanzo Wilder's father did for his son was to give him a sense of values. Children will be interested perhaps in a comparison of prices then and now.*

Almanzo was eating breakfast before he remembered that this was the Fourth of July. He felt more cheerful.

It was like Sunday morning. After breakfast he scrubbed his face with soft soap till it shone, and he parted his wet hair and combed it sleekly down. He put on his sheep's-gray trousers and his shirt of French calico, and his vest and his short round coat.

Mother had made his new suit in the new style. The coat fastened at the throat with a little flap of the cloth, then the two sides slanted back to show his vest, and they rounded off over his trousers' pockets.

He put on his round straw hat, which Mother had made of braided oat-straws, and he was all dressed up for Independence Day. He felt very fine.

Father's shining horses were hitched to the shining, red-wheeled buggy, and they all drove away in the cool sunshine. All the country had a holiday air. Nobody was working in the fields, and along the road the people in their Sunday clothes were driving to town.

Father's swift horses passed them all. They passed by wagons and carts and buggies. They passed gray horses and black horses and dappled-gray horses. Almanzo waved his hat whenever he sailed past anyone he knew, and he would have been perfectly happy if only he had been driving that swift, beautiful team.

At the church sheds in Malone he helped Father unhitch. Mother and the girls and Royal hurried away. But Almanzo would rather help with the horses than do anything else. He couldn't drive them, but he could tie their halters and buckle on their blankets, and stroke their soft noses and give them hay.

Then he went out with Father and they walked on the crowded sidewalks. All the stores were closed, but ladies and gentlemen were walking up and down and talking. Ruffled little girls carried parasols, and all the boys were dressed up, like Almanzo. Flags were everywhere, and in the Square the band was playing "Yankee Doodle." The fifes tooted and the flutes shrilled and the drums came in with rub-a-dub-dub.

"Yankee Doodle went to town,
Riding on a pony,
He stuck a feather in his hat,
And called it macaroni!"

Even grown-ups had to keep time to it. And there, in the corner of the Square, were the two brass cannons!

The Square was not really square. The railroad made it three-cornered. But everybody called it the Square, anyway. It was fenced, and grass grew there. Benches stood in rows on the grass, and people were filing between the benches and sitting down as they did in church.

Almanzo went with Father to one of the best front seats. All the important men stopped to shake hands with Father. The crowd kept coming till all the seats were full, and still there were people outside the fence.

The band stopped playing, and the minister prayed. Then the band tuned up again and everybody rose. Men and boys took off their hats. The band played, and everybody sang.

"Oh, say, can you see by the dawn's early light,
What so proudly we hailed at the twilight's last gleaming,
Whose broad stripes and bright stars through the perilous night,
O'er the ramparts we watched were so gallantly streaming?"

From the top of the flagpole, up against the blue sky, the Stars and Stripes were fluttering. Everybody looked at the American flag, and Almanzo sang with all his might.

Then everyone sat down, and a Congressman stood up on the platform. Slowly and solemnly he read the Declaration of Independence.

"When in the course of human events it becomes necessary for one people . . . to assume among the powers of the earth the separate and equal station. . . . We hold these truths to be self-evident, that all men are created equal. . . ."

Almanzo felt solemn and very proud.

Then two men made long political speeches. One believed in high tariffs, and one believed in free trade. All the grown-ups listened hard, but Almanzo did not understand the speeches very well and he began to be hungry. He was glad when the band played again.

The music was so gay; the bandsmen in their blue and red and their brass buttons tootled merrily, and the fat drummer beat rat-a-tat-tat on the drum. All the flags were fluttering and everybody was happy, because they were free and independent and this was Independence Day. And it was time to eat dinner.

Almanzo helped Father feed the horses while Mother and the girls spread the picnic lunch on the grass in the churchyard. Many others were picnicking there, too, and after he had eaten all he could Almanzo went back to the Square.

There was a lemonade-stand by the hitching-posts. A man sold pink lemonade, a nickel a glass, and a crowd of the town boys were standing around him. Cousin Frank was there. Almanzo had a drink at the town pump, but Frank said he was going to buy lemonade. He had a nickel. He walked up to the stand and bought a glass of the pink lemonade and drank it slowly. He smacked his lips and rubbed his stomach and said:

"Mmmm! Why don't you buy some?"

"Where'd you get the nickel?" Almanzo asked. He had never had a nickel. Father gave him a penny every Sunday to put in the collection-box in church; he had never had any other money.

"My father gave it to me," Frank bragged. "My father gives me a nickel every time I ask him."

"Well, so would my father if I asked him," said Almanzo.

"Well, why don't you ask him?" Frank did not believe that Father would give Almanzo a nickel. Almanzo did not know whether Father would, or not.

"Because I don't want to," he said.

"He wouldn't give you a nickel," Frank said.

"He would, too."

"I dare you to ask him," Frank said. The other boys were listening. Almanzo put his hands in his pockets and said:

"I'd just as lief ask him if I wanted to."

"Yah, you're scared!" Frank jeered. "Double dare! Double dare!"

Father was a little way down the street, talking to Mr. Paddock, the wagon-maker. Almanzo walked slowly toward them. He was faint-hearted, but he had to go. The nearer he got to Father, the more he dreaded asking for a nickel. He had never before thought of doing such a thing. He was sure Father would not give it to him.

He waited till Father stopped talking and looked at him.

"What is it, son?" Father asked.

Almanzo was scared. "Father," he said.

"Well, son?"

"Father," Almanzo said, "would you—would you give me—a nickel?"

He stood there while Father and Mr. Paddock looked at him, and he wished he could get away. Finally Father asked:

"What for?"

Almanzo looked down at his moccasins and muttered:

"Frank had a nickel. He bought pink lemonade."

"Well," Father said, slowly, "if Frank treated you, it's only right you should treat him." Father put his hand in his pocket. Then he stopped and asked:

"Did Frank treat you to lemonade?"

Almanzo wanted so badly to get the nickel that he nodded. Then he squirmed and said:

"No, Father."

Father looked at him a long time. Then he took out his wallet and opened it, and slowly he took out a round, big silver half-dollar. He asked:

"Almanzo, do you know what this is?"

"Half a dollar," Almanzo answered.

"Yes. But do you know what half a dollar is?"

Almanzo didn't know it was anything but half a dollar.

"It's work, son," Father said. "That's what money is; it's hard work."

Mr. Paddock chuckled. "The boy's too young, Wilder," he said. "You can't make a youngster understand that."

"Almanzo's smarter than you think," said Father.

Almanzo didn't understand at all. He wished he could get away. But Mr. Paddock was looking at Father just as Frank looked at Almanzo when he double-dared him, and Father had said Almanzo was smart, so Almanzo tried to look like a smart boy. Father asked:

"You know how to raise potatoes, Almanzo?"

"Yes," Almanzo said.

"Say you have a seed potato in the spring, what do you do with it?"

"You cut it up," Almanzo said.

"Go on, son."

"Then you harrow—first you manure the field, and plow it. Then you harrow, and mark the ground. And plant the potatoes, and plow them, and hoe them. You plow and hoe them twice."

"That's right, son. And then?"

"Then you dig them and put them down cellar."

"Yes. Then you pick them over all winter; you throw out all the little ones and the rotten ones. Come spring, you load them up and haul them here to Malone, and you sell them. And if you get a good price, son, how much do you get to show for all that work? How much do you get for half a bushel of potatoes?"

"Half a dollar," Almanzo said.

"Yes," said Father. "That's what's in this half-dollar, Almanzo. The work that raised half a bushel of potatoes is in it."

Almanzo looked at the round piece of money that Father held up. It looked small, compared with all that work.

"You can have it, Almanzo," Father said. Almanzo could hardly believe his ears. Father gave him the heavy half-dollar.

"It's yours," said Father. "You could buy a sucking pig with it, if you want to. You could raise it, and it would raise a litter of pigs, worth four, five dollars apiece. Or you can trade that half-dollar for lemonade, and drink it up. You do as you want, it's your money."

Almanzo forgot to say thank you. He held the half-dollar a minute, then he put his hand in his pocket and went back to the boys by the lemonade-stand. The man was calling out,

"Step this way, step this way! Ice-cold lemonade, pink lemonade, only five cents a glass! Only half a dime, ice-cold pink lemonade! The twentieth part of a dollar!"

Frank asked Almanzo:

"Where's the nickel?"

"He didn't give me a nickel," said Almanzo, and Frank yelled:

"Yah, yah! I told you he wouldn't! I told you so!"

"He gave me half a dollar," said Almanzo.

The boys wouldn't believe it till he showed them. Then they crowded around, waiting for him to spend it. He showed it to them all, and put it back in his pocket.

"I'm going to look around," he said, "and buy me a good little sucking pig."

The band came marching down the street, and they all ran along beside it. The flag was gloriously waving in front, then came the buglers blowing and the fifers tootling and the drummer rattling the drumsticks on the drum. Up the street and down the street went the band, with all the boys following it, and then it stopped in the Square by the brass cannons.

Hundreds of people were there, crowding to watch.

The cannons sat on their haunches, pointing their long barrels upward. The band kept on playing. Two men kept shouting, "Stand back! Stand back!" and other men were pouring black powder into the cannons' muzzles and pushing it down with wads of cloth on long rods.

The iron rods had two handles, and two men pushed and pulled on them, driving the black powder down the brass barrels. Then all the boys ran to pull grass and weeds along the railroad tracks. They carried them by armfuls to the cannons, and the men crowded the weeds into the cannons' muzzles and drove them down with the long rods.

A bonfire was burning by the railroad tracks, and long iron rods were heating in it.

When all the weeds and grass had been packed tight against the powder in the cannons, a man took a little more powder in his hand and carefully filled the two little touchholes in the barrels. Now everybody was shouting,

"Stand back! Stand back!"

Mother took hold of Almanzo's arm and made him come away with her. He told her:

"Aw, Mother, they're only loaded with powder

and weeds. I won't get hurt, Mother. I'll be careful, honest." But she made him come away from the cannons.

Two men took the long iron rods from the fire. Everybody was still, watching. Standing as far behind the cannons as they could, the two men stretched out the rods and touched their red-hot tips to the touchholes. A little flame like a candle-flame flickered up from the powder. The little flames stood there burning; nobody breathed. Then—BOOM!

The cannons leaped backward, the air was full of flying grass and weeds. Almanzo ran with all the other boys to feel the warm muzzles of the cannons. Everybody was exclaiming about what a loud noise they had made.

"That's the noise that made the Redcoats run!" Mr. Paddock said to Father.

"Maybe," Father said, tugging his beard. "But it was muskets that won the Revolution. And don't forget it was axes and plows that made this country."

"That's so, come to think of it," Mr. Paddock said.

Independence Day was over. The cannons had been fired, and there was nothing more to do but hitch up the horses and drive home to do the chores.

That night when they were going to the house with the milk, Almanzo asked Father,

"Father, how was it axes and plows that made this country? Didn't we fight England for it?"

"We fought for Independence, son," Father said. "But all the land our forefathers had was a little strip of country, here between the mountains and the ocean. All the way from here west was Indian country, and Spanish and French and English country. It was farmers that took all that country and made it America."

"How?" Almanzo asked.

"Well, son, the Spaniards were soldiers, and high-and-mighty gentlemen that only wanted gold. And the French were fur-traders, wanting to make quick money. And England was busy fighting wars. But we were farmers, son; we wanted the land. It was farmers that went over the mountains, and cleared the land, and settled it, and farmed it, and hung on to their farms.

"This country goes three thousand miles west, now. It goes 'way out beyond Kansas, and beyond the Great American Desert, over mountains bigger than these mountains, and down to the Pacific Ocean. It's the biggest country in the world, and it was farmers who took all that country and made it America, son. Don't you ever forget that."

A STRANGE GAME OF HIDE-AND-SEEK

Olive W. Burt

This story tells of a lifelong interest beginning in childhood. The modest little book from which this chapter comes gives many examples of Burbank's keen observations and ingenious experiments when he was still only a boy. The book is easy to read as this episode shows and is one of a long series of popular biographies, Childhood of Famous Americans. *They are especially valuable for children who find reading difficult.*

"All who're out may come in free!" The children playing in the big shady yard took up the cry, but no one came in to the hide-and-seek "home."

"Luther!" Lizzie shouted as loud as she could. "Luther! Don't you hear? You can come in free!"

"Oh, he's gone off somewhere," said Henry crossly. "He's always forgetting that he's playing a game. Come on! I'll race you to the brook. Last one there's a Red Man!"

Away ran Henry, as fast as his bare feet could carry him across the grass, with Sarah and Lizzie close behind.

Alfred hung back. He couldn't beat the others to the brook and he didn't want to be a Red Man. He would go look for Luther.

It was a summer afternoon in the year 1856. The yard where the children were playing was around the old Burbank house. It was a lovely yard. Tall elm trees gave shade, and old apple trees spread their limbs to make good climbing easy.

Bright flower beds here and there made pretty

patterns against the grass. Some were round, some were diamond-shaped, and some beds were in the form of hearts. Farther down the lot were the vegetable garden and the orchard.

The house itself was of red brick. The front windows looked out on the country road that wound past, wide and dusty, to the town of Lancaster, Massachusetts, three miles away. It was a big, squarish house, with a white frame wing snuggled up against one end. In this wing Luther, the oldest of the "three little Burbanks," had been born seven years before.

Now Alfred, the "middle-between" little Burbank, ran across the yard toward the rock wall. It separated his mother's garden from the meadow. He was pretty sure he knew where to find his brother.

Alfred made no noise as he climbed over the wall and went searching among the deep grass and daisies and clover blossoms. It wasn't long before he came upon Luther, half-hidden in the grass. Alfred stood and watched him, wondering what his brother could be doing.

Luther was still playing hide-and-seek, but his playmates were not boys and girls. They were honeybees!

He had hidden from the other children in the deep clover of the meadow behind the rock wall. As he sat there waiting for a good chance to come in free, his bright blue eyes were alert. He looked at the clover blossoms and the bees that droned above them. As he watched, he saw something he had never noticed before.

A big, fat honeybee came zooming over the wall. It stopped on a blossom. Then it pushed its hairy body deep into the pink cup of the flower. It buried its head among the curled petals as if it wanted to get every drop of nectar.

Luther smiled as he watched the greedy bee. He was still smiling when the bee backed out of the flower, spread its wings and flew away. Luther watched it fly a little distance and light on another pink blossom.

As the boy watched, he forgot the game and his playmates in the yard. He was interested in the flight of this fat, greedy bee. It flew right over daisies and buttercups. It paid no attention to the beautiful red roses that spilled over the garden wall.

Luther didn't blame the bee for passing over the daisies and buttercups. They were not nearly so fragrant as the clover. But to fly right past the roses as if he couldn't see them! Luther couldn't believe it. He got to his feet and followed the bee.

Luther was not afraid of losing this bee and following another. To his clear blue eyes each bee was different from every other bee. Long ago he had noticed that every daisy in the field was different from its neighbors. Each rose, too, had its own special form and color, so that anyone who looked closely enough could tell it from all others.

He was still watching the bee when Alfred found him. "What are you doing?" Alfred asked.

Luther told him about the bee, but Alfred didn't care what the bee did. "You spoiled our game," he reminded Luther. "Henry and the girls have gone home."

Luther was sorry. "I forgot," he said.

Just then their mother's voice came across the meadow. "Luther!" she called. "Alfred!"

It was suppertime already! The two little boys started up through the meadow toward the house.

They looked a great deal alike as they ran along together, though Luther was seven and Alfred was not yet five years old. They were dressed alike too. Both wore jeans—long trousers made of heavy gray cloth—and cotton shirts. They wore neither shoes nor stockings. Mr. Burbank was a well-to-do farmer, and there was good lumber in his woods and fine red clay for bricks in the hollow. The lumber and bricks brought him extra money. But Mrs. Burbank knit all the family stockings by hand, and it took a long time. The boys wore them only when they dressed up on Sundays.

Luther was rather small for his age, with light yellow hair that curled up in front. His eyes were blue and merry, and he was fond of jokes and tricks. Alfred was large for his age and more sturdily built than his brother.

When the boys reached the house, they found that their mother had already set the table. Two-year-old Emmy was in her high chair, pounding her spoon against her mug.

Luther went to the table and started to count the plates. His mother smiled at him.

"It is only Cousin Levi," she said. "Better get washed, Luther."

Luther hurried to the wash bench near the pump in the big kitchen. He was glad it was Cousin Levi, for now he could find out about the bee. And he was hungry and wanted his supper. Luther was shy with strangers. Whenever he found an extra place set for someone he didn't know, he would slip away and stay in the meadow while the family ate. Sometimes he would sit under the open kitchen window so that he could hear the talk. Many of his father's visitors were preachers or teachers or students who knew the things Luther himself wanted to know.

But Cousin Levi was different. Luther was never shy with this tall, good-natured teacher who explained things to him.

As soon as he had a chance, after grace was said, Luther asked Cousin Levi about the bee.

"He spoiled our hide-and-seek game!" Alfred said crossly.

"Luther was playing hide-and-seek with the bee!" Cousin Levi laughed. "And I think I can explain why the bee's goal was always clover blossoms."

Luther stopped eating to listen.

"It seems that some instinct causes a bee to go to only one kind of flower in a day," Cousin Levi went on. "If he starts on clover blossoms, he goes to clover blossoms all day long. If he starts with roses, he goes only to roses. In that way, he fills his pouch with only one kind of nectar. His fuzzy back gets covered with only one kind of pollen—"

"What's pollen?" asked Alfred.

"It's a sort of flower dust that makes plants grow," Cousin Levi answered. "Roses must have pollen from other roses, and daisies must have pollen from other daisies if they are to form seeds so that we can have new plants next year."

"I thought the bees' job was just to make honey," Luther said. "I didn't know that they had two jobs to do."

"And maybe the pollen-carrying job is the more important," Mr. Burbank suggested.

"I don't think so," Alfred said. He spread a big spoonful of honey on his brown bread. "I think making honey is more important."

"Me, too! Me, too!" shouted Emmy, and everyone laughed.

But Luther was thinking, "I'm glad I played hide-and-seek with that bee!"

from DR. GEORGE WASHINGTON CARVER

Shirley Graham and George D. Lipscomb

One of the most original scientists this country has ever produced was the mild-mannered, dedicated Negro, Dr. George Washington Carver. These two chapters show the tragic beginning and provide just a glimpse of the wonderful fruition of a life of service. Every young American should read the whole biography with gratitude for and pride in the achievements of this great and humble man.

Was the Tiny Boy Worth a Horse?

"Heraus! Heraus mit sie! I say—get up!"

It was still dark outside, but down in the kitchen the German farmer was shaking the wooden ladder that led to the boy's place under the eaves.

"Get up—you! *Raus mit!* Or—must I come up?" Now the voice was threatening and the tiny black boy shivered as he tumbled off his pallet. They said he was six or seven years old, plenty old enough to milk the cow, tend the hog and chickens and do something about keeping weeds from choking the already sparse garden. But the rusty little legs and arms were like pipe-stems, his hands bony, with long, curling fingers, his face was pinched. In that little dark face, his eyes burned like coals of fire. And, even though he could not speak, Frau Carver had noted that he saw everything.

Yesterday, he had hoed in the garden for many hours. His back still ached with fatigue. Now, spindly legs still trembling with sleep, he clumsily crawled down the ladder and there in the kitchen was Frau Carver, still swathed in yards and yards of sleeping clothes, on her head a nightcap. But how glad he was to see her!

"No! No, *mein Mann,"* she was saying to her husband. "He is too small. After yesterday, he is too tired. I have work for him to do in the house this morning. He cannot go."

"And who will help me in the fields?" the farmer asked angrily. "Have we money? Our crops, poor as they are, will rot. We will starve and he also!"

"God is good," the woman's voice was soothing. "Not a sparrow falls that he does not know. Let be the little fellow. Soon he will be big and strong." The little boy's eyes were fast upon her, drinking in every word.

"O weh!" exploded Farmer Carver. "I had a *horse*—" he paused significantly, "and now," his eyes fell on the shrinking little boy—*"this!"*

There was a twinkle in his wife's eyes as she replied, "He was not so much of a horse—that one!"

"Stupid!" And the man went out slamming the door behind him.

Frau Carver laid her large hand on the little boy's head. His eyes were slowly filling with tears. It was true. He couldn't talk.

"Bah," she laughed. "He does not mean that. Quick now, make the fire. Once he has something in that stomach, all will be well."

And the clean, starched smell of her wide skirts filled his being with comfort.

The distant Ozark hills showed black against a faintly colored sky as Farmer Carver crossed the yard with its numerous outhouses and approached the huge barn. He sighed as he thought how empty it now was. He stamped his feet partly to keep them warm and partly because of the helpless rage. Of course, that child could help him very little, but what was he to do? Once he would have looked out over blue grass pasture land and a checkerboard of wheat and corn prairie. Once the large frame house of his nearest neighbor could not be seen for the thick orchard of fruit trees. But, now, the land itself seemed starved and beaten and only the smoked blackened ruins of his neighbor's house remained.

More than any other border state, Missouri had been torn and devastated by the War between the States. Since 1854 when an Act of Congress left the issue of slavery to be decided by the individual states, Kansas and Missouri had been caught in the struggle between free and slave states. Pro-Union and Pro-Southern groups made the war a peculiar horror. And the prosperous German farmers on the Ozark plateau suffered most. Hard-working, industrious immigrants, they had come to settle new homes in this land of plenty. The idea of slavery was abhorrent to them. When they needed extra help, they sometimes bought a few slaves and treated them as they were accustomed to treating hired help in Europe—as dependent members of their household. This attitude did not endear the German farmers to their slave-owning neighbors and when difficulties arose, it was upon the immigrants that their fury was lashed.

Moses Carver saw his land and ownings dwindle before the storm. He could not hire men to work his farm and he would not encourage the traffic of poor human beings, most of whom he suspected had been kidnapped.

At that time, Carver's wife had Mary, a soft-spoken, gentle slave girl, to help about the house. Mary's husband was owned on a huge plantation not many miles away. Often she had begged the German farmer to buy him, but George was a valuable slave, and his owner was a hard master. Sometimes weeks passed before George could get away to see his wife and three children. So it was a long time before they knew he was killed—falling from an ox team, they said. After that Mary was very silent, except at night when she sang her baby to sleep.

Farmer Carver's face softened as he looked across the field at the tumbled log cabin where Mary and her children had lived. Of course his wife was right. How could he expect that poor sick baby to work? He'd never be strong.

He struggled with the heavy barn door, finally getting it back upon its rusty hinges. His eyes fell upon the dust-covered harness hanging high above an empty stall. His anger stirred faintly again. But she had no right to say the horse was worthless! That he would not forgive!

Five years had passed since that bitter cold night when he had hurried home from the village, disturbed by that ominous notice: "Keep a careful watch on your slaves! Nightriders have crossed the border!" The settlers in Diamond Grove were bolting their doors and locking their gates with caution. Snatching slaves was more profitable than horse-thieving or rustling cattle. Though the War between the States was nearing an end, slaves still brought good prices in the markets of Arkansas and Texas.

When he reached home, Mary had already gone to her cabin. He heard her softly singing to her babies as he examined the latch. He had put his horse up, carefully bolting the door. Nightriders would take anything.

Susan had already heard the news and was worried. He spoke lightly of the whole matter.

"But I hear they crossed the river with some slaves," his wife said.

"Probably headed back the other way then."

"You can't be sure," Susan replied.

"Well, they'll not bother us. They can see I've got no slaves such as they want."

"Perhaps we'd better bring Mary and the children into the house to live," Frau Carver suggested.

"Oh, they'll be all right. The slavers are looking for men to work."

But he had been wrong. Late in the night he heard the scream. It was Mary. He grabbed his gun and ran out into the yard. But in the blackness he could see nothing. Only the galloping of horses and the slave woman's muffled cries came back to him out of the night. He rushed to the cabin. On the ground outside, her head bleeding, lay Mary's little girl. The little boy stood over his sister, whimpering. Inside, the cabin was empty. Mother and baby were gone!

By this time Frau Carver was calling.

There were no telephones in those days. It was several hours later that Farmer Carver reached the village of Diamond Grove and rounded up help. He was not alone in his trouble. Several slaves had been stolen that night and soon a posse was formed. Farmer Carver could not go with them. The little slave girl had died before he left the house, and Frau Carver was almost hysterical. One of the women offered to return with him to her.

"Could we go back in your cart?" Farmer Carver asked. "My horse is faster than anything the nightriders have. I'd like to let one of the men ride fast on horseback to follow the raiders."

This was agreed upon.

"What shall we do if we catch up with them," asked one of the men. "They won't give up your slaves easily."

"Bargain with them," answered Farmer Carver. "My wife says we must get Mary back. I'm not a rich man, but I'll pay anything in reason."

"Did you bring money with you?" asked a second man.

Farmer Carver frowned. "No, and you'll need money. I'll tell you," he thought a moment, "give them the horse if necessary, but," he added quickly, "only if necessary. If they'll return, let them do so, and I'll pay them."

The men rode off. Days passed with no word. But nearly a week later they appeared at Farmer Carver's farm and told what had happened.

The nightriders had evaded them, thrown them off the trail and appeared gone. But the posse had waited at the border and finally they had come upon them trying to slip across. No shots were fired for fear of killing the slaves, and finally the thieves agreed to take the horse in exchange for the mother and baby.

"Tie him to a tree, retire out of sight. We'll examine the horse, and, when you hear us blow a horn, come and get your slave and her baby."

The men did not trust them, but a storm had come up and they realized they were at the mercy of the nightriders. So they had tied the horse to a tree and gone six hundred paces around the bend of the river. When they heard the horn it was far away and they knew that the nightriders had already put a mile or so between them. They dashed forward, found the baby soaking wet and shaking with cold on the ground by the tree, but the mother was nowhere about. The nightriders had tricked them and had taken her off with them.

When Frau Carver heard this story, tears had run down her cheeks. She had taken the dirty, soggy bundle in which lay the still form of the child. At first, they thought it was dead, but after a long time her tender ministrations brought some warmth back into the chilled frame. For days and weeks a racking cough choked the feeble breath until it seemed the baby could not live and even when life seemed promised, the baby's growth and development seemed stunted. But Frau Carver would not be discouraged.

"Mary's child must live—he will live!" She said it over and over again.

And at last, Mary's child did take a grip on life. He stood, he walked. He grew a little, but he could not speak. The violent cough, it seemed, had torn his vocal chords. Try as he might, he could not form words. Sometimes he uttered little squeaking noises.

Of Mary they had never heard again. So all that they had gotten for their valuable horse was this poor, weakened, speechless child. Farmer Carver shook his head dismally. What was he to do? He moved from one morning chore to another, hardly noticing that the sun was shining. Then he felt a gentle tug on his coat.

There beside him stood the little boy. He was smiling and pointing towards the house. Farmer Carver understood.

"So," he said heartily, "breakfast is ready. Well, I am ready for it. *Raus mit!*"

And taking the little brown hand in his, the big farmer strode across the yard. The little boy smiled happily. Frau Carver was right, as usual. The big man didn't mean it!

. . . .

"Gentlemen, I Give You the Peanut!"

For three days now the Ways and Means Committee of the House of Representatives had been listening to reasons why they should or should not pass a certain tariff bill which had come up before the house. The bill had been introduced as an emergency bill and was designed to protect the producers of this country from infringement of their rights by putting a high tariff on the same products as they came into the country. Rice, for instance, could be raised in China for a few cents a bushel. In 1921 China was not at war and coolies worked for next to nothing. It cost so little to raise the rice that even after shipping it over here, it could sell for much less than the rice raised in our own country. Our growers did not want such competition.

The Congressman from South Dakota quite agreed—about rice and wheat and corn. But, as the Congressman from Pennsylvania said, and not too softly, the hearings were becoming tedious. Before the Committee had come spokesmen for meat packers, poultry farmers, dairymen, manufacturers, date growers, walnut growers. All of them brought statistics which they presented in a highly efficient manner. Now, to cap the climax somebody from the Virginia-Carolina Cooperative Peanut Exchange was complaining because they could not sell their peanuts! This was carrying the matter too far. Peanuts! Monkey-food, boys called them. Fine to munch at a circus, but surely nobody was seriously thinking of including *peanuts* in a tariff bill!

The Congressman from Michigan got up and wandered out. Another man representing the New York Peanut Association was pointing out that "whereas the present tariff imposes duty of three-eighths of one cent per pound on unshelled peanuts and three-fourths of one cent on shelled peanuts it affords no protection to American producers. We are asking that—" The voice went on. Sheets were being rustled. Somebody dropped a book.

One of the officials of the United Peanut Growers Association groaned audibly and whispered to the man beside him, "It's no use, Bill. We're sunk!"

"Steady," whispered back the other man, "it's two-thirty. This room's so crowded, we can't see who's in the back. Maybe he's here."

The speaker had finished and the chairman fitted his glasses and peered at the sheet before him. "Thank you, Mr. Smith. Now," he looked closely, "Mr. Carver—is Mr. Carver in the room?"

The two officials held their breath. There was a movement near the door where several men were standing. No one had come forward, and the chairman said, "We'll go on. I guess Mr. Carver is not here. Will Mr. "

"Pardon me, sir," a high, shrill voice was heard in the back of the room, "this case is heavy and awkward. It's difficult to get through."

Heads were turned and a way cleared in the aisle. Then the Congressmen saw the slender, slightly stooped Negro, in his green-black alpaca, carrying a large wooden case. Under his arm was the old golf cap. Having reached the front of the room, he eased the case to the floor, stuffed the cap in his pocket and stood waiting. The chairman stared at him.

"What—what—?"

"I am George Washington Carver."

"Oh—oh, yes. You've come to speak on the tariff."

Several gentlemen in the room could not help laughing. One man asked bluntly, "What do you know about the Hawley-Smoot bill?" There was laughter.

But the old man turned and with a twinkle in his eye said, "Not a thing. Do you?" When the laughter had died down he added, smiling, "I've come to talk about peanuts!"

The chairman had to rap for order. He said

rather sternly, "Very well, Mr. Carver, will you please come to the stand? You have ten minutes."

They leaned forward to see as the unusual figure stepped up, opened his case and began talking.

"I've been asked by the United Peanut Growers Association to tell you something about the possibility of the peanut and its possible extension," he began. "I come from Tuskegee, Alabama, where I am engaged in agricultural research work. I have given some attention to the peanut and can tell you that it is one of the very richest of all the products of the soil—rich in food value, rich in properties of its chemical constituents, and wonderfully rich in possibilities for utilization."

The Congressmen were leaning forward, their eyes eager. Now the Negro opened his case and was removing the contents: bottles of every size, description and color, little boxes, several small plaques.

"If I may have a little space to put these things down," he suggested. And the clerk quickly cleared the table for him.

"Thank you," said Mr. Carver. "Now I should like to exhibit them to you. I am just going to touch a few high places here and there, because in ten minutes you will tell me to stop. These are a few of the products which we have developed from the peanut." He held up a tube. "This is breakfast food containing peanut and sweet potato—twin brothers. It is wholesome, easily digested and delicious in flavor. A perfectly balanced diet with all the nutriments in it could be made from the sweet potato and peanut."

One of the Congressmen took the tube in his hand and examined it.

"Here is ice cream powder made from the peanut," continued Mr. Carver. "Simply mixed with water, it produces an unusually rich and delicious ice cream, not to be distinguished from ice cream made with pure cream." He held up several small bottles of different color. "In these bottles are dyes extracted from the skin of peanuts. I have found thirty different dyes. They have been tested in the laboratory and found to hold their colors and to be harmless to the skin. Here is a substitute for quinine. We can hardly overestimate the medicinal properties of the peanut. They are many and varied. These are various kinds of food for live stock. You will find that cattle thrive on them and the increase in milk is pronounced."

He looked up at the wall clock and remarked. "I see my time is about up. I should like to say that the soil and climate of the South is particularly suited to the cultivation of peanuts and that they could be produced in much greater quantities if a larger market for them were developed."

He stopped and began gathering up his bottles. The Congressmen looked at each other with amazement. Mr. Garner, from the back of the room, called out, "Mr. Chairman, all this is very interesting. I think his time should be extended."

"Very well, gentlemen," answered the chairman, "do you all agree?"

"Yes! Yes!" they answered in one voice.

"Will you continue, Mr. Carver," asked the chairman, smiling.

"I shall be happy to do so, sir."

From the front row Mr. Rainey asked, "Is the varied use of the peanut increasing?"

"Oh, yes," came the quick reply, "we are just beginning to know its value."

"In that case, is it not going to be such a valuable product that the more we have of them here the better we are off?"

"Well, now that depends. It depends upon the problems that these other gentlemen have brought before you," declared Mr. Carver, with a smile.

"Could we get too much of them—they being so valuable for stock food and everything else?" asked a man at the back of the room.

"Well, of course, we would have to have protection for them." There was laughter. "That is, we could not allow other countries to come in and take over our rights."

"I thought you said you didn't know anything about tariff," called out a voice.

"Well, I know it's what keeps the other fellow out of our business!" replied the old man. When the laughter had died down he went on, "I wish to say here in all sincerity that America produces better peanuts than any other part of the world, so far as I have been able to find out."

"Then," said Mr. Rainey, "we need not fear these inferior peanuts from abroad at all. They would not compete with our better peanuts."

"Well, you know that's like everything else. You know some people like oleomargarine just as well as they do butter. So sometimes you have to protect a good thing."

"The dairy people did not ask for a tax on oleomargarine," Mr. Oldfield spoke up, "but they did put a tax on butter."

"And," said Mr. Garner, "they did use the taxing power to put it out of business."

"Oh, yes, yes, sir. That is all the tariff means—to put the other fellow out." There was much laughter again. The twinkling eyes turned to the chairman, "Maybe—maybe—I'd better stop!"

But the chairman leaned forward, wiping his eyes, "Go ahead, brother. Your time is unlimited."

"Well," picking up a small bottle, "here is milk from peanuts."

Mr. Oldfield laughed. "Don't you think we ought to put a tax on that peanut milk so as to keep it from competing with the dairy products?"

"No, sir. It is not going to affect the dairy product. It has a distinct value all its own."

"Why won't it replace the dairy product?" someone asked.

"We do not now have as much milk and butter as we need in the United States."

"How does it go in punch?" asked a teasing voice.

"Well," came the grave answer, "I'll show some punches."

"Attaboy!"

"Here is one with orange, here one with lemon, and this one with cherry!" Each time holding up a bottle with different colored liquids. "Here is instant coffee which already has in it cream and sugar, here is the preparation for making regular coffee. Here is buttermilk, Worchestershire sauce, pickles—all made from the peanut!"

There was a moment of breathless silence. Then someone asked, "Did you make all those products yourself?"

"Yes, sir, they are made in the research laboratory. That's what a research laboratory is for. The sweet potato products number one hundred and seven up to date."

Mr. Garner leaned forward, "What? I didn't catch that last statement."

"From sweet potatoes we have made ink, relishes, pomade, mucilage, to mention only a few things. But I must stick to peanuts." There was laughter. "Here are mock oysters which would fool most of you. I have developed recipes for mock meat dishes from peanuts. They are delicious. We are going to use less and less meat as science develops the products of nature."

"So, you're going to ruin the live stock business!" came a voice.

"Oh, no, but peanuts can be eaten when meat can't. Peanuts are the perfect food. They are always safe. God has given them to us for our use. He has revealed to me some of the wonders of this fruit of His earth. In the first chapter of Genesis we are told, 'Behold, I have given you every herb that bears seed upon the face of the earth, and every tree bearing seed. To you it shall be meat.' That's what He means about it—meat. There is everything there to strengthen, nourish and keep the body alive and healthy."

The chairman cut in here to ask, "Mr. Carver, where did you go to school?"

"The last school I attended was Agricultural College of Iowa. You doubtless remember Mr. Wilson, who served in the Cabinet here so long, Secretary James Wilson. He was my teacher for six years."

Several Congressmen nodded their heads. "What research laboratory do you work in now?" asked one.

"I am at Tuskegee Institute, Tuskegee, Alabama."

Mr. Carew rose, "You have rendered this committee a great service."

"I think," said Mr. Garner, "he is entitled to the thanks of the committee."

Every member stood up, clapping heartily.

"Did the Institute send you here or did you come of your own volition?"

"I was asked to come by the United Peanut Growers Association to talk about," he paused and his eyes twinkled again,—"peanuts!"

There was more warm, hearty laughter. One Congressman called out, "Come again soon, and bring the rest of your products with you."

The bottles had been carefully replaced in the case. The chairman leaned forward and said sincerely, "We want to compliment you, sir, on the way you have handled your subject."

Dr. Carver bowed with gracious dignity, presented his brief to the clerk and walked quietly from the room.

"Well, I'll be blowed!" The official of the United Peanut Growers Association wiped the perspiration from his brow.

"And you were going to tell him what to say!" commented his companion.

"Aw, shut up!" grinned the official.

The committee moved that the hearings were finished. Its members rose, adjourned to another room and voted to include the peanut in the Emergency H.R. 2435 Tariff Bill.

In the late afternoon sunshine an insignificant black man paused one moment under the sleeping arch, then descended the Capitol steps.

It was over. Now, he could go back to his laboratory!

from THE WRIGHT BROTHERS

Quentin Reynolds

The Wright Brothers, *one of the fine books in the Landmark Series, carries the two brothers through their successful flight at Kitty Hawk, but the foundation for that triumph is to be found in the second chapter given here "Get It Right on Paper." The book is fascinating and easy reading.*

Learning from Mother

Susan Wright wasn't like other mothers.

She was younger and prettier than most other mothers, and she liked to laugh and she liked to play games with her three youngest children; Wilbur, who was eleven; Orville, who was seven; and Katharine, who was four.

The other mothers would shake their heads and say, "Susan Wright spoils those children; lets 'em do anything they want. No good will come of it."

But Susan Wright only laughed. In the summer she'd pack a picnic lunch and she, the two boys and little Kate (no one ever called her Katharine) would go and spend a day in the woods. Mrs. Wright knew the name of every bird and she could tell a bird by his song. Wilbur and Orville learned to tell birds too.

One day they sat on the banks of a river near Dayton, where they lived. Wilbur and Orville were fishing. Everyone called Wilbur "Will," and of course Orville was "Orv." The fish weren't biting very well. Suddenly a big bird swooped down, stuck his long bill into the river, came out with a tiny fish, and then swooped right up into the sky again.

"What makes a bird fly, Mother?" Wilbur asked.

"Their wings, Will," she said. "You notice they move their wings and that makes them go faster."

"But Mother," Will said, not quite satisfied, "that bird that just swooped down didn't even move his wings. He swooped down, grabbed a fish, and then went right up again. He never moved his wings at all."

"The wind doesn't just blow *toward* you or *away* from you," she said. "It blows *up* and *down,* too. When a current of air blows up, it takes the bird up. His wings support him in the air."

"If we had wings, then we could fly too, couldn't we, Mother?" Wilbur asked.

"But God didn't give us wings." She laughed.

"Maybe we could make wings," Wilbur insisted.

"Maybe," his mother said thoughtfully. "But I don't know. No one ever did make wings that would allow a boy to fly."

"I will some day," Wilbur said, and Orville nodded and said, "I will, too."

"Well, when you're a little older maybe you can try," their mother said.

That was another thing about Susan Wright. Most other mothers would have thought this to be foolish talk. Most other mothers would have said, "Oh, don't be silly, who ever heard of such nonsense!" But not Susan Wright. She knew that even an eleven-year-old boy can have ideas of his own, and just because they happened to come from an eleven-year-old head—well, that didn't make them foolish. She never treated her children as if they were babies, and perhaps that's why they liked to go fishing with her or on picnics with her. And that's why they kept asking her questions. She always gave them sensible answers.

They asked their father questions too, but he

was a traveling minister and he was away a lot.

"It's getting chilly," Mrs. Wright said suddenly. "Look at those gray clouds, Will."

Wilbur looked up. "It's going to snow, I bet," he said happily.

"No more picnics until next Spring," his mother said. "Yes, it looks like snow. We'd better be getting home."

As they reached home, the first big white snowflakes started to fall. They kept falling all that night and all the next day. It was the first real snowstorm of the year.

In the morning the wind was blowing so fiercely that Wilbur found it hard to walk to the barn where the wood was stored. The wind was so strong it almost knocked him down. He burst through the kitchen door with an armful of wood for the stove, and he told his mother about the wind.

"The thing to do is to lean forward into the wind," she said. "Bend over, and that way you get closer to the ground and you get under the wind."

That night when Wilbur had to make the trip for more wood, he tried his mother's idea. To his surprise it worked! When he was bent over, the wind didn't seem nearly so strong.

After a few days the wind stopped, and now the whole countryside was covered with snow. Wilbur and Orville, with little Kate trailing behind, hurried to the Big Hill not far from the house.

Orville's schoolmates were all there with their sleds. It was a good hill to coast down because no roads came anywhere near it, and even if they had, it wouldn't have mattered. This was 1878 and there were no automobiles. Horse-drawn sleighs traveled the roads in winter. The horses had bells fastened to their collars, and as they jogged along the bells rang and you could hear them a mile away.

Most of the boys had their own sleds; not the flexible fliers boys have now, but old-fashioned sleds with two wooden runners. No one ever thought of owning a "bought" sled. In those days a boy's father made a sled for him.

The boys who had sleds of their own let Wilbur and Orville ride down the hill with them. Ed Sines and Chauncey Smith and Johnny Morrow and Al Johnston all owned sleds, but they liked to race one another down the long hill. When this happened Wilbur and Orville just had to stand there and watch. Late that afternoon the boys came home, with little Kate trailing behind, and their mother noticed that they were very quiet. She was wise as well as very pretty, and she soon found out why they were unhappy.

"Why doesn't Father build us a sled?" Wilbur blurted out.

"But Father is away, Will," his mother said gently. "And you know how busy he is when he is at home. He has to write stories for the church paper and he has to write sermons. Now suppose we build a sled together."

Wilbur laughed. "Whoever heard of anyone's mother building a sled?"

"You just wait," his mother said. "We'll build a better sled than Ed Sines has. Now get me a pencil and a piece of paper."

"You goin' to build a sled out of paper?" Orville asked in amazement.

"Just wait," she repeated.

Get It Right on Paper

Will and Orv brought their mother a pencil and paper, and she went to the minister's desk and found a ruler. Then she sat down at the kitchen table. "First we'll draw a picture of the sled," she said.

"What good is a picture of a sled?" Orville asked.

"Now Orville, watch Mother." She picked up the ruler in one hand and the pencil in the other.

"We want one like Ed Sines has," Orville said.

"When you go coasting, how many boys will Ed Sines's sled hold?" she asked.

"Two," Wilbur said.

"We'll make this one big enough to hold three," she said. "Maybe you can take Kate along sometimes." The outline of a sled began to appear on the paper. As she drew it she talked. "You see, Ed's sled is about four feet long. I've seen it often enough. We'll make this one five feet long. Now, Ed's sled is about a foot off the ground, isn't it?"

Orville nodded, his eyes never leaving the drawing that was taking shape. It was beginning to look like a sled now, but not like the sleds the other boys had.

"You've made it too low," Will said.

"You want a sled that's faster than Ed's sled, don't you?" His mother smiled. "Well, Ed's sled is at least a foot high. Our sled will be lower—closer to the ground. It won't meet so much wind resistance."

"Wind resistance?" It was the first time Wilbur had ever heard the expression. He looked blankly at his mother.

"Remember the blizzard last week?" she asked. "Remember when you went out to the woodshed and the wind was so strong you could hardly walk to the shed? I told you to lean over, and on the next trip to the woodshed you did. When you came back with an armful of wood you laughed and said, 'Mother, I leaned 'way forward and got under the wind.' You were closer to the ground and you were able to lessen the wind resistance. Now, the closer to the ground our sled is the less wind resistance there will be, and the faster it will go."

"Wind resistance . . . wind resistance," Wilbur repeated, and maybe the airplane was born in that moment. Certainly neither Will nor Orville Wright ever forgot that first lesson in speed.

"How do you know about these things, Mother?" Wilbur asked.

"You'd be surprised how much mothers know, Will." She laughed. She didn't tell the boys that when she was a little girl at school her best subject had been arithmetic. It just came naturally to her. It was the same when she went to high school. And when she went to college, algebra and geometry were her best subjects. That was why she knew all about things like "wind resistance."

Finally she finished the drawing. The boys leaned over the table to look at it. This sled was going to be longer than Ed's sled and much narrower. Ed's sled was about three feet wide. This one looked as if it would be only half that wide.

"You made it narrow," Wilbur said shrewdly, "to make it faster. The narrower it is, the less wind resistance."

"That's right." His mother nodded. "Now let's put down the exact length of the runners and the exact width of the sled."

"But that's only a paper sled," Orville protested.

"If you get it right on paper," she said calmly, "it'll be right when you build it. Always remember that."

"'If you get it right on paper, it'll be right when you build it,'" Wilbur repeated, and his mother looked at him sharply. Sometimes Will seemed older than his eleven years. Little Orville was quick to give you an answer to anything, but as often as not he'd forget the answer right away. When Will learned something he never forgot it.

"Mother, you make all your clothes," Wilbur said thoughtfully. "You always make a drawing first."

"We call that the pattern," his mother said. "I draw and then cut out a pattern that's exactly the size of the dress I am going to make. And . . ."

"If the pattern is right, it'll be right when you make the dress," he finished. She nodded.

"Now you two boys get started on your sled." She smiled. "There are plenty of planks out in the barn. Find the very lightest ones. Don't use planks with knots in them. You saw the planks to the right size, Will—don't let Orville touch the saw."

"May we use Father's tools?" Wilbur asked breathlessly.

His mother nodded. "I don't think your father will mind. I know you'll be careful with them. Just follow the drawing exactly," she warned once more.

The two boys, followed by little Kate, hurried out to the barn. Both realized that this was an important occasion. Wilbur always chopped the wood for the stove when his father was away, but he had never been allowed to use the gleaming tools that lay in his father's tool chest.

Three days later their sled was finished. They pulled it out of the barn and asked their mother to inspect it. She had her tape measure with her and she measured it. The runners were exactly the length she had put down in her drawing. In fact, the boys had followed every direction she had given them. The runners gleamed. Orville had polished them with sandpaper until they were as smooth as silk.

"We thought of one other thing, Mother," Will said. "We found some old candles in the woodshed. We rubbed the runners with the candles. See how smooth they are?"

Mrs. Wright nodded. She had forgotten to tell the boys that, but they'd thought it out for themselves. "Now try your sled," she told them.

Followed by Kate, the boys dragged their new sled to the hill only half a mile away where their pals were coasting. They looked at the new sled in amazement. It was long and very narrow. It looked as though it wouldn't hold anyone. The runners were thin compared to those on their own sleds.

"Who made that for you?" Ed Sines asked.

"Mother showed us how," Wilbur said proudly. Some of the boys laughed. Whoever heard of a boy's mother knowing how to make a sled?

"It looks as if it would fall apart if you sat on it," Al Johnston said, and he laughed too.

"Come on, we'll race you down the hill," another cried out.

"All right, two on each sled," Wilbur said. He wasn't a bit afraid. He was sure the drawing had been right, and because he and Orv had followed the drawing, he knew that the sled was right.

They lined the four sleds up. Will and Orv sat on their sled, but it didn't "fall apart." Suddenly Wilbur got an idea.

"Get up, Orv," he said. "Now lie down on the sled . . . that's it . . . spread your legs a bit." Will then flopped down on top of his brother. "Less wind resistance this way," he whispered.

"Give us all a push," Ed Sines yelled.

And then they were off. It was an even start. The four sleds gathered speed, for at the top the slope was steep. Will looked to the right. Then to the left. He brushed the stinging snow out of his eyes but he couldn't see the other sleds. He looked behind. They were straggling along, twenty and now thirty feet in back of him. The new sled skimmed along, the runners singing happily. Both Will and Orv felt a strange thrill of excitement. They approached the bottom of the long hill. The other sleds were far, far behind now.

Usually when the sleds reached the bottom of the hill they slowed down abruptly and stopped. But not this sled. It kept on; its momentum carried it on and on a hundred yards farther than any of the other sleds had ever reached. Finally it stopped.

Shaking with excitement, Will and Orv stood up.

"We flew down the hill, Orv," Will said breathlessly.

"We flew," Orv repeated.

Now Ed and Al and Johnnie ran up, excited at what had happened. No sled had gone so far or so fast as the one Will and Orv had built.

"You *flew* down the hill," Ed Sines gasped. "Let me try it?"

Wilbur looked at Orv, and some secret message seemed to pass between them. They had built this sled together, and it was the best sled there was. They'd always work together building things.

"Orv," Will said, "I've got an idea. This sled can do everything but steer. Maybe we can make a rudder for it. Then we can make it go to the right or to the left."

"We'll get Mother to draw one," Orv said.

"We'll draw one, you and I," Wilbur said. "We can't run to Mother every time we want to make something."

By now little Kate had come running down the hill.

"You promised," she panted. "You said you'd take me for a ride."

"Come on, Kate." Will laughed. "The three of us will coast down once. And then you can try it, Ed."

They trudged up the hill, pulling the sled. Two words kept singing in Wilbur's ears. "We flew . . . we flew . . . we flew. . . ."

The Old Testament presents a galaxy of hero tales unsurpassed in variety and interest. But whether the story is about David and Goliath or Joseph and his brothers or Samuel or Samson or Solomon, these Old Testament heroes have one characteristic which differentiates them from the heroes of most other tales. They carry with them a sense of their responsibility and close relationship to their God. When they sin, they defy God's commands—what God tells them is right. When they undertake impossible tasks, it is because they

OLD TESTAMENT STORIES

are strong in the strength of the Lord. When they are discouraged, confused, or defeated, they seek God's guidance and help, and obtain it. These are religious concepts to be built into children's lives and our own. Children like these old stories because the heroes are men of action. There is violence, but there are also fortitude and faith. Whether the story is about David the giant killer or Joseph the dreamer, who became a practical man of affairs, or Samson, who was betrayed by his own weakness and redeemed himself only by his death, there are moral and spiritual implications in the story. It is true that children may sense the deeper significance of these stories only vaguely, but a dramatization or even a discussion of the tale will clarify and reinforce the meaning. Great characters, dramatic conflicts, suspense, and terrifying action may make these stories memorable, but it is the reiterated emphasis upon man's relationship to God that makes them significant.

DAVID AND GOLIATH

A shepherd boy against a giant, a sling shot against armor of brass! But the boy knows that the Lord "saves not with sword and spear," and so, strong in the strength of the Lord, he is unafraid and conquers. Here is a drama made to be played and spoken by children and its implications never to be forgotten.

When Saul was king over Israel, the Philistines called together their armies for war against the Israelites. The Philistines were gathered at Shochoh, and King Saul and the men of Israel were gathered by the valley of Elah and they drew up in battle line facing the Philistines. And the Philistines stood on a mountain on one side, and Israel stood on a mountain on the other side, and there was a valley between them.

Then there came out a champion from the camp of the Philistines named Goliath of Gath. He was six cubits and a span high.[1] He had a helmet of brass on his head, and he was armed with a coat of mail that weighed five thousand shekels of brass. He had greaves of brass upon his legs and a javelin of brass between his shoulders. The staff of his spear was as big as a weaver's beam and the spear's head weighed six hundred shekels of iron. A shield bearer walked before the champion.

Goliath shouted across the valley to the armies of Israel and said to them, "Why have you come out in battle array? Am not I a Philistine and you are the servants of Saul? Choose a man from among you and let him come down to meet me. If he can fight me and kill me then will we be your servants, but if I overcome him and kill him, then shall you be our servants and serve us." And Goliath shouted again, "I defy the armies of Israel this day. Send me a man from among you that we may fight together."

When Saul and the Israelites heard the words of the champion, they were greatly frightened and knew not what to do. And Goliath the Philistine drew near, morning and evening for forty days, and shouted his challenge to the Israelites.

Now in Bethlehem, there was an old man named Jesse, who had eight sons, and the youngest was called David. The three oldest sons were Eliab, Abinadab, and Shammah, and they had followed King Saul to battle. David went with them, but later he returned to Bethlehem to care for his father's sheep. One day, Jesse said to David, "Take a measure of parched corn and these ten loaves and run quickly to the camp where your brothers are. And carry these ten cheeses to the captain of their thousand and find out how your brothers fare."

So David rose up early in the morning and left the sheep with a keeper and set off for the camp of the Israelites as his father had commanded him to do. He came to the camp just as the Israelites were making ready to go into battle. For the Israelites and the Philistines were both drawn up in battle line, army against army. For no man had accepted the challenge of Goliath the champion.

David left his supplies with a man who looked after such things and ran quickly into the battle lines looking for his brothers. Just as he found them and was talking to them, Goliath of Gath, champion of the Philistines, came out of the ranks and shouted his same words again, and David heard them: "Give me a man from among you that we may fight together."

Again the men of Israel fled from the champion and were sore afraid. They said to David, "Did you see this man who has come out to defy Israel? Surely the man who is able to kill this Philistine, King Saul will reward with great riches and give him his daughter in marriage and make his father's house free in Israel."

Then David said to the men standing by him, "What did you say shall be done for the man who overcomes yonder Philistine and takes away the shame of Israel? For who is this Philistine that he should dare to defy the armies of the living God?"

"David and Goliath." From I Samuel 17:1–54, as adapted by May Hill Arbuthnot

[1] Over nine feet tall.

And the people told him again what King Saul would surely do for the man who could kill the Philistine.

But when Eliab, the oldest brother, heard what David said, he was angry with his young brother and said to him, "Why have you come here and with whom did you leave those few sheep in the desert? I know your arrogance and the wickedness in your heart. You have come here because you want to watch this battle."

And David said, "What have I done now? And what cause have you to speak to me like that?" And he turned away from his brothers, and talked again with the men who answered him as before. And some of the words David spoke the men repeated to King Saul, and the king sent for David.

When David came before the king, the boy said, "Let no man's heart be afraid because of that Philistine. Your servant will go and fight with him."

But Saul looked at David and replied, "How can you expect to go against this Philistine to fight with him? You are only a boy, and Goliath has been a man of war from his youth."

Then David told the king this story. "Sometimes, when your servant was a shepherd with his father's sheep, a lion or a bear would come and take a lamb out of the flock. Then I would go after him and attack him and take the lamb out of his mouth. And when the beast rose against me, I would catch him by the beard, smite him, and kill him. Your servant killed both the lion and the bear, and this Philistine shall fare the same, for he has defied the armies of the living God. Moreover, the Lord who delivered me out of the paw of the lion and out of the paw of the bear, He will deliver me out of the hand of this Philistine."

So Saul said to David, "Go and may the Lord be with you."

Then, the king put his own armor on David. He put a helmet of brass on his head and armed him with a coat of mail. He also girded him with a sword over his armor. And David struggled to go, for he wanted to try the armor. But he said to Saul, "I cannot wear these, for I have not proved them."

And he took off the king's armor. Then David took his staff in his hand and he chose five smooth stones out of the brook and put them in a shepherd's bag which he had with him and, with his sling in his hand, he went out to meet the Philistine.

The Philistine came near to David, keeping his shield bearer directly in front of him. But when he came near enough to see David, he scorned him, for he saw that he was only a youth, ruddy and fair of face. And Goliath called out, "Am I a dog that you come against me with sticks?" And he cursed David and said, "Come on, and I'll give your flesh to the birds of the air and the beasts of the field."

David replied to the Philistine, "You come to me with a sword, a spear, and a shield, but I come to you in the name of the Lord of Hosts, the God of the armies of Israel, whom you have defied. This very day the Lord will deliver you into my hands, and I will smite you and take your head from your body and this day I will give your dead body and the dead of the camp of the Philistines to the birds of the air and the wild beasts of the earth. This will I do that all the earth may know there is a God in Israel. And all this assembly shall know that the Lord saves not with sword and spear. For the battle is the Lord's, and He will give you into our hands."

And when David had finished speaking, Go-

liath drew near to meet him, and David ran towards the Philistine. And as he ran, he put his hand in his bag and chose a smooth stone. This he put in his sling and took aim. The stone struck the Philistine in his forehead, and he fell upon his face on the ground.

So David prevailed over the Philistine with a sling and with a stone and smote the Philistine and killed him. But there was no sword in David's hand.

Therefore, David ran and stood over the Philistine and took the champion's own sword out of its sheath and slew him and cut off his head. When the Philistines saw that Goliath, their champion, was dead, they fled. Then, the men of Israel arose and shouted and pursued the Philistines and plundered their tents.

David took the head of Goliath to Jerusalem, but he put Goliath's armor in the Philistine's tent.

SAMSON

Samson is the tragic story of a great and godly man who stubbornly insisted upon having his own way and upon his right to get even with his enemies, forgetting that "'Justice is mine,' saith the Lord." Yet in the days before Israel had kings, Samson was their judge and ruled them well for twenty years. Then, again, he used his great strength for vengeance and paid dearly for his folly. The end of his story leaves the reader with feelings of admiration and pity for this remarkable man.

Now there was a certain man of Zorah whose name was Manoah, and he and his wife were childless. But one day, an angel of the Lord appeared to the woman and said to her, "You are going to bear a son. See that you drink no wine or liquor nor eat anything that is unclean. When your son is born, no razor is ever to be used on his head; for the boy is to be a Nazarite, given to God from the day of his birth. And he shall deliver Israel from the hand of the Philistines."

In time, it came to pass as the angel had told the woman. She bore a son and called his name Samson. The Lord blessed the child and he grew up and the spirit of the Lord began to work within him.

Samson went down to Timnath and saw a woman there who pleased him, so he returned to his father and mother and said, "I have seen a woman in Timnath, a daughter of the Philistines; she pleases me and I want her for my wife."

Then his father and his mother said to him, "Is there no girl among all your own people that you must take a wife from the Philistines, our enemies?"

But Samson said, "She pleases me well. Get her for me in marriage."

So Samson and his mother and father went down to Timnath, and when they came to the vineyards of Timnath, behold a young lion came roaring out against Samson. And the spirit of the Lord came upon him mightily, and he tore the lion apart with his hands as if it were no bigger than a kid. But he told not his father or his mother what he had done.

Samson talked with the woman of Timnath, and she pleased him well, so the marriage arrangements were made. After a time, he returned to take her for his wife and on the way, he turned aside to see the carcass of the lion he had slain. Behold there was a swarm of bees and honey in the carcass, which he took out with his hands and began to eat. When he came to his father and mother, he gave them the honey to eat also, but he did not tell them that he had taken it out of the carcass of the lion.

When they came to the woman of Timnath, Samson made a great feast, as was customary for the bridegroom to do. And the Philistines sent thirty young men to be with him. Samson said to them, "I will now tell you a riddle. If you can solve it within the seven days of this feast, I will give you thirty sheets and thirty changes of garments. But if you cannot solve the riddle, then you shall give me thirty sheets and thirty changes of garments."

Then he told them his riddle. "Out of the eater came forth meat and out of the strong came forth sweetness."

The young men of the Philistines thought about the riddle for three days, but they could not solve it. On the seventh day they said to Samson's wife, "Coax your husband to tell you the answer to this riddle. If you don't find out for us,

"Samson." From Judges 13–16, as adapted by May Hill Arbuthnot

we'll burn you and your father's house. Have you brought us here to take away from us everything that we have?"

So Samson's wife wept before him and said, "You hate me. You don't really love me at all. You have put forth a riddle to my countrymen and have not told it to me."

"I have not told the answer to my father nor my mother," Samson said, "so why should I tell it to you?"

Then his wife wept and begged Samson so hard to tell her the answer to the riddle that he finally told her, and she told the Philistines. Then the Philistines said to Samson, "What is sweeter than honey and what is stronger than a lion?"

And Samson said to them, "If you had not plowed with my heifer, you would not have found out my riddle."

And Samson slew thirty men of Ashkelon and took their spoils and gave them to the thirty Philistines who had solved the riddle. Then he was so angry that he returned to his father's house, and his wife was given to a man who had been his companion and friend.

But it came to pass in the time of the wheat harvest, that Samson decided he wanted his wife. When he went to the house, her father would not let him in, saying, "I thought, of course, that you utterly hated her, so I gave her as a wife to your companion. But is not her younger sister fairer than she? Why not take the younger sister instead of her?"

Then Samson turned away without answering, but he said to himself, "Though I do the Philistines an injury, I shall be blameless because of what they have done to me."

And he went out and caught three hundred foxes and, turning the foxes tail to tail, he put a torch between each pair of tails and set the brands on fire. He turned the foxes loose in the standing grain of the Philistines, and so burnt up all the standing grain of the Philistines and the shocks and also their vineyards and their olive groves.

"Who has done this?" said the Philistines, and the people answered, "Samson, the son-in-law of the Timnite, because his wife was given to his companion."

The Philistines then burned the wife and her father. And Samson said to them, "Because you have done this, I shall take my revenge on you, and after that I will cease."

And Samson smote the Philistines hip and thigh, with great slaughter. Afterwards he went away and dwelt in a cleft of the rock Etam. But the Philistines followed him there, and the Judeans, where they camped at Lehi, cried out, "Why are you come against us?"

The Philistines answered, "To bind Samson are we come up, to do to him as he has done to us."

Then three thousand of the men of Judah went to the top of the rock Etam and said to Samson, "Know you not that the Philistines are our rulers? What have you done to us?"

And Samson answered, "As they did to me so I have done to them."

"But we must turn you over to our rulers," they said. "We have come to bind you and deliver you into the hand of the Philistines."

"Then swear to me that you will not fall upon me yourselves," Samson said.

And they answered him saying, "No, that we will not do. We will bind you fast and deliver you into their hands, but we ourselves will surely not kill you."

So they bound him with two new cords and brought him from the rock to Lehi where the Philistines were and they shouted against him. But the spirit of the Lord came mightily upon Samson, and the ropes on his arms became as flax that had been burned with fire and his bonds melted from his hands. Then he found the jawbone of an ass and, taking it in his hand, he slew a thousand men with it and he cried aloud,

"With the jawbone of an ass
Heaps upon heaps of men have I slain.
With the jawbone of an ass
I have slain a thousand men."

Then when he had finished speaking, he cast away the jawbone and he was sore athirst and he called on the Lord and said, "Thou hast given thy servant great deliverance. Shall I now die of thirst?"

And the Lord smote a hollow place, and water gushed out. After Samson had drunk of this water, his spirits revived. He went forth from there and became a great judge in Israel and he governed Israel for twenty years in the time of the Philistines.

After a time, Samson loved a woman in the valley of Sorek, whose name was Delilah. The lords of the Philistines came to the woman and said to her, "See if you can entice him to tell you wherein his great strength lies. And find out how we can overpower him so that we can take him prisoner and punish him for what he has done to us. If you will do this, we will everyone of us give you eleven hundred pieces of silver."

So Delilah said to Samson, "Tell me, I pray you, what is the source of your strength and what will overpower you?"

And Samson answered her, "If I were bound fast with seven green withes that were never dried, then I should be as weak as any other man."

Then the lords of the Philistines brought Delilah the seven green withes that had never been dried, and she bound him with them. Now there were men lying in wait in an inner room, and she said to Samson, "The Philistines are upon you, Samson."

But Samson broke the withes as a thread of tow would break when it comes near the fire. So the source of his strength was not known.

And Delilah said to Samson, "Behold you have mocked me and told me lies. Tell me now, I pray you, what would overcome your strength?"

And Samson replied, "If I were bound fast with new ropes that had never been used, then should I be weak as other men."

So Delilah took new ropes and bound him with them. Then she cried, "The Philistines are upon you, Samson."

And the men who were lying in wait fell upon him but he broke the ropes off his arms like thread.

And again Delilah said, "Again you have mocked me and told me lies. Tell me what there is that will hold you?"

And Samson said, "If you weave seven locks of my hair into your web."

So Delilah did this while Samson slept and she fastened his hair with a pin and cried out, "Samson, the Philistines are upon you."

And Samson waked from his sleep and pulled out both the loom and the web.

And Delilah said to Samson, "How can you say, 'I love you' when your heart is not with me? You have mocked me three times and you have never told me wherein your great strength lies." This she said to him over and over until his soul was vexed unto death, and he told her his whole heart.

He said, "No razor has ever been used on my head, for I have been a Nazarite, dedicated to God from my birth. If I were to be shaved, then my strength would go from me, and I would become weak like any other man."

Delilah knew then that he had told her his secret. So she sent for the lords of the Philistines and said, "This time he has told me his whole heart." Then they brought her the money they had promised, and Delilah put Samson to sleep on her knees. While he was sleeping, she sent for a man to shave off the seven locks of Samson's hair, and he became helpless and his strength left him.

So she said, "The Philistines are upon you, Samson."

And Samson woke from his sleep and thought, "I will escape as I have before. I will shake off my bonds." But he did not know that his strength had left him and the spirit of the Lord had departed from him.

Then the Philistines seized him, put out his eyes, and brought him down to Gaza bound with fetters of brass. They put him in a prison where he had to grind the grain. But his hair began to grow as soon as it was shaved off, and this the Philistines did not notice.

After a time, the lords of the Philistines gathered together to offer a great sacrifice to their god Dagon and to rejoice together because, they said, "Our god has delivered into our hands, Samson, our enemy."

And when the people saw the blind Samson, they praised their god that he had delivered to them their enemy, the destroyer who slew many of them.

Now it came to pass, when they were merry that they said, "Bring Samson to us that he may make sport for us." And the blind Samson was led out of the prison and he made sport for the Philistines, between the pillars of the hall.

And Samson said to the boy who led him by the hand, "Suffer me to feel the pillars that support the building, that I may lean against them."

The building was full of men and women and the lords of the Philistines were all there and on the roof there were about three thousand men and women, all watching Samson make sport for them.

And Samson cried to the Lord and said, "O Lord God, remember me I pray you, and strengthen me, I pray you, only this once, O God, that I may be avenged upon the Philistines for my two eyes."

Then Samson took hold of the two middle pillars upon which the building stood, one with his right hand and the other in his left. And Samson said, "Let me die with the Philistines." And he bowed himself with all his might, and the house fell upon the lords of the Philistines and upon all the people that were therein. So that the dead which Samson slew at his death were more than they which he slew in his life.

THE STORY OF JOSEPH

The story of Joseph and his brothers is one of the greatest epics in literature. It is the drama of the brothers' hate of a favored younger brother and their crime against the boy. They paid dearly for their ill deed to the lad, but years later, Joseph showed them how God had turned their evil to good. It is also the story of a pampered younger son, a dreamer of dreams, who dared to dream greatness for himself when he was only a stripling. Perhaps because of this, Joseph, too, had to suffer many ills before his dreams came true. But what saved Joseph from his own youthful arrogance, his brothers' jealousy, the wrath of his employer, and the misery and inaction of a long prison term were his complete innocence and his reliance on God's guidance in all he said and did. That guidance changed Joseph the dreamer into Joseph the practical man of affairs and active ruler of a great land. His reliance on God kept him free, too, from every taint of bitterness and resentment against those who had ill used him. When the brothers came before him at last, they found only compassion, generosity, and deep affection.

The Coat of Many Colors

Now Jacob, who was sometimes called Israel, had twelve sons, but he loved the youngest boy, Joseph, best of all. When Joseph was seventeen years old, Jacob made him a coat of many colors. Then the brothers saw that their father loved this boy more than he loved them and they hated Joseph and could not speak peaceably to him.

They hated him still more when he told them about a dream he had dreamed. He said, "Hear, I pray you, my brothers, this dream which I have dreamed. We were binding sheaves in the field and, lo, my sheaf arose and stood upright, and behold, your sheaves stood round about and bowed down to my sheaf."

His brothers said, "Shall you indeed rule over us?" And they hated him more and more for his dream and his words.

But Joseph dreamed still another dream which he told to his brothers. "Behold, I have dreamed again," he said. "And in this dream the sun and the moon and eleven stars all bowed down to me."

When Joseph told this dream to his father, Jacob rebuked him saying, "What is this dream that you have dreamed? Do you mean that your mother and I and your eleven brothers shall indeed bow down to you?"

The brothers hated Joseph still more, but Jacob, although he reproved the boy, remembered his saying.

After this, Jacob's eleven sons went to Shechem to feed their father's flocks, and Jacob said to Joseph, "Your brothers are feeding my flocks in Shechem. Go, I pray you, and see whether all is well with them and bring me word."

So Joseph set off for Shechem, but when he came there he could not find his brothers. He was wandering in the field when a man saw him and asked him what he was seeking. Joseph replied, "I am looking for my brothers. Tell me, I pray you, where are they feeding their flocks?"

And the man answered, "They have left this place, but I heard them say, 'Let us go to Dothan.' "

So Joseph set off for Dothan, and he found his brothers there. But they, when they saw him coming, plotted together to kill him. They said, one to another, "Behold, the dreamer comes! Let us kill him and throw his body into the pit. We can say some evil beast has killed and eaten him. Then we'll see what becomes of his dreams."

"The Story of Joseph." From Genesis 37, 39, 40, 41, and 43 as adapted by May Hill Arbuthnot

But Reuben, the oldest brother, wished to save the boy; so he said, "No, we must not kill him. We must shed no blood. Lay no hand upon him, but rather cast him into this pit, here, in the wilderness." This he said in order that he might get the boy out of their hands and deliver him safely to their father once more. The brothers agreed.

So, when Joseph was come to them, they stripped him of his coat of many colors and threw him into an empty pit where there was no water. Then they sat down to eat and as they were eating, they saw coming towards them a great company of Ishmaelites with their camels, bearing spices and balm and myrrh from Gilead to Egypt. When Judah, one of the brothers, saw the caravan, he said, "What good will it do us if we slay our brother and hide his blood? Come, let us sell him to these Ishmaelites. Then our hand will not be upon him, for he is our brother."

The others agreed to this plan. So, they lifted Joseph out of the pit and sold him to the Ishmaelites for twenty pieces of silver, and the Ishmaelites went away with Joseph to Egypt.

After they were gone, the brothers took Joseph's coat of many colors and dipped it in the blood of a goat. Then they took the coat to Jacob and said, "This we have found. Do you know whether or not it is your son's coat?"

And Jacob knew the coat and he cried out, "It is my son's coat. An evil beast has killed Joseph and devoured him." And Jacob wept and mourned for his son for many days. All his sons and daughters rose up to comfort him, but he refused to be comforted and said, "I will go down to my grave mourning for my son Joseph." And he wept the more.

Joseph In Egypt

The Ishmaelites took Joseph to Egypt where they sold him to Potiphar, one of King Pharaoh's officers, a Captain of the Guard. The Lord was with Joseph. He prospered in the house of his Egyptian master and found favor in his eyes. For when Potiphar saw that all Joseph did in his house was a success, because the Lord was with him, he made him overseer of his household and put him in charge of all his property. And because of Joseph, the Lord blessed the Egyptian's house and his fields and Potiphar had no more worry about his possessions.

Joseph grew to be a handsome and a goodly young man. Potiphar's wife liked him and wanted him to do her will instead of his master's. But when she urged Joseph to do something dishonorable he refused, saying, "Behold my master has given everything he has into my hand. He trusts me, and I will do no wickedness against him and in the eyes of my God."

This made the woman angry, so she turned against Joseph and told her husband lies about his overseer. Potiphar believed her, and his wrath was kindled and he had Joseph thrown into the prison where the king kept his prisoners bound. But the Lord was with Joseph and he found favor in the sight of the jailer. This man turned over to Joseph's hand all the prisoners in his charge and again Joseph's work was a success. He looked after everything that needed to be done, and the jailer did not have to oversee anything. Whatever Joseph did, the Lord prospered him.

It came to pass that Pharaoh, King of Egypt, was angry with his butler and his baker, and he sent them to the same prison where Joseph was, and they were put in Joseph's charge. One morning, Joseph came to them and found them looking sad, so he asked them, "Why are you looking so gloomy?"

"Because we have each of us dreamed a dream," they said. "And there is no one here to tell us what our dreams mean."

"Interpretations belong to God," Joseph said. "But tell me your dreams, I pray you."

So the chief butler told his dream first. He said, "In my dream a vine was before me, and on the vine there were three branches, and these budded, and the blossoms shot forth and clusters of grapes grew on them. And Pharaoh's cup was in my hand, so I squeezed the grapes into the cup and gave it to Pharaoh."

Joseph answered, "This is the meaning of your dream. The three branches are three days. Within three days Pharaoh will summon you and restore you to your place, so that you shall place Pharaoh's cup in his hand as you used to do when you were his butler. When this happens, and it is well with you, I pray you show kindness to me. Mention me to Pharaoh that he may release me from this prison. For indeed I was stolen away out of the land of the Hebrews, and here I have done nothing wrong that I should be put into this dungeon."

Now when the baker saw that the interpretation of the butler's dream was good, he also told his dream to Joseph. He said, "In my dream I had three white baskets upon my head. And in the uppermost basket there were all manner of baked foods for Pharaoh. But the birds did eat them out of the basket on my head."

And Joseph said, "This is the meaning of your dream. The three baskets are three days. Within three days Pharaoh shall summon you and hang you on a tree, and the birds shall eat your flesh."

On the third day, which was Pharaoh's birthday, he held a feast for all his servants. He sent for the chief butler and the chief baker. The chief butler he restored to his duties again and he gave the cup into Pharaoh's hand as before. But the chief baker Pharaoh hanged, as Joseph said he would do. But when the chief butler was restored to his place, he did not keep Joseph in mind but forgot him.

So Joseph remained in prison for two more years. Then, King Pharaoh himself dreamed, and in his dream he stood by a river. Seven fat and beautiful cattle came up out of the river and fed in the meadow. Then seven lean, ugly cattle also came up out of the river and devoured the seven fat cattle. So Pharaoh woke, but he slept again and dreamed the second time. In his dream seven ears of corn came up on one stalk, thick and good, and behold seven thin ears, blasted by the east wind, sprang up after them and devoured the seven thick, good ears. When morning came, Pharaoh's spirit was troubled and he called for all the magicians and wise men of Egypt to tell him what his dreams meant. But not one of them could interpret Pharaoh's dream for him.

Then Pharaoh's butler said to the king, "This day I remember my faults. For when you were angry with your servants and put both me and the baker in prison, we dreamed a dream one night, he and I. And there was a young man in the prison, a Hebrew, who had been a servant to the Captain of the Guard, and we told our dreams to him. He interpreted our dreams for us, and everything happened just as he told us it would. I was restored to my office, and the baker was hanged, as the young Hebrew told us."

When King Pharaoh heard this, he sent for Joseph at once. They brought him hastily out of his dungeon, and he shaved himself and changed his raiment and was brought at once to Pharaoh.

The King said, "I have dreamed two dreams and none can say what they mean. But I have heard that you can understand dreams and can interpret their meaning."

Joseph replied, "It is not in me but it is God, who shall give Pharaoh an answer of peace."

Then Pharaoh told Joseph his two dreams, and when Joseph had heard them he said, "Pharaoh's dreams are one. God has shown Pharaoh what he is about to do. The seven good cattle and the seven good ears of corn are seven years, and the dream is one. The seven thin cattle and the seven empty, blasted ears of corn, which came after them, are seven years of famine. This which I have spoken is what God is about to do to Pharaoh. There shall be seven years of plenty throughout all the land of Egypt. Then there shall arise seven years of famine, and all the plenty shall be forgotten in the land of Egypt and famine shall consume the land, and it shall be very grievous. Because the dream was doubled, it means that God will shortly bring it to pass. Pharaoh, therefore, should look for a man who is discreet and wise and set him over the land of Egypt. And let him appoint officers to take up a fifth part of all the corn and other foods that are gathered in the plenteous years and let them store the food in the cities. And that food shall be a store against the seven years of famine that are to come to the land of Egypt, that the land shall not perish from the famine."

This plan was good in the eyes of Pharaoh, and he said to his courtiers, "Can we find such a man as this, a man filled with the spirit of God?"

Then Pharaoh said to Joseph, "Since God has showed you all this, there is surely no man so wise and discreet as you are. I will set you over my house, and my people shall be ruled according to your word. Only on the throne will I be greater than you. Behold, I have set you over all the land of Egypt."

King Pharaoh took the ring off his finger and put it on Joseph's finger and arrayed him in vestures of fine linen and put a gold chain around his neck. And Pharaoh made Joseph ride in the second chariot which he had, and the people cried before him, "Bow the knee!" And Joseph was ruler over all the land of Egypt.

Later, Pharaoh gave Joseph as his wife, Asenath, and before the years of famine set in, two sons were born to them. The firstborn he called Manasseh, and the second he called Ephraim. And Joseph traveled everywhere throughout all the land. In the plenteous years the land produced great crops, and Joseph gathered the food and stored it in the cities. And the corn he stored was like the sands of the sea. There was so much he could no longer count it.

But at last, the seven years of plenty came to an end and the seven years of want began. The lack of food was over all the lands, only in Egypt was there food. And when the Egyptians began to be hungry, they cried to Pharaoh for food, and Pharaoh said to them, "Go to Joseph and do what he tells you."

So Joseph opened the storehouses to the Egyptians, and all the other countries also came to Joseph to buy corn, for the famine was sore throughout the lands.

"And your sheaves . . . bowed down to my sheaf."

Now, in Canaan, when Jacob, the father of Joseph, heard that there was corn in Egypt, he said to his sons, "Why do you sit staring at each other and do nothing? Behold I have heard there is corn in Egypt. Go there and buy food for us that we may live and not die."

So, ten sons of Jacob traveled to Egypt with other people from the land of Canaan. But their father Jacob would not let Benjamin, the youngest boy, go with them lest something happen to him. Benjamin and Joseph were the children of the same mother, and Jacob loved them more than he loved his other sons.

Now Joseph was, of course, the governor over all the land of Egypt, and the people who wished to buy corn had to go to him. So, his ten brothers bowed low before him with their faces to the earth. They did not know him, but he knew them at once, and he remembered his dreams about them. He spoke harshly to them as if they were strangers, for he did not want them to recognize him.

"Where do you come from?" he asked, and they told him they came from the land of Canaan. "You are spies," Joseph said roughly. "You have come to see the nakedness of this land."

"No, my Lord," the brothers replied. "We have only come to buy food. We are honest men, the sons of one father, and no spies."

And again he accused them of being spies and they replied, "There are twelve of us, the sons of one father. The youngest son has remained at home with our father, and one son is no more. But we have come, not to spy, but to buy food."

Joseph said, "If this is true, you will have to prove it to me. Let one of you return home and bring your youngest brother to me. The rest of you shall stay in prison until the two return. Then we shall see whether there is any truth in what you say, for by Pharaoh's life, I believe you are spies."

Then Joseph put them all in prison for three days. After that, he said. "If you be true men, prove it to me and live, for I do fear God. One of you shall remain here in prison, and all the others shall return to Canaan with corn for the famine in your houses. But you must bring your youngest brother to me so that the truth of your words shall be proved. Do this and live."

When the brothers heard this, they said to one another, "This has happened to us because we are guilty concerning our brother, Joseph."

And Reuben said to his brothers, "You remember I begged you not to sin against the child Joseph, but you would not listen to me. Now, perhaps Benjamin's blood will be required of us."

All this they said because Joseph had been speaking to them through an interpreter so they did not think he could understand their words. But, of course, he did understand them, and when he heard what Reuben said, he turned away and wept. Then he returned to the brothers and bound Simeon before their eyes. And Joseph secretly commanded his steward that their sacks should be filled with corn and every man's money restored to his sack. Besides this, he gave them enough provisions to last them for the journey home.

The nine brothers loaded their asses with the corn and set off for home. But on the way, they stopped at an inn and one of them opened his sack to give his ass some corn, and in the sack he found his money. The brothers were frightened when they discovered what had happened. Their hearts failed them, and they said, "What is this that God has done to us?"

When they reached home, they told Jacob about the governor of all Egypt who had spoken roughly to them and accused them of being spies. And they told Jacob everything that had happened, and when they emptied their sacks, every man found his money inside.

When he had heard their story and seen all the money, Jacob said, "You have bereaved me of my sons. Joseph is no more. Now, Simeon is gone, and you would take Benjamin from me. Everything is against me."

And Reuben spoke to his father, "If I do not bring Benjamin and Simeon back to you, you may kill my own two sons."

But Jacob was not satisfied. "No," he said, "Benjamin shall not go down to Egypt. His own brother Joseph is dead, and if something happens to Benjamin, it will bring my gray hairs with sorrow to the grave."

A Feast in the Land of the Egyptians

The famine was sore in the lands. After awhile Jacob and his sons and their families had eaten all the corn which they had brought out of the land of Egypt. So Jacob said to his sons, "Go again to Egypt and buy food."

But Judah protested, "The Egyptian did solemnly swear to us, 'You shall not see my face if you do not return with your youngest brother.' "

"But why did you tell the Egyptian that you had another brother?" Jacob asked. "It was an ill thing to do to me."

"The man asked us all sorts of questions, and we had to answer him truly," the brothers replied. "He asked, 'Is your father yet alive? Have you another brother?' We answered his questions for we could not know that he would say, 'Bring your brother to me.' "

Then Judah said to his father, "Send the lad Benjamin with me, and we will go at once. I will be responsible for him. For we must have food that we may live and not die, both we and thou and also our little ones."

At last Jacob said, "If this must be, go now, and take with you a present for the man—a little balm and a little honey, spices, myrrh, nuts, and almonds. And be sure to take double money in your hands to pay back the money that you found in your sacks which, perhaps, was an oversight. Take your brother Benjamin also and may

God Almighty have mercy on you and on your brother that the man may send him back to me, lest I again be bereaved."

So the nine brothers took Benjamin with them, a present for the Egyptian, and double money in their hands and set off for Egypt. They came at last before Joseph and bowed low before him. And Joseph, when he saw his brother Benjamin, commanded his stewards to prepare a great feast and to bring all these brothers to eat with him. And the steward did so, and he brought the brothers to Joseph's house. The brothers were frightened. They thought that perhaps because of the money that was returned to them, the Egyptian might now fall upon them and make them his slaves. So they talked to the steward at the door of Joseph's house and said, "Oh sir, we came down the first time to buy food. But when we came to the inn on our way home, every man's money was in his sack. We do not know who put it there, but this time we have brought double that money to pay for food."

And the steward replied, "Peace be with you. Fear not. Your God and the God of your fathers has given you treasure in your sacks. I had your money. It is well with you." And he brought Simeon to them, and led them into Joseph's house, where they could wash themselves and make ready for the feast. And the steward saw that their asses were also fed.

When Joseph came home, the brothers brought him their presents and they bowed themselves to the earth before him, and he asked them how they fared and said, "Is your father well, the old man of whom you spoke? Is he yet alive?"

And they answered, "Thy servant, our father, is alive and well," and again they bowed themselves to the earth.

Joseph lifted up his eyes and saw his own brother, Benjamin, and said, "And is this your younger brother, of whom you spoke? God be gracious to you, my son." And then, Joseph was so moved at the sight of his brother that he had to leave the room in haste to find a place where he could weep unseen. In his own room he wept; then he washed his face and returned to the feast where he restrained himself and bade the steward set out the food.

The servants set Joseph's food before him and he ate by himself. The brothers also had their food set before them by themselves, for the Egyptians who were there might not, according to their laws, eat with any Hebrews. But Joseph kept sending special dishes from his table to Benjamin's place until the lad had five times as much as anyone else. Everyone ate and drank and made merry with Joseph.

After the feast, Joseph commanded his steward, "Fill the men's sacks with food, as much as they can carry, and put every man's money in the mouth of his sack. But put my own silver cup in the sack of the youngest brother together with his corn money."

So the steward did as Joseph commanded him, and as soon as the morning was come, the men were sent on their way with their asses laden with the sacks of food. Before they had gone very far, Joseph called his steward and said to him, "Up, follow these men and when you overtake them, ask them why they have rewarded good with evil. Say to them, 'One of you has my lord's silver cup from which he drinks.' "

The steward did this, and when he spoke these words to the brothers, they cried out, "Why would my lord speak to us like this? God forbid that we should do any such thing. Don't you remember how we brought back the money we found in our sacks? How then could my lord think we would steal gold or silver out of his house? But search us, and if the cup is found on anyone of us, that one shall die and the others shall be slaves to your master."

Then they speedily opened up their sacks, and the steward searched them, from the sack of the oldest brother to the youngest. And the cup was found in Benjamin's sack. The brothers cried out and tore their clothes, and after they had reloaded their asses, they returned to the city.

The brothers came again before Joseph and fell down before him and Joseph spoke. "What is this that you have done? You might know that I would find you out."

And Judah said, "What can we say, my lord, to prove our innocence? God is punishing us for our sins, and now we are here, the slaves of my lord, both we and he in whose possession the cup was found."

"No," said Joseph, "I could not think of doing

such a thing, God forbid. Only the man in whose hand the cup was found shall stay here to be my servant. The rest of you shall go in peace to your old father."

Then Judah came close to Joseph. "My lord, I pray, let me speak a word in your ear and do not let your anger blaze against me, for I know right well that you are as powerful as Pharaoh. You asked about our father and brother, and we told you that our father was old and the boy a child of his old age, a little one, the only one left of the mother whom Jacob loved. The other child Joseph is no more, so this boy my father loves more than any of us. When we told our father that you would not see us again to sell us corn unless we brought this lad with us, he said to us, 'You know the wife I loved had but two sons. One is gone from me, and if any mischief should befall this boy, it would bring my gray hairs in sorrow to the grave.' So, then, I became surety for my brother Benjamin. Now therefore, I pray you, let me become your servant instead of the lad and let him go in peace to my father."

When Joseph heard Judah plead for the boy, he could restrain himself no longer and he said to his attendants, "Have everyone withdraw from this room except these brothers." And Joseph was left alone with his brothers, and he made himself known to them. "I am Joseph," he cried. "Does my father yet live?" And he wept as he spoke, and his brothers were so overcome with fear that they could not answer him.

"Come nearer to me," Joseph said, and when they came nearer, he continued, "I am your brother Joseph, whom you sold into slavery in Egypt. But do not be grieved nor angry with yourselves for what you did. God sent me ahead of you to this land to save life. For two years now, famine has prevailed over all the land, and there are still five years to come when there will be no ploughing and no reaping. God sent me ahead of you to save a remnant of the earth and so to preserve you and your posterity. So now it was not you who sent me here but God. And it is God who has made me a father to Pharaoh, a ruler over all the land of Egypt and the cause of this great deliverance. Go now in haste to my father Jacob and tell him what I have said. And tell him not to tarry there in the land of Canaan, but come to me and you shall all dwell in the land of Goshen and be near me with all your children and your children's children and your flocks and your herds and all that you possess. And here will I nourish you for the five remaining years of the famine lest any of you fall into poverty. And say to my father that your own eyes and the eyes of Benjamin have seen me and you have heard my words. And tell my father of my glory in Egypt and all the things you have seen. Make haste now, and bring my father to me."

Then Joseph wept and embraced his brother Benjamin and Benjamin wept too on Joseph's neck. And Joseph kissed all his brothers and they talked together.

Then the news was heard in Pharaoh's palace, and everyone began to speak of it and to say, "Joseph's brothers are come."

Pharaoh was pleased with the news and said to Joseph, "Tell your brothers to load their asses and go into the land of Canaan to fetch your father and your household. Come to me and I will give you some of the best land in Egypt for you and your family and you shall eat the fat of the land. Tell your brothers to take wagons from Egypt to bring back their wives and little ones and your father too. Never mind your goods, for the best of all Egypt will be yours."

So Joseph gave his brothers wagons, as Pharaoh had commanded, and he gave them provisions for the journey. He also gave each man a rich garment, and to Benjamin he gave three hundred pieces of silver and five changes of raiment. And to his father, Joseph sent ten asses laden with the good things of Egypt and ten she asses laden with corn, bread, and meat. And Joseph warned his brothers not to quarrel with each other on the journey.

When the brothers came to the land of Canaan and their father Jacob, they told him, "Joseph, your son, is still alive and he is governor over all of the land of Egypt!"

But Jacob was stunned by the news and did not believe them. Then the brothers told him all the words Joseph had spoken to them and all the splendor of his life in Egypt. But still Jacob could not believe their stories until he saw the wagons Joseph had sent to bring his father to

Egypt. Then Jacob believed the stories and his spirits rose. "It is enough," he said. "I believe you. My son is still alive and I shall see him again before I die."

So Jacob set off for Egypt with all of his sons and their wives and their little ones in the wagons which Pharaoh had sent. And Judah went ahead to tell Joseph that his father was coming.

So Joseph went out in his chariot and drove to meet his father. And they embraced each other and wept for joy, and Jacob said, "Now, my son, I can die in peace for I have seen your face and know that you are still alive."

And Joseph preserved his father and his brothers and all their households in the land of Egypt.

BIBLIOGRAPHY

ANIMAL STORIES

ALDRICH, MARY M., *Too Many Pets,* ill. by Barbara Cooney, Macmillan, 1952. The arrival of each new pet in the Gay family is a cause of rejoicing among the children and for a few groans from the parents. From angleworms to a dog, the pets are entertaining and so are the children. 6–10

ANDERSON, C. W., *Billy and Blaze,* ill. by author, Macmillan, 1936. 6–10

Black, Bay and Chestnut, ill. by author, Macmillan, 1939. 10–14

Blaze and the Gypsies, ill. by author, Macmillan, 1937. 6–10

Blaze Finds the Trail, ill. by author, Macmillan, 1950. 5–8

Deep Through the Heart, ill. by author, Macmillan, 1940. 10–14

High Courage, ill. by author, Macmillan, 1941. 10–14

Salute, ill. by author, Macmillan, 1940. 7–12

BEATTY, HETTY BURLINGAME, *Little Wild Horse,* ill. by author, Houghton, 1949. A small boy's dream comes true—a real ranch in the West and the taming of a little wild horse to be his very own. 3–7

BELL, THELMA HARRINGTON, *Yaller-Eye,* ill. by Corydon Bell, Viking, 1951. When Randy forgets to feed old Yaller-Eye, the cat wanders away to find food and loses her foot in a trap. Randy, full of remorse, has to contend with his daddy who thinks the cat should die. Fine story of a mountaineer family and a boy's love for his pet. 6–9

BIALK, ELISA, *Jill's Victory,* ill. by Edward Shenton, World Pub. Co., 1952. City-bred Jill has much to learn from her farm cousins. This is a story of adjustment to new standards of achievement. When Jill wins her 4-H membership, she is as proud as her cousins are when, after failing, she wins in the horse show. 10–14

Taffy's Foal, ill. by William Moyers, Houghton, 1949. A little girl meets two major problems in one year—her father's second marriage and the death of her adored horse. The stepmother relationship is well handled. 7–12

Wild Horse Island, ill. by Paul Brown, Houghton, 1951. Horses, mystery, and good family relationships make this story of life in northwestern Montana unusually interesting. It is easy to read, and as in all of Mrs. Bialk's books, there is good character development and lively plot. 9–12

BUFF, MARY and CONRAD, *Dash and Dart,* ill. by authors, Viking, 1942. The first year in the life of twin fawns is beautifully told and illustrated. The cadenced prose of the text reads aloud well and the pictures in sepia or full color are exquisite. 5–8

BURT, OLIVE, *Prince of the Ranch,* ill. by Bob Myers, Bobbs-Merrill, 1949. Prince, a city-bred collie, learning to herd sheep, is suspected of being a killer. His master defends the dog and both eventually prove themselves first-rate workers. A good dog story and a good western. 10–14

COGGINS, HERBERT, *Busby & Co.,* ill. by Roger Duvoisin, Whittlesey, 1952. Keeping a beaver as a pet is not easy, as Jerry Gardner soon realized. Plenty of adventures, excitement, and a delightful style make this a good story to read aloud. 6–10

COOPER, PAGE, *Pat's Harmony,* ill. by Olive Grimley, World Pub. Co., 1952. This is a heart-warming story of affection between a great horse and a girl who believed in him. Minor characters are also well drawn. 10–14

CREDLE, ELLIS, *The Flop-Eared Hound.* (See Bibliography, Today in the United States: Negro Stories.)

DELAFIELD, CLELIA, *Mrs. Mallard's Ducklings,* ill. by Leonard Weisgard, Lothrop, 1946. A beautiful picture-book with interesting text of the seasonal cycle of ducks from egg to winter flight. 6–8

DENNIS, MORGAN, *Burlap,* ill. by author, Viking, 1945. A worthless old farm dog suddenly proves himself by helping to capture an escaped circus bear. 6–9

DOWNEY, FAIRFAX, *Free and Easy, the Story of a Narragansett Pacer,* ill. by Frederick Chapman, Scribner's, 1951. This semihistorical story of a unique breed of horses is also an adventure tale and a romance. Stella O'Dare rescues one of these horses from the sea, and after a courageous exploit wins it for her own. 10–14

DUDLEY, RUTH, *Hank and the Kitten,* ill. by Louis Darling, Morrow, 1949. An easy-to-read story about a small dog and its efforts to escape the devotions of a stray kitten. The conclusion and the illustrations are equally satisfying. 4–8

EARLE, OLIVE L., *Thunder Wings,* ill. by author, Morrow, 1951. This authentic record of the development of the ruffed grouse from the egg to maturity is well told and illustrated. 6–10

FLACK, MARJORIE, *Story about Ping,* ill. by Kurt Wiese, Viking, 1933. 6–9

Tim Tadpole and the Great Bullfrog, ill. by author, Doubleday, 1934. 7–9

Topsy, ill. by author, Doubleday, 1935. 4–7

Wag-Tail Bess, ill. by author, Doubleday, 1933. 6–9

FROST, FRANCES, *Maple Sugar for Windy Foot,* ill. by Lee Townsend, Whittlesey, 1950.

Sleighbells for Windy Foot, ill. by Lee Townsend, Whittlesey, 1948.

Windy Foot at the County Fair, ill. by Lee Townsend, Whittlesey, 1947.

The same delightful people and the same little pony lend adventure, warmth, and fun to these choice stories of American family life. 9–14

GATES, DORIS, *Little Vic*, ill. by Kate Seredy, Viking, 1951. When Pony River, a Negro boy, sees Little Vic, he believes that the colt will be as great a horse as his sire Man O'War. The boy endures every hardship willingly in his devotion to the colt. A moving, well-told story. 9–12

GEORGE, JOHN and JEAN, *Meph, the Story of a Pet Skunk*, ill. by Jean George, Dutton, 1952. This is not only the story of a tame skunk but also the story of the reclamation of an eroded farm and its effect on an embittered farmer and his unhappy son. Meph enlivens the tale with his antics. 11–16

Vison, the Mink, ill. by Jean George, Dutton, 1949. The vicious mink is not an appealing hero, but this book is a fine record of its life. 11–15

Vulpes, the Red Fox, ill. by Jean George, Dutton, 1948. This story of a red fox and his hunters is superbly told and illustrated. It will delight readers from ten to any age. The hunters win but Vulpes has lived a good fox life. 10–14

GLICK, CARL, *Mickey Wins His Feathers*, ill. by Bill Crawford, Whittlesey, 1948. Humorous adventures of that absurd horse Mickey and his master in Indian territory, with bad men and trickery galore. 8–12

HADER, BERTA and ELMER, *The Big Snow*, ill. by authors, Macmillan, 1948. Beautiful pictures of small animals preparing for a winter that was worse than they dreamed. They struggled through with the help of human friends. Caldecott Award. 5–10

HENDERSON, LUIS, *Amik, the Life Story of a Beaver*, ill. by author, Morrow, 1948. Fascinating account of the wisdom and skills of the beavers; accurate and full of absorbing details. 10–14

HENRY, MARGUERITE, *Album of Horses*, ill. by Wesley Dennis, Rand McNally, 1951. 8–14

Justin Morgan Had a Horse, ill. by Wesley Dennis, Wilcox and Follett, 1945. 10–16

King of the Wind, ill. by Wesley Dennis, Rand McNally, 1948. 8–14

Little-or-Nothing from Nottingham, ill. by Wesley Dennis, Whittlesey, 1949. 7–12

Misty of Chincoteague, ill. by Wesley Dennis, Rand McNally, 1947. 8–12

Sea Star, Orphan of Chincoteague, ill. by Wesley Dennis, Rand McNally, 1949. 8–12

Animal stories by this author are invariably dramatic and exciting but never sensational and they are written with fidelity to horse or dog nature. Moreover, her human characters are never stereotypes but well-drawn, unique individuals. *Album of Horses* gives brief accounts of all the different breeds of horses. King of the Wind was the great Arabian horse which sired the ancestors of our modern race horses. This sometimes tragic but always exciting tale won the Newbery Medal. Little-or-Nothing from Nottingham is a circus dog which has temper tantrums because he can never find the bones he buried the night before. Misty is a little wild horse, caught and tamed by two island children. This little horse is now in Mrs. Henry's own stable. Sea Star is an orphaned colt, also from Chincoteague Island, rescued by the same children. These books are so superbly illustrated by Wesley Dennis that the stories are forever associated with the pictures.

JOHNSON, MARGARET, *Snowshoe Paws*, ill. by author, Morrow, 1949. 6–8

JOHNSON, MARGARET and HELEN, *Barney of the North*, Harcourt, 1939. 7–10

The Runaway Puppy, Harcourt, 1942. 5–7

A Spaniel of Old Plymouth, Harcourt, 1937. 7–10

Stablemates, Harcourt, 1942. 7–10

The Story of Rickey, Harcourt, 1939. 5–7

Tally-Ho, Harcourt, 1936. 7–10

KJELGAARD, JIM, *Big Red*, ill. by Bob Kuhn, Holiday, 1945. 12–16

Kalak of the Ice, ill. by Bob Kuhn, Holiday, 1949. 10–14

Snow Dog, ill. by Jacob Landau, Holiday, 1948. 12–16

These stories are justly popular. They are well written, with plenty of action and both human characters and animals are well drawn. Big Red is an Irish setter, the constant companion of Danny Pickett. Their adventures together climax in tracking down a huge outlaw bear. Kalak, known to the Eskimos as the "mist bear," is a heroic figure in her struggle to protect her cubs and survive. Snow Dog, part Husky and part Staghound, is an orphan struggling for survival in the north woods until he is befriended by a lone trapper.

KNIGHT, ERIC, *Lassie Come Home*, ill. by Marguerite Kirmse, Winston, 1940. A popular story of a collie's faithfulness to her master and ability to track her way home over great distance. 10–16

KNIGHT, RUTH ADAMS, *Halfway to Heaven*, ill. by Wesley Dennis, Whittlesey, 1952. This is a great story for family reading and one that neither children nor adults will forget. It is the story of the dedicated life of one young monk of the St. Bernard Hospice, high in the Alps. His love for the magnificent dogs with which he works, particularly the famous Barry, the dog he trained, will be shared by the readers of this inspiring story of service. 10–14

LATHROP, DOROTHY, *Hide and Go Seek*, ill. by author, Macmillan, 1938. 7–10

Who Goes There? ill. by author, Macmillan, 1935. 7–9

Who Goes There tells about a winter picnic for birds and animals in the forest. *Hide and Go Seek* is about flying squirrels. Both are exquisitely illustrated.

LIPKIND, WILLIAM and MORDVINOFF, NICOLAS, *The Two Reds*, Harcourt, 1950. The two Reds, boy and cat, both city dwellers, were enemies because they both yearned for the same goldfish but for different reasons. How they became friends is hilariously told by Will Lipkind and illustrated by Nicolas Mordvinoff. 4–8

LIPPINCOTT, JOSEPH WHARTON, *Wilderness Champion*, ill. by Paul Bransom, Lippincott, 1944. 10–14

MC CLOSKEY, ROBERT, *Make Way for Ducklings*, ill. by author, Viking, 1941. Since this episode really happens in Boston each year, it is largely realistic with a few thoughts and words permitted the sagacious Mrs. Duck. Caldecott winner. 4–8

MC CLUNG, ROBERT M., *Spike, the Story of a Whitetail Deer*, ill. by author, Morrow, 1952. This clear, factual story of the first year in the life of a whitetail deer pleases young children and makes good reading for the older ones. 5–10

Stripe, the Story of a Chipmunk, ill. by author, Morrow, 1951. These easy-to-read animal stories by a scientist and artist are well told, interesting to read to five-year-olds, and good reading for slow readers of nine and ten. Pictures and format are attractive. The story covers the first year in the life of a chipmunk. 5–10

MC MEEKIN, ISABEL MC LENNAN, *Ban-Joe and Grey Eagle*, ill. by Corinne B. Dillon, Watts, 1951. An excellent race horse story with well-drawn children and grownups and an absorbing plot. Mrs. McMeekin is well qualified to write these stories. She herself is a Kentuckian, and a rider. Her husband is in charge of racing at Churchill Downs. She heard the story of Grey Eagle from her grandfather who saw the race. 9–11

Kentucky Derby Winner, ill. by Corinne B. Dillon, McKay, 1949. A boy-centered horse story of unusual value. It concerns young Jackie Spratt and his passion for "Risty" (Aristides), the horse which eventually won the first Kentucky Derby. Fine people, good horse lore, and considerable humor make this a memorable story. 9–14

MEADER, STEPHEN, *Red Horse Hill,* ill. by Lee Townsend, Harcourt, 1930. Bud Martin is happy when he wins a chance to work with horses in a New Hampshire village. In the process, he discovers a great racer. 11–16

NEWBERRY, CLARE, *April's Kittens,* ill. by author, Harper, 1940.
Babette, ill. by author, Harper, 1937.
Barkis, ill. by author, Harper, 1938.
Marshmallow, ill. by author, Harper, 1942.
Mittens, ill. by author, Harper, 1936.
Percy, Polly and Pete, ill. by author, Harper, 1952.
Clare Newberry's drawings of cats are so entrancing the slight stories do not matter. *Percy, Polly and Pete* is the best story, and the lesson to small cat lovers who hug their kitties too hard is pleasantly administered. 5–8

O'BRIEN, JACK, *Silver Chief, Dog of the North,* ill. by Kurt Wiese, Winston, 1933.
Silver Chief to the Rescue, ill. by Kurt Wiese, Winston, 1937.
Popular but somewhat stereotyped adventures of dog and master. 10–14

O'HARA, MARY, *Green Grass of Wyoming,* Lippincott, 1946. 12–adult
My Friend Flicka, Lippincott, 1941. 10–14
Thunderhead, Lippincott, 1943. 10–14
These books are a trilogy about the McLaughlin's horse ranch, where the problems are complicated by a bad wild-horse strain. How Ken gentles the wild filly Flicka and her son Thunderhead, who is also a problem horse, makes for exciting reading.

RAFTERY, GERALD, *Snow Cloud,* Morrow, 1951. A white stallion escaped from a master he hated and became a wild horse in the Vermont hills. Ken sees the horse, loves it at first sight, and eventually domesticates it once more. 10–16

RAWLINGS, MARJORIE KINNAN, *The Yearling,* ill. by N. C. Wyeth, Scribner's, 1939. This is a poignant story of growing up, when the boy Jody learns to face and accept the tragic necessity of disposing of his pet deer, which has become a menace to the family's livelihood. 10–adult

RECHNITZER, F. E., *Bonny's Boy,* ill. by Marguerite Kirmse, Winston, 1947. A story of a boy's loyalty in raising a motherless puppy. 10–14

REYNOLDS, BARBARA, *Pepper,* ill. by Barbara Cooney, Scribner's, 1952. This amusing story of a boy's attempt to domesticate a baby raccoon and the complications that developed as Pepper matured is especially popular with boys. 8–12

ROBINSON, TOM, *Buttons,* ill. by Peggy Bacon, Viking, 1938. Wonderful picture-story of an alley cat who became a gentleman. 6–10
Greylock and the Robins, ill. by Robert Lawson, Viking, 1946. A gay story with a happy ending of a battle between a hungry old cat and a mother robin. 6–8

ROUNDS, GLEN, *Stolen Pony,* ill. by author, Holiday, 1948. A moving story of a pony stolen by horse thieves and abandoned when it was found he was blind. A faithful dog guides the pony home. 8–12

SCOTT, SALLY, *Binky's Fire,* ill. by Beth Krush, Harcourt, 1952. A frightened puppy becomes—to his own surprise—the hero of the evening.

SEREDY, KATE, *Gypsy,* ill. by author, Viking, 1951. Children of any age and all cat-loving adults will enjoy Miss Seredy's magnificent pictures and simple account of a growing kitten. 4–

SMITH, E. BOYD, *Chicken World,* ill. by author, Putnam's, 1910. Beautiful picture-book of domestic fowls. 4–10

STEARNS, DAVID M., *Chuckle,* ill. by Sharon Stearns, Farrar, 1939. The story of a puppy who weathered a flood in company with a woodchuck.
Sniffy, ill. by Sharon Stearns, Farrar, 1940. Appealing story of a skunk.

STONG, PHIL, *Honk: the Moose,* ill. by Kurt Wiese, Dodd, Mead, 1935. This is undoubtedly one of the most amusing animal tales we have. A hard winter drives a hungry moose into the cozy confines of a livery stable and the problem is to get rid of him. Kurt Wiese's pictures add to the hilarity. 9–12

WALDECK, THEODORE J., *Jamba the Elephant,* ill. by Kurt Wiese, Viking, 1942.
Lions on the Hunt, ill. by Kurt Wiese, Viking, 1942.
The White Panther, ill. by Kurt Wiese, Viking, 1941.
Authentic and exciting stories of wild animals. 10–14

WARD, LYND, *The Biggest Bear,* ill. by author, Houghton, 1952. The Orchard family said, "Better a bear in the orchard than an Orchard in a bear." But Johnny was bound to get a bear and he did. A prize tale with wonderful pictures. 4–8

WEISGARD, LEONARD, *Pelican Here, Pelican There,* ill. by author, Scribner's, 1948. Gorgeous modernistic pictures of a Florida pelican blown by a hurricane to Alaska. What he sees on his return trip is good geography, good art, and real fun. 5–10

TODAY IN THE UNITED STATES

ARDIZZONE, EDWARD, *Little Tim and the Brave Sea Captain,* ill. by author, Oxford, 1936. A picture-book of life at sea with five-year-old Tim as the hero. This first story has been succeeded by numerous books about Tim, all with fine pictures and very popular. 4–9

ASSOCIATION FOR CHILDHOOD EDUCATION, *Told under the Blue Umbrella,* ill. by Marguerite Davis, Macmillan, 1933. A collection of realistic stories. 4–10

AUSTIN, MARGOT, *Barney's Adventure,* ill. by author, Dutton, 1941. A good circus story for the kindergarten age. 4–9

BALET, JAN B., *Amos and the Moon,* ill. by author, Oxford, 1948. A distinguished picture-book telling about Amos' struggles to capture the moon. 4–7

BELL, THELMA HARRINGTON, *Mountain Boy,* ill. by Corydon Bell, Viking, 1947. Randy, a mountain boy, was good at reading wood lore but determined not to read reading. How his mother broke down his resistance makes a delightful story in homespun style. His next adventure is with Yaller-Eye, his cat. See Bibliography, Animal Stories. 6–9

BIALK, ELISA, *Taffy's Foal.* (See Bibliography, Animal Stories.)

BRINK, CAROL RYRIE, *Family Grandstand,* ill. by Jean M. Porter, Viking, 1952. A university professor's lively family is the center of this amusing story. Their house is so close to the football field that the children can watch the games from the attic window and the hero of the gridiron is not only their hero but their problem too. 10–13

BULLA, CLYDE, *A Ranch for Danny,* ill. by Grace Paull, Crowell, 1951. This sequel to *Surprise for a Cowboy* continues the experiences of Danny in the West. Two cowboy songs with music are included. 7–10

CHASTAIN, MADYE LEE, *Bright Days,* ill. by author, Harcourt, 1952. Like *Loblolly Farm* and *Steamboat South* this story has warmth, humor, and a delightful assortment of people. The numerous Fripseys, Marcy the heroine, and a beloved teacher are fine foils for the hateful Gynn who must always win at everything. 9–12

CLEARY, BEVERLY, *Ellen Tebbits,* ill. by Louis Darling, Morrow, 1951.
Henry and Beezus, ill. by Louis Darling, Morrow, 1952.
Henry Huggins, ill. by Louis Darling, Morrow, 1950.
These stories are fun to read aloud to almost any age group and most nine- or ten-year-olds can read them for themselves. Whether Henry is trying to take a stray dog home, or standing by while Beezus buys a bicycle of the wrong sex, these stories are hilarious Americana. 8–12

CREDLE, ELLIS, *The Flop-Eared Hound* (See Bibliography, Today in the United States: Negro Stories).
Goat That Went to School, ill. by author, Grosset & Dunlap, 1940. Here is another mountaineer story in Miss Credle's sympathetic style. The goat threatened to be a nuisance, but proved his value in a storm. 7–10

DALGLIESH, ALICE, *America Travels,* ill. by Hildegard Woodward, Macmillan, 1933.
Blue Teapot, ill. by Hildegard Woodward, Macmillan, 1931. 9–10
Book for Jennifer, ill. by Katherine Milhous, Scribner's, 1940. 9–12
Relief's Rocker, ill. by Hildegard Woodward, Macmillan, 1932. 9–10
Roundabout, ill. by Hildegard Woodward, Macmillan, 1934. 9–10
The Smiths and Rusty, ill. by Berta and Elmer Hader, Scribner's, 1936. 8–10
Wings for the Smiths (sequel to *The Smiths and Rusty*), Scribner's, 1937. 8–10
Miss Dalgliesh's nice stories of the everyday activities of children are climaxed by *The Bears on Hemlock Mountain,* which is a thriller. (See Bibliography, Historical Fiction: American.)

DAVIS, LAVINIA R., *The Wild Birthday Cake,* ill. by Hildegard Woodward, Doubleday, 1949. This is a full-bodied story of a little boy living intensely in his outdoor environment, with minor adventures appropriate to his age. Enchanting pictures add to the beauty and interest of this fine book. 5–9

DU SOE, ROBERT C., *Three Without Fear,* ill. by Ralph Ray, Jr., Longmans, 1947. Dave Rogers, shipwrecked off the coast of California, is rescued by two Indian children. The three children lead a Robinson Crusoe existence of incredible hardship and survive only through the fortitude and ingenuity of the two Indians. 10–14

ENRIGHT, ELIZABETH, *The Four-Story Mistake,* ill. by author, Rinehart, 1942.
The Saturdays, ill. by author, Rinehart, 1941.
Then There Were Five, ill. by author, Rinehart, 1944.
Thimble Summer, ill. by author, Rinehart, 1938.
The Saturdays, The Four-Story Mistake, and *Then There Were Five* tell the story of the Melendy children, first in New York City, where they evolve a scheme for taking turns on successive Saturdays in spending their allowances, and in the second two books in the country. *Thimble Summer* is a delightful story of the adventures of a little girl on a Wisconsin farm today. 8–12

ESTES, ELEANOR, *Ginger Pye,* ill. by author, Harcourt, 1951. Newbery Award, 1952.
The Middle Moffat, ill. by Louis Slobodkin, Harcourt, 1942.
The Moffats, ill. by Louis Slobodkin, Harcourt, 1941.
Rufus M., ill. by Louis Slobodkin, Harcourt, 1943.
Ginger Pye, like *The Moffats,* is a lively family story. The children make and solve their own problems often with hilarious results. Louis Slobodkin's pen-and-ink sketches illustrate the Moffat books with humor and unerring characterization. 9–12

GARST, SHANNON, *Cowboy Boots,* ill. by Charles Hargens, Abingdon-Cokesbury, 1946. On his uncle's ranch, Bob learns cowboy skills with many discouragements and great persistence. He finally wins his boots. 9–12

GATES, DORIS, *Blue Willow,* ill. by Paul Lantz, Viking, 1940. The story of Janey Larkin, the daughter of migrant workers, who longed for a real home. 9–12
Sarah's Idea, ill. by Marjorie Torrey, Viking, 1938. A girl story of California ranch life and a coveted burro. 8–10

GRAY, ELIZABETH JANET, *The Fair Adventure,* ill. by A. K. Reischer, Viking, 1940. Generally rated as one of our best girl stories, this is an effective picture of a lovable, modern family. 12–14

HARRIS, ISOBEL, *Little Boy Brown,* ill. by André François, Lippincott, 1949. This story concerns a city boy's day in the country and his return to his confined skyscraper life. 5–8

HAYWOOD, CAROLYN, *"B" Is for Betsy,* ill. by author, Harcourt, 1939.
Little Eddie, ill. by author, Morrow, 1947.
Between *"B" Is for Betsy* and the Eddie books, there are many titles. Each relates the mild adventures of suburban children at home, at school, or in the community. Eddie has more humor than most of them. 5–10

HENDERSON, LE GRAND, *Augustus and the River,* ill. by author, Bobbs-Merrill, 1939. This is the first of innumerable Augustus books about a happy-go-lucky migrant family, who have fun anywhere. 7–12

HOLBERG, RUTH, *Rowena Carey,* ill. by Grace Paull, Doubleday, 1949. A delightful story of a fat, horse-loving little girl who never gets a horse but does achieve jodhpurs and an occasional ride. 9–12

JONES, ALLETTA, *Peggy's Wish,* ill. by Mary Stevens, Abingdon-Cokesbury, 1949. A strenuous, redheaded orphan yearns in vain to be adopted. Her summer on the Meredith farm is a heaven-sent opportunity except for the presence of two members of the family who seem to dislike her. The happy ending comes after considerable excitement. 8–12

KINGMAN, LEE, *The Quarry Adventure,* ill. by Barbara Cooney, Doubleday, 1951. There is a heart-warming quality about this author's *Best Christmas* that is also to be found in this story of the reformation of a bookworm thrown suddenly into the midst of a family of seven children, an emergency, and a mystery. 10–12

LANSING, ELIZABETH H., *The Pony That Kept a Secret,* ill. by Barbara Cooney, Crowell, 1952. This is a welcome sequel to *The Pony That Ran Away.* Both books center on the activities of the twins, Ted and Sue, and their pony Twinkle. In *The Pony That Kept a Secret* the adorable two-year-old Robbie is both the villain and the hero of a mystery.

LAWRENCE, MILDRED, *Peachtree Island,* ill. by Mary Stevens, Harcourt, 1948.
Sand in Her Shoes, ill. by Madye L. Chastain, Harcourt, 1949.
Tallie, ill. by Paul Galdone, Harcourt, 1951.
Miss Lawrence writes warmly and understandingly of little girls in the process of making difficult adjustments. The locale of each story is different and so are the lively heroines. Sharing work and responsibility with grownups is stressed, but so are adventures, play, and gaiety. These and other books by Miss Lawrence are deservedly popular with girls. 9–12

LENSKI, LOIS, *Cowboy Small,* ill. by author, Oxford, 1949. This should be one of the most popular of all the "Small" books, for every detail of cowboy gear and work is described and illustrated. 4–8
The Little Airplane, ill. by author, Oxford, 1938. 3–7
The Little Auto, ill. by author, Oxford, 1934. 3–7
The Little Sail Boat, ill. by author, Oxford, 1937. 3–7
The Little Train, ill. by author, Oxford, 1940. 6–8
Papa Small, ill. by author, Oxford, 1951. 4–8
(See also Bibliography, Today in the United States: Other Minority Groups.)

LIPKIND, WILLIAM and MORDVINOFF, NICOLAS, *Even Steven,* Harcourt, 1952. If this is not down to rock bottom realism, it is the kind of ranch, cowboy, crooks, and heroism that children dream about. Hobie chooses Steven for his own horse and together they save the day with ease and éclat. A five-year-old dream and great fun! 4–6

MC CLOSKEY, ROBERT, *Blueberries for Sal,* ill. by author, Viking, 1948. A picture-story about Sal and her mother, who tangle with a bear and her cub. Eventually, each mother gets her own child and blueberries, too. 3–7
Lentil, ill. by author, Viking, 1940. Amusing story of a boy living in a small middle western town who saves the day with his harmonica. 8–12
One Morning in Maine, ill. by author, Viking, 1952. Another Sal story with glorious pictures of Maine woods and water. This time Sal has lost her first tooth, but after the first shock, life goes on serenely and there is "Clam chowder for lunch!" 3–7

MC GINLEY, PHYLLIS, *The Most Wonderful Doll in the World,* ill. by Helen Stone, Lippincott, 1950. A small girl cannot distinguish between things as they are and as she dreams they might be. A lost doll becomes more and more remarkable until the real doll is a shock when it is found. Gentle, humorous treatment of a common ailment!

NORTH, STERLING, *Greased Lightning,* ill. by Kurt Wiese, Winston, 1940. The story of a small boy and his pet pig, pestiferous but dearly loved. 8–10

PETERSHAM, MAUD and MISKA, *The Box with Red Wheels,* ill. by authors, Macmillan, 1949. This entrancing picture book is the Petershams at their colorful best. The mysterious "box" which so attracts the animals contains a delightful baby, who is as charmed with the barnyard animals as they are with her. 4–8

RENICK, MARION, *Pete's Home Run,* ill. by Pru Herric, Scribner's, 1952.
Nicky's Football Team, ill. by Marian Honigman, Scribner's, 1951.
These stories have no literary qualities but they do introduce children successfully to football, baseball, and good sportsmanship. 7–10

ROBINSON, THOMAS PENDLETON, *Trigger John's Son,* ill. by Robert McCloskey, Viking, 1949. Trigger is an orphan in the process of being adopted when he decides to inspect his future parents. He gets off the train prematurely, falls in with a boys' gang and a blind hermit, and action begins. Boys delight in Trigger's scrapes and good intentions, and Robert McCloskey's sensitive drawings add to the fun. 10–14

SAUER, JULIA, *The Light at Tern Rock,* ill. by Georges Schreiber, Viking, 1951. A Christmas story set against the wild beauty and isolation of a lonely sea-girt lighthouse. The story is beautifully told and illustrated, and the moral problem involved makes it unusual. 9–12

SCHNEIDER, NINA, *While Susie Sleeps,* ill. by Dagmar Wilson, Scott, 1948. Pleasantly cadenced text tells about the creatures that sleep the darkness through and those that wake and work at night. Ends with the bright new day. Reassuring and appealing. 4–7

SINGMASTER, ELSIE, *The Isle of Que,* ill. by Elmer Hader, Longmans, 1948. A teen-age story of a boy's growing up, of close family affection and fun, and of the boy's conquest of a life-long fear. 12–16

TORREY, MARJORIE (pseud. for T. Chanslor), *The Merriweathers,* ill. by author, Viking, 1949. Strong family affection, an energetic attack on problems, and a genuine friendliness make the seven Merriweathers a delightful family to read about. 12–16

TRESSELT, ALVIN, *Follow the Wind,* ill. by Roger Duvoisin, Lothrop, 1950.
Hi, Mister Robin! ill. by Roger Duvoisin, Lothrop, 1950.
Rain Drop Splash, ill. by Leonard Weisgard, Lothrop, 1946.
Sun Up, ill. by Roger Duvoisin, Lothrop, 1949.
White Snow, Bright Snow, ill. by Roger Duvoisin, Lothrop, 1947.
These picture-stories and others by the same author-artist team are little dramas of weather and seasonal changes. *White Snow, Bright Snow* won the Caldecott Award. 4–6

TUDOR, TASHA, *Pumpkin Moonshine,* ill. by author, Oxford, 1938. This Halloween story makes a good introduction to the small, beautifully illustrated books of Tasha Tudor. 4–7

TUNIS, JOHN R., *The Duke Decides,* ill. by James MacDonald, Harcourt, 1939.
The Iron Duke, ill. by Johan Bull, Harcourt, 1938.
The best college stories we have for the pre-college boy. *The Iron Duke* is about an Iowa boy's adjustments to Harvard. *The Duke Decides* finds him a member of the Olympic track team. 12–16
The Kid Comes Back, Morrow, 1946. The readjustment of a boy back from the Service. Another baseball story. 12–14
Kid from Tomkinsville, ill. by J. H. Barnum, Harcourt, 1940. Roy Tucker, a small-town boy, makes a big-league baseball team. Fine story of his training, mistakes, and triumphs. All the Tunis books are popular sports stories with a strong emphasis on community ideals. 11–15

WILSON, HAZEL, *Herbert,* ill. by John Barron, Knopf, 1950.
Herbert Again, ill. by John Barron, Knopf, 1951.
Island Summer, ill. by Richard Floethe, Abingdon-Cokesbury, 1949.
The Owen Boys, ill. by William Sharp, Abingdon-Cokesbury, 1947.
Herbert is a younger Homer Price and his adventures and vicissitudes are equally funny. *The Owen Boys* and

Island Summer are family stories with amusing ups and downs but with the boys as the center of interest. These are decidedly boy stories and extremely popular. 8–12

WOOLLEY, CATHERINE, *David's Railroad,* ill. by Iris Beatty Johnson, Morrow, 1949. For six-year-olds, this is a significant story of a small boy's obsession with his electric railroad. David neglects his chores, grows genuinely naughty, but is finally transformed into a "solid citizen."
Railroad Cowboy, ill. by Iris Beatty Johnson, Morrow, 1951. David's interest in his electric train is now broadening to an intense concern with real trains. His club of train fans really sees trains and travels. 6–8

YATES, ELIZABETH, *Mountain Born,* ill. by Nora Unwin, Coward, 1943.
A Place for Peter, ill. by Nora Unwin, Coward, 1952. Peter is a little boy in the first book, growing into farm activities and enjoying the companionship of a pet lamb. Through his pet, Peter comes to know birth, death, and the continuity of life. In the second book, Peter is a sturdy thirteen-year-old but in unhappy conflict with his father. Again, farm animals and activities help both Peter and his father. 10–14

Negro Stories

BEIM, LORRAINE and JERROLD, *Two Is a Team,* ill. by Ernest Crichlow, Harcourt, 1945. Two little boys find that they get more done as a team than singly. That they are of two different races makes no difference; it's the team that is important. 6–9

BIANCO, MARGERY, *Forward, Commandos!* ill. by Rafaello Busoni, Viking, 1944. Amusing story of a happy gang which includes one Negro child. Good relationships and good play. 7–9

BONTEMPS, ARNA, *You Can't Pet a Possum,* ill. by Ilse Bischoff, Morrow, 1934. Shine Boy was lonely until Butch, a yellow pup, wandered into his life. The delectable possum dinner that celebrates their adventures makes a mouth-watering conclusion. 8–10

BURGWYN, MEBANE HOLOMAN, *Lucky Mischief,* ill. by Gertrude Howe, Oxford, 1949. This book combines the virtues of being a good mystery, a story about 4-H activities, and a picture of a substantial, rural Negro community. The feud between two boys is finally dissolved in their devotion to their pet steers. 10–14

CREDLE, ELLIS, *The Flop-Eared Hound,* ill. with photographs by Charles Townsend, Oxford, 1938. Boot-jack's dog is always misbehaving and being given away, until finally, the dog proves his worth and becomes a permanent member of the family. 6–9

EVANS, EVA KNOX, *Araminta,* ill. by Erick Berry, Putnam, 1935.
Araminta's Goat, ill. by Erick Berry, Putnam, 1938.
Jerome Anthony, ill. by Erick Berry, Putnam, 1936.
Favorites with all children, these stories are unexcelled for mild humorous realism. 7–10

FAULKNER, GEORGENE, and BECKER, JOHN, *Melindy's Medal,* ill. by C. E. Fox, Messner, 1945. A humorous and tender story of a little Negro girl's achievement. 8–12

HUNT, MABEL LEIGH, *Ladycake Farm,* ill. by Clotilde Embree Funk, Lippincott, 1952. This joyous story of a Negro family beginning a new life on a farm has its tragic moments too. The family faces them frankly and courageously and their competence and friendliness help them. A delightful family group by any standard, and a first-rate story with unusual social values. 9–12

JACKSON, JESSE, *Call Me Charley,* ill. by Doris Spiegel, Harper, 1945. The story of the ups and downs in a young Negro's friendship with a white boy in a white community. 9–12

LANG, DON, *On the Dark of the Moon,* ill. by Nedda Walker, Oxford, 1943. A moving story of a little Negro boy's love for his pet raccoons and possum. 9–14

LATTIMORE, ELEANOR FRANCES, *Junior, a Colored Boy of Charleston,* ill. by author, Harcourt, 1938. An understanding story of a little colored boy's efforts to earn money for his family. 8–10

MEANS, FLORENCE CRANNELL, *Great Day in the Morning,* Houghton, 1946. Another lovable Negro girl experiences the bitterness of racial prejudice but has the courage to go on. At Tuskegee she comes to know Dr. Carver and decides to become a nurse. 12–14

North American Indian Stories

ABEITA, LOUISE, *I Am a Pueblo Indian Girl,* told by E-Yeh-Shure', Morrow, 1939. A young Pueblo Indian girl describes with simplicity and beauty the things that are familiar and important to her. 8–12

ARMER, LAURA, *Dark Circle of Branches,* ill. by Sidney Armer, Longmans, 1933.
Waterless Mountain, ill. by author and Sidney Armer, Longmans, 1931.
Two fine stories of Navaho Indian life, although they are difficult for children because of their mysticism and lack of action. 12–14

BAILEY, FLORA, *Summer at Yellow Singer's,* ill. by Ralph Ray, Macmillan, 1948. Two children spend a summer with the Navaho Indians and enter completely into the Indian way of life. A good story and authentic description of modern Navaho life. 8–12

BLEEKER, SONIA, *American Indian Tribes,* ill. by Althea Karr, Morrow, 1950—
Indians of the Longhouse, the Story of the Iroquois.
The Apache Indians, Raiders of the Southwest.
The Sea Hunters, Indians of the Northwest.
The Cherokee, Indians of the Mountains.
The Crow Indians, Hunters of the Northern Plains.
Factual narratives with good story interest, these books written by an anthropologist give children authentic information about the family life, work and play, customs, and history of each tribe.

BRONSON, WILFRID S., *Pinto's Journey,* Messner, 1948. A fine adventure story about a Navaho Indian boy of modern times. Brilliant pictures in color. 8–10

BUFF, MARY, *Dancing Cloud,* ill. by Conrad Buff, Viking, 1937. 8–10

CLARK, ANN NOLAN, *In My Mother's House,* ill. by Velino Herrera, Viking, 1941. This is a fine story written with simplicity and beauty about the Tewa Indian children. 8–12
Little Navajo Bluebird, ill. by Velino Herrera, Viking, 1943. This is the story of a little Navaho girl who loves her home and the old ways of life, but who learns to accept the idea of going to the white man's school. Miss Clark's books are beautifully written and show deep sympathy and understanding of Indian ways. 8–12

COBLENTZ, CATHERINE CATE, *Blue and Silver Necklace,* ill. by Edwin Earle, Little, 1937. A little Hopi girl tries to adjust to new ways of living in the white man's school. 10–12
Sequoya, Longmans, 1946. The story of a great Cherokee Indian who developed the Cherokee alphabet and taught his people to read. 12–14

HAYES, FLORENCE, *Hosh-Ki, the Navajo,* ill. by Charlotte

Anna Chase, Random House, 1943. An Indian boy adjusts to new ways. 10–12

MALKUS, ALIDA SIMS, *Stone Knife Boy,* ill. by Herbert Morton Stoops, Harcourt, 1933. Boy returns from the government school to his Taos pueblo only to find himself under suspicion for going back on the old ways. He helps bring about better understanding. 12–14

MCGRAW, ELOISE JARVIS, *Moccasin Trail,* Coward, 1952. Although this story centers on a white boy's decision to leave the Crow Indians, who rescued and raised him, and return to his own people, it tells much about the Indians, their ideals, customs, and limitations. A powerful story. 12–adult

MOON, GRACE, *Chi-Weé and Loki,* ill. by Carl Moon, Doubleday, 1926. 8–12

PHELPS, MARGARET, *Chia and the Lambs,* ill. by Ann Eshner, Macrae Smith, 1944. A graceful story of a little Indian girl and her lamb. 8–10

Other Minority Groups

ANGELO, VALENTI, *The Bells of Bleecker Street,* ill. by author, Viking, 1949. 10–14

The Golden Gate, ill. by author, Viking, 1939. 10–12

Hill of Little Miracles, ill. by author, Viking, 1942. 10–14

Nino, ill. by author, Viking, 1938. 10–12

Paradise Valley, ill. by author, Viking, 1940. 8–12

In *The Bells of Bleecker Street* twelve-year-old Joey finds himself the accidental possessor of a toe from the statue of St. John. His struggles to return the toe, his adventures with his gang, and his father's return from the war make an amusing story and bring this Italian neighborhood vividly to life. *Nino* is the story of the author's own childhood in Tuscany. *The Golden Gate* tells of Nino's first years in America and his family's adjustment to their new home and country. *Hill of Little Miracles* shows Rieco, who was born with one leg too short, starting on the road to normalcy. This book abounds with the good nature and gaiety of the Italians on Telegraph Hill. *Paradise Valley* is the sensitive story of a little Mexican boy who lived in an old railroad caboose in Nevada.

ASSOCIATION FOR CHILDHOOD EDUCATION, *Told under Spacious Skies,* ill. by William Moyers, Macmillan, 1952. 6–12

Told under the Stars and Stripes, ill. by Nedda Walker, Macmillan, 1945. 8–12

The first book is made up of regional stories. The second book is an anthology of short stories about various minority groups in our cities and throughout the country.

BAKER, CHARLOTTE, *Necessary Nellie,* ill. by author, Coward, 1945. Some little California-Mexican children prove to the judge that their stray dog Nellie is really "necessary." 5–9

DE ANGELI, MARGUERITE, *Henner's Lydia,* ill. by author, Doubleday, 1936. 7–10

Skippack School, ill. by author, Doubleday, 1939. 8–12

Thee, Hannah! ill. by author, Doubleday, 1940. 8–12

Up the Hill, ill. by author, Doubleday, 1942. 8–12

JUSTUS, MAY, *Here Comes Mary Ellen,* ill. by Helen Finger, Lippincott, 1940.

Lucky Penny, ill. by Frederick T. Chapman, Aladdin, 1951.

Mountain people come vigorously alive in these and other stories by this author. Mary Ellen is an appealing little girl and the two boys with their dogs and mules make a lively tale. 8–12

LANSING, E. H., *Shoot for a Mule,* ill. by Susanne Suba, Crowell, 1951. This Kentucky mountaineer story has feuds and a shooting match into the bargain. Our hero is bound to get a mule of his own and he succeeds. Humorous, exciting, and fun to read. 8–12

LENSKI, LOIS, *Bayou Suzette,* ill. by author, Lippincott, 1948.

Blue Ridge Billy, ill. by author, Lippincott, 1946.

Boom Town Boy, ill. by author, Lippincott, 1948.

Judy's Journey, ill. by author, Lippincott, 1947.

Prairie School, ill. by author, Lippincott, 1951.

Strawberry Girl, ill. by author, Lippincott, 1945.

These regional stories are a remarkable contribution to the child's understanding of the people, work, and conditions in different sections of this country. The titles indicate locale or work. *Prairie School* is the story of courage and resourcefulness with which a teacher and children met the Dakota blizzard of 1949, which marooned them in their schoolhouse. Every book is a good story with lively characters. 8–12

LOWNSBERY, ELOISE, *Marta the Doll,* ill. by Marya Werten, Longmans, 1946. Hanka, a little Polish girl, longs for a soft, cuddly doll such as her American cousins have. Her sister Marysia gives up a new skirt to buy the doll. Hanka and her doll Marta are inseparable and share together all the pleasant adventures of everyday living. 7–10

MEANS, FLORENCE CRANNELL, *Across the Fruited Plain,* ill. by Janet Smalley, Friendship Press, 1940. A story of migrant fruit pickers, their problems, courage, and warm family affection. 12–14

MILHOUS, KATHERINE, *The Egg Tree,* ill. by author, Scribner's, 1950. This beautifully illustrated picture-book of an Easter egg tree in rural Pennsylvania has started egg trees blooming all over this country. Authentic folk art and bright colors made it the Caldecott winner. 6–8

OAKES, VANYA, *Willy Wong, American,* ill. by Weda Yap, Messner, 1951. Here is the old struggle of a little Chinese boy to be accepted as a hundred per cent American. A good family story.

POLITI, LEO, *A Boat for Peppe,* ill. by author, Scribner's, 1950.

Juanita, ill. by author, Scribner's, 1948.

Little Leo, ill. by author, Scribner's, 1951.

Pedro, the Angel of Olvera Street, ill. by author, Scribner's, 1946.

Song of the Swallows, ill. by author, Scribner's, 1949. Caldecott Award.

These appealing picture-stories have slight plots but a tender beauty that is unique. Pedro and Juanita show the Christmas and Easter customs of the Mexican colony at Olvera Street in Los Angeles. The swallows are the famous birds of San Capistrano Mission. Peppe takes part in the blessing of the fishing boats at Monterey, but Little Leo journeys to Italy and converts a whole village of children to the charms of playing Indian. 5–8

SEREDY, KATE, *A Tree for Peter,* ill. by author, Viking, 1941. A story of shanty town, complicated by a rather confusing symbolism, but a beautiful story with some of Kate Seredy's finest pictures. 8–12

SEYFERT, ELLA, *Little Amish Schoolhouse,* ill. by Ninon MacKnight, Crowell, 1939. A modern story of Amish life, describing their customs, a wedding, a Christmas celebration, and their school. Their deep desire to keep their own school and ways seems reasonable in this appealing little tale.

SIMON, CHARLIE MAY, *Lost Corner,* ill. by Howard Simon, Dutton, 1935. This tells the story of two Ozark children who make a new friend when they are lost in the mountains. 10–12

TUNIS, JOHN R., *Keystone Kids,* Harcourt, 1943. A fine sports story for the teen age. The happy solution to anti-Semitic feeling is achieved by the children. 12–16

WARNER, GERTRUDE, *Children of the Harvest,* ill. by Janet Smalley, Friendship Press, 1940. Another story of migrant workers, their troubles, and triumphs. 12–16

WILSON, LEON, *This Boy Cody,* ill. by Ursula Koering, Watts, 1950.

This Boy Cody and His Friends, ill. by Ursula Koering, Watts, 1952.

Joyous stories of Cody Capshaw, his family, friends, and neighbors in the Cumberland Mountain region. House building, fiddle making, berrying, riddles, tall tales, livestock, pets, and a tag-along small sister add interest, complications, and fun to Cody's adventures. 9–12

TODAY IN OTHER LANDS

China

HANDFORTH, THOMAS, *Mei Li,* ill. by author, Doubleday, 1938. The pleasant adventures of a little Chinese girl at the Fair. A picture-book which won the Caldecott Medal for 1939. 5–8

LATTIMORE, ELEANOR FRANCES, *Little Pear and His Friends,* ill. by author, Harcourt, 1934. 6–10

Three Little Chinese Girls, ill. by author, Morrow, 1948. 7–10

LEWIS, ELIZABETH, *China Quest,* ill. by Kurt Wiese, Winston, 1937. 12–16

Ho-Ming, Girl of New China, ill. by Kurt Wiese, Winston, 1934. 12–16

When the Typhoon Blows, ill. by Kurt Wiese, Winston, 1942. 12–16

LIANG, YEN, *Dee Dee's Birthday,* ill. by author, Oxford, 1952. Dee Dee is Chinese, but any child of any country would like to have a birthday celebration such as Dee Dee has in Pekin. 3–7

LIDE, ALICE, *Yinka-Tu the Yak,* ill. by Kurt Wiese, Viking, 1938. A curious story of a Mongol boy and his adventures with his pet yak. Wonderful pictures by Kurt Wiese add to the interest of the book. 9–12

MUHLENWEG, FRITZ, *Big Tiger and Christian,* ill. Rafaello Busoni, Pantheon, 1952. Here are nearly six hundred pages packed with adventure, people, and strange places in a story so unusual no one who reads the first chapter will want to put it down. An English and a Chinese boy carry through a dangerous mission for General Woo in wartime China. They travel by truck, ponies, and camel, encounter kindly people and villains, but come through it all competently and with their sense of humor intact. 12–adult

TREFFINGER, CAROLYN, *Li Lun, Lad of Courage,* ill. by Kurt Wiese, Abingdon-Cokesbury, 1947. Story of a Chinese boy who compensates for his fear of the sea by a four months' vigil on a barren mountaintop, alone. He learns a new way of life for himself and his people. 9–12

WIESE, KURT, *Fish in the Air,* ill. by author, Viking, 1948. An amusing account of what happened to a small boy who would buy the largest kite in the market. Lovely, bright pictures. 6–8

WOOD, ESTHER, *Pepper Moon,* ill. by Laura Bannon, Longmans, 1940. 5–7

Silk and Satin Lane, ill. by Kurt Wiese, Longmans, 1939. 9–12

YOUNG, EVELYN, *Wu and Lu and Li,* ill. by author, Oxford, 1939. Picture book of Chinese toddlers, appealing and beautiful. Older boys and girls can study the costumes for dramatizations. 5–6

England and Ireland

RANSOME, ARTHUR, *Coot Club,* ill. by author and Helene Carter, Lippincott, 1935.

Peter Duck, ill. by Helene Carter, Lippincott, 1933.

Pigeon Post, ill. by Mary E. Shepard, Lippincott, 1937.

Swallowdale, ill. by Helene Carter, Lippincott, 1932.

Swallows and Amazons, ill. by Helene Carter, Lippincott, 1931.

We Didn't Mean to Go to Sea, ill. by author, Lippincott, 1938.

Winter Holiday, ill. by Helene Carter, Lippincott, 1934.

This is a series of books about English children living in the Lake district of England. The children spend most of their time outdoors, and meet emergencies with resourcefulness and intelligence. 12–14

STREATFEILD, NOEL, *Ballet Shoes,* ill. by Richard Floethe, Random House, 1937.

Circus Shoes, ill. by Richard Floethe, Random House, 1939.

Theater Shoes, ill. by Richard Floethe, Random House, 1945.

The "Shoes" books are a series of gay tales with vocational themes. 10–14

VAN STOCKUM, HILDA, *The Cottage at Bantry Bay,* ill. by author, Viking, 1938. The story of the escapades of the lively O'Sullivan children—Michael, Brigid, and the twins Francie and Liam. 10–14

Francie on the Run, ill. by author, Viking, 1939. This sequel describes Francie's adventures after he leaves the hospital, where his clubfoot has been operated on, until he reaches home. 10–14

Pegeen, ill. by author, Viking, 1941. This tells of the scrapes and misdeeds of Pegeen, a mischievous orphan, who has come to live with the O'Sullivans. 10–14

France

BISHOP, CLAIRE HUCHET, *Pancakes Paris,* ill. by Georges Schreiber, Viking, 1947. A half-starved postwar French child receives a miraculous package of American pancake mix. How he meets two American soldiers and gets the directions for the pancakes translated makes a heart-warming tale. 8–12

Twenty and Ten, ill. by William Pene du Bois, Viking, 1952. During the Nazi occupation of France, nineteen French children with their teacher were asked to feed and hide ten Jewish children. How these fifth graders shared their food and managed with their teacher held in jail is a moving and satisfying story. 9–12

COATSWORTH, ELIZABETH JANE, *The House of the Swan,* ill. by Kathleen Voute, Macmillan, 1948. Exciting, modern mystery tale about two American orphans in France. 9–14

Holland

DE JONG, MEINDERT, *Dirk's Dog Bello,* ill. by Kurt Wiese, Harper, 1939. The story of a boy's love for his much too large and hungry dog. A fine picture of present-day Dutch life. Hard reading. 10–12

DODGE, MARY MAPES, *Hans Brinker; or the Silver Skates,*

Scribner's, 1932, ill. by Hilda Van Stockum, World Publishing, 1946. 10–12

VAN STOCKUM, HILDA, *A Day on Skates,* ill. by author, Harper, 1934. A Dutch schoolmaster takes his flock on a day's skating tour. 8–10

Mexico and South America

BANNON, LAURA, *Manuela's Birthday,* ill. by author, Whitman, 1939. A popular and lively story with brilliant pictures. 6–9

BEIM, LORRAINE and JERROLD, *The Burro That Had a Name,* ill. by Howard Simon, Harcourt, 1939. An amusing story of a boy's attachment for a burro. 6–9

BURBANK, ADDISON, *The Cedar Deer,* ill. by author, Coward, 1940. Breathless action and a good picture of primitive and modern life in Guatemala. 10–12

CLARK, ANN NOLAN, *Secret of the Andes,* ill. by Jean Charlot, Viking, 1952. Cusi lives among the great peaks of the Andes mountains, guarding a hidden herd of royal llamas and learning from old Chuto the sacred traditions of his Incan ancestors. Even after his journey to the world of men, Cusi knows that his destiny lies in the remote heights cherishing the flock. 10–14

CREDLE, ELLIS, *My Pet Peepelo,* photographs by Charles Townsend, Oxford, 1948. Delightful story of a little Mexican boy who finds he just can't bear to sell his pet turkey, because something you love is better than money. 7–12

DESMOND, ALICE CURTIS, *The Lucky Llama,* ill. by Wilfrid Bronson, Macmillan, 1939. A charming picture of boy and llamas. 10–12

ELIOT, FRANCES, *Pablo's Pipe,* ill. by author, Dutton, 1936. Quiet, slow-moving, but satisfying, this tale makes an excellent center for a Mexican play or pageant. 8–12

GARRETT, HELEN, *Angelo the Naughty One,* ill. by Leo Politi, Viking, 1944. The amusing reform of a small Mexican boy who did not like to take baths. 6–9

GILL, RICHARD C. and HOKE, HELEN, *Paco Goes to the Fair,* ill. by Ruth Gannett, Holt, 1940. The story of two Indian children in the mountains of Ecuador, who use some ancient Inca dye instead of the cheap imported red, while their parents are at the fair. 9–12

HADER, BERTA and ELMER, *Story of Pancho and the Bull with the Crooked Tail,* ill. by authors, Macmillan, 1942. A very funny story of a little Mexican boy's accidental capture of a ferocious bull. Pictures in brilliant colors. 5–9

HALL, ESTHER GREENACRE, *Mario and the Chuna,* ill. by J. M. de Aragon, Random House, 1940. A chuna is an Argentine bird that can spit a pebble out of its beak with unerring aim. A really funny story with a good picture of primitive rural life. 9–12

LIDE, ALICE A., *Aztec Drums,* ill. by Carlos Sanchez M., Longmans, 1938. Early civilization in Mexico, well described but incidental to a thrilling story. 10–14

LONG, EULA, *Far Away Holiday,* ill. by author, Morrow, 1947. The struggles of a little Mexican girl to make a proper flower wand for the church procession almost fail. A pleasant picture of family life.

MALKUS, ALIDA, *The Silver Llama,* ill. by author, Winston, 1939. Appealing, well-written picture of Peruvian Indians. 10–14

PARISH, HELEN RAND, *At the Palace Gates,* ill. by Leo Politi, Viking, 1949. Appealing adventure story of a small Peruvian hillbilly living on his own in the city of Lima. When he saves the president from plotters, the conclusion is naturally triumphant. 9–12

SAWYER, RUTH, *The Least One,* ill. by Leo Politi, Viking, 1941. A touching little tale of a boy's love for his donkey and his deep religious faith that the little burro will come back to him. 8–10

TARSHIS, ELIZABETH K., *The Village That Learned to Read,* ill. by Harold Haydon, Houghton, 1941. A robust story with humor and an amusing moral. Important in its focus on the national drive for literacy. 10–12

Pacific Islands

CROCKETT, LUCY HERNDON, *Lucio and His Nuong,* ill. by author, Holt, 1939. An amusing picture-book and a story popular from second grade to high school. Six-year-old Lucio and a huge water buffalo are the principal characters in a story of the Philippines. 8–12

SPERRY, ARMSTRONG, *Call It Courage,* ill. by author, Macmillan, 1940. This Newbery Medal book is an exciting adventure story and also the tale of one boy's conquest of fear. 10–12

Scandinavian Countries

BESKOW, ELSA, *Pelle's New Suit,* ill. by author, Harper, 1929. 3–8

BURGLON, NORA, *Children of the Soil,* ill. by Edgar Parin d'Aulaire, Doubleday, 1932. (Sweden)

Deep Silver, ill. by Peter Hurd, Houghton, 1938. (Norway)

The Gate Swings In, ill. by Richard Floethe, Little, 1937. (Sweden)

Sticks Across the Chimney, ill. by Fritz Eichenberg, Holiday, 1938. (Denmark)

Good stories with wholesome ideals and rousing plots centered around mysteries. 10–14

HENRY, MARGUERITE, *Auno and Tauno,* ill. by Gladys R. Blackwood, Whitman, 1940. The entertaining picture-story of a small Finnish boy who skips out of school where he is supposed to remain. The device by which he escapes tickles children. (Finland) 6–9

Switzerland

CHONZ, SELINA, *A Bell for Ursli,* ill. by Alois Carigiet, Oxford, 1950. One of the most beautiful picture-stories to come out of Europe, this is also an exciting adventure story of a small Swiss boy determined to have the largest bell to ring in the spring processional. 6–9

GAGGIN, EVA R., *An Ear for Uncle Emil,* ill. by Kate Seredy, Viking, 1939. A humorous but very long story about a little girl who manages to have her masculine doll, "Uncle Emil," transformed into a coquettish female. 10–12

Eskimo Stories

DOONE, RADKO, *Nuvat the Brave,* ill. by Hans Wallen, Macrae-Smith, 1934. An Eskimo boy overcomes his cowardice. 10–12

FREUCHEN, PIPALUK, *Eskimo Boy,* ill. by Ingrid Vang Nyman, Lothrop, 1951. This epic tale, translated from the Danish, is the grimmest, most terrifying picture of Eskimo life we have had. It is the story of a boy's fight to save his family from starvation. The realistic details make it unsuitable for young children, but the heroism of the boy and his deeds are good for older children to read about. 10–12

LIPKIND, WILLIAM, *Boy with a Harpoon,* ill. by Nicolas Mordvinoff, Harcourt, 1952. Here are "Will and Nick" in serious vein and Will Lipkind turns out to be an anthropologist of parts. This is a substantial story of Eskimo life for younger children than Freuchen's book, but it too should banish forever the igloo stereotype of Arctic life. An absorbing story of a boy's attempts to rid himself of a derogatory nickname and win a respected place in the community of men. 7–10

Other Countries

BENARY-ISBERT, MARGOT, *The Ark,* trans. by Clara and Richard Winston, Harcourt, 1953. This first juvenile to come out of West Germany is an appealing story of a mother and four children trying to reëstablish themselves in a postwar city. Two freezing attic rooms seem to them a miracle of good luck after the refugee camps. Somehow the mother makes a home which becomes a center of hope, kindness, and even fun for many people. This lively story is told with humor, beauty, and fine characterizations. 10–14

BOTHWELL, JEAN, *The Little Flute Player,* ill. by Margaret Ayer, Morrow, 1949. This is Jean Bothwell's fourth book about India, and certainly it is one of the most beautiful. Minor disasters stalk Teka, the little flute player of the village, and grow into tragedy when the famine comes. This ten-year-old boy takes his father's place and saves his family from starvation. 8–12

BROWN, MARCIA, *Henry—Fisherman,* ill. by author, Scribner's, 1949. Small Henry of the Virgin Islands yearns for the day when he can go fishing with his father. When that day comes, he dodges a big shark and comes home in triumph, "a fisherman for true." Lithe, brown bodies against the clear, brilliant colors of island and sea add to the beauty and grace of this brief tale. 7–10

BUCK, PEARL, *The Big Wave,* prints by Hiroshige and Hokusai, Day, 1948. Significant story built around the theme that "life is stronger than death." Two Japanese boys adventure together, survive a terrible catastrophe, and begin life anew. 9–14

DAVIS, NORMAN, *Picken's Exciting Summer,* ill. by Winslade, Oxford, 1950.

Picken's Great Adventure, ill. by Winslade, Oxford, 1949. Picken is an African boy, the son of a chief, but he is a typical eight-year-old of any land. He rescues a small monkey that becomes his constant companion and their adventures together make two exciting stories. 7–10

JONES, ELIZABETH ORTON, *Maminka's Children,* ill. by author, Macmillan, 1940. The story is not important, but is written with great charm and tenderness. This tale of Czechoslovakia has lovely pictures and childlike humor. 10–12

PRISHVIN, MIKHAIL, *The Treasure Trove of the Sun,* trans. from the Russian by Tatian Balkoff-Drowne, ill. by Feodor Rojankovsky, Viking, 1952. This Russian story is beautiful in format, pictures, and content. An orphaned brother and sister nearly lose their lives in a cranberry bog, but are saved by an orphaned dog. 8–12

RANKIN, LOUISE, *Daughter of the Mountains,* ill. by Kurt Wiese, Viking, 1948. A little Tibetan girl undertakes a long and perilous journey alone to retrieve her beloved dog. She is sustained by a deep religious faith. 9–12

SEREDY, KATE, *Chestry Oak,* ill. by author, Viking, 1948. An involved and difficult story with a deeply significant theme—the fall of an ancient house and its rebirth in a new land. The boy Michael and his great horse Midnight are the central figures of the tale. 10–14

The Singing Tree, ill. by author, Viking, 1939. 10–14

WEIL, ANN, *Red Sails to Capri,* ill. by C. B. Falls, Viking, 1952. An unusual story about the discovery of the Blue Grotto at Capri, told entirely in dialogue. Considerable suspense and delightful people, especially the mother who cooks by the length of a song, will make this a book to remember. 9–12

HISTORICAL FICTION[1]

American

ALBERT, EDNA, *Little Pilgrim to Penn's Woods,* ill. by Esther Brann, Longmans, 1930. A little girl and her family leave Germany to make a new home in the Pennsylvania colony. 12–14

ALCOTT, LOUISA MAY, *Little Women,* ill. by Jessie Willcox Smith, Little, 1934 (1868). Although this forerunner of modern realism for children and young people is chiefly a story of family life, it is also a story of life in Civil War times. Recent editions by World Publishing Company and Grosset & Dunlap have added to its attractions, but it still remains a girl's book. 12–16

BAILEY, JEAN, *Cherokee Bill, Oklahoma Pacer,* ill. by Pers Crowell, Abingdon-Cokesbury, 1952. A fine story of a boy and his horse. The setting is on the Kansas-Oklahoma border at the time of the opening of the Cherokee Strip. 12–14

BLEEKER, SONIA, *American Indian Tribes.* (See Bibliography, Today in the United States: North American Indian.)

BULLA, CLYDE ROBERT, *Riding the Pony Express,* by Grace Paull, Crowell, 1948. An easy-to-read story of a boy who carried the mail in an emergency. 8–10

The Secret Valley, ill. by Grace Paull, Crowell, 1949. A Missouri family go to California in search of gold, but find other treasures instead. 8–10

CARR, MARY JANE, *Children of the Covered Wagon: a Story of the Old Oregon Trail,* ill. by Bob Kuhn, Crowell, 1943. An excellent story of a pioneer family on a journey from Missouri to the Willamette Valley, Oregon, in 1844. 9–12

Young Mac of Fort Vancouver, ill. by Richard Holberg, Crowell, 1940. Outstanding for fine characterizations and authentic historical background. This is a story of a thirteen-year-old Scotch-Indian boy who accompanies a group of French fur traders on a trip down the Columbia River to Fort Vancouver, Washington. 12–14

CAUDILL, REBECCA, *Tree of Freedom,* ill. by Dorothy B. Morse, Viking, 1949. An outstanding pioneer story, which gives a detailed picture of life in 1770, near Louisville, Kentucky. The story involves some stormy family relationships and appealing characters. 12–14

CHILDHOOD OF FAMOUS AMERICANS SERIES, Bobbs-Merrill. These fictionalized, easy-to-read biographies of over sixty famous Americans—national heroes, scientists, baseball players, writers, musicians, etc. are extremely popular with children. They should be used chiefly with slow readers but even good readers like them and they serve as introductions to more substantial biographies.

[1] Bibliography for historical fiction and biography compiled largely by Miss Mildred Phipps, supervisor of work with children, Pasadena Public Library, and Miss Gladys English, formerly supervisor of work with children, Los Angeles Public Library.

They are printed in large type with silhouette pictures. A few titles will serve to indicate the scope. 8–10

Mason, Miriam, *William Penn: Friendly Boy,* 1944.

Stevenson, Augusta, *Abe Lincoln: Frontier Boy,* 1932; *Andy Jackson: Boy Soldier,* 1942; *Clara Barton: Girl Nurse,* 1943.

Van Riper, Guernsey, Jr., *Lou Gehrig: Boy of the Sandlots,* 1949.

Wagoner, Jean Brown, *Louisa M. Alcott: Girl of Old Boston,* 1943.

COATSWORTH, ELIZABETH, *Away Goes Sally,* ill. by Helen Sewell, Macmillan, 1934. 10–12

Boston Bells, ill. by Manning de V. Lee, Macmillan, 1952. 6–10

Five Bushel Farm, ill. by Helen Sewell, Macmillan, 1939. 10–12

The Fair American, ill. by Helen Sewell, Macmillan, 1940. 10–12

Sword of the Wilderness, ill. by Harve Stein, Macmillan, 1936. 10–14

The White Horse, ill. by Helen Sewell, Macmillan, 1942.

The Wishing Pear, ill. by Ralph Ray, Macmillan, 1951. 6–10

Away Goes Sally, Five Bushel Farm, The Fair American, and *The White Horse* deal with the adventures of Sally and her cousin Andrew. The last one is the most exciting. The cousins are captured by pirates and sold as slaves to the sultan of Morocco. In *Boston Bells* John Singleton Copley, the artist, lived on Boston's Long Wharf during the time of the press gangs. In *Sword of the Wilderness* young Seth Hubbard is captured by Indians during the French and Indian Wars. *The Wishing Pear* is based on a true incident about a little boy of the Plymouth colony who was lost in the woods and taken to an Indian village in 1621.

COBLENTZ, CATHERINE CATE, *The Falcon of Eric the Red,* ill. by Henry C. Pitz, Longmans, 1942. In the New World settlement of Vineland, Jon and his falcon play a gallant part. Falconry and a fine historical story of Greenland make this an unusually good book. 10–12

CRAWFORD, PHYLLIS, *"Hello, the Boat!"* ill. by Edward Laning, Holt, 1938. A resourceful family journey from Pittsburgh to Cincinnati in 1816 aboard a steamboat fitted out as a store. 9–11

DALGLIESH, ALICE, *The Bears on Hemlock Mountain,* ill. by Helen Sewell, Scribner's, 1952. This adventure story is based on an historical epsiode. There weren't supposed to be any bears on Hemlock Mountain, but there *were,* as poor Jonathan proved to all concerned. This is not only a thriller, it is a chiller, this good author's very best! 5–10

DE ANGELI, MARGUERITE, *Thee, Hannah!* ill. by author, Doubleday, 1940. A vivid picture of Quaker life in old Philadelphia is given in this story of lively Quaker Hannah. Beautiful illustrations in color and black and white. 8–10

DOUGLAS, EMILY, *Appleseed Farm,* ill. by Anne Vaughan, Abingdon-Cokesbury, 1948. Ten-year-old Penny hears about a visit Johnny Appleseed once made to her family's Indiana farm. 8–10

EDMONDS, WALTER D., *Cadmus Henry,* ill. by Manning de V. Lee, Dodd, Mead, 1949. The Civil War from the Confederate side is the scene of this humorous and appealing tale of a young soldier's misadventures. 12–14

The Matchlock Gun, ill. by Paul Lantz, Dodd, Mead, 1941.

Tom Whipple, ill. by Paul Lantz, Dodd, Mead, 1942.

These books, written by a successful novelist are vigorous and unusual. *The Matchlock Gun* (Newbery Medal) relates the heroism of a small boy and his mother during an Indian raid. *Tom Whipple* is the incredible story of a farm boy who set off to see the Czar of all the Russians and did. 10–12

FOLLETT, HELEN, *House Afire!* ill. by Armstrong Sperry, Scribner's, 1941. An amusing story of Peter Stuyvesant's efforts to reduce the fire hazards of New Amsterdam and clean it up besides. 9–11

GENDRON, VAL, *The Fork in the Trail,* ill. by Sidney Quinn, Longmans, 1952. A young boy sets up a trading post on the route to the West during the Gold Rush Days. A good picture of the period. 12–14

GRAY, ELIZABETH JANET, *Beppy Marlowe of Charlestown,* (1715), ill. by Loren Barton, Viking, 1936.

The Fair Adventure (modern), ill. by Alice K. Reischer, Viking, 1940.

Jane Hope (1860), Viking, 1933.

Meggy MacIntosh (1775), ill. by Marguerite de Angeli, Viking, 1930.

This is Elizabeth Gray's fine series about North Carolina. The period of each book is indicated. The series shows the changes in manners, customs, and problems of one region. 12–16

GREY, KATHERINE, *Hills of Gold,* ill. by Tom Lea, Little, 1941. 9–11

Rolling Wheels, ill. by Frank Schoonover, Little, 1937. 12–14

Rolling Wheels tells of the long heroic journey from Indiana to California by pioneers seeking their fortune in the West. *Hills of Gold* is a sequel in which the Lambert family join the California gold rush.

HINTERNHOFF, JOHN, *Barry's Boys,* ill. by Clifford N. Geary, Holt, 1952. The adventures of a young midshipman on board the first ship in our Colonial navy. 12–14

HODGES, C. WALTER, *Columbus Sails,* ill. by author, Coward, 1939. Fiction but based on facts, and tremendously moving. This is a popular book. 12–14

HOLLING, HOLLING C., *Paddle-to-the-Sea,* ill. by author, Houghton, 1941.

Seabird, ill. by author, Houghton, 1948.

Tree in the Trail, ill. by author, Houghton, 1942.

Perhaps the first book is more geography than history for it is the account of an Indian boy's toy canoe which follows our Great Lakes to the sea and back. *Seabird* is a story of American ships in terms of one family of shipbuilders. In *Tree in the Trail* a cottonwood tree on the Santa Fe trail to California was a landmark for Indians and white men. All three books are superbly illustrated. 10–12

KOHLER, JULILLY H., *Harmony Ahead,* ill. by Peter Burchard, Aladdin, 1952. Fifteen-year-old Allan Ward is the hero of this well-documented story of Robert Owen's group which travels down the Ohio River to New Harmony, Indiana, in 1825. 12–14

LENSKI, LOIS, *Puritan Adventure,* ill. by author, Lippincott, 1944. Massachusetts is the scene of this vivid tale of Colonial times when a gay young aunt from England visits a strict Puritan family bringing gayety and laughter with her. 12–14

MALKUS, ALIDA, *Colt of Destiny,* ill. by Manning de V. Lee, Winston, 1950. A vivid picture of the California mission days. 12–16

Little Giant of the North, ill. by Jay Hyde Barnum, Winston, 1952. This rousing adventure story helps to answer the question of why the French got on with the

Indians and the English failed. This tells of Henry Kelsey's success in 1688 of getting the Indians to work with him. 10–14

MASON, MIRIAM, *The Middle Sister,* ill. by Grace Paull, Macmillan, 1947.

Susannah, the Pioneer Cow, ill. by Maud and Miska Petersham, Macmillan, 1941.

Easy-to-read, entertaining stories of pioneering. The first one is about a timid little girl trying to keep her small apple tree safe. The second one centers on a home-loving cow which went pioneering with great reluctance. 8–10

Caroline and her Kettle Named Maude, ill. by Kathleen Voute, Macmillan, 1951. An amusing story of a little pioneer girl who asked for a gun but was given a kettle. How she uses this kettle as a weapon will delight young readers. 8–10

MC GRAW, ELOISE JARVIS, *Moccasin Trail.* (See Bibliography, Today in the United States: North American Indian.)

MC MEEKIN, ISABEL, *Journey Cake,* Messner, 1942. Six motherless children, in the care of an intrepid old free Negro woman, journey through the wilderness to join their father in Boone's Kentucky. Followed by *Juba's New Moon.* Both books have good historical details. 10–12

MEADER, STEPHEN W., *Jonathan Goes West,* ill. by Edward Shenton, Harcourt, 1946.

Red Horse Hill, Harcourt, ill. by Lee Townsend, 1930.

River of the Wolves, ill. by Lee Townsend, Harcourt, 1948.

Who Rides in the Dark? ill. by James MacDonald, Harcourt, 1937.

Exciting stories, with historical background and usually an element of mystery, these and other books by this author are well written and exceedingly popular. 10–14

MEADOWCROFT, ENID, *Along the Erie Towpath,* ill. by Ninon MacKnight, Crowell, 1940. A good story about opening the Erie Canal. 10–12

By Secret Railway, ill. by Henry C. Pitz, Crowell, 1948. A story of a white boy's rescue of a freed Negro who had been carried south again, illegally. 11–14

By Wagon and Flatboat, ill. by Ninon MacKnight, Crowell, 1938. In the post-Revolutionary period a family travels from Gray's Ferry to Ohio in a Conestoga wagon and a flatboat. 10–12

On Indian Trails with Daniel Boone, ill. by Lloyd Coe, Crowell, 1947. Thrilling adventures of the Boone family as they move west into the Indian country. 8–10

MEANS, FLORENCE CRANNELL, *A Candle in the Mist,* ill. by Marguerite de Angeli, Houghton, 1931. Pioneer life in a Minnesota settlement in the 1870's is difficult, but fifteen-year-old Janey faces it with high courage. 12–14

MEIGS, CORNELIA, *Covered Bridge,* ill. by Marguerite de Angeli, Macmillan, 1936.

Master Simon's Garden, ill. by John Rae, Macmillan, 1929.

Willow Whistle, ill. by E. B. Smith, Macmillan, 1931.

These well-written stories of other days and ways are not easy reading but they are rewarding books for the able child. Action and theme carry the interest. Characters are less memorable. 10–14

RIETVELD, JANE, *Nicky's Bugle,* ill. by author, Viking, 1947. Nicky was a Wisconsin pioneer on the side. His main business in life was earning enough money to buy a glorious bugle. His adventures were astonishing and often hilarious. 9–12

SWIFT, HILDEGARDE R., *The Railroad to Freedom,* ill. by James Daugherty, Harcourt, 1932. A true story of a Negro slave who helped her people to freedom during the Civil War. 10–14

WILDER, LAURA INGALLS, *By the Shores of Silver Lake,* ill. by Helen Sewell and Mildred Boyle, Harper, 1939. 10–12

Farmer Boy, ill. by Helen Sewell, Harper, 1933. 9–11

Little House in the Big Woods, ill. by Helen Sewell, Harper, 1932. 9–11

Little House on the Prairie, ill. by Helen Sewell, Harper, 1935. 9–11

Little Town on the Prairie, ill. by Helen Sewell and Mildred Boyle, Harper, 1940. 11–14

On the Banks of Plum Creek, ill. by Helen Sewell and Mildred Boyle, Harper, 1937. 9–11

These Happy Golden Years, ill. by Helen Sewell and Mildred Boyle, Harper, 1943. 12–14

These seven books cover the saga of a pioneer family and the childhood of the author to the time of her marriage. This is the family invincible, able to stand up to misfortunes and tragedies because they are strong in love and loyalty. No American child should miss these books. 9–14

European

BUFF, MARY, *Apple and the Arrow,* ill. by Conrad Buff, Houghton, 1951. This is the stirring story of William Tell and his son Walter, with many dramatic illustrations by Swiss-born Conrad Buff. 10–12

COBLENTZ, CATHERINE CATE, *Beggar's Penny,* ill. by Hilda Van Stockum, Longmans, 1943. A fine historical story of the siege of Leyden by the Spanish. 11–12

The Bells of Leyden Sing, ill. by Hilda Van Stockum, Longmans, 1944. A story about the English exiles' last year in Leyden before sailing for America. Contains some new historical information, exciting and long secret. 11–13

DAVID, JULIAN, *The Three Hanses,* ill. by Warren Chappell, Little, 1942. A novel, based on facts, about Hans Christian Andersen. 10–14

DE ANGELI, MARGUERITE, *The Door in the Wall,* ill. by author, Doubleday, 1949. When Robin, son of Sir John de Bureford, is stricken with an illness that leaves his legs paralyzed and his back bent, it is Brother Luke who helps him to find a "door in the wall" and nurses him back to strength and courage. This tender and beautiful book is not only a valuable addition to children's literature of the medieval period, but it should bring courage to any child crippled with polio. Newbery Award. 8–10

DIX, BEULAH M., *Merrylips,* ill. by Frank T. Merrill, Macmillan, 1925. About a little lass who longed to be a boy when England was in the midst of civil war. 10–12

EATON, JEANETTE, *Betsy's Napoleon,* ill. by Pierre Brissaud, Morrow, 1952, New ed. When Napoleon first went to St. Helena he stayed at Betsy's home. This story faithfully follows her memoirs. 10–12

EVERNDEN, MARGERY, *Knight of Florence,* ill. by Rafaello Busoni, Random, 1950. The art of Florence in the middle ages as it affects the life of a noble family whose eldest son aspires to be an artist. 10–12

GIBSON, KATHARINE, *Oak Tree House,* ill. by Vera Bock, Longmans, 1936. Almost fairy tales, these whimsical stories of medieval times are charmingly written. An oak tree house is what every child would like, a complete house in a tree with cat and dog and finally the young king himself. 8–9

GILBERT, JANE, *Imps and Angels,* ill. by Nedda Walker, Dutton, 1946. An English town devoted to the building of a great cathedral has the usual number of active boys whose pranks are diverting and eventually lead to the solution of a mystery. Fine details of guilds and building crafts. 10–14

GRAY, ELIZABETH JANET, *Adam of the Road,* ill. by Robert Lawson, Viking, 1942. When Adam, by mischance, loses both his father and dog, he seeks them on the highways and byways of thirteenth-century England. 6–9

HEWES, AGNES, *Boy of the Lost Crusade,* ill. by Gustaf Tenggren, Houghton, 1923. A French boy joins the Children's Crusade in the hope of finding his father. 12–14

KENT, LOUISE, *He Went with Christopher Columbus,* ill. by Paul Quinn, Houghton, 1940. 12–14
He Went with Marco Polo, ill. by C. LeRoy Baldridge, Houghton, 1935. 12–14
He Went with Vasco da Gama, ill. by Paul Quinn, Houghton, 1938. 12–15
The adventures of boys who accompanied the three great explorers of the middle ages.

KNIGHT, RUTH ADAMS, *Halfway to Heaven,* ill. by Wesley Dennis, Whittlesey, 1952. An inspiring story of a young priest of the St. Bernard Hospice and the dogs which were trained to rescue travelers from the storms and avalanches of the dangerous pass from Italy to Switzerland. 12–14

LEIGHTON, MARGARET, *Judith of France,* ill. by Henry C. Pitz, Houghton, 1948. Teen-age girls or superior readers of twelve will enjoy this romantic historical novel about Charlemagne's spirited granddaughter. The pathetic pawn of kings, she comes into her own at last. 12–16

MAGOON, MARIAN AUSTIN, *Little Dusty Foot,* ill. by Christine Price, Longmans, 1948. Absorbing story of the far-traveled merchants of medieval days. The young "dusty-foot" and his talking magpie are a delightful pair, and their adventures have proved exceedingly popular. 10–14

PYLE, HOWARD, *Men of Iron,* ill. by author, Harper, 1891. The training of knights, the clash of battle and all the glamor of feudal England under Henry IV. 12–14
Otto of the Silver Hand, ill. by author, Scribner's, 1888. The appealing story of a boy whose father, a German robber baron, places him in a medieval monastery to assure his safety. 10–12

STEIN, EVALEEN, *Gabriel and the Hour Book,* ill. by Adelaide Everhart, 1906. A French peasant boy helps a medieval monk illuminate a book. 9–11

SUTCLIFF, ROSEMARY, *The Armourer's House,* ill. by C. Walter Hodges, Oxford, 1951. Tamsyn moves to live with her uncle's family in London. He is a famous armourer and his pretty wife and lively children show Tamsyn London in the time of Henry VIII. The children even see the king and the doomed Anne Boleyn. Delightful characters and vivid details make this a rewarding story. 10–14
Queen Elizabeth Story, ill. by C. Walter Hodges, Oxford, 1950. Perdita's dearest wish is realized when she sees the great Queen Elizabeth. 10–12

Ancient Times

COE, FREDERICK L. *Graven with Flint,* ill. by Robert Hallock, Crowell, 1950. The adventures of two Cro-Magnon boys. 12–14

CROWELL, PERS, *The First Horseman,* ill. by author, McGraw, 1948. A convincing picture of prehistoric times is given in this story of man's first attempt to domesticate the horse. 12–14

GERE, FRANCES, *Boy of Babylon,* ill. by author, Longmans, 1941. This lively story with many pictures gives a good idea of life in ancient Babylon. 10–12

JONES, RUTH FOSDICK, *Boy of the Pyramids; a Mystery of Ancient Egypt,* ill. by Dorothy Bayley Morse, Random, 1952. Kaffe, a ten-year-old Egyptian boy whose home is near the ancient city of Memphis, watches the building of a pyramid on the desert and sees the Nile in flood. 10–12

KJELGAARD, JIM, *Fire-Hunter,* ill. by Ralph Ray, Holiday, 1951. The adventures of a prehistoric boy with saber-toothed tigers, mammoths, and cave bears. 12–14

LOWNSBERRY, ELOISE, *A Camel for a Throne,* ill. by Elizabeth T. Wolcott, Houghton, 1941. A daughter of the pharaoh is brought up as a commoner. How her identity is finally made known is an exciting story, rich with historical details. 10–14

MEADOWCROFT, ENID, *The Gift of the River, a History of Ancient Egypt,* illustrations adapted from Egyptian sources by Katharine Dewey, Crowell, 1937. Adapted from source material in both text and pictures. A useful book for children studying ancient history. 9–12

MORRISON, LUCILE, *The Lost Queen of Egypt,* ill. by Franz Geritz, Lippincott, 1937. This story of ancient Egypt solves the mystery of the disappearance of the young queen, when her husband Tutankhamen, king of Egypt, dies. 12–14

RIENOW, LEONA, *The Bewitched Caverns,* ill. by Allen Pope, Scribner's, 1948. The life and times of Cro-Magnon man are portrayed in an exciting way, through two primitive children who solve a hair-raising mystery. 9–14
The Dark Pool, ill. by Allen Pope, Scribner's, 1949. A continuation of the adventures of the Cro-Magnon brother and sister. Reveals even more of the brutality and violence of primitive man's existence. It shows also a developing moral code. 9–14

SHORE, MAXINE, *The Captive Princess,* ill. by Kreigh Collins, Longmans, 1952. Story of the Roman conquest of Britain in which a Druid princess falls in love with a Roman soldier. 12–14

SNEDEKER, CAROLINE DALE, *The Forgotten Daughter,* ill. by Dorothy Lathrop, Doubleday, 1933. When Chloe's Greek mother died, she suffered many hardships until her Roman father remembered her and made a home for her in Rome. An interesting picture of ancient Greece and Rome. 12–14
Theras and His Town, ill. by Whitson Haring, Doubleday, 1924. Life in ancient Athens and Sparta from the point of view of a small Athenian school boy. 10–12

BIOGRAPHY

Collections of Biographies

BEARD, ANNIE E. S., *Our Foreign-Born Citizens; What They Have Done for America,* Crowell, 1946. Short biographies of famous American men and women and their contributions in art, science, business, and politics. 12–16

COTTLER, JOSEPH, *Heroes of Civilization,* ill. by Forrest W. Orr, Little, 1931. Among the thirty-five famous people living in different countries and at different periods are: Marco Polo, Madame Curie, Louis Pasteur, Edward Jenner, and Albert Einstein. 10–14

DAUGHERTY, SONIA, *Ten Brave Men,* ill. by James Daugherty, Lippincott, 1951. Good accounts of such national heroes as Roger Williams, Patrick Henry, Thomas Jefferson, and Andrew Jackson. 11–14

FARJEON, ELEANOR, *Ten Saints,* ill. by Helen Sewell, Oxford, 1936. Stories of St. Francis, St. Christopher, and other less well-known saints, beautifully told. 8–12

FENNER, PHYLLIS, compiler, *Yankee Doodle; Stories of the Brave and the Free,* ill. by John Alan Maxwell, Knopf, 1951. Excerpts from books of American historical fiction by such outstanding authors as Elizabeth Coatsworth, Constance Skinner, Esther Forbes. 9–12

FOSTER, GENEVIEVE, *Abraham Lincoln's World,* ill. by author, Scribner's, 1944. This pageant of world happenings during the lifetime of Lincoln makes history real for children and illumines the character and achievements of Lincoln himself. 12–14

Augustus Caesar's World; A Story of Ideas and Events from 44 B.C. to 14 A.D., ill. by author, Scribner's, 1947. The relationship of people and happenings in the Roman Empire which, at the time, included most of the known world. 12–14

Birthdays of Freedom, ill. by author, Scribner's, 1952. This book, sponsored by the American Library Association, records the growth of freedom in the world. It begins with the Declaration of Independence, and then goes back in time to ancient Egyptians, the Hindus, Chinese, Greeks, and so on over the centuries. 10–14

George Washington's World, ill. by author, Scribner's 1941. The life of Washington is related against a background of events and of people living in other parts of the world at that time. 12–14

KUNITZ, STANLEY J. and HAYCROFT, HOWARD, *The Junior Book of Authors,* 2nd ed. revised, Wilson, 1951. Brief biographies of more than 280 authors and illustrators of children's books.

MCCONNELL, JANE and BURT MORTON, *Presidents of the United States,* portraits by Constance Joan Narr, Crowell, 1951. Sketches of their lives are closely interwoven with the political and economic changes of the nation. 12–14

MONTGOMERY, ELIZABETH RIDER, *Story behind Great Books,* ill. by Friedebald Dzubas, Dodd, Mead, 1946.

Story behind Great Stories, ill. by Elinore Blaisdell, Dodd, Mead, 1947.

Story behind Modern Books, Dodd, Mead, 1949. Short sketches about authors and illustrators of children's books, with notes about the books they have written.

MORGAN, JAMES, *Our Presidents,* Macmillan, 1949. Brief biographies of our presidents from Washington to Truman, with short accounts of each presidency. 12–14

RICHARDSON, BEN ALBERT, *Great American Negroes,* ill. by Louise Costello, Crowell, 1945. Vivid accounts of twenty-one Negroes who have overcome prejudice and who have contributed to American culture in many fields. 12–16

SICKELS, ELEANOR M., *In Calico and Crinoline, True Stories of American Women, 1608–1865,* ill. by Ilse Bischoff, Viking, 1935. Their role in the settlement of the country and in its economic, social, and cultural development. 12–16

SIMON, CHARLIE MAY, *Art in the New Land,* ill. by James McDonald, Dutton, 1945. Stories of famous American artists from Benjamin West to Grant Wood, with illustrations and descriptions of their work. 12–14

Figures in American History

AULAIRE, INGRID and EDGAR PARIN D', *Abraham Lincoln,* ill. by authors, Doubleday, 1939. 6–10

Benjamin Franklin, ill. by authors, Doubleday, 1950. 6–10

Buffalo Bill, ill. by authors, Doubleday, 1952. 6–10

George Washington, ill. by authors, Doubleday, 1936. 6–10

Leif the Lucky, ill. by authors, Doubleday, 1952. 6–10

AVERILL, ESTHER, *King Philip, the Indian Chief,* ill. by Vera Belsky, Harper, 1950. This is the story of the chief of the Wampanoag Indians of New England, who led his tribe and others in fighting against the colonists in 1675. 12–14

BELL, MARGARET E., *Kit Carson, Mountain Man,* ill. by Harry Daugherty, Morrow, 1952. A short, dramatic biography with large print and many illustrations. 8–10

DAUGHERTY, JAMES, *Abraham Lincoln,* ill. by author, Viking, 1943. A substantial biography that compares favorably with Carl Sandburg's. 12–16

Daniel Boone, original lithographs in color by the author, Viking, 1939. Awarded the Newbery Medal in 1940, *Daniel Boone* is a vigorously written and illustrated biography of a rugged American. 12–16

Of Courage Undaunted, across the Continent with Lewis and Clark, ill. by author, Viking, 1951. This stirring account of the Lewis and Clark expedition gives young readers a clear understanding of the courage and resourcefulness of the explorers. 12–16

Poor Richard, ill. by author, Viking, 1941. A beautifully written and illustrated book which emphasizes Franklin's patriotic achievements. 12–16

DAVIS, JULIA, *No Other White Men,* maps by Caroline Gray, Dutton, 1937. An unforgettable account of the Lewis and Clark expedition, not only of the explorations but of the friendship which existed between the two great leaders. 12–14

EATON, JEANETTE, *Leader by Destiny: George Washington, Man and Patriot,* ill. by Jack Manley Rosé, Harcourt, 1938. A definitive biography which shows Washington as a very human, often bewildered man with a gift of inspiring confidence in other men. 12–16

Narcissa Whitman; Pioneer of Oregon, ill. by Woodi Ishmael, Harcourt, 1941. This inspiring story of the great pioneer woman is based on early letters and memoirs. 12–16

That Lively Man, Ben Franklin, ill. by Henry C. Pitz, Morrow, 1948. Franklin's many-sided career from printer to colonial ambassador to France and England is well portrayed. 10–14

Washington, the Nation's First Hero, ill. by Ralph Ray, Morrow, 1951. A short dramatic biography with many attractive illustrations. 9–12

Young Lafayette, ill. by David Hendrickson, Houghton, 1932. Lafayette's vivid personality, high ideals, and sense of adventure have made him one of the beloved figures in the history of our country. 12–16

FAST, HOWARD, *Haym Salomon; Son of Liberty,* ill. by Eric M. Simon, Messner, 1941. A moving story of the great Polish Jew who helped finance the American Revolution. Difficult reading at elementary level. 12–16

FISHER, GEORGE CLYDE, *The Life of Audubon,* ill. with paintings and drawings by John James Audubon, Harper, 1949. This biography of the famous naturalist by a former staff member of the American Museum of Natural History is glorified by superb reproductions of Audubon's own paintings both in black and white and full color. 10–14

FORBES, ESTHER, *America's Paul Revere,* ill. by Lynd Ward, Houghton, 1946. Vigorous prose and superb illustrations make this book a treasure for children to own. It is not easy reading but will do much to illumine the history of that day. 12–16

FOSTER, GENEVIEVE, *Abraham Lincoln*, ill. by author, Scribner's, 1950.
Andrew Jackson, ill. by author, Scribner's, 1951.
George Washington, ill. by author, Scribner's, 1949.
These books are simply written and cover outstanding achievements of the hero from birth to death. 9–12

GARST, DORIS SHANNON, *Jim Bridger, Greatest of the Mountain Men*, ill. by William Moyers, Houghton, 1952. An exciting story of a farm boy who went into the West when it was a wilderness and became the most famous of the mountain men. 12–16

GOTTSCHALK, FRUMA, *The Youngest General, a Story of Lafayette*, ill. by Rafaello Busoni, Knopf, 1949. The author had access to unusual original sources in writing this well-documented life of Lafayette. The lively, fascinating text will bring both Lafayette and Washington vividly to life for young readers. 10–14

GRAHAM, SHIRLEY, *The Story of Phillis Wheatley*, ill. by Robert Burns, Messner, 1949. This book tells the story of a remarkable woman, a young Negro poet who lived in Boston in revolutionary days. 12–14

HAVILAND, VIRGINIA, *William Penn: Founder and Friend*, ill. by Peter Burchard, Abingdon-Cokesbury, 1952. (Makers of America Series.) An easy-to-read biography of the great Quaker who founded Pennsylvania. 9–12

HAWTHORNE, HILDEGARDE, *Give Me Liberty*, ill. by Woodi Ishmael, Appleton-Century, 1945. An exciting biography of one of our most colorful colonials, Patrick Henry. 12–14

HOGEBOOM, AMY, *Christopher Columbus and His Brothers*, ill. by author, Lothrop, 1951. Unlike other biographies of Columbus in that the author presents him as one of four brothers all working together on plans for exploration and discovery. 9–12

HOLBROOK, STEWART H., *America's Ethan Allen*, ill. by Lynd Ward, Houghton, 1949. Spirited illustrations in color add to the dramatic story of the "Green Mountain Boys" and their fighting leader. 10–16

HUNT, MABEL LEIGH, *Better Known as Johnny Appleseed*, ill. by James Daugherty, Lippincott, 1950. The life of John Chapman, "American pioneer, missionary, and apple lover," based on old legends and reminiscences, gathered by the author during many years of research. 12–16

JUDSON, CLARA INGRAM, *Abraham Lincoln, Friend of the People*, ill. by Robert Frankenberg; Kodachromes of the Chicago Historical Society Lincoln dioramas, Wilcox and Follett, 1950. An excellent biography of Lincoln which shows much research. 10–14
City Neighbor; the Story of Jane Addams, ill. by Ralph Ray, Scribner's, 1951. The life of the great woman who founded Hull House in Chicago. 10–14
George Washington, Leader of the People, ill. by Robert Frankenberg, Wilcox and Follett, 1951. Beautiful illustrations and well-written text make this an outstanding book. 10–14
Thomas Jefferson, Champion of the People, ill. by Robert Frankenberg, Wilcox and Follett, 1952. A well-documented biography of one of the great figures in American history. 12–16

LANDMARK BOOKS, Random, 1951. This series is a distinguished addition to children's knowledge of their country. Written by notable authors, the books are sometimes biographies and sometimes they enlarge upon great moments in history or great movements. They are freshly and vigorously written, and although many of them lend themselves to use in social studies, they are equally valuable for the child's private library. So far, this series has had many imitators but no rivals. There are, however, individual biographies which are finer than some of these.
Adams, Samuel Hopkins, *The Pony Express*. 10–12
The Santa Fe Trail. 10–12
Brown, John Mason, *Daniel Boone*. 13–16
Considine, Robert, *The Panama Canal*. 11–14
Cousins, Margaret, *Ben Franklin of Old Philadelphia*. 11–14
Daugherty, James, *The Landing of the Pilgrims*. 11–14
Trappers and Traders of the Far West. 11–14
Fisher, Dorothy Canfield, *Our Independence and the Constitution*. 12–14
Fisher, Dorothy Canfield, *Paul Revere and the Minute Men*. 11–14
Holbrook, Stewart, *Wild Bill Hickok Tames the West*. 11–14
Hunt, George, *The Story of the U. S. Marines*. 11–14
Janeway, Elizabeth, *The Vikings*. 12–14
Jennings, John, *Clipper Ship Days*. 13–16
Kantor, MacKinlay, *Gettysburg*. 13–16
Lee and Grant at Appomattox. 13–14
Kjelgaard, Jim, *The Explorations of Père Marquette*. 10–12
Lawson, Marie, *Pocahontas and Captain John Smith*. 11–14
Mayer, Jane, *Betsy Ross and the Flag*. 10–12
McNeer, May, *The California Gold Rush*. 10–12
Nathan, Adele, *The Building of the First Transcontinental Railroad*. 10–12
Neuberger, Richard L., *The Lewis and Clark Expedition*. 10–12
Owen, Russell, *The Conquest of the North and South Poles*. 11–14
Pratt, Fletcher, *The Monitor and the Merrimac*. 11–14
Reynolds, Quentin, *Custer's Last Stand*. 10–12
The Wright Brothers. 10–12
Shippen, Katherine B., *Mr. Bell Invents the Telephone*. 11–14
Sperry, Armstrong, *The Voyages of Christopher Columbus*. 11–14
Tallant, Robert, *The Louisiana Purchase*. 14–16
Tallant, Robert, *The Pirate Lafitte and the Battle of New Orleans*. 10–12
White, Ann Terry, *Prehistoric America*. 11–14

LAWSON, ROBERT, *They Were Strong and Good*, ill. by author, Viking, 1940. These stories of the author's four grandparents and his mother and father are told with humor and affection and illustrated with large black and white drawings. 9–12

LE SUEUR, MERIDEL, *Chanticleer of Wilderness Road*, ill. by Aldren A. Watson, Knopf, 1951. Young readers not ready for the more difficult Rourke biography of David Crockett will find this one completely satisfying. Legends, tall tales, and facts are humorously woven together. 10–14

LISITZKY, GENEVIEVE, *Thomas Jefferson*, ill. by Harrie Wood, Viking, 1933. A well-written book about a brilliant and great American for mature and superior readers. 12–16

MEADOWCROFT, ENID, *Abraham Lincoln*, ill. by Kurt Wiese, Crowell, 1942. A good biography of Lincoln for younger readers, giving them the usual anecdotes of his childhood, and carrying him through the war years to his death. 10–12

MEANS, FLORENCE CRANNELL, *Carvers' George*, ill. by Harve Stein, Houghton, 1952. A well-written and moving account of the great Negro scientist from his tragic infancy to his triumphant old age, honored and beloved by his own people and the world. 8–12

NOLAN, JEANNETTE COVERT, *Andrew Jackson,* ill. by Leej Ames, Messner, 1949. This fictionalized biography of Jackson with its simplification of political issues and amplification of the man's romance and achievements will appeal to young readers. 12–16

The Story of Clara Barton of the Red Cross, ill. by W. C. Nims, Messner, 1941. An outstanding account of the great nurse who organized service to the wounded during the Civil War. 12–16

PEARE, CATHERINE OWENS, *Mary McLeod Bethune,* Vanguard, 1951. The story of a great Negro woman who has dedicated her life to the education of her people. 12–19

ROGERS, FRANCES and BEARD, ALICE, *Paul Revere, Patriot on Horseback,* ill. by author, Lippincott, 1943. A readable account of Revere, easier to read than Miss Forbes' book. 12–15

ROURKE, CONSTANCE MAYFIELD, *Audubon,* with twelve colored plates from original Audubon prints, Harcourt, 1936. This is a fascinating account of Audubon's life and travels from Florida and the Louisiana bayou to the Ohio and Mississippi rivers, drawing and painting as he went. It does perpetuate the now exploded myth of Audubon as the lost dauphin of France. 12–16

Davy Crockett, ill. by James MacDonald, Harcourt, 1934. One of the liveliest accounts we have of the legendary Davy. 12–16

SANDBURG, CARL, *Abe Lincoln Grows Up,* ill. by James Daugherty, Harcourt, 1928. The finest account we have of Lincoln's childhood and youth from the author's famous adult book, *Abraham Lincoln, the Prairie Years.* 12–16

SHIPPEN, KATHERINE, *Leif Eriksson, First Voyager to America,* Harper, 1951. Well-written, exciting biography of the explorer of Vineland. 11–13

STEFFENS, LINCOLN, *Boy on Horseback,* ill. by Sanford Tousey, Harcourt, 1935. The boyhood of Lincoln Steffens, taken from his autobiography. 12–16

SYME, RONALD, *Champlain of the St. Lawrence,* ill. by William Stobbs, Morrow, 1952. A vivid account of this great explorer's struggle to establish New France in America. 12–14

Columbus: Finder of the New World, ill. by William Stobbs, Morrow, 1953. A brief book about the life of Columbus and the three voyages of discovery. 10–14

La Salle of the Mississippi, ill. by William Stobbs, Morrow, 1952. Well-documented and interestingly written biography of this daring French explorer. 12–14

VANCE, MARGUERITE, *The Lees of Arlington; the Story of Mary and Robert E. Lee,* ill. by Nedda Walker, Dutton, 1949. The childhood romance and happy home life of Robert and Mary Lee will interest older girls. 12–14

Martha, Daughter of Virginia; the Story of Martha Washington, ill. by Nedda Walker, Dutton, 1947. History, romance, and biography are combined in this story of Martha Dandridge, the belle of colonial Virginia, who became the first lady of the United States. 12–14

Patsy Jefferson of Monticello, ill. by Nedda Walker, Dutton, 1948. A delightful biography of a beguiling young heroine with pleasant glimpses of her father, Thomas Jefferson. 10–14

YATES, ELIZABETH, *Amos Fortune, Free Man,* ill. by Nora S. Unwin, Aladdin, 1950. The moving account of a Negro slave who purchased his own freedom and became a benefactor of his race. Newbery Award. 12–16

Other Historical Figures

BAKER, NINA BROWN, *Sir Walter Raleigh,* Harcourt, 1950. The many-sided aspects of Raleigh's character are well portrayed and the Elizabethan background is fully drawn. 12–14

BENZ, FRANCIS E., *Pasteur, Knight of the Laboratory,* ill. by James MacDonald, Dodd, Mead, 1938. A good account of the crusader for the health of humanity. 12–14

BOUTET DE MONVEL, MAURICE, *Joan of Arc,* ill. by author, Century, 1907. This superbly illustrated picture-biography is also available in French. It is a book to own both in schools and homes. 10–14

BULLA, CLYDE, *Song of St. Francis,* ill. by Valenti Angelo, Crowell, 1952. The appealing story of St. Francis of Assisi presented in simple fashion for the youngest readers. 7–10

HUNT, MABEL LEIGH, *"Have You Seen Tom Thumb?"* ill. by Fritz Eichenberg, Lippincott, 1942. An entertaining biography of Charles Sherwood Stratton, midget in P. T. Barnum's circus. 11–14

IVES, MABEL LORENZ, *He Conquered the Andes, the Story of San Martin, the Liberator,* ill. by Forrest Orr, Little, 1943. Unusually appealing account of a great patriot. Popular with boys. 10–14

JEWETT, SOPHIE, *God's Troubadour, the Story of Saint Francis of Assisi,* ill. by Elinore Blaisdell, Crowell, 1940. Beautiful illustrations add to the appeal of this story of a favorite saint. 10–14

JUDSON, CLARA INGRAM, *Soldier Doctor; the Story of William Gorgas,* ill. by Robert Doremus, Scribner's, 1942. A lively account of the man whose work against yellow fever made possible the building of the Panama Canal. 10–12

KING, MARIAN, *Elizabeth, the Tudor Princess,* ill. by Elinore Blaisdell, Stokes, 1940. Girls like this well-written biography of a great queen in the making. 12–14

MALVERN, GLADYS, *Dancing Star, the Story of Anna Pavlova,* ill. by Susanne Suba, Messner, 1942. Girls like especially the details of the dancer's early training and the glamor of her triumphs. 10–14

MCNEER, MAY YONGE, *John Wesley,* ill. by May McNeer and Lynd Ward, Abingdon-Cokesbury, 1951. The rather somber story of the founder of the Methodist church with large illustrations in rich colors, which make this gallant man more than ordinarily appealing. 10–14

NOLAN, JEANNETTE COVERT, *Florence Nightingale,* ill. by George Avison, Messner, 1946. This warm, readable biography of Florence Nightingale stresses her work rather than her personal life. 12–14

ROOS, ANN, *Man of Molokai, the Life of Father Damien,* ill. by Raymond Lufkin, Lippincott, 1943. This book tells of his work for the lepers on the island of Molokai for whom he gave his life. 12–16

SYME, RONALD, *Cortes of Mexico,* ill. by William Stobbs, Morrow, 1951. The tremendous adventure of the conqueror of Mexico makes an exciting story. 12–14

TREASE, GEOFFREY, *Sir Walter Raleigh, Captain and Adventurer,* Vanguard, 1950. Raleigh's adventures on land and sea are set against the romantic background of Elizabethan England. Vivid details. 12–14

VANCE, MARGUERITE, *Marie Antoinette, Daughter of an Empress,* ill. by Nedda Walker, Dutton, 1950. A sympathetic portrait of the lonely young queen is presented against the background of the rising tide of revolution in France. 12–14

WOOD, LAURA NEWBOLD, *Louis Pasteur,* ill. with photographs, Messner, 1948. The story of one of the world's great scientists, whose experiments and research made a great contribution to modern medicine and surgery. 12–14

Raymond L. Ditmars, ill. with photographs, Messner, 1944. The early struggles of a young scientist to obtain and study the snakes that became his lifework. 10–14

WOODHAM-SMITH, CECIL, *Lonely Crusader; the Life of Florence Nightingale, 1820–1910,* McGraw, 1951. Special emphasis on her early life and character development which led to her career in nursing. 14–16

Musicians

BENET, LAURA, *Enchanting Jenny Lind,* ill. by George G. Whitney, Dodd, Mead, 1939. The romantic and appealing story of the "Swedish Nightingale." 12–14

BUNN, HARRIET, *Johann Sebastian Bach,* ill. by Rafaello Busoni, Random, 1942. Easy-to-read, but a more advanced study than the Wheeler and Deucher story of Bach. 10–14

EWEN, DAVID, *Story of George Gershwin,* ill. by Graham Bernbach, Holt, 1943. Memories of an American composer of popular music by a personal friend. 12–16

Tales from the Vienna Woods: The Story of Johann Strauss, ill. by Edgard Cirlin, Holt, 1944. The composer of some of the world's greatest and best-loved dance music is presented against the background of romantic nineteenth-century Vienna. 12–14

GOSS, MADELEINE, *Beethoven, Master Musician,* ill. by Carl Schultheiss, Holt, 1946. A sensitive and thwarted genius portrayed with rare sympathy. 12–16

Unfinished Symphony; The Story of Franz Schubert, ill. by Carl M. Schultheiss, Holt, 1941. His creative genius, the simplicity of his nature, and a feeling for his music are all blended in this portrait of a great composer. 12–16

PURDY, CLAIRE LEE, *He Heard America Sing; The Story of Stephen Foster,* ill. by Dorothea Cooke, Messner, 1940. A sympathetic picture of the folk-song composer. 12–14

Artists

DEUCHER, SYBIL, *Millet Tilled the Soil,* ill. by Dorothy Bayley, Dutton, 1939. Millet is a difficult hero to reduce to child size, but this is a popular book and introduces the most frequently used pictures of the artist. 8–12

DEUCHER, SYBIL and WHEELER, OPAL, *Giotto Tended the Sheep,* ill. by Dorothy Bayley, Dutton, 1938. A picture of fourteenth-century Italy and of the shepherd boy who became an artist. 8–10

RIPLEY, ELIZABETH, *Leonardo da Vinci; a Biography,* Oxford, 1952. The many reproductions of his drawings and paintings reveal his extraordinary genius. 12–14

Writers

BECKER, MAY L., *Presenting Miss Jane Austen,* ill. by Edward Price, Dodd, Mead, 1952. This picture of the life and times of Jane Austen written by a devotee will interest older girls. 14–16

GRAY, ELIZABETH JANET, *Young Walter Scott,* end papers by Kate Seredy, Viking, 1935. One of the fine biographies written for young people, outstanding for its literary style and appealing picture of the man. 12–14

MASON, MIRIAM E., *Yours with Love, Kate,* ill. by Barbara Cooney, Houghton, 1952. One of the first kindergarten teachers in America, Kate Douglas Wiggin also became a well-loved author of children's books. 12–16

MEIGS, CORNELIA, *Invincible Louisa,* ill. with photographs, Little, 1933. An absorbing life of Louisa May Alcott, the beloved author of *Little Women.* 12–16

PROUDFIT, ISABEL, *River Boy, the Story of Mark Twain,* ill. by W. C. Nims, Messner, 1940. An excellent life of the author of Tom Sawyer for older boys and girls. 10–14

Treasure Hunter, the Story of Robert Louis Stevenson, ill. by Hardie Gramatky, Messner, 1939. A full-length biography of a favorite children's author. 10–14

BIBLICAL TIMES

BARNHART, NANCY, *The Lord Is My Shepherd,* ill. by author, Scribner's, 1949. A beautiful book in text and format which tells the Bible stories briefly but with considerable use of Biblical language. 9–14

BOWIE, WALTER RUSSELL, *The Bible Story for Boys and Girls,* ill. by Edward and Stephani Godwin, Abingdon-Cokesbury, 1951. Here is a continuous story of the New Testament from the birth of Christ, through the Pauline journeys to John's vision of the Holy City. Good to read aloud. 6–10

CEDER, GEORGIANA D., *Ann of Bethany,* ill. by Helen Torrey, Abingdon-Cokesbury, 1951. A little Jewish girl warns Joseph and Mary of King Herod's search for the Christ Child. 9–11

Ethan, the Shepherd Boy, ill. by Helen Torrey, Abingdon-Cokesbury, 1948. Ethan is working with his uncle in the hills near Bethlehem at the time of the Nativity. Told with sincerity and beauty. 9–11

JONES, MARY ALICE, *Bible Stories,* ill. by Manning de V. Lee, Rand McNally, 1952. Sixteen stories from the Old Testament and four from the New Testament are simply told and gorgeously illustrated with twenty-six pictures in full color. For parents to use with children as an introduction to Bible stories. 5–9

LILLIE, AMY MORRIS, *Nathan, Boy of Capernaum,* ill. by Nedda Walker, Dutton, 1945. How the presence of Jesus in his village changed the life of a ten-year-old boy. 10–12

LONG, LAURA, *The Chosen Boy,* ill. by Clotilde Funk, Bobbs-Merrill, 1952. The story of Moses who led his people from slavery to the promised land. 9–12

MALVERN, GLADYS, *Behold Your Queen!* ill. by Corinne Malvern, Longmans, 1951. There is romance, drama, and suspense in this story of Esther, Queen of Persia. 12–14

Tamar, ill. by Corinne Malvern, Longmans, 1952. How the teachings of Jesus changed the lives of the people of Capernaum. 12–16

MENOTTI, GIAN CARLO, *Amahl and the Night Visitors,* narrative adaptation by Frances Frost, ill. by Roger Duvoisin, Whittlesey, 1952. This beautifully told and illustrated book of the Christmas opera tells how the Three Kings stopped to rest at a poor shepherd's house and the wonderful results of their visit. A book to treasure and reread each Christmas. 7–adult

VANCE, MARGUERITE, *While Shepherds Watched,* ill. by Nedda Walker, Dutton, 1946. A beautiful retelling of the Nativity story. 7–9

SHIPPEN, KATHERINE B., *Moses,* Harper, 1949. The story of a great leader's sense of dedication to his people and to God. 12–14

INDEX

1 2 3 4 5 6 7 8 9 10 11 12 13 14 15 16 17 18 19 20 21 22 23 24 25 62 61 60 59 58 57 56 55 54 53